Conversations

with

Tibor.

Brody McVittie

Foreword: Tibor's Son, Emil Fidler

I have wanted to have a written recording of my father's life for many years now. I remember when I was growing up he would tell me these wild stories about his life, and I would think to myself what an incredible journey my father has led. I always believed that other people would appreciate his unbelievable true-life stories as well.

I have known Brody for over three years now, and he has become a wonderful friend to my family and I. This project is truly special to me, and because of him, it has become a reality. With Brody's descriptive writing style, I believe that any reader will be able to imagine what it might have been like, to live the wild and amazing life that my father has had.

I hope you enjoy reading it.

Introduction.

Tibor Gyorgy Fidler sits across the coffee shop table from me, and his eyes say:

Boy, have I got a story to tell you.

Before, he parts his robust lips to say:

"Boy, have I got a story to tell you."

Over the course of my bi-weekly encounters with Tibor, I'm to learn of a life fully-realized; fully-realized and fantastical, and, to a writer, vivid in both the recounting of adventures too bold for a writer's imagination, and quite frankly, vivid well beyond this writer's humble hopes of completely recounting.

Here then, in the pages to follow, are my interpretations of the life and adventures of one Tibor Fidler—a phenomenal man full of life…life earned and reflected in the luster of the words he parts his lips to tell.

Coffee Shops and Crushing Poverty.

Tibor tells me he grew up poor, and he means it.

"Poor."

It's our first sit-down—the first of what I already hope to be many, and admittedly, I'm still learning the degrees of his various inflections, and the influence over-annunciation can have regarding the severity of the story to follow.

So it's early, and I'm new, and undeniably, Tibor can be a difficult man to understand—

--unless he really, really wants you to understand, you see—

"*Poor.*"

--like he wants me to understand, right now.

His lips look dry, robust as they are, and I swear I would lose count of the cracks in them should I have the time or reason to count. Before I can start, he's speaking again, annunciating in a strange tongue, telling me again with those eyes—and without really needing to tell me—that he grew up

"Poor."

and that I have no damn idea just how poor

Poor

really was for him.

He sits across the table from me, and he's reading me the-way-I-am-and-better than the way I'm reading him, and when he's satisfied the pause between cracked lips has been sufficient, he parts them once more, and begins to tell me the first of the tales I'm going to spend the next forever reciting.

…

Before he does, it's best if I take a moment, in my mind and on your page, to recount my first impressions of this man.

I suppose it's best to start at the beginning—not only the facts I've collected regarding an extraordinary man's extraordinary origins, but also my impressions upon our first meeting, some weeks ago, in a coffee shop.

Born on November 15th, 1930 in Hungary, Budapest, perhaps the first most-interesting thing about Tibor is that there are *two* of him.

Tibor Gyorgy Fidler arrived in the world about five minutes before Emil Fidler, and as I am to learn, five minutes is just about the longest stretch of time they were ever apart. Twins were a rarity in pre-war Budapest—hell, by Tibor's recollection, twins were a rarity in all of Europe in the years leading up to the Second World War.

Born to Tibor Ference and his wife Racz Anna, a couple who had married some eight years prior in the small city of Andacs, Hungary, the twins joined a daughter, Piroska, who had been born four years before, and by all accounts was thrilled to have two new 'dolls' to play with.

Named as such for the ice blue of their eyes, Tibor tells me they were a 'big deal' back in those days—hell-raising and enjoying life—as much as life could be enjoyed in pre-war Eastern Europe.

...

He's older now, obviously, and some years ago the 'two' of him was tragically whittled to one, but I can tell he's still got some hell raising left. His shoulders are broad, his hands are rough and calloused—the longer he speaks, the more involved the tale, the more the shoulders sag and the less the hands dance…as though recalling the deluge of memory places an invisible weight across his back. The posture goes a little, but the eyes never surrender.

They're three shades bluer than the blue of blue eyes today, and tell me at-least-if-not-more than his mouth and the totality of him. I find my eyes, humble in comparison, spend a good deal of time absorbing the words from his lips and then translating their true meaning in his gaze.

This is but one of my duties in transcribing this man's life—between the thick, rich drawl of his still-very-much-Hungarian accent and visible passion injected into each and every story, I'm swimming in information instantly. The lines across his forehead, broad and taut against somewhat tanned and way too youthful skin (--provided my math, based on his year of birth, holds true--) dance the way his words do when he gears up to tell me words after

"Poor"

here in the coffee shop I'm meeting this extraordinary man in.

He goes on for a moment, stirring absently at the fresh cup of coffee placed in front of him, and as he gets me through the formative years, I take a look around the table, only beginning to understand the undertaking we're embarking on together.

Together, because Tibor's son Emil—yes, named for his twin brother Emil—sits in what's left of the booth beside his Dad, and for his part, patiently absorbs information he's patiently absorbed many times before. What's *left* of the booth, because Emil is six-six and at least two-seventy, but only about two of those pounds are fat. I had met him first through my day job at a local gym—despite his intimidating presence, I found him warm and engaging, which was a blessing, as he was dating Teala, a beautiful co-worker who I'd grown close to. Teala and Emil had approached me about the idea of meeting Tibor, here, at the coffee shop beside the gym, and I figured I'd hear him out.

This, of course, was before the first ten minutes of the many ten minutes we'd spend on any particular subject, and this subject just happens to be

"Poor"

and being it,

and, being a writer,

Poor

is something I know plenty about.

So Teala sits beside me, being stunningly beautiful because being stunningly beautiful is something she knows plenty about, and she's watching him with ice blue eyes of her very own, just a shade shier of the blue of Tibor's, but still the kind of ice blue guys like Emil and I—guys with brown eyes—tend to make a fuss over. Emil is taking turns, patiently listening and non-patiently stealing gazes from Teala, and I'm thinking of how granite jaws are hereditary as I watch both Fidler men in the booth across from me.

The differences are noted as well—Emil is distinctly darker than his dad; I'm to learn that mom is Filipino (--and looks about old enough to be Emil's sister, but we'll get to that--) and the boy has a half-foot on his father, but they're both ruggedly handsome, all sharp features wide shoulders.

I'd figured this initial visit would be appropriately awkward—couldn't imagine sitting in front of a total stranger on Day One and feeling up to spilling my life story—but, as I'm to learn, Tibor is full of surprises, and as hand-offs go, Emil and Teala are sufficiently pleased at their handling of this particular one.

We're here, the four of us, and the coffee is warm and so is the sentiment, and, ten words past

"Poor"

I've got the feeling that I'm in for one hell of a ride.

...

Poor, for me meant growing up some six concessions from somewhere on a map, and playing with small pieces of wood I told myself were anything other than, small pieces of wood.

Poor, for Tibor meant huddled together with his father Tibor Ference and mother Racz Anna; huddled between twin brother Emil and sister Piroska…huddled between the brothers and sisters and sons and daughters of the fathers and mothers hunkered down in a hollowed tunnel below the earth. Poor meant sleeping to the serenading sounds of hammering jackboots—hundreds strong—of soldiers soldiering in what used to be their home city of Budapest, some years before the World War he was a part of, in this first War of the Wars of his life, living underground as the Hungarian Revolution raged on the streets he used to call safe.

When it comes to

"Poor"

I think to myself as I begin transcribing his words on the paper next to the second coffee on the first visit—Tibor wasn't lying when he told me I had no damn idea what the word meant.

And all I can think is

I'm in

and

I'm doing this

—transcribing the story of this man's life, not as a favor to stunningly beautiful Teala and stunningly big Emil—

I'm doing this because I can't wait to hear what he's going to tell me next.

...

What follows then, are the words just after—and then all of the words that followed.

Or, succinctly, to quote the man himself...

"Boy, have I got a story to tell you."

Just How Poor, Poor Can Be.

Tibor walks to school, Day One, with no shoes on his feet. He does this because he owns no shoes. The socks he kind-of wears kind-of count, *because they're something, right?*

He tells himself this as he saunters down cobblestone streets, excited at the prospect of this whole *education* thing, the things it could mean for his future. Emil saunters some seven steps south, equally shoeless and equally excited.

Between the two of them, the boys have about two functional, whole socks, and about two semi-functional—so one-or-two-toes-sticking-through-one-or-two-holes socks. Still, its school and it's new and it's a glimmer of hope where, traditionally, there just hasn't been one.

The sun washes Tibor's face as he approaches the halfway-part of the walk to school—a little over an hour in what should be a two-hour trek—one way—and all he can think of is how great this whole education thing is going to be.

…

This whole education thing sucks. It's Day Twenty, and he's still shoeless—only now he's shoeless and miserable, because it's lunchtime and the thing about lunch time when you're shoeless is that you're goddamn lunch-less, too. It was just something he never bothered to think about—why would he? School is to be for education, not illustrating and exacerbating class divides by sticking everyone in a fenced and poorly kept auditorium guarded by what he has discovered to be stone-faced heartless-bastard teachers.

Teachers, who, it's worth noting, are ruler-hand-slapping dictators. Still, he sighs, surveying his makeshift must-be-just-like prison, he's here, and he's hungry, and, by God, it's time he does something about it.

Over there, underneath Mr. Heiml and Mr. Heiml's overtly-aggressive hook nose, lingers the first of the five tables filled with children who can afford lunch…each day, they produce delicatessens from tiny tin lunch boxes; sandwiches and hot soups from canteens, fruit and fresh vegetables from whatever containers contain fruit and fresh vegetables.

And all the while, Tibor and many, many more children like him sit, far from the protection of Mr. Heiml and Mr. Heiml's beady little dead-stone-marble eyes, on the tables littered with those who would eat litter, just to have something to eat at all.

No, this simply won't sit…not the way he's sat for the past nineteen days, discovering on Day One that Poor sucks and Poor really, really sucks when you're surrounded by people who aren't nearly as poor, or worse, aren't poor at all.

So there's a plan formulating, Day Twenty, and it's a good one.

The mark's name is Hadja, and Hadja is a mark for two reasons. The first—and less important, if there is such a thing when borderline-starvation is concerned, relates directly to Hadja's size.

Or, more specifically, lack thereof.

This will be relevant in a moment—because—and far, far more importantly than size or lack thereof—is the fact that Hadja

that motherfucker

has a lunch prepared for him

Every.
Single.
Day.

So Tibor watches him, today, Day Twenty, the way he's watched him since about Day Two-and-a-half; the Day he discovered the difference between having food to eat, and *not*.

From his perch atop a stone slab lunch table (it's been the same perch since the revelation, Day Two-and-a-half, and it's been devoid of food the entirety of his residency) Tibor eyes young, under-sized Hadja, and thinks that as much as the boy may need the nourishment, Tibor needs it just that little bit more.

He catches Mr. Heiml's overly-aggressive gaze, and his eyes do not waiver…the protector of the 'halves' will have to be adequately humbled, and adequately inefficient, if his plan is to work. So he spits, physically manifesting eighteen-and-a-half days of displeasure, and leans over his left shoulder to whisper in Stugard's ear.

Stugard

because he's much bigger than Hadja

and

because he's the other half of the plan.

…

It's five, six minutes later, and Tibor makes a beeline for Mr. Heiml. This, of course, is part of the plan—a necessary distraction in order to allow Stugard to move into position. Considering the size—and therefore lack of speed—of Stugard, his timing must be precise. A bead of perspiration dances erratically across his young, strained brow as Tibor meets the daunting figure's gaze.

Mr. Heiml is looking at his with those cold, dead eyes…

"Aargh!"

Eyes which double in size, instantly, the moment after Tibor accidentally -on-purpose catches his big, naked-because-the-sock-has-a-hole-in-it toe on a jagged edge of schoolyard concrete and topples headfirst onto the ground.

He knows his pantomime must be divine, so he writhes there, twisting and contorting his young frame while grabbing his sock-but-no-shoe-because-he's-poor, foot in his tiny hands and crying as loud and as aggressively as he can.

As Mr. Heiml dashes toward him, leaving the fat, rich, well-fed table of youths unprotected, Tibor bites down on his lip to hide his smile.

Twenty days with no lunch.

There will not be a twenty-first.

…

Through the tears, Tibor peers around Mr. Heiml's hulking and now-hunched frame, stealing glances between cries and exaggerated descriptions of imagined agonies. Heiml is also feigning concern, trying to pry Tibor's hungry little fingers apart long enough to inspect the damage; doubtless the extent of his actual worry is simply shutting his cries so he can return to his table of rich, well-fed bastards.

A table of rich, well-fed bastards and one grinning, giant-in-comparison Stugard, who is grinning because he's reached his position, and giant-in-comparison because said position is directly in young Hadja's face.

Even his shadow appears menacing, blanketing the smaller boy in darkness as he peers up from the corners of his sandwich…he would meet Stugard's gaze, if Stugard were in fact gazing down in silent intimidations, but this is not yet to be…

…because Stugard is looking at Tibor, and waiting for the signal.

A moment for the clouds to clear, and the "pain" to subside, and Tibor, between tears imagined and real

--because damn it, he's hungry—

gives Stugard the wink.

Recognizing the pre-determined call-to-action, Stugard hesitates only for Tibor's wailings to crescendo once more, knowing the noise will do well to drown out the cries.

He cocks his ham-sized fist, eager to commence the crying.

…

From the dirt, Tibor has a perfect view of the beating young Hadja is receiving. Confident Stugard has appropriately doled out both bruising and dread, he reduces the pitch of his cries, and allows Mr. Heiml's investigations to continue unmolested. Once the teacher/guardian has appropriately determined that nothing has been broken, he allows the man to assist him to his feet, still selling the injury as he limps back toward an already returned and waiting Stugard.

A nod, a handshake, and another wink, and Stugard is satisfied that his payment is coming…Tibor waits a moment, watching patiently from his perch atop a stone slab table, for the bell to ring, signifying the end of a productive lunch break.

On his way back to the confines of the classroom, he's sure to position himself directly beside a wounded and shaking Hadja, one who, with his head sunken in embarrassment, has perfectly managed to disguise his beating from the ever-watchful Heiml. Tibor reminds himself to pay Stugard more than they agreed upon—his powers of intimidation are even greater than previously advertised.

"Hadja, yes?"

The boy, still shaking, manages to look up from the corner of an ever-blackening eye.

"I'm Tibor."

"Hello."

His voice is timid, small, defeated—perfect. Tibor knows he has him right where he wants him.

"I saw what happened—that boy, Stugard, put a beating on my brother much the same way."

Hadja's eyes fall.

"He won't go near him now, though…not after what happened."

It takes Hadja longer than anticipated to take the bait—for a moment, Tibor is half-convinced his scheme may not come to fruition, and the poor boy may have taken a beating simply for said beating's sake.

They're close to the entrance door now, and if they make it inside, Tibor will be required to go left, while his mark will spend the afternoon in the damned east wing, to the right…

No time, he recognizes…he has to press if his plan is to work.

"I can make sure it never happens to you again."

Hadja half steps, stopping almost on a dime, and nearly sending the mass of boys behind careening onto the cold pavement. The herd, momentarily, remains frozen. Over a growing din of commotion, Tibor swears he sees a dark circle forming under the boy's right eye as well, though he has yet to fully raise his head.

"How?"

His voice is quiet, subdued; he looks as though the weight of mouthing the words may send him toppling to the ground.

For a moment—and a moment only—Tibor almost regrets his scheme.

And then his stomach rumbles low, and he doesn't regret anything, at all.

"I'll protect you."

"How?" An octave louder, perhaps, but that is all. The head remains hung, both the increasingly blackened and possibly swollen other eye are still veiled and low.

"That boy is a bully. I stood up to him, I beat on him a little—if you're with me, he'll know better than to try anything again."

Hadja doesn't answer, but moves a little, enough to begin the somber procession toward the impending-doom of afternoon classes.

"Why are you doing this for me?"

Ah. Satisfied the bait has been taken, he slings his arm protectively around the somewhat-shaking-yet-somewhat-comforted Hadja as they pass the funnel-point of the front door.

"I just hate to see good people hurt by jerks like that."

"Thank you…"

"See, the thing of it is…."

Here it comes. Tibor sighs, does his best to appear instantly forlorn, disheveled. He knows it's time to grease the wheel.

"…my family doesn't have any money, and I haven't had anything to eat in days. I feel a little weaker than I should, you know?"

Gauging Hadja's reaction, he senses his ruse is rooting deep within the boy's brain, and casting off fear of revelation, decides to press to the conclusion.

"If there's any way you could convince your parents to add a little something to your lunch tomorrow, I know I'd have the energy to fend off that jerk…if I feel anything like today—I just don't know."

"And you're sure you can do this for me? You really can—k-keep him away?"

Tibor throws his arm protectively around the boy, careful not to apply too much strength; he knows that, right now, the weaker he appears, the better.

"Buddy, it would be my pleasure."

A grin, and a cough to trail it, just for effect.

"From this day on, I will be your protector."

Confident the bait has been sufficiently taken, Tibor gives the still-shaking boy a firm pat on the shoulder, and separates himself, doing his best to both hide his grin and ignore the rumbling in his stomach as he makes his way to class.

Day Twenty-One is a Good One.

Better than Twenty, for sure—and the prospects, Tibor thinks as he tears into another bite of a fresh baguette—the prospects for Day Twenty-Two are greater still. From across the schoolyard, Stugard gives Tibor a toothy grin, and there are bits of lettuce in there too—his portion of today's robust meal was well-deserved. He is careful not to let his gaze linger, however—his charge sits on the bench beside him, and his eyes, though comparatively settled thanks to the presence of his newfound protector, still wander as though anticipating further troubles.

Twenty-One minutes ago, when the bell for lunch break sounded, Tibor found his way to the schoolyard a half-step behind Hadja, and was pleased to see a fat paper bag with his name etched on it sitting on the seat he's sure the boy had no trouble reserving for him.

A quick exodus to the washroom—prefaced by a promise to immediately return, of course—facilitated a rendezvous with an over-eager Stugard, and yielded the towering brute a half of his baguette, as well as an apple and a fistful of crackers.

The baguette had been agreed upon—the apple was not really an issue, but the crackers were both the result of an escalating and pointless debate, and the fact that the fist holding the fistful of crackers was impressive…hence why said fist facilitated their dealings and feedings in the first place.

So some eleven minutes ago, having literally broken bread over the negotiations, Tibor returned

Here

his bench and perch, just slightly underneath Mr. Heiml's oblivious glass-gaze, to enjoy the first of what ought-to-be many refreshing meals.

Nine, and the Things no Nine Year Old Should Ever See.

The boy is running, and he is scared.

Terrified, really—all of eight, nine years old, blue eyes careening violently from alleyway to alleyway as he crisscrosses the debris-strewn cobblestone streets. He knows they're out there—Axis soldiers, patrolling his native Budapest—and he knows they will shoot him on sight for breaking curfew.

Still, young Tibor Fidler navigates the worn alleyways, ignoring the throbbing of his naked feet as they cascade against cracked macadam road. If the pain from jagged stone bothers the boy as it tears into his flesh, his expression does not betray it. His eyes dance continuously, searching the alcoves and shadows for something particular, lingering not on any one shapeless mass, but ever onward toward the next.

He's hunting, this boy, and thus far his prey has eluded him.

Tibor rounds a corner—perhaps a half-pace too aggressively, and careens headlong into a wooden cart left toppled on the pathway. Its contents long since rummaged through, he ignores the bleeding of his feet, the newfound bleeding from his head, and collects himself. Running his hand violently across the length of his increasingly-crimson scalp, he swats at the locks of thick blond hair dancing with the edges of the fresh wound, forces a sigh, and continues running as fast as he possibly can.

His target is close, now—if Piotr's fevered words are to be believed anyway. Piotr, one of the five children of the Tisoka family, and one of five, times two, families living with Tibor in an underground conclave just below the battle-worn roads he crashes through, just one of many who discovered something decidedly grisly on a rare surface-side exploration some hours ago.

He was too scared; Piotr was, to venture back onto the surface following the thundering of Axis regiment lines above the bunker, so it came to Tibor to do what must be done. This of course, is nothing new—over the course of the past however-many months since the occupation, young Tibor has made these mad excursions as pedestrian as dodging random mortar shells and occasional gunfire bursts can be.

He thinks of this fleetingly, allows a desperate grin to cover his features, swatting away the blood threatening to cover the same as he approaches the square in the heart of what-used-to-be-his city.

His breath leaves him momentarily, as he spots his target…a soldier, slumped wearily against the façade of what was once a corner store…and, more importantly, slung lazily across his right shoulder…

…A soldier's rifle.

Hoping that his breath has left him, as well—and for more than just a moment—Tibor edges ever closer toward the roadway, which separates him from this fallen soldier. His eyes, wide and at times matted with hair or rivulets of mud or rivulets of blood--or all three—remain fixated on the rifle, searching for any rise and fall from its' pedestal, sure signs of a life he would very much rather be extinguished.

The jagged rock he suddenly clutches in his right palm will do little to save him should Piotr's inspired-information be incorrect…the bullet from the rifle he so desperately desires is intended for far greater use than claiming the life of an overly ambitious and equally *hungry* Hungarian daredevil.

So he waits, and he watches, inching ever closer and allowing his other senses to numb as the building's refuge threatens to leave him, there on the opposite corner of what he prays to be a dead infantryman. They would do little but betray him, anyway—his ability to hear, for instance, is completely and utterly useless at this point. Intermittent gunfire and the sound of parading jackboots are omnipresent in young Tibor's day-to-day existence; startling at every new firing would have left him without wits months ago.

No, the only thing that matters is the eyes…and his do not stray, peering fingertip-first into the light of the open day. Heaving what must be a heavy sigh, could he hear it, Tibor Fidler damns both his luck and his God, and crawls headfirst from the safety of the shadows of war-torn buildings.

As the sun washes violently across his bloodstained features, he does not stop.

There is a certain freedom to abandoning the trappings of perceived safety— the wash of the sun, the rush of air contribute to a newfound and entirely invigorating sense of invulnerability. The noises are there still, mortar fire and the click clacking of spent shell cases off of cobblestone somewhere close, but right now, at this moment, young Tibor Fidler feels as though he's impervious.

All-encompassing dread and terror will dull eventually; the tugging of fear at his coattails seems to be a pace behind as he nears his target. He hears shouting somewhere close, but he's moderately certain it is neither directed to or about him, so he steadies his gaze, finding himself across the street and beside the what-had-better-be body in a series of relatively non-accelerated heartbeats.

Heartbeats, he's elated to discover, his sleeping target is decidedly *without*; dead, there, and not breathing, and Tibor is doing enough for the both of them, crouched and exhausted and exhilarated as he thumbs at the strap securing the rifle to the dead man's shoulder. The clasps and canvas feel large and alien to him as he sets about his task, the weight of the rifle and the man bearing it a great deal more than he'd anticipated.

BOOM

BOOM

everywhere, suddenly, around him—for a moment, he's as stiff as the corpse he now lies against, confident the echo of mortar shells must mean the opposition stands directly above him. The thrill and eagerness and generalized numb of distant gunfire has washed away, replaced by the immediate punch-to-the-guts the adrenaline spike provides.

Tibor plays possum, resting on the shoulder of the gunman he intends to rob, on the side of a building ravaged by the war he's confident has returned, as long as his lungs allow. Finally, the need to breathe wins the battle with his better judgment, and he gasps for air, sure that the next thing he hears will be the

BOOM

BOOM

of the bullets as they imbed into his brain.

As his eyes open, wide and wild and positively throbbing, the micro second it takes them to inform his brain that

No,

there are no storm-troopers above him and

No,

he's not about to die,

feels as though it's at least *two* forevers.

He remains there, longer than he should, yet still somehow not long enough, at least for the fingers that snake across dead shoulders and the rifle strap restraining them. It comes easy—far easier than it should, as though the ghost of the soldier has tired of allowing it to prop him against the rubble. Two tugs and it's free and it's his, and the dead infantryman nods his approval, as the sudden lack of support sends him slumping and sets Tibor free.

He's up and alert instantly—Tibor, that is—the dead soldier, readjusted and relaxed, resumes his silent patrol, and the horrified and somehow steadfast boy is away in a moment, back to the relative comfort of the shadows and the solace they provide.

Clamor and commotion beckon him onward, and, armed now as he is, young Tibor finds his feet falling toward the chaos, instead of far, far from it.

Piotr was right—his prize clutched tightly in his tiny hands, this boy of eight or nine familiarizes himself with the firmness of the rifle stock as he offers a silent

Thank You

to the fates for rewarding his bravery.

Still, his mission is but half over; the hunt is still the goal, and the tool clutched tightly between bruised and bent fingers is but one of many he will need to facilitate its end. He thinks of these things, and countless others, in the time and ravaged city blocks between Piotr's observation and the motivations behind its recovery.

Were he capable of exhaustion—would the war and the terror and the fear and the oppression to relent long enough for him to truly succumb to the totality of it—young Tibor would be fully within its grip by the time his target presents himself, there, across another obliterated and otherwise, thankfully, empty square some two obliterated squares away.

He's sixteen, hands high, magnificent and healthy and sinewy and fat, and as Tibor does his best to find something remotely close to a vantage point, he's a goddamned gift from God.

He's a horse,

and

--if he's lucky—

he's dinner for families.

For *days*.

Somewhere deep down he realizes the weight of this—the responsibility of feeding his family, and Piotr, and Piotr's family, and families other than his and other than Piotr's—simply should not rest on his shoulders alone. That the width—shoulder to shoulder—of a boy eight or nine years old far too slight to carry both burdens and horse meat back to a bunker devoid of hope.

Still, the sigh he sighs in knowing only lasts so long, and he's only got so many sighs in him, so instead he sets his sights, rests his elbows on a somewhat-sturdy concrete ledge, and cocks the rifle a boy of eight or nine years old should know nothing of cocking. The breaths he draws are labored and they are riddled with fear and electricity and unbridled youth—the fingers he holds the rifle with are tiny and *too* and they sweat and they dance, erratically and haphazardly along the cold hard ridges of the weapon.

He swears the animal looks at him—in defiance and with a certain majesty and a certain sadness—and he swears he's looking back with sadness, as well, and regret and understanding—and all of the things he swears to himself he's looking back with…things other than malice and urgency and a deep, deep hunger.

It's the hunger that forces his too tiny trigger finger around the cold, unforgiving, not-tiny-enough trigger: it's the hunger that won't let his sad, regretful, understanding eyes close as he squeezes that trigger just as hard and as violently as his too tiny finger can.

BOOM

and the majestic animal explodes violently in front of him and

BOOM

He's blown nearly off of his feet;

Feet he collects underneath him to run as violently and as far away as he can.

This was part of the plan, he swears, over the swearing of the soldiers attracted, undoubtedly, to the

BOOM

and the violence and the sight of the animal killed in the square they surround, now, swearing and shooting and

BOOM

BOOM-ing

in his and every other general direction.

He stumbles and crawls and spits and swears—all the swear words a boy of eight or nine can swear—yet he finds a new vantage point, and he makes himself as small as he can, hunched over and shivering and waiting for the

BOOM
BOOM-ing to stop.

It does, eventually—time kind of runs away from him, strewn amongst debris and rubble as the thundering of footsteps resonates and reverberates all around him. Figuring the soldiers must have given up the search for the horse murderer—or, more likely, found a suitable replacement to punish for the crime—Tibor sighs, commits himself to remain there, and mercifully, falls asleep.

...

This, too, is by design, and when the thundering of canons on some far off cobblestone street slams him back into reality, Tibor is pleased to see that some hours have passed.

The comfort of the rifle stock--having acted as both pillow and security blanket--has his head positively radiating as he realizes his work is not quite done.

Resigning himself to his task, he starts, standing listlessly on unsteady feet, eyes steeled to purpose as he begins the trek back to the scene of the crime. Horse thievery is punishable by death—for murdering, in essence, an enlisted soldier, his entire family, if discovered, would be executed.

That the invaders have no sense of humor (--and that they would consider an animal an enlisted officer says nothing for the intelligence of their enlisted officers--) keeps his mind placated as young Tibor darts deeply and swiftly toward the detritus. Rounding a familiar corner with resounding finality, he's pleased to note that:

1) The body of the slain Stallion remains exactly where his life so unceremoniously ended.

And,

2) Not a single soldier remains to stand guard over the grisly scene.

Proof positive there is a God, Tibor gently reminds himself, edging closer to the mass of flesh. His eyes are heavy and tired, despite the forced slumber, from the constant scanning of the shadows surrounding him. He grips the rifle at least twice as tightly now, grits his teeth in resolve. The first part—the rifle, and Piotr's assurances that said weapon would be readily available; the shooting, and the hiding, and the waiting—all seem pedestrian compared to the task he faces now.

The second part—the part where he feeds his family, and Piotr, and the rest of the Tisoka family, and the rest of the associated and assembled families living in squalor and terror with him—well, that's the necessary part of the task.

Which should help to make *this*—

--the third part--

--the part where he cuts a dead horse into tiny little pieces—

--something less horrible than the most horrible part of an already horrible day.

...

The tools he finds are crude, but sharp. Sharp enough to sear flesh and sinew and muscle and ligament and tendon and bone; sharp enough to do it, and fast.

Not fast enough, should his resolve waiver the way he subconsciously knows it very well might…but then, the fear of capture and execution—perhaps even with similar crude, sharp instruments—steels his mind to the most necessary of necessary evils.

...

Quartering an animal is a most difficult undertaking. There's the unpleasantness, sure; the wrenching and heaving and sweating and tearing that comes from wrenching and heaving and sawing and tearing…this, Tibor discovers very, very quickly, and with a force and a nausea that threatens to overtake him with each and every wrenching…this is pretty much what he pictures hell to be like.

He starts at the shoulder—not for any particular methodology or knowledge, simply because this way he can keep one eye fixated on the disappeared storm troopers ahead of him. Nervously, he lifts the stallion's powerful front leg, and with as much reverence and respect as a half-starved boy of eight or nine can muster, he draws his knife's blade across the thin skin of the animal's armpit.

He pulls up and away—as up and as away as his tiny arm will allow, progressively working his haphazard blade underneath the leg and shoulder, trying not to topple over or faint or be set upon by some angry soldier, or some angry soldiers. Eventually, mercifully, his grisly work is finished, and the front leg of the horse is his.

With no wasted motion he steels away, back to the relative safety of a debris-strewn building, and finding the cleanest, most concealed corner he can, places the meat upon the floor. Once more, he ensures he was at no point spotted or followed, and returns to the task, determined to harvest his powerful prize before the darkness of night or war set upon him once again.

He's behind the horse, suddenly—as suddenly as his feet and his exhaustion will allow, and he's sawing shallow cuts into the meaty flesh, working from the anus of the beast up to where he feels the hip point attach to the spine. This only yields Tibor half of the result the front leg has; the rear of the animal is nearly twice the size, and he can barely support the weight of the leg against his body while he works.

Feverishly he continues, rearward cuts now biting into some bone in what must be the beast's pelvis. Just as the weight of the leg begins to topple him, he exposes the hip joint—with maddening resolve he hacks at the ligaments surrounding it, survivors' instinct and guilt racing each measure of his strike.

It falls, he imagines, just as a tree might—not cleanly, and not without jagged splinters and a layer of dusting. He tells himself the raw tendon and pooling blood are no different, thinks of the families he's sawing for when his stomach churns and he falls, exhausted and somehow not-yet-defeated.

His prize—the powerful rear leg—lies in wait beside him.

The dreadful spectacle continues. The sun, perhaps tired of bearing witness to the atrocities of the day, begins to cast shadows across Tibor's now-naked back as he sets to work on the back of the horse. The retching has somewhat subsided as he peels the skin from the upper side—Tibor tells himself it is this way simply because it *has* to be—he has neither the time nor the energy, unfortunately, to feel remorse any longer.

Frustration has grown in its stead—he's exhausted and distraught and probably emaciated…he hasn't eaten anything of substance in days, and judging by the physique of the animal he carves to sustain him, sustenance for enlisted soldiers (--since the animal he's quartering clearly was--) outweighs any meal he's had from his family's hand in years.

So the anger sets in, sometime after removing the horse skin and exposing two cords of rich muscle running from the hip towards the powerful shoulder. By the time he's extracting the meat from alongside the rib cage he's beyond reproach. There is something primal in the kneading and tearing away of the meat…for the first time in the forever-of-the-day he's endured, there are no gunshots permeating his senses, no clatter of boots across makeshift supply lines to steal his attention.

No, there is only Tibor, resplendent atop his fallen prey, elbow deep in viscera and guts. He feels an eerie sense of peace—the peace that comes from desolation and exhaustion and the moments just north of human limitation, the moments that can define a man…

…the moments that can forge a boy.

He finds himself in the rending, carving amongst the ribs until he discovers one that has no fight-back left in it. His victory is complete as he discovers the tenderloin can be torn from the body by hand—the feeling of the meat submitting to his tiny grasp fills him with a sense of purpose.

A sense of purpose, and of delight.

Suddenly the young boy realizes his place in the world, atop the animal he killed on the streets lined with the bodies of those both recognized and unrecognizable to him. He tears his trophy free, ignoring the tremor in his tiny hand as he feels the blood race the length of his arm.

Eyes wild, head throbbing, the boy of eight or nine, too frail to turn the animal over, settles for half of the available meat, carefully collects his prizes and darts back across the unforgiving alleyways that have birthed him this evening. Overhead, the moon observes silently, proud to bathe a boy better suited to the violence of the dark, perhaps thankful the sun and light surrendered such an effective little solider.

...

"When I returned to the bunker,"

Tibor's eyes, a little wild, his lips dry.

Even now, decades later, it's clear to me that particular day has been branded across his soul, and that in recounting it, he's right back atop that damn horse.

"I could see it in their eyes—the adulation, the joy; a kind of quiet reverence…I had become a man in their eyes."

His eyes close momentarily. When he opens them, they positively radiate.

"A man—

--and maybe something else."

Block Life.

Thirteen families live in the tiny used-to-be-red bricked building...a modest two-story affair, Tibor tells, piss-stained hallways, all Communist-chic architecture and me. He's in Unit Number One—he and Emil, and Mom and Dad and his older sister; five humans in a space that could comfortably house two. Complaining about lack of space isn't an issue for a sixteen-year old—specifically, a sixteen-year old mature enough to recognize that, when you have thirteen families living in a twelve-unit Communist walk-up, you simply make do.

Everyone older—meaning at least the patriarch of the thirteen families—are employed just down the street at Bingyar; a massive Germany road-making factory. Tibor, in his younger years, often marveled at how so many people could work within Bingyar's gated walls, when the roads the company produced were anywhere *but*...however, his father, and the father next door, and the father next door were always rather dismissive when they spoke of just what the hell they did there, and so 'road making' was the description he accepted when all thirteen trucked off to work every day.

Tibor is just happy that they do, disappear every day, as it leaves him to steal glances at the various wives and daughters who remain to toil amongst piss-stained hallways and oppressive humming fluorescent lights. Stealing glances isn't the only thing happening on hot hazy summer days; the young voyeur prides himself on becoming something of a super-spy, aware of all the happenings occurring within his used-to-be-red-bricked eco-system.

Of particular and increasing note, for example—the tragedy developing in Unit Three. Torok Steve is a drinker, and an abuser, and his wife, Torok Ne, is becoming increasingly abused. Steve lives with Ne and their two daughters, Ica and Iren, and from the muffled cries he hears when he presses his ear to the rotting drywall, Ica and Iren are close to being abused themselves.

So he watches, Tibor does, and waits for moments between wailings and the crashes of whiskey bottles upon walls. He comes by in the quiet times, peering his head around the corner, offering handkerchiefs for wet faces while feeling a certain degree of shame; crying eyes, it turns out, shine just a little brighter under oppressive lights.

One such afternoon—an afternoon following a particularly intense evening, he finds Torok Ne stumbling down the hallway, her bruised knee buckling under the weight of the clothesbasket she labors beneath. He knows she's headed for the attic—twice weekly she makes the trek, laboring under blackened eyes as she struggles up the steps. He helps her when he can—helps her the way he intends to when he reaches out his hands, wrestling her crushingly fragile fingers from the weave of the basket he finds himself suddenly—gladly—burdened with.

They speak softly as they climb the broken and heaving stairs leading to the attic—the air hangs thick and hot around them, and for a moment, Tibor swears it must be getting to him…he almost fools himself into thinking the poor woman is actually smiling. The weaving of the basket cuts into his fingers, and the throbbing threatens to distract him—until he notices the shape of Torok Ne's legs under the flimsy, stained sun dress. His focus wavers—his investigation yields less about the floral pattern on the cotton, and more about the hips swinging lazily against it. It brushes his leg, the flimsy cotton dress…and instantly, he's thankful for the presence of the cumbersome wicker basket, the way it hides his burgeoning member.

They reach the summit, thankfully, and Tibor finds himself maintaining an iron grip on the basket. Torok Ne pleads with him to release it—his shame demands he does not. Feeling his face turn three shades of crimson, he utters something foolish about wanting to help, and averts his eyes from hers when she reaches to grab crumpled laundry from within, her face and hands now mere inches from his.

Her skin is tanned and taut, and, save for the discoloration of the ring around her swollen right eye, unmarked or marred. For a woman who has seen hell, she looks astonishingly beautiful—though her husband must forbid makeup, Torok Ne's eyes shine brilliantly an emerald green, in strict defiance of the ugliness surrounding her.

Her eyes linger on his, and sixteen years of age and Communism and the oppression Communism brings won't allow him to recognize the intent behind her gaze. So they fall, her emerald eyes, and she returns to her labors. As he counts the freckles adorning her must-be-blushing-because-she-sure-as-hell-isn't-wearing-makeup cheeks, he tells himself that—should the opportunity arise—he'll never pass up the opportunity to express to this beautiful woman just how beautiful she is.

...

As luck would have it, the opportunity arises exactly two weeks later. It's a Tuesday, and today, the bruising and swelling seems to be across the opposite side of the face—so left—and when he notices that Torok Steve has left as well, Tibor seizes the opportunity to spend some time with the battered woman.

She's washing the floor, and the reason he almost falls headlong into her has less to do with the soapy water cascading the sides of his feet…and more to do with Torok Ne herself. She's bent over, scrubbing at least as furiously as he finds his heart beating, and she's wearing that floral print, flimsy summer dress again. He's behind her, and as he offers his best

"Hello"

--in the least-pubescent voice his still-pubescent vocal cords can muster—

her

"Hello"

back is offered while her back is still towards him. Meaning he's looking at the end of Torok Ne he's been dreaming of, incessantly, for at least every night in the last two weeks. From his vantage point, (lurking as innocently as a sixteen year old can lurk in such situations) he's certain he can discern both color and contour of her undergarments. She pretends not to notice, although Tibor is moderately sure he catches her glance over her shoulder on a couple of uncomfortable moments—before returning to her chores, always scrubbing for spots that require her to extend her body just *that much* more. He's in the midst of imagining the terrible things he would do to her, this beautiful, battered woman—her screams of

"Tibor"

and

"TIBOR"

echoing so loudly in his ears that he nearly misses the much-quieter

"Tibor"

she offers in reality and beneath him.

So it's

"Tibor?"

again and this time with a pause and a question mark, because for his part, Tibor is far-removed from the oppressive realities of humming florescent lights and whiskey-stained walls.

"Yes?"

and with less baritone than he would like, but still, he's happy to have been able to voice any response, at all. His eyes shift far later than they have any right to, and he can feel his cheeks flush with blood, but for her part, Torok Ne seems not to mind.

She's smiling and *still*, and it's rare and it's noted, and when she asks

"Would you mind running to the well for some more water?"

he's running with the bucket in hand, and yet still nowhere nearly as fast as his mind is.

...

His hands shake with excitement and adrenaline and the surge that excitement and adrenaline bring. It makes holding the bucket--awkward and heaving and tipping with fresh water from the well in the courtyard—almost impossible at worst, and cumbersome as hell at best. Tibor would much rather be watching this beautiful, tragic woman scrubbing those floors...he corrects himself mid-thought.

He would much rather be taking this beautiful, tragic woman on those floors.

Heart racing almost as fast as his feet, Tibor rounds the last corner there on the first floor, swearing softly and losing more of the well water than he should in the process. She's there and waiting and heaving from the exertion of scrubbing, and he hopes, maybe from something *more* as well.

She motions him towards her, and her smile is as widely spread as her legs, and what happens next happens, mercifully, in some heightened version of time.

Time that—kindly--seems to slow for them, there under the oppressing hum of fluorescent lights.

...

No one is home—at least, mercifully, no one who would mind or notice is home—and so Tibor takes his time. Takes his time, at least as much as any red-blooded sixteen-year old can...meaning the foreplay is the duration and only that Torok Ne guides him through. He's clumsy with the clasp adorning her cotton dress; clumsier still with the clasp adorning the garment beneath. He breathes an audible sigh of relief when she's appropriately undressed; loses all breath when she is naked and turns to face him.

What happens next happens much more slowly than it has any right to; between the thrusting and the contortions that follow, Tibor is elated and amazed—and, he discovers, in tune with the needs this beautiful, tragic woman has. She stirs softly underneath him, there on the still-drying floor once they've finished, and he holds her the way he imagines a man is supposed to. Her breathing slows, becomes rhythmic, and suddenly he's left alone, heart racing, unable to join her at rest should her husband come home from work early and find the pair of them naked and entwined.

His heart breaks to leave her, but he must, and if she's awake while he fastens his trousers and tousles his hair, she does her damndest to fool him. Torok Steve isn't due home for hours still, but part of not-quite-being-a-man-yet dictates Tibor is still lacking in certain social graces...and so, as he turns to leave her, closing the whiskey-stained door quietly behind him, he does not see the single tear running down the side of Torok Ne's beautiful face.

...

Time passes. An uncertain amount, filled with the occasional—and always unplanned—sexual encounters, usually following particularly violent evenings. Torok Steve emerges in the mornings, reeking of alcohol and violence and leaving in his wake the kinds of things alcohol and pre-dispositions to violence leave.

So Torok Steve saunters off to work, leaving Torok Ne home to pick up pieces both literal and metaphorical. Torok Steve also leaves two increasingly beautiful daughters. Ica is older than Tibor by a few years—she's twenty-two, or twenty-three; Iren is a couple of years her junior, at eighteen. Both are beauties in their own right, despite the ugliness of their surroundings...Ica, with her raven hair and piercing blue eyes, possesses the longest set of legs Tibor—or any Hungarian, for that matter—has ever seen. Of this, it seems, she is increasingly aware...rarely does she pass Tibor in a darkened hallway without a seductive sway of that hair, exposing the elegant nape of a neck, he reckons, he would give his least-favorite fingers to chew on. Those legs constantly carry her away from him, yet Tibor—drunk with the confidence only sleeping with a mature woman can instill on a just-post-pubescent boy—reckons it will only be a matter of time before said stems are wrapped aggressively around him.

Thoughts such as these continue to occupy the totality of Tibor's time, even when, against his protests and wailings, his mother convinces some hard Hungarian bastard to hire him.

It sucks, this job—but so does Communism and the crushing oppression that comes with it—so if hours of back-breaking manual labor can provide even a modicum of financial relief for his over-burdened family, then hours of back-breaking manual labor it is.

So, for more days in a week than he would like to, Tibor spends twelve hours unloading slabs from the backs of trucks, all the while cursing both the crushing oppression of Communism and the ever-increasing callouses forming on his hands. The only redeemable element of the job, Tibor realizes—and realizes rather quickly—is the scenery.

Konti Utca Street snakes a quarter-mile from the waterfront, and as a result, is a hub and a bastion for trade and industry. The unofficial 'gate way to Hungary' is littered with merchants and makeshift warehouses, teaming with hustlers and vagabonds and sailors and businessmen.

And,

(Thank God)

--hookers.

Dozens of them parade the chaos of the strip daily, flashing their wares and plying their trade amongst the appreciative throngs of over-eager sailors and handsy Johns. Tibor may be young, but he's street-wise enough to recognize the towering Mafia enforcers prowling the corners; everyone behaves, he imagines, because they *have* to. Young or old, there is no imagination required for the results of 'damaging the goods' along the Konti Utca.

So his toilings are tempered with the maturations that accompany his environment—within two months, he has grown exponentially in both the amounts of callouses adorning his palms and the acquired ability to cat-call like the heartiest of sea-men.

Grown too, in stature—although the newfound ripples of sinew and cords of muscle still belie the rigors of the trade, the results are both welcomed by Tibor and noticed by the targets of his increasingly bold come-hitherings.

...

It's Tuesday, and Tuesday, like the Tuesdays before, and oppressively, like the Tuesdays to follow, find Tibor toiling semi-productively…for every truck bed unloaded there are a half-dozen ladies-of-the-night to coo after, and he does, emboldened by the routine and the banality of the task at hand—until he sees something, there on the back of a truck a quarter-mile down the Konti Utca that instantly changes Tuesdays forever.

Torok Ica—Torok Ne's beautiful, raven-haired daughter emerges from the stairwell adjoining the fish monger directly across the street from his vantage point, there on the back of the just-unloaded truck. This is significant enough to leave him staring, slack-jawed and starry-eyed for two reasons.

One-that particular stairway has been granted almost mythical status to the young men who toil around it—quite literally, the translation is 'Stairway to Heaven,' because it leads directly to the series of make-shift apartments the girls take paying customers to—far removed, no doubt, from the prying eyes of their dutiful wives and

Two-Torok Ne, Ica's poor, battered mother is convinced Ica works a secretarial job at an esteemed office decidedly *nowhere close* to the Konti Utca.

The realization hits him harder than a whiskey-powered backhand from Ica's father, Torok Steve

--Daddy's little girl

(--his beautiful, voluptuous, decidedly exotic little girl)

--is a prostitute.

A prostitute who—as her John saunters, satisfied, onto the street beside her, descending finally, and obviously, by the kiss on her cheek and the not-so-subtle cash he hands her in lieu of a handshake—

fixes her beautiful blue eyes across the street, and stops, transfixed, upon meeting his.

So, yeah—

--goodbye Tuesdays.

…

He has seen the look before, he realizes—and in a haze because she's staring at him and he's staring at her; it is the look of a deer upon realization they're in the hunter's cross-sight.

It is resignation, bewilderment, disdain, and defiance. Only more, somehow…for surely no prey in any hunter's cross-sight has been possessed of beauty such as Ica's. Tibor does his best not to fall outright from the back of the truck; transfixed, his body twitches in tandem with the movement of his target—this stunning beauty has much to answer for, and both know it best to have such conversations before inevitable awkward glances across apartment hallways.

When she moves, its first and its fast, and he has a half-mind to turn and run.

But,

eyes,

and hers hold him and his other half-mind—the one currently churning and charging south of his waist won't let him move anywhere but closer to her. And he does, hoping his jumping down from the bed of the truck looks as cool as he desperately needs it to, feet hitting the cobblestone a half-heartbeat after hers.

So he's lost in the race and the fight, before realizing he's in either, and she's on him, not the way he would prefer—and it's all Tibor can do to keep his other half-mind from poking her from beneath the fabric of his torn jeans, so close to him this beautiful woman comes.

Her hands move quickly, too; she's shouting obscenities in broken English and not-much-better Hungarian, all

"If you say anything, I'll have you killed,"

and

"Do you see the man watching us across the street?"

and

he does, partly because he is the biggest, meanest man Tibor has ever seen

and

"He's the biggest, meanest man you have ever seen."

Yeah, she's moving quickly and gesturing wildly and her moves are too, and maybe if Tibor was paying attention the biggest, meanest man he's ever seen is moving too and towards them, but

eyes,

and hers aren't moving, at all.

So neither does his, and he's telling himself it's because he's cool and tough *enough*; but looking at her looking at him they both know his eyes aren't moving because they *can't*.

Ica sees it too, changing tactics as quickly as her aggressively quick hand gestures, which slow down as well; just enough to send a shiver down his spine when one comes to rest somewhere north

--but not north enough—

of the secret he only kind-of desperately wants to hide under his jeans.

Her voice is Hungarian and only; and the way she's looking at him when she whispers

"So, are you going to keep our little secret?"

they might as well be the only two on the whole of the Konti Utca.

He opens his mouth to answer, and it's all

"I'll do any-everything you want me too,"

but before he can use his manliest voice

her lips are covering his lips the way he's been wanting them to, every frozen moment in the litany of frozen moments since he spotted her spotting him across the street.

Across the street, like where the biggest, meanest man he's ever seen remains, satisfied the way he *must be* since what looked like a problem turned out to be just another passionate negotiation.

Torok Ica takes him by the hand, there amongst the hustlers and vagabonds and sailors and businessmen, and when the "Stairway to Heaven" opens up to young Tibor, the confidence that comes from bedding both mother and impossibly-beautiful daughter comes hard and,

God Bless Youth

comes again.

…

Tibor walks home with the strut of a sixteen-year old who has bedded both a beautifully voluptuous, decidedly exotic twenty-two year old….and her mother.

So pretty much like no other sixteen-year old has strutted, ever, and said strut is far better for it. It's on his mind—really, how could it not be—and it's all-encompassing and it makes both the passing of time and cobblestones on the walk home better and by degrees.

He's practically levitating the length of the sidewalk, blessing the effects his conquests have granted his ego, and, somewhere dark and small and yet embarrassingly intimate in the back of his mind, he's thinking of neither Torok Ne nor Torok Ica.

No, his mind wanders to Ica's younger sister, Torok Iren, the sole remaining female living - life of fear under Torok Steve's roof, and wonders what wonders his confidence could gain should he climb that mountain, as well.

…

"You didn't."

I put the pen down, align the corners of my note paper earnestly, and yet absently, if for no other reason than my eyes are scanning his for the slightest sign of exaggeration.

He just smiles at me, there across the table, as if silently encouraging me to bombard him with vocalizations of my disbelief.

"You didn't—

The wattage of his grin increases.

"—let me finish the story."

"There's no way."

"Iren was some three, four years younger than Ica, but in many ways, she was just as beautiful—"

I pick up the pen, shake my head and follow his lead. Of all the stories I have heard, or have yet to, this is one of the tamer ones, and from what I have gathered, the crushing coercion of Communism has a way of heightening emotion, so as my pen races to follow, I'm forced to smile.

Thankful, more than anything else, to be along for the ride.

...

Iren was some three, four years younger than Ica, but in many ways she was just as beautiful. Iren's hair was dark (though a couple of shades shy of Ica's) and long, (though a couple of strands shorter.) She was too, though in recollection it could have more to do with the height of the heels her older sister favored than any genetic pre-disposition the second daughter of Torok Steve lacked.

Her smile he remembers most and most fondly, the way she flashed it more than any Communist had a right to. Iren may not have had the kind of secret to keep from her parents that her older sister had—she had secrets, nonetheless.

Paramount among them was a paramour—surely something worthy of the absolute ire of Torok Steve, who, amongst his catalogue of faults, honestly believed any girl with a smile such as Iren's was oblivious to the attentions received by boys deemed unworthy. (So, *all* boys.)

Including a young man just a few months shy of Tibor named Sular, who worked a block away from the Konti Utca, slaving behind a factory wall making pencils and other office equipment. Sular was a nice enough boy, and, from the conversations Tibor struck up with him, seemed to genuinely love Iren.

Problem was, Tibor reasoned he loved her—or, at least lusted after her—a little bit more.

Even the crushing oppression of Communism relented daily for lunch, at which time Tibor and his crew from the 'Utca' would venture farther up the block, meeting the working boys of various factories and stores and backs-of-trucks for games and leisure and lunch amongst the dilapidated ruins of a once-proud storefront. They affectionately called it 'home base,' and it *was*, a haven for all the posturing and gossiping and outright exaggerating testosterone-fueled boys are prone to do, away from the prying eyes and cupped ears of stifling adults.

For his part, Tibor kept his conquests to himself, realizing after many sleepless nights spent listening to Torok Steve wail on his wife that any illumination on his activities could lead to a wailing of his own—or worse, for poor Torok Ne.

Still, he made friends despite his lack of boasting and story-telling, instead earning respect for his athletic endeavors, including a particularly nasty natch for slap boxing and hide-and-seek.

His physical dominance assured his ascension in the boy's social hierarchy, and he was privy to many secrets during his lunch breaks at home base. He silently scoffed at descriptions of the rooms above the fabled 'Stairway to Heaven;' he knew the truth, the un-upholstered furniture and patchwork drywall a far cry from braggadocios accounts of Corinthian leather and luxurious goose-down duvets atop silk sheets adorning beds bigger than they have any right to be.

He was shrewd enough to keep this information to himself, and soon he could not account for all of his newfound friends on fingers *and* toes. Some, in retrospect, were barely worth remembering—some, for one reason or another, stood out more than others.

And then there was Sular.

...

"I think I love her, Tibor."

Tibor slumps onto the dirt beside him, the dust cloud he creates simply adds to the layer he's accumulated from a solid half-day's work.

Sular shifts slightly; the factory he toils at must have some modicum of cleanliness or hygiene and the maintenance of—for all the boys rough housing daily in the abandoned storefront, he's always the least dirty.

Tibor might have the presence of mind to recognize the boy's somewhat alien regards to the somewhat mandatory physical component of daily lunchtime—he might even catalogue the decidedly feminine features of the boy speaking whimsically of love—instead he's lost, as always and as he has been, lately—on feelings of his own.

For Torok Ne,

Torok Ica

--and, now that the boy with the well-manicured eyebrows mentions it—

for Torok Iren, too.

"They live in my building,"

is all he can offer, the difficulty of forming words oppressive like Communism, when all he can think of is Iren's dark

(though a couple of shades shy of Ica's)

long

(though a couple of strands shorter)

hair,

and the feeling of accomplishment that he's destined to feel whilst *pulling* it.

So yeah, Sular, maybe he gets it, this

"I think I love her, Tibor"

thing,

gets it because he reckons he might, just a little, too.

"So you see her?"

Sular's big almond eyes light up the way big almond eyes do, and Tibor can sense where he's going with his line of questioning before

"You...*talk* to her?"

escapes his lip-glossed looking lips.

"I do—I mean, I can; she's like, right across the hallway—

(he doesn't say whiskey-stained)

--I see her all the time—

(he doesn't mention that it's more like hears her, and crying)

--you know?"

Sular nods, impatiently and eagerly in equal measures, assuring that while,

no,

he doesn't know,

he sure would like to believe him.

"Can you get a message to her Tibor? Please, it would mean the world to me. Since they started keeping us extra hours, I only get to see her on weekends, and that's *if* her mother will let her outside."

It's more like if her father doesn't get drunk on Friday and beat her, and she can't go outside until the bruises fade, but Tibor doesn't have the heart to tell him, and Sular doesn't look like he has the heart to take it.

"Sure, Sular. I can get a message to her…"

Sular looks as though Communism just died.

"…under one condition."

"Name it, Tibor. Anything. Everything. I'm so excited…"

Ever the hustler, Tibor grins.

"I'm going to need your lunch."

The boy is already in the midst of stuffing a half-eaten sandwich into his paper bag, and sliding the paper bag his way…

"Everyday."

…

Torok Iren is looking at him,

looking at him with eyes bigger than they have any right to be, and she's saying something and he can't hear her, because her eyes are saying something *else*.

It's a look he's seen before—if not on her face, then on the faces of the other women she's closest to; her mother and her older sister…so women he's close to, too.

The look, his confidence tells him, says

"I want you"

and with more enthusiasm than both mother and sister, more because of the exuberance that comes with youth, of which Torok Iren is resplendent in.

He doesn't hear the

"—to tell Sular something for me, as well"

that follows, because his eyes are following here and not her lips, and when they finally fall it's only to her hips, and because they're bigger than they have any right to be, as well.

The rest is just *noise*, her softly-spoken and half-hearted pleas to deliver messages to her half-man boyfriend; and while Tibor likes Sular well enough to convey said messages, he's not above naming the conditions for his courier services.

They come with a cost—blame the crushing domination of Communism—and the cost is the kiss she's currently (and worth noting, not at all reluctantly) kissing onto his lips…lips, worth noting, not at all tired from persuading the latest member of the Torok clan to taste.

What follows is not-at-all negotiated upon; needless to say, he spends the *next as long as he humanly can* exploring hips bigger than they have any right to be, and areas south.

He's already forgetting expressions of love he's supposed to communicate on her behalf; his mouth and his body and her mouth and her body are busy communicating expressions of their own.

It might be love and it might not—intertwined and mid-communication it sure feels like it, and could he conceive anything other than the act of really *really* trying to, Tibor might take a moment to imagine what the effects of bedding a mother and *both* of her beautiful daughters is bound to do to his already-inflated sense of self-worth.

Tailors and Terrible Things.

"Sof Pupos was a villain"

Tibor tells me, so I write

"Sof Pupos was a villain"

in the notepad I bring with me to Tibor's when I write. I've learned enough, in our times together, to realize when one of his stories could have a fairly lecherous bent; it's in the pitch of his voice as he begins to sing his song. Tonight, he's an octave higher than he has been lately—I grip my pen tight, draw breath to mirror his own, and set upon the journey he exhales to tell me.

…

"He was a tailor, you see—at least officially. Yeah, he owned a shop on the edge of the Konti Utca; which was interesting in its own right—all of the wealthy patrons who could afford his services worked nowhere remotely close to the docks. They'd come, mind you—Sof Pupos was, amongst other things, renowned for his custom wares—it's just that none of us blue-collar boys could dream of draping ourselves in those fabrics."

The beautiful red brick—a contrast to the sea-weathered storefronts littering the quarter-mile surrounding it—served as both a tailor shop and front for those seeking to escape the crushing oppression of Communism. Sof, as it turns out, was notorious for taking large sums of money to secure passage out of Hungary, into Austria.

Tibor knew this—hell, everyone working the length of the Utca knew this. He was relatively sure that the wealthy patrons who frequented his shop knew this too—though, given their collective wealth, he imagined they would have no need to escape what was--for him and those with his combined family income—pretty much hell.

Walking past the shop on his way to work, he figured he'd have money too one day—certainly enough to retain the services of Sof Pupos—and whichever of *those* he sought, as well. Today, walking past the opulent and untarnished red brick of the shop, he's daydreaming of an escape that he's been told might never come. Still, he's all of sixteen—he figures he's got years to devise a suitable escape plan. He's musing this—the way one tends to when the years behind have yet to color the years to come—when a ghastly figure darkens the just-passed doorway. For a moment, he's convinced he's seeing a phantasm—so ghastly is the hunched figure, so maniacal in movement, that he's sure the apparition will vanish as suddenly as it appeared.

It lingers, locking eyes with his, and parts a pair of dried lips to speak from a mouth that harbors no teeth.

In the moment it takes to vocalize the reason for such an interruption, Tibor realizes with abject dread that the apparition he's beholding is Sof Pupos, himself.

Over his cackling laugh, Tibor takes measure of what has turned out to be less a monster, and more a *semblance* of a man. He's short—comically so, even—from his vantage on the sidewalk, two steps below the door Sof just burst out of, Tibor still stands a head taller. His eyes are black and entirely too close together, lording over a crooked nose, centered between two deeply recessed cheeks. They rise, his cheeks, in time to anchor another smile, one completely devoid of warmth and prelude to a series of words that twist and turn, escaping out of the black hole sucking air from the morning he suddenly wishes he didn't wake up to.

"Hello, dear boy."

...

He ushers him into his shop, mumbling less important words between the ones that stick, words like

"Dear boy"

and

"Need your help"

stoking his sense of dread if not his curiosity. Sof Pupos, somewhat revered, somewhat reviled, presents more of a curious figure than a menacing one—the shock of his appearance having subsided, Tibor hesitantly agrees to both enter his shop and hear his proposal. He tells himself that, by making the man's acquaintance, he could cultivate a necessary contact should the need for escape ever arise—hell, should he ever be able to dress as dapper as he'd like, it couldn't hurt to know the greatest clothier on the Utca.

So he chalks it up to a sense of adventure, climbing the steps Sof presented himself from, figuring a couple of minutes late for work could be sacrificed for a little relationship building. All the while, the man natters on, his gnarled, elongated fingers and somewhat sweaty palm resting firmly on the square of his back. Were he to dwell on such things, Tibor might wonder how a man so dependent on the precision of said hands could allow them to become so weathered—still, his mind is occupied by the honeyed words dripping from a toothless grin.

"You're a fine young man. What's your name, son?"

"Tibor, sir."

Sir, because it's customary, and sir, because the stories of Sof Pupos among the poor have painted him as a savior of sorts—despite the contrary image the old man presents, he's deserving of such respect.

For the moment, leastways—should the hand move somewhere south from current vantage between his shoulder blades, Tibor knows his opinions will change. The moments that pass, mercifully, pass uneventfully—Sof, in between preparing a pot of coffee and fumbling through various receipts strewn atop his countertop, have set his hands to more timely work. Tibor sits cautiously at the edge of a ridiculously opulent velvet-feeling chair—

when, minutes later, he's presented with a mug of coffee, he decides the time for pleasantries is at an end.

"What can I do for you, Mr. Pupos?"

"You, my boy, can help me in a very specific way, with a task of a very specific nature. You'll be compensated for your time—compensated quite well, actually. Tell me—

Tibor draws the mug to his lips, mind racing, wondering what the infamous villain is about to ask of him.

"—how do you like the coffee?"

He smiles, Sof does, and it's an image that Tibor knows he'll never forget. There's nothing overtly malicious about the man—rather, his wickedness is the result of his advanced age, the ravages of time more responsible for his ghastly personage than any perceived intent.

"Delicious, sir."

He's stalling—the coffee is good, sure, but hardly noteworthy…and certainly no reason to derail the course of the response. Noting the warmth of the blend racing down the back of his throat, he's acutely aware that while the man's physical prowess may be in decline, his mental acumen is razor sharp. He surmises that the stories—spoken in hushed whispers and of orchestrating daring escapes—must be accurate. There's a power, of sorts, to this strange man—it is impacted by the impressiveness of the shop he finds himself sipping coffee in, and in stark contrast to whatever ailing limits the man from the tasks he must obviously delegate—tasks like the one he's two sips from being tasked with.

"What can I help you with, Mr. Pupos?"

"Direct, boy. I appreciate that. You strike me as an ambitious young man—just the sort I have use for. You see, young sir, my…restrictions…prevent me from accomplishing a myriad of necessary endeavors."

His eyes break contact; his glance darts to a meticulous suit resting upon a mannequin.

"Ah, I still get by, boy. The hands—no matter how they may look—remember the dance well enough."

"I'm quite sure they do. Everyone has heard of your suits—my father, in fact--

"Has one? I'm delighted!"

"—I'm sorry…no. He's always wanted one. We just…

"Say no more, boy. I understand. And, I'm pleased to tell you, I can help with your current situation. The task at hand will be compensated for, upon completion. Compensated quite handsomely."

"As you say, sir. If I may be so bold, what is it that I can do for you?"

"Not what, my dear boy…

…*who*."

…

I put my pen down. This will require some explanation; the song in Tibor's voice has risen, clear indication that the story is about to get risqué. I've learned that these stories are saved for days where his beautiful wife won't be listening in—the man's love for her prevents him from sharing any previous-to-her amorous adventures.

"Now, you have to understand—it was a different time. I was younger; a little more…unbridled…back then. I don't want to come across as lecherous—I simply ask you to put yourself in my shoes."

I remember my teens

I tell him with my eyes and my smile—and with the utmost sincerity.

"I was young and poor, and hopeless—living in the most hopeless of circumstances. As such, I relished any opportunity to mask my desolation…and, what better way than with a woman?"

I pick up the pen, trying to suppress my smile. Having somewhat survived the ravages of adolescent hormones; I'm fighting flashes of fond memories as he returns to regaling me with one of his.

...

"Her name is –

He hears him; he's listening at least as intently as he can. The name rings hollow, the way one does with no sensory input to make it real—instead, he focuses on the following description, becoming increasingly warm, stirred cumulatively by caffeine and the magics of teenage biochemistry.

"She's a rare beauty, young Tibor. Seasoned, perhaps, by a few more winters than yourself—but no less radiant, I assure you."

The description that follows only serves to warm him further. By the time he reaches the bottom of the mug, he's entirely sure that agreeing to follow Sof Pupos into his tailoring shop is well worth the explanation Emil will have to improvise to explain his absence on the Utca.

"Raven hair, so long it could touch her backside, were if not kept neatly tied in a high ponytail—the latest in fashion in Paris, you understand. Her breasts, young man—should you be so interested, are magnificent; high and pert and with a symmetry, you'll learn, that is actually quite uncommon. In my profession, one learns to appreciate such qualities—the width of the hips, the resplendent elevation of the buttocks."

"She sounds lovely."

The villain laughs, a cold, calculated, soulless current escapes that vacuous hole he calls a mouth.

"Lovely indeed, my son. Lovely indeed."

"If you don't mind my asking, Mr. Pupos—

"Sof, son. Call me Sof."

--if you don't mind my asking, Sof—why are you telling me about this girl?"

He leans in closer, Sof does, and for the first time Tibor becomes acutely aware of what must be a deformity presenting itself from under the rich fabric he's draped over his back. It protrudes—violently—just below the base of his neck, a mass of tissue looking akin to a mountain. From straight on, the man almost gets away with the disguise of it, despite the overly-hunched posture; this close, the villain's face inching ever more towards his own, the sight is unmistakable.

Sof Pupos might be a monster after all—the Hunchback of Notre Dame, from the story he read as a child, rather than the apparition he initially mistook him for.

So he leans in close, this monster, and with a toothless grin befitting both countenance and reputation, he says,

"I want you to fuck her."

…

He isn't quite sure if the 'gasp' is audible or just inside his own head; either way, he knows at once that his reaction betrays him. Until this very moment, the events of the morning have been astonishing in both their unfolding and good fortune; making the acquaintance of one of the most powerful men on the Konti Utca, gaining access to his inner sanctum, a proposed business opportunity. All had worked to disarm the more…ghastly…aspects of their savior; now, his intentions revealed, Tibor is appropriately dumbfounded.

"I…beg your pardon, sir?

"Sof."

"I'm sorry Sof—I think I must have misheard you."

"I can assure you, young Tibor, that you did not."

"This lovely woman—Sosha—I am going to compensate you to couple with her. And compensate you quite handsomely."

The word *compensate* resonates just slightly less than the words *resplendent elevation of her buttocks* do; he's swimming in his thoughts, tasting coffee and possibility as Sof lists off various sweet-sounding adjectives above him. By the time he uses the *fifth* word Tibor has never heard, he's in; hedonistic pleasures circling the lobes of his brain where rational thought should be. They agree to the terms of the deal—a hefty sum, plus the carnal reward for Tibor—the transaction to be consummated at a specific time and location for Sof. The details reveal that the woman—this Sosha—is a prostitute; were he of a sounder mind, he might remember his father's insistence that 'the devil is in the details'; as he shakes the villain's hand, consummating the deal, he's blissfully unaware that there might be a touch of malice to Sof's proposal.

Still, he's a teenager, and his biology demands he copulate—and with as many women as humanly possible—so if he lies with a sex worker at the request of a hunchbacked villain, he knows at least he will have a story to tell one day. So he's up from the lavish seat in the lavish shop, and he's ending the handshake with a hug—because, *why-the-hell-not*—and he's practically skipping out the door, figuring he deserves the rest of the day off.

…

The afternoon sunlight streams through the window; given the time of day, he finds the illumination annoying—a distraction, penetrating his eyes, taking away from the task at hand. Beneath him, Sosha writhes and moans the way he assumes professionals do; were he capable, he might question Sof's insistence that, in bending her over, he bend her over the open window here, on the second floor of the whorehouse he bends her over in. He's already utilizing every technique he can imagine to prevent himself from becoming overly excited; Sof had been very insistent as to when the event takes place, and, to the best of his knowledge, some three positions in, he started a little *early*. So the sunlight in his eyes is just another complication—as she writhes with a rhythmic, increasing fury, he hopes the villain presents himself promptly. He's not entirely sure why he's been tasked with coupling—or why Sof is insistent it be with this…particular…professional, but he's certainly thankful nonetheless. Sosha is an experienced lover, and in the time since he arrived at the humble apartment complex at the end of the Utca—known to just about everyone in Hungary—until she gladly accepted the payment Sof had provided, she's been nothing if not inspiring.

He couldn't have imagined a woman would do *that*—the thing she did just before he undressed her and just after he insisted the room they occupy have the number '203' on the door. Now, thirty thrusts deep, he's thinking there might be something to the whole paid-love thing and actually beginning to enjoy the illumination the midday sun provides when a shadow presents itself, there on the periphery of his vision. It darkens the day, metaphorically; Tibor muses that nothing short of an eclipse could dampen the warmth he feels from her body and the world outside the window.

Nothing, save the sight of Sof Pupos, violently pleasuring himself just outside the window.

It's alarming the way it *should* be; he stiffens, and poor Sosha senses it, her cry beneath him indicates her surprise a moment before her scream beneath him ensures that damn sun isn't playing havoc on his vision. They stop in tandem, the rhythm of their dance violently stolen by the grim visage of the hunchback purposefully pleasuring himself to the tune of their transaction. He continues unabated, despite his discovery—were he of the right mind, Tibor might even appreciate his dedication. The totality of the tailors' plan-- only now creeping across corners of his mind better occupied by fuck--Tibor stands his ground, dumbfounded and still somehow no less aroused.

He had incorrectly assumed that poor Sosha had been owed a favor—as Sof's lewd countenance is magnified by the vitriol now escaping that black hole of a mouth, he realizes the intent behind his hiring.

"You dirty little whore, Sosha—you refused to lie with me; my money, you say, isn't good enough? Who do you think paid for the fuck you're receiving now?"

She screams again, Sosha does, but makes no effort to leave the situation Tibor is all at once accomplice to; instead, they stand fast, neither attempting to perceive a modesty already stolen.

"Never in a million years, you say? Oh my misguided little flower—feel my vessel behind you, working at my behest—you cause me climax after all!"

Had he an ear for such things, the repugnance of his proclamations might detract from the beauty of the act itself. A slave to the hormones drumming violently against the base of his brain, he barely hears the villain's commands to continue. So when he begins again, it is of his own volition—he takes it as a compliment that poor Sosha receives his direction compliantly. Beneath him, she could be sobbing or she could be laughing—the ghastly image outside the window is both alarming and comical, after all—but the act continues just the same, and Tibor for one is grateful for it. She's beautiful, after all—beautiful in a way that ensures this mustn't be the first atrocious situation to befall her, given her profession; he makes a mental note, in between the rhythms of his dance, to apologize to her at a later date. *Meaning he'd like to see her again*; it may be her professionalism, but he's fooled into believing that, upon finishing their grisly transaction, she'd be open to seeing him again, too.

And the thought of it, *finishing*, has him desperately trying not to—the way she moves beneath him edging him ever closer to climax. Outside the window, the cacophony of wailings from the villain indicate he's about to himself; at the sight of it, Sosha swears violently, almost interrupting the cadence of the act Tibor is so intent on continuing.

There's a reason that washes over one after climax; at the sobering sight of Sof Pupos culminating his best-laid plan, Tibor dreads the moment that he may, too. But she's moving, still, and in a way that does little for his sense of self-restraint—before long he's finishing as well.

Sense washes over him the moment he's climaxed; beneath him, Sosha suddenly *isn't*; in an instant she's halfway across the room and halfway dressed, and, despite his euphoria, Tibor can't help but feel a sense of disgust clawing at the pit of his stomach. Lower, of course, there is only the feeling of conquest, an endorphin rush telling him that he's accomplished something magnificent—the look on Sosha's face, flushed with a sense of embarrassment that must be foreign in her line of work—tells him that perhaps he should focus on the stomach feeling, rather than the one in his loins.

Outside the open window, the soundtrack of Sof's maniacal laughter drowns out the softness of her speaking voice; she offers him a last look before having collected the rest of her clothing, if not her decency, she disappears from the room they've rented. Tibor stands suddenly alone; in the several moments it takes him to collect his clothing, he's debating chasing her down the hallway she's disappeared to. Pulling up his pants, he feels the thickness of the cash stuffed into the front pocket and remembers the nature of the transaction—despite his lust for her and his appreciation for her dedication, he knows the matter of greater import waits just beyond that window.

The realization that Sof Pupos, the man with the keys to freedom from the crushing oppression of Communism and the detritus his life has become, owes him, one guides his hand if not his heart as he anchors it against the window of the second floor in the whorehouse, offering one last look over his shoulder before he heaves himself out onto the sidewalk below.

A handshake and a slightly uncomfortable hug and his transaction completed, he politely refuses the villain's invitation for lunch, heading off home instead, a story and a reason awaiting Emil and his pending questions of why he missed work today.

Being Seventeen in Communist Budapest is the Worst.

Tibor's father is the best carpenter in the whole damned country, and the Fidler family still struggles to put food on the table. If a serving of meat, he tells me, was the size of a deck of cards, it was divided amongst the entirety of the household.

So, while other teenagers were focused on education and girls, Tibor sought to follow the footsteps of his father, provider in a way that, ideally, would mean something *other* than shooting horses.

Fortunately, a family friend—one *Lengyel Kardi*—owns a beautiful, hand-crafted furniture store just off of the Konti Utca—and, fortunately, he's looking for apprentices. Tired of hauling bags off the backs of trucks, Tibor relished the opportunity for new employment.

"A good man, Lengyel"

Tibor tells me, weathered features betraying a hint of mischief—

"but perhaps I wasn't of the…*maturity* required for such a position, at my delicate age. Despite my recklessness—or maybe even a little because of it—I manage to hold the position for a year, before my inquisitiveness gets the best of me."

Lengyel, as it turns out, has been receiving visits—with ever-increasing frequency—from his brother's wife.

"He was decent looking, I suppose; though not decent-looking enough that I attributed her flirtatious laugh to anything other than the fact that Kardi was the most successful man on all of the Utca."

Tibor's tone rises as he describes the man—and, more importantly, the woman—and my pen races to keep up, realizing that this is going to be one of *those* stories.

"She was beautiful, of course—far too beautiful for him, naturally, but during those times, anyone with their own business was something of a celebrity."

He looks at me, and his eyes say
Poor,

so his lips don't have to.

...

Tibor watches from his vantage point, huddled adjacent a mercilessly squeaky staircase, and does his best to peer through the posts. What he sees moves him the way it tends to, beautiful women and teenagers, and as he watches the clumsy man fumble with the straps on her bra, he knows that he could do *better.*

She throws her hair with the abandon of a woman who isn't married herself, and she most certainly is—the ring adorning her finger glistens against the harsh fluorescent light, and Tibor knows enough about Mrs. Kardi to know that *this* stunning brunette is not her. She is, however, *a* Mrs. Kardi—specifically and to Lengyel's much more handsome, and much more poor, younger brother Schtuart.

Tibor's been working for Lengyel for two weeks now; not nearly long enough to respect the man's boundaries, just long enough to know he's best to avoid the man's detection. The bastard has a temper, and a reputation if-not-outright-penchant for flying off the handle. While Tibor is sure the man counts his father as one of his closest friends, he doubts very much that said bond would outweigh walking the tightrope a witness to his illicit affair would doubtlessly create.

And so he hides and he watches, taking notes all the while Lengyel kisses the exposed neck of his brother's wife. Her hair dances, ever more violent as their lust spills across what—if Tibor does say so himself—is the finest handcrafted tabletops in all of Communist Budapest. He counts the freckles on her back; catching the muscles writhe and defy the fabrics of half-torn cotton weaves.

Her cries grow louder, lamentation and pleasure tangled in tandem, soft skin and hard wood. He takes a great many things away from the experience, the romantic in him excusing Lengyel's frantic hands and emotional-connectivity shortcomings. He overlooks the over-enthusiastic thrusts and the wholly unattractive grunting, forgives the sheen of sweat threatening to stain the oak already, just three gyrations in. He takes the tear-reinforced mascara racing the length of her rosy cheeks as she indulges what he can only imagine are the man's basest desires.

To Tibor, the act is more than the observed tangle of brunette hair against unforgiving—distractingly balanced—furniture; this is a visceral demonstration of *power*. Not in the sense of the vigor behind the fucking…no, that is entirely lacking—and so much so that Tibor makes a mental note to never age—but in the way a beautiful and beautifully taken woman submits to such a *not*-beautiful man.

The observation excites and terrifies him the way he imagines the fornication *should* and to a boy his age; the realization that getting what one wants with women has less to do with the kinds of physical attributes he and Emil were blessed with, and more to do with the kinds of material attributes they, devastatingly, were not.

So they're sad, these observations from a banister, the way they should be transformative—and rather than being enthralled with the possibilities, he's enthralled with an all-too-familiar feeling of despair. Her hair flies, and his heart follows, and all at once it's flailing the way that horse's hair flailed when he shot it for food.

Helplessness feeds the yearning he's feeling, and beyond the banister and below she's climaxing or pretending to—and Lengyel's not

pretending,

and even to a somewhat-inexperienced-but-entirely-game Tibor, he recognizes that the duration of this tryst is leaving something to be desired.

Like he desires the power—if nothing else—that the man possesses, and he shifts his weight and freezes, fearing he's given himself away…but now, coupling completed, the entirety of their focus below is set to the untangling. So he waits, baited breath, until she's fastened what he observes to be overly complicated garments, sighing with a resignation even a seventeen year old can recognize. Lengyel, for his part, looks satisfied…though the repulsion threatens to topple him, Tibor will not allow his eyes to waiver from the sweaty, breath-labored man buttoning his trousers.

This,

he tells himself,

is *power*.

And if anything is to be learned from the unfortunate exchange, it is that—in this, the thousand-thousandth example—the world is a cold bastard, and that for whatever duration Communist Hungary will allow him to live, he'd better take each and everything that he can, lest he lose it to some writhing, premature-ejaculating *better* man.

They move, and somehow the world does to, and he's left shaking, huddled against a beautifully crafted banister—maybe the only sturdy thing in the whole of Eastern Europe today, week two into a job and a world he suddenly realizes he simultaneously wants nothing and everything from.

…

Hard work and hopelessness are strange bedfellows, but he makes the best of it. He whittles away at the wood below and before him, and he whittles away at the existentialism that just kind of comes with it, floating in the air there in the furniture shop like so much sawdust.

He breathes it,

the sawdust

and the sadness too, and he swears with each and every ever-more aggressive whittling that he won't die like the way he's been forced to live. The anxiety builds while the wood diminishes—changing and evolving and sculpting into form as his mental state unravels.

There's an angst, he supposes, that kind of comes with the territory at seventeen—still, the gnawing at him does anything but dissipate as the weeks since his voyeuristic episode disappear, and the sanctity of age does nothing to settle a troubled mind. He watches from afar as the tryst continues—her visits come more often, and for his part, he does to—and all the while, Tibor works, undaunted by his increasing proximity to the lust filling the spaces between the furniture he tells himself he shows up to create.

Curiosity turns to disdain the way it tends to, and by tryst ten-teen, he's no longer concerned with hiding his voyeuristic inclinations. He's also convinced that Lengyel is no longer concerned with his voyeuristic inclinations, and there's a time or two he swears he catches the couple watching him. The realization feels anything but welcome, the latest in a soul-crushing series of tangibly oppressive moments, a stare telling him that he's not good enough.

He catalogs it and maybe whittles the wood underneath him a little harder, a quiet retaliation, telling himself that he will not be held underfoot by a system he did not choose to be born into.

Tiny Crimes--

Crushingly, a year passes this way. Seasons bleed together for the first time in his young life, the winter wind whispers into his ear for the first time in his eighteen snows, telling him that this pace will be unrelenting, and perhaps ever-increasing. He walks to work everyday, bracing himself against the harshness of the climate, bracing himself against the visuals from a still-torrid and somehow still-undiscovered affair, bracing himself for the latest in a line of days that do no service toward his dreams of a better life.

He's thinking of these things, amongst a myriad of others, when a shrill sound splits the winter wind, startling the young man from his silent machinations.

He turns his head toward the sight of the disturbance; a rotund and ruby cheeked woman huddled under the canopy attached to a tiny cement hovel. She calls again, his name and other sweetness, and he forgives the wind for biting him as he makes his way to her, recognizing as he advances that the woman in question is Mrs. Andorsch.

She urges him onward, a welcome distraction from the winds of both winter and his mind, and it isn't long before he's welcomed into her modest living room, sat across from a bowl of hot soup and the subject, he's to learn, of her summons: her son Paul.

Paul is a boy he's known for years, from their school days together, and shared summers patrolling the Konti Utca, two in a seemingly endless sea of wild young men looking for something more. So the conversation is almost as warm as the soup, and though their paths had strayed farther apart in the years following puberty, they're quick to rekindle slightly worn friendships. Mrs. Andorsch and her soup helps, and he isn't long into his second bowl before she gets to the point of this impromptu invitation.

It turns out that Paul needs a job, the way all boys need jobs in Communist Budapest, and, as Lengyel is too busy fucking his brother's wife in order to make rational decisions or quality carpentry, Tibor makes an executive decision that even admits may be a touch above his pay grade.

And, so he leaves, with both a belly full and a new partner. Now, two bracing the cold on the way to a somewhat, unscrupulous work environment.

...

He's worried for two, maybe three minutes after pushing through the snow and the front door. He pictures Lengyel, despite being the single wealthiest man he has ever known, rejecting Paul's employment on principle, despite the fact that the workload is piling up, and productivity is being pounded down at a relentless pace.

He keeps his head down as he ushers Paul towards the small, reddish workbench beside his—the boys work furiously to clean it of dust both *saw* and *other*, and before long the makeshift station is decorated with a healthy assortment of the kind of tools one would not stop ponder the boy's proficiency with.

Paul strikes Tibor as an observant boy; his eyes dance from the bench to the darkened recesses of the stockpiles, and back to the bench again—so it is of little surprise that Tibor is the second to notice Lengyel's entrance into the room.

Their eyes meet—Tibor to Lengyel, Lengyel to Paul, Paul to Tibor and Lengyel back to Tibor—and the moment's fall like sawdust from the freshly cleaned table as no one draws breath to speak.

Or explain—figuring there is no sense, Tibor simply nudges Paul, drawing his attention back to the scraps of wood they'd been in the process of stripping prior to Lengyel's arrival. Paul takes the hint and returns to his work diligently; after an eternity of quiet observation, Lengyel simply smiles, half-snorts, and turns on his heels, leaving his employees to their task.

...

So he's not the *worst* boss, Tibor tells himself, telling Paul of his extra-marital affairs in the weeks that follow the boy's tension-filled first day. He does so because he has too—Mrs. Lengyel has been making ever-increasing visits to the shop to see her husband, and Tibor feared the boy would confuse his unfortunate wife for the ravishing woman they observe Mr. Lengyel making love to on a semi-daily basis. Again, the boy is nothing if not vigilant—the adulteress had offered little more than a smile the boss's way before Paul guessed at the nature of their relationship. Granted, his taking her on the boy's workbench ten minutes later confirmed his suspicions—still, Tibor felt that an explanation was in order, so close had the boys become.

They watched the coupling together, at times, and usually only because their productivity was halted by the impromptu use of their workspace—together cowered behind the banister, snickering and offering commentary at the inherit flaws in Lengyel's lovemaking game.

They're at it again today; this session is proving to be particularly laborious; deciding the performance too ghastly to observe, Tibor nudges Paul from his snickering commentary, pointing silently to the roof access door some ten paces behind their vantage point.

"Fresh air,"

he whispers into his partner's ear, and with the skilled dexterity of youth spent silently observing salacious acts, the boys move without detection into the freedom of the afternoon air. Eyes strained, Tibor finds solace on the building's edge, legs dangling freely over the side of the proud three-story building.

Ever the adventurer, Paul lights one of his loathsome cigarettes—a habit Tibor knows Mrs. Andorsch would blame on him, even though he's never seen the appeal—and begins a steadfast exploration of the perimeter. Moments pass deliriously, the heat from the overhead sun playing with Tibor's perception of time.

He's thinking happy thoughts—

--so escaping the crushing oppression of Communism—

when a frenzied cry from the opposite corner of the roof fools Tibor into thinking maybe Lengyel has finally unlocked the mystery of the female orgasm.

He's congratulating himself on the humor of his silent musing when Paul and the revolting scent of his cigarette eclipse his overhead sun.

"Tibor!"

His daze interrupted by violent shaking, Tibor draws breath to respond, ingesting a mouthful of cigarette smoke.

"Jesus—Tibor!"

His wits come back slower than they should—in the stirring Tibor recognizes that his momentary respite must have been decidedly longer in duration. He breathes fire, his response exaggerated by the wisps of smoke that follow his words as he mouths

"Paul, what the fuck" —

as eloquently as one stirred from peaceful rest can. Assuming they've been discovered, he's in the midst of formulating an excuse for being on the roof when Paul suddenly and mysteriously whispers,

"You have to come see this,"

and vanishes, leaving the sun to pierce his freshly-opened eyes.

Swearing at the abruptness of it all, Tibor shakes his head, rising from his fog and the corner of the roof to stumble towards Paul, who is gently fidgeting with what appears to be an old, discarded toilet strewn amongst a pile of similarly dispatched and dilapidated items.

Exhuming the last of his violently ingested smoke, Tibor makes little effort to disguise his displeasure as he joins Paul beside the junk pile.

"Look, Tibor—in the toilet."—

His push is delivered with half-hearted intention; just hard enough to rock Paul from his protective vantage of both the toilet and the treasures apparently concealed within the cracked bowl—should a joke be played on him, he makes note to deliver the next with more vigor.

Peering sleepily into the water-free bowl, Tibor is assured of two things—

one-Paul is going to receive a physical manifestation of his frustrations because

two-the bowl is empty, devoid of even rain water, exposed as it is on the roof he was pleasantly napping on.

"No Tibor,"

Paul offers, sensing the proverbial smoke surely pouring from his nostrils, pouring smoke *not-proverbially* from his and insisting

"lift the tank cover."

This push has a little more malice in it; Paul rocks on his heels, dropping his cigarette in the process. Rather than rush to recover it, he remains steadfast in his urgings—sensing the frenzy in his voice, Tibor decides to humor the jest once more, lifting the porcelain cover and

stopping dead

because he's overcome with the realization that,

"I wasn't joking."

Paul wasn't joking.

Tibor looks down at the stacks

and

stacks

and

stacks

of cash literally filling the tank of the toilet, there on the roof of Lengyel's furniture shop, and for a moment he's certain of the fact that he must still be daydreaming.

As if on cue, Paul offers a push back—hard enough to assure a bewildered Tibor that

no,

he's not dreaming

and

"Yes"

--thank you, Paul—

he's staring at more money than he's ever seen in his young, crushingly-oppressed life.

It's beautiful, colored paper reflecting in the sun, and all at once talking to him the way he's sure that Paul is,

whispering

"Take me,"

softly, and still louder than whatever-the-hell Paul is *not-whispering* in his other ear.

If he had an angel on one shoulder, and a devil on the other—like he saw on some cartoon once, over at a friend's-who-could-afford-a-television-house—he's reasonably sure that both would be in agreement, and that he should listen to the cash when it tells him,

"Take me,"

again and the way he was really hoping it would.

Paul's over his shoulder—the one where the angel would be—and he's delirious and devilishly speaking, telling him,

"Take it,"

with maybe a

"Let's,"

beforehand and in ever-increasing tones, and all at once and before he can think he's

taking it

the way the voices in-and-around his head really want him to.

He counts it, right there on the rooftop; all forty thousand of it—a number that, until this very moment, Tibor wasn't even sure he could count to.

It feels like sex in his hands

--so pretty much the best thing ever—

and he's losing count for all the daydreaming he's doing, thoughts of what he could do with forty-thousand getting in the way of his attempt to stay disciplined in the counting.

His fingers are shaking as he throws Paul his fair share, and the shaking has nothing to do with the fear of discovery…a year of watching Lengyel and his trysts assures him a post-coital rooftop jaunt just isn't happening.

So he knows it's the money; the representation of an escape from the only hell he's ever known that has him shaking the way he is and gripping at least as hard as he can to a tangible way out.

He thinks of Emil, his other-and-better half, and how he would tell him to leave the money the way even the proverbial angel on his shoulder wouldn't; for the briefest of moments his shaking fingers falter, and he actually contemplates

not

taking all of this fucking money.

And then he remembers the crushing oppression of Communism, and how much he really, really hates it *here*, and how forty thousand could get he and his loved ones as far away as far away goes.

It sets on him like a fever, dreaming of making off like those outlaws he's seen on TV, too, and to somewhere where he could have a television of his own.

Hell, he could have two—big ones—and the house to store them in—and so he decides that he shouldn't *imagine* what his twin will say when he can just experience it.

This is the only justification he needs, shoving the rest of the cash down the front of the pants he holds together with a piece of twine, and the symbolism is not lost on him as he places the toilet tank carefully in place. Paul is at his side instantly, and his pants are visibly weighted too as they make their way to the rooftop stairs; two bandits illuminated by a lazy afternoon sun, the only witness to what he hopes is the perfect crime.

The only witness, he's reassured, discovering Lengyel exactly where they left him, underneath *not*-Mrs. Lengyel and, for once, he blesses the man's newfound stamina.

--*Tall Punishments.*

Tibor feels a great many emotions leaving the front door of Lengyel Kardi's carpentry shop—guilt, he recognizes with a grin—just isn't one of them. He and Paul race down the Konti Utca, shouting now, over the din of activity along the ever-bustling storefronts. In between the dodging of craftsmen and their street-side wares they agree to meet at a coffee shop around the corner—each will retreat only to stash their ill-gotten gains. Fortunately for Tibor, his stop will serve to accomplish an additional purpose. Emil will be home, doubtless having accomplished a day's labor at the nearby Ganz automotive plant—surely, he'll be suitably exhausted and thus, Tibor hopes, more receptive to the more…*morally questionable* aspects of his discovery.

He recites his pitch as he navigates the cobblestone streets toward his home, practicing appropriate inflections and earnest reasoning, all the while aware that the convincing will probably prove more difficult than the getting away with it.

He rounds the corner to his modest dwellings, surveying the windows from a safe perimeter. Failing to spot activity, Tibor somewhat assuredly approaches the front door, noting that, despite his false confidence, his hand still shakes as he reaches for the doorknob.

His plan rests on the convincing of his decidedly *better* half; should his parents or sister happen upon his half of the forty-thousand he knows he'll have more explaining to do…and that father's strap will doubtlessly be employed before he's finished.

So it's a delicate turning of the doorknob as Tibor peers inside—confident he's not been discovered, he ushers himself hurriedly inside, chastising himself only for the rustling of the bills against the fabric of his decidedly shallow pockets.

He makes his way cautiously to the relative sanctity of his bedroom—sanctity in that no one appears yet to be home, relative because he shares his bedroom with both siblings. It could be worse, he muses, peering hungrily at every potential hiding spot within the modest walls—he could be sharing the room with both siblings and parents; the latter of which, he knows, are more likely to investigate the contents of rooms shared with troubled youth.

Thankfully, horse-killing heroics earned him both the benefit of the doubt and a semi-private living space; Tibor knows many families in the derelict building can afford no such luxury. This lends itself to hiding exorbitant sums of money, and so he *does*—figuring underneath his dirt-stained mattress so-obvious-it's-clever, Tibor hurriedly stuffs the

stacks

and

stacks

and stacks of cash; noticing a series of distinct mounds presenting themselves upon his hasty conclusion, Tibor leaps upon his mattress with the vigor of a boy trying desperately to hide his half of forty-fucking-thousand dollars.

He's midway through accomplishing his latest task—rolling furiously over the suddenly unbearable surface of what was already a highly uncomfortable mattress when a voice from somewhere *too close* stops him mid-turn.

It's *his* voice, though he did not speak it, and he rises instantly, turning to face his face,

so Emil,

at once both relived it's the family member he's including in his plan and terrified that he's faced with the convincing.

He makes his best

I'm not hiding anything

face—which is exponentially harder to do when you share a face with the one you're trying to deceive—and, in doing so, hopes with everything he has that Emil doesn't notice the perspiration accumulating on his brow.

He *does*, or is in the process of discovery, so Tibor goes for the misdirection, all

"Emil, you have to come with me right now,"

a half-sentence before the

"Tibor, what the hell are you doing in here?"

that follows.

Follows, and he does, if and only because Tibor grabs his hand and leads him frenetically from the compromised sanctity of his stash spot.

…

He sits directly across from him, Emil does, and as Tibor nervously thumbs the mug of his coffee, there in the coffee shop they've convened in, and does his very best to look anything *but*.

Nervous, and he knows he's failing miserably—to his left, Paul is sweating and profusely and not doing his best—even remotely—to mask the fact that the two of them brought his twin here for anything other than something nefarious. Emil just stares, eyes moving only to intimidate either boy across from him in turn; Paul is moments from breaking, Tibor not all that far behind.

He clears his throat, absently pawing at the bead of sweat that seems to always appear at the most inopportune moments…aside from horse-killing and the crushing oppression of communism, this moment may well number among the hardest of his young, yet wizened, life. He opens his mouth to speak, and for moments numbering far too many, not a sound comes out. Beside him, Paul clears his throat and it may as well be a gunshot; Emil's eyes do not move from their intended target.

"We found—

Paul elbows him violently from underneath the coffee shop table—Tibor is amazed that, given the glare from his twin, his partner-in-crime would request any further culpability on his part, but he offers it just the same.

"Paul found cash, Emil. Lots of cash. Enough to get us—

His twin's lips move, words come out.

"Enough to leave, with the whole family—and never come back," Tibor offers as response to the somewhat expected

"How much?"

Emil delivers with a decidedly troubling lack of rage.

In truth, Tibor had prepared for a more incendiary reaction; upon revealing to him both the nature and subsequent details of the heist, he was sure the telling would be met with both verbal *and* physical assault.

Thus, he had recounted it slowly and in a measured tone; sitting beside a slack-jawed Paul across the table from his twin, Tibor momentarily allows himself relief, thumbing aimlessly at the sweat dancing the length of the knuckles on his clenched fists.

Clenched in preparation to strike back if need be; years of brotherhood informing him that sometimes rational decisions can only be reached following steadfast violence—the decided lack of which telling Tibor that the reaction to his crime is both wholly unexpected and his next words totally unperceivable.

So he beats Emil to the punch, metaphorically, offering an earnest

"We could leave tonight"

to sweeten the deal, hoping to crack the façade icily studying his features from across the coffee shop table. Still the retort is withheld; the only break to the tension supplied by Paul's near hyperventilating somewhere to his left.

And this is no help, a minor distraction from the greater game at play—a game of wills and intent, two sharing a singular face and trying to mask intent between sips of bitter coffee.

Tibor's hand shakes as he presses his mug to his mouth, and he silently admonishes his weakness as he swallows the burnt blend. Emil either doesn't notice or doesn't care, his eyes remaining locked, appearing at once utterly soulless and yet full of scheming; to hide his great and growing anxiety, Tibor takes another healthy sip. Paul breaks, snorting violently into a just-raised sleeve, and Tibor breaks his battle of wills just long enough to turn, a death-stare accompanied by the most violent elbow-to-the-ribs the confines of the coffee shop booth will allow.

The follow-up sneeze, instigated by the dying embers of the first, crashes traumatically from intended target; said elbow-to-the-ribs causing particles of snot and saliva to detail the window pane to Paul's left.

Still, Emil's countenance does not change.

Emboldened by the break in tension, Tibor forfeits his silent game of wills—his attention already turned to the weaker of his accomplices, he begins the necessary proceedings as though his plan has been agreed upon.

"Paul, go home. Don't say a fucking word to your mother, understand? Tomorrow, at first light, I'll go to see Sof Pupos. We'll pay him enough—just enough—out of my share to ensure passage to Austria. You tell your mother in the morning—at nine a.m., and not a moment before; otherwise she'll wonder why the hell you're not headed to work, and why I haven't yet been by for breakfast. Emil—

He allows a pause to his feverish planning, offering Emil one final retort, verbal or otherwise, before assuming 'silent rage' equals 'silent agreement.' When the blow doesn't come, he draws thankful breath to continue his dissertation.

"Emil, you and I will tell Mom and Dad promptly after supper. We'll need the better part of the night to convince them – God knows our precious sister will take hours to pack her belongings. I'll flash just enough of the cash to make the dream real—the concept of freedom should do for punctuation. Come morning, I'll steal away to Sof with payment of passage—enough from my share to secure you and your mother, Paul."

"I'll pay you back…"

"—you're Goddamned right you will. Emil, I know that look; don't worry, Sof owes me a favour."

Shaking the memory of Sof's toothless grin and subsequent diddling from his already-troubled mind, Tibor finishes the rest of his now-chilled coffee with the authority of a general leading his troops to battle.

Emboldened by the startling lack of resistance his own private coup has yielded, he rises from the coffee shop table with the assurance of an already-freed man.

As he leaves a healthy tip atop the counter, Tibor is impressed to note that his hand is no longer shaking.

…

He steals away amidst the morning fog; he can't tell if it's thicker today or just in his mind, nervous as he is dancing along the narrow streets. His mind races in tandem with his feet, troubled thoughts driving the footfalls he chastises himself for making so heavily. Sweat both clings to and escapes his brow; he's becoming accustomed to its presence at his temples.

Had he the time, he might reflect on the events of the night before—the tension with his brother, and the steadily rising sense of dread as they neared the home he'd stolen him from hours before. He might analyze the subsequent discussion with his parents—with his sister—over the course of three tense hours, hours he'd have preferred to be sleeping, spent instead consoling a weeping mother and restraining an overjoyed sibling.

He searches for breath that hasn't quite returned; clears a throat still burning from a day full of exasperated *selling*—selling a dream that he now has to make reality.

And all at once he's a provider again; savior of sorts, although the thought of securing passage to freedom appeals to him infinitely more than the thought of shooting some poor animal for food. He gives thought to his brother at moments like these—how someone so the same on the outside can have the luxury of burden less existence the way he could only dream of. He wonders if this is why his theft--and subsequent proposal--was met with little resistance—if Emil somehow silently understood that grand designs and the risk-takings associated with their implementation fell distinctly outside of his wheelhouse.

It is as though his crime is diluted somehow—by servicing the escape from the crushing oppression of Communism, robbing a man of a life's earnings justified and acceptable and something approaching understood. He pacifies himself to these atrocities under guise of 'serving the greater good' and gives them little thought now, racing toward the latest tension-filled component of an already-exhausting plan.

It's early—the streets of the Konti Utca are only now starting to fill with the shopkeepers, swindlers, and laborers that will crowd its narrow cobblestones come midday. He rounds the final corner towards Sof's shop with dexterity unencumbered by guilt. Breath following both heart rate and footfall, accelerated and only climbing as he spots his intended target within the large pane glass window of his modest tailoring shop.

If red brick could look tired, the walls surrounding the store window certainly would, if only for housing a villain such as the proprietor. If red brick could talk, Tibor shudders at the thought of the horrors it might convey. Still, today the red brick and the villain within are a necessary evil—Sof Pupos is renowned for two things; a penchant for the objectification of the fairer sex, and securing passage for Hungarians to the relative safety of Austria. It is the second that forces Tibor to darken the tailor's doorstep this eerie morning, and though he takes no joy in it, he's comforted by the daydreaming his plans afford him.

The fog lifts, literally, as he opens the door to the shop…it stays on the metaphorical tip, matched by the relative delirium in his head as he recites his proposal internally for the final time. Spying his intended audience hunched behind the modest oak counter, he approaches with the caution of a man *not* hurrying because he's stolen a ridiculous sum of money that could be discovered at any moment.

Under the muted light of the tailoring shop—muted the way it always seems to be, he notices, wondering how the man can perform his duties with any semblance of proficiency—Sof appears a character out of a dime mystery magazine. His nose crooked and gnarled and a portent of the personality attached to its owner, is leaking a clear substance as he approaches. His eyes, ever so slightly too close to one another, seem to shine underneath the muted overhead light. He stops whatever maniacal task he was performing before Tibor's entrance and sneers, the appropriate visage considering both previous encounters and the slightly subversive purpose behind today's visit. Tibor approaches with the gravity of a man holding heavy secrets; as if sensing his need, Sof's grin widens with every apprehensive step.

"Your clothes"

he begins with a croak

"are ill-fitting, Mr. Fidler."

"Yeah, uhm—that's not why I'm here, Sof."

"A shame."

And a sigh. A decided taste of disappointment rides its echo.

"You would look rather smart with a tighter pair of slacks…hold on, I may have something in the back…"

"I'm in a hurry—I actually came to you about *other* business."

His inflection is appropriately noticed. Sof Pupos stops dead in his tracks, doubtless thoughts of presenting Tibor with whatever abomination of tight dress slacks he's been storing for special occasions replaced by the unspoken urgency the word *other* belies.

He turns, and a renewed sense of menace washes over Tibor.

Despite being the worst-kept secret on the Utca, Sof Pupos regards his side business with an admittedly warranted level of protection; still, Tibor had assumed his …previous…encounter with the man would have allowed him some level of admission both base desires and otherwise-sheltered proclivities. The crooked man's reaction indicates that he may have been wrong. He opens his mouth to say something, Sof does, and Tibor knows what will follow is not going to serve his purpose.

Deciding that a night full of tense negotiations has left him apprehensive to further engagements, Tibor decides that he'd best beat the tailor to the punch. He produces the stack of cash he'd hidden against the band of his ill-fitting pants, just as Sof mouths the first consonant of whatever venom he'd intended to pepper the coming rebuttal with.

The intended effect takes place—Sof's jaw, once moving to mouth, in no uncertain terms, the foulest of profanities, now hangs cartoonishly agape. No sound escapes his maw.

"*Other* business that needs to take place immediately."

The man's eyes, ever so slightly too close to one another, remain fixated upon the stack of cash as Tibor outlines both his plan and the urgency it requires. Sof, instructed to secure passage for the intended escapees, appears unable to close his mouth, transfixed upon the paper swaying slightly in slightly sweating palms.

An eternity passes—an eternity or a moment, and either way Tibor has not the time. He forces the healthy stack of cash into the tailor's shaking hands; for another eternity Tibor wonders what it is about money that can make a man's palm tremble so.

"No, son."

The words come softer than any the man has uttered in his presence; Tibor, over the beating of his heart in his ears, doubts he hears them at all. The speaking makes him force his point, pushing the cash harder toward the chest, now, a gnawing in the pit of his own stomach growing even as he feels the money press into his savior's. He is alarmed at the force all at once presented against his own. Sof Pupos—the greasiest villain on the Bakony—is rejecting his offer.

"I'd hoped you'd come for anything but *this*."

Inflection on the last word, an indication that Sof had some kind of idea as to what would bring him to the shop…instantly Tibor wishes it were just for tight pants and sexual harassment.

"You know."

"All of the Utca knows, son. Lengyel Kardi spent the night knocking on the door of every shop-owner, laborer, and miscreant for a half-mile. He came to me, even, ranting about the theft of his hard-earned savings—and of his intentions to punish those who are found to be in its' possession…tell me, son, are you late to work?"

Resignation tastes funny, Tibor tells himself; all at once he is unsure whether the fear of discovery or the fleeting promise of freedom hurt his heart more. He opens his mouth for breath that won't come, the distance between thoughts and words doubtless telling the tailor of his involvement in the heist.

So he merely looks—as least dumbfounded as he can—and in between catching breath that won't come, the plans he'd formulated the night before come crashing down around him. He thinks of Emil, and how he's stealing away with the rest of the family, waiting for him to return with instructions for passage to Austria. He thinks of Paul, on his way at this very moment to Lengyel's shop, the illusion of normalcy to buy time until Tibor could join him, a half-day to work before escaping at lunch. He thinks of Paul's poor mother, her features giving way to those of his own, imagining the look of disappointment sure to cloud their faces once word of his failure reach their collective ears. He is lamenting on this and a great number of other things, trapped in an eternity and a moment, when Sof's weathered--yet somehow delicate and precise—fingers rest upon his shoulder.

He turns on his heels and runs, at least as fast as his burdened feet will carry him. He grips the cash tightly in his right hand, the thought of concealing it no longer renting space in his troubled head. He reckons that where he's headed it won't matter anyway, so he ignores the slack-jawed passers-by as he careens wildly onto the cobblestone streets.

Sof had tried to block his escape from the shop, reaching with strange hands to restrain him; Tibor nearly doubled him over on his way out the door. The plight of the tailor interests him little—he's relatively sure the man will be fine following the scuffle. What he is *un*sure of, as he rounds the corner in the opposite direction from the pre-determined rendezvous spot, is how *he'll* turn out, knowing where he's going, and most importantly, why. He knows that Emil awaits him at the coffee shop—knows that Paul will be there soon as well; set to leave Lengyel's employ—unbeknownst to the carpenter, forever—upon the commencing of the lunch hour.

So time is of the essence, the way it kind of has been since this caper started—were he capable of acknowledging it, Tibor might feel a sense of relief at the thought of an ending to the events of the past twenty-four hours. Instead, priority having shifted from escape to protection, he rounds the final corner, thinking only of the slight difference between the soldiers he'd hid from as a child and the looks on the collective faces as he enters the building marked

POLICE

holding a wad of recently-stolen-and-recently-reported cash.

And they grab him, these

Police

before he has a chance to mouth any other words than

"You've been looking for

and

"me"

but the me is more of an

"*oomph*"

because he's tackled to the cold floor of the police station before he can complete his sentence.

...

They smack him around a bit,

these detectives do

before sitting Tibor in a cold steel chair in the middle of a comically-over-lit room. Fresh bruises make it hard to read the names on their respective badges, badges worn on the hips of the otherwise-uniform-less duo assigned, apparently, to this investigation.

And the names look like they could be *Franctz* and *Kleisher*—or *Grantz* and *Kroehner*; Tibor gives up trying to discern their correct titles, identifying them as *tall asshole*, and *not-as-tall asshole* instead. *Not-as-tall asshole* resumes with the slapping, and this one is across his less-bruised cheek, and Tibor reasons in between flashes of lightning that *not-as-tall asshole* must be compensating for his distinct lack of stature.

It turns out that they knew about the robbery the night before—Sof Pupos was telling the truth, after all. They hadn't ruled Tibor and Paul out as suspects, given their proximity to the cash yesterday, but were apparently waiting to see if they showed up to work today before questioning. When Paul arrived, claiming Tibor was sick and wouldn't be joining him, Lengyel had called and informed the assholes; when Paul didn't report back to work following the lunch hour break, their suspicions were all but confirmed.

Paul's whereabouts—and Tibor's staunch denial that the boy had anything to do with the robbery—are the reasons for the bruises, which the assholes promise will continue to come should he not give up the location of his alleged accomplice.

So he maintains that he's acted alone, and that he stole the cash to escape his horrible (lie) family and the crushing oppression of Communism (not lie) and the assholes beat him because they don't believe him and they really,

really

seem to like the Communism part. They tell him to lead them to his friend, and he refuses, and he's accosted for it; they tell him he's going to jail and he laughs and they accost him a little harder. This goes on, Tibor figures, for the better part of an hour. He can't quite tell the passage of time there in his superbly-lit prison, but he knows he's been rocking back and forth in that steel chair with every percussive slap—and the residual ringing in his ears—for what feels like a punishment-not-fitting-the-crime length of time.

Really, these two have no sense of humor—he offers to return the money, and he's struck upside the head for taking it in the first place. Granted, *Krantz* and *Chreschler* have a point—theft of this magnitude is, technically, illegal—but surely they couldn't blame him for seeking to escape a regime where police brutality is simply part of the interrogation process. Tibor takes his beating like the man-he-isn't-quite-yet; he gives up neither his accomplices or his intentions for taking the cash, stating simply that he acted alone and on impulse, and that he showed up to the station after the realization that he simply couldn't live with himself for committing (lie) the crime.

They press him for Paul's whereabouts the same; they tell him that they have his description out to uniform cops, that they're patrolling the Bakony and blocks out for miles, that they'll have him by nightfall. Tibor laughs, spits blood for effect. He's always figured he was a tough kid—one doesn't kill horses for food in wartime without a little grit—but he's pleasantly surprised at both his resilience and the apparent inefficiency of the city's police force. In between concussive blows, he reminds himself to tempt fate and attempt escape from this hellhole again.

At the sight of the blood, the taller of the two—*Frontz*, maybe—assures him in a harsh German accent that the beating they've given him is akin to one a father gives an unruly child...his own father having never laid a hand on him, Tibor takes the man at his word, the ringing in his ears subsiding long enough to hear that he won't be struck again. This comes as relief—the lesson already having been learned, he resolves to never attempt to do the right thing again.

Next time,

he tells himself

he'll run like hell.

...

It turns out, there will be no running today. Tibor figures he was in the room for another hour, two tops before they brought Paul and his brother in, sat them down in the bright room right beside him and commenced with their respective beatings. Turns out the detectives aren't half bad at their job— they'd commissioned beat cops to follow Paul from Lengyel's directly to the coffee shop and a waiting Emil.

Figuring that the boy with the same face as the one they'd been beating must have been in on it, they arrested him without a second thought the moment Paul sat at the booth. Emil's coffee, last Hungarian comfort before the sanctity of Austria, hadn`t even cooled on the countertop.

The three of them, swollen and defeated and somewhat resigned to their collective fate, waited another hour, and have made the hours since home behind the steel bars of a piss smelling holding cell.

"20 years—

Paul isn't taking it well.

--20 fucking years!"

It's a lie and he knows it—and he knows Emil knows it, cool as he is and laid out on the solitary, probably-piss-stained cot in the corner of the cell. Paul, on the other hand, readily believed the shorter of the two detectives when he stopped beating him long enough to tell him the likely outcome of the endeavor.

And so it's,

"20 fucking years!"

even though it's *not*—and as if his day hasn't been difficult enough, he's now responsible for assuring the weaker of his fellow criminals that the best years of their lives won't be spent behind bars just like these.

"They're just trying to scare us."

From his vantage point, there on the floor of the cell, leaned against the wall adjacent the probably piss-stained cot, Tibor can see all of the comings-and-goings in the lobby of the tiny one-room, two-cell police station. Silently, he muses if it's almost-comforting lack of size influenced his decision to run directly into its walls, instead of the anywhere else he *should* have; Paul's continual wailings pulls him back to reality long enough to offer his insights to their current dilemma.

"You see, no one has walked through those doors since we've been here. The detectives left at least an hour ago, and no official charges have been laid. They mean to scare us, nothing more. Twenty years—*hmmph*. We won't spend the night in here."

"What the fuck do you know? They say twenty years—you don't think they can do it? They're not supposed to beat us either, Tibor, and clearly they have no issue with that!"

"Ah, they're making a point. What did you expect? Besides, the short one was heavy-handed *before* they brought you in—it didn't make as much sense to beat us afterwards. Nothing a couple of days won't fix."

"And he hits like a girl."

Levity from Emil—a good sign, Tibor reckons. He's been silent, for the most part, since his arrival to the station…he can only pray that he was able to convey the failure of their escape attempt to the rest of his family. Sitting helplessly in his cell, defeated and more than a little disdainful, Tibor vows that, should he be granted his freedom from this hell, he'll endeavor to make their next escape stick.

And he's fantasizing about it, somewhere between daydream and visualization when the door to the quaint station rocks on its hinges. Instantly, he's torn from his momentary respite; the door hasn't swung open since their collective relocation. His eyes strain; through swollen tissue he makes out a disturbingly familiar form—though he can't clearly make out the features, the posture is unmistakable. Peering through bars is oddly reminiscent of peering from behind a banister—and so at once the ghastly form is unmistakable.

Lengyel Kardi.

Paul, judging solely from the frantic pitch of his cry, recognizes him as well. Emil, thankfully, remains silent. For a moment, Tibor blames his impaired vision for the man's appearance—when, after a half-dozen forced blinks, his visage remains the same, the gravity of the situation weighs on him for perhaps the first time.

He looks the way he does mid-coitus; his massive shoulders rolled forward, his forehead dotted with perspiration. Hell, Tibor reckons, he's wearing his climax face as he addresses the lone officer stationed behind the desk.

"What do you mean, surrendered himself?"

So much for good deeds.

The officer begins to explain the events that landed both he and his accomplices in the cell—straining to hear, he's comforted in the regaling of the tale, and the account of how Tibor claims to have acted alone.

"Then why, pray tell, are the other two sitting in there with him?"

"Mr. Kardi, the details of the investigation"

"And where the fuck is my money?"

"Mr. Kardi, the detectives will contact you in the morning."

"He knows—that little bastard…"

"We've recovered fifty percent of the funds, Mr. Kardi. More importantly, the boy has assured us he will aid in retaining the full amount."

"I'll *kill* him!"

Police brutality aside, Tibor reckons the officer can't abide death threats in the police station. He swallows hard anyway, the crushing oppression of Communism leaving the purported rigidity of 'laws' somewhat open to interpretation. Paul's cries increase violently and by degrees; Emil remains stoic. The officer looks as though he intends to stop him—Tibor seizes the opportunity to blink heavy eyelids. His moment is interrupted by a particularly fever-pitched cry—sighing, he adds *never-involving-Paul-again* to his growing checklist of things to do differently *next* time.

His weary, bruised eyelids open to witness Kardi, distraught and disheveled, charging the cell. Were he of a sounder mind, he might comment on how the man should reserve such zeal for his extra-marital trysts. Instead, he exhales slowly, attempting to maintain a modicum of control before the man reaches the bars, a mixture of exuberant shakes and consonant-driven spittle.

He offers something, Lengyel does, and it's bold and it's violent and it's phrased as a promise; it doesn't carry the weight it may have when Tibor began his tutelage. So it's another sigh, slightly less measured than the first, and delivers a response just audible above Paul's wailings.

"I'll bring you the rest of the money."

It's enough to stop him, mid-insult.

"And what of your accomplices? I assume you've distributed my money between you—this one has the same face, for Christ's sake…was he under my employ as well, masquerading as you, you little shit?! Huh, boy? Were you the one to discover my private property, on a rooftop you had no business accessing?"

"You'll get the money, Mr. Kardi."

"You're goddamned right, Fidler! I'll get my money, and I'll watch you rot."

The officer, appearing to have more concern for the welfare of his charges than the detectives, does his best to calm Lengyel down. He's still waving maniacally, attempting to rattle the cell bars and shouting colorful obscenities as the officer grabs the collar of his shirt, half-dragging him back toward the desk.

Grateful for his removal, Tibor manages to blink again before Paul, nearing outright convulsion, tackles him to the cell floor. He's incoherent, rambling there on top of him, and as Tibor dodges torrents of spittle and tears, he doubts—for the first time since he turned himself in—that he will get away with the robbery the way he was hoping to. Amongst the flailing and his subsequent escape from it, he makes another mental note—this time, to never scheme with the weak-minded again. Eventually, his dexterity pays off and he's free; pulling himself to his feet and leaving his attacker a sobbing heap on the cell floor, he offers an apologetic look Emil's way.

His twin remains unchanged, simply staring through the cell bars, seemingly past a still-foaming Lengyel, and straight out the modest police station doors. The weight of the situation suddenly presses on Tibor the way Paul *tried* to; seeing his twin so distant, so withdrawn, the gravity of the situation—coupled with the oppression of incarceration—burdens him, intangible weight on already-weary shoulders. The realization forces him back to the cell floor; he comes to rest beside a still-weeping Paul, and the rhythm of his lamentations eventually rocks him to sleep.

...

He's dreaming of freedom. He's in a field, under the midday sun, somewhere decidedly better. Emil is beside him and he's laughing—laughing with no hint of the stoicism that seemed to cloud his visage in the any-everywhere other than here, and this dream. So there's wheat and women, because all of his happiest dreams have them in it, and they're dancing and he's dancing and the sun is getting warmer and

"Fidler!"

He wakes violently, a pair of hands tearing him away from the sanctity of his dream. Paul stands over him, frantic as before, and he's all at once awake and yet too groggy to *dodge* the combination of tears and sweat that fall to explode off the cheek underneath a just-opened and still swollen eye.
"Tibor, wake up!"

"Fidler!"

Another voice—lower, yet with no lesser urgency; one that instantly merits the totality of his attention. On his way to its' source, his still-weary eyes scan the perimeter of his cage...once he's established that Emil still sits silently atop the probably piss-stained mattress, he focuses on the face attached to the rumblings.

It belongs to one of the detectives; mercifully, not the one responsible for the heaviness still clinging to his eyes. The taller of the two, all pockmarks and thinning hair, doubtless physical reflection of the rigors of a thankless job under the most oppressive of regimes. Despite his fearsome visage and thundering voice, there is a distinct softness to the otherwise cold blue of his eyes—Tibor reckons that if he's to learn of his impending doom, there exists no police officer better suited to its delivery.

He stands, shaking off the weaker of his accomplices once more, and his heavy feet approach the bars opposite the detective. He does his best to hold the man's gaze, refusing to meet any impending judgement with lesser resolve. He takes account of the man—the rigidity of his jaw, the flexion of the muscle as he clenches teeth before drawing the breath that will almost certainly administer his punishment. It is as though the starkness of the man encapsulates the coldness of the city he exists in—if he possessed even the fraction of a chance to escape his reaches forever, he knows that the chance he took was worth it.

Behind the detective, Tibor notices the tiny police hall is decidedly fuller than it was before he drifted to sleep. He can faintly hear the more violent of the cops questioning Lengyel as to where *he* got the money; the carpenter's apparent desperation at the line of questioning forces a grin across sore features. His detective, *Franctz* or *Gantz*, seems unamused by what he can only assume is a decidedly cocksure grin—Tibor swallows it quickly, not wanting to mistake the kindness in the man's eyes for weakness.

"You've got a visitor."

The man offers a scornful gaze, turns on his heels, and heads back toward the relatively-controlled chaos at the desk across from the police station door. Following his retreat, Tibor takes account of Lengyel, swearing and sweating and doing his best to explain that

"The cash—so—some of it belonged to my wife's brother…I was just holding it for them"

or some such nonsense—Tibor catches fragments, his eyes dancing among the collected assortment of police officers and what appears to be interested civilians huddled around what has become a makeshift audience hall, his humble cell as stage of sorts.

He's searching for a familiar face—perhaps his father has learned of what happened, and come to offer some miraculous explanation, some alibi that will exonerate them from the more malicious aspects of the crime they've been so punished for. Tibor sighs, realizing his turning himself in appears to have offered him no absolution. A pregnant moment passes, and then another, and still no one materializes from amongst the sea of uniformed oppressors—no familiar face, no angel of mercy. Paul, having overheard the detective and doubtless hoping for the same, joins him at the front of the cell, his ever-present sobs a soundtrack of sorts, and drowned out only by the frantic cries of Mr. Kardi himself.

Finally, as the laughter of the officers appears to reach a crescendo—and Lengyel is forced down onto the bench adjacent to the desk, the crowd begins to part. A figure emerges, moving slowly toward the cell and presenting itself painstakingly into focus.

Sof Pupos, the villain who holds both his emancipation and his incarceration in gnarled hands, offers a knowing grin.

"Mr. Fidler."

He's appropriately shocked—why would the man offer his testimonial to the police, knowing they'd be sure to reason that he didn't come to his shop for an expensive new suit? Sof Pupos is a great many things; chief among them is a fiercely protective guard of secrets. Knowing they'd be…interested…to discover the man was responsible for stewarding dozens of Hungarians into Austria, Tibor is baffled by the man's brazen appearance. Should he call for the detective, just now, he's sure he could gain a new cellmate.

So his response, defeated and exhausted, bruised and puzzled, does little to hide the tone of astonishment pitifully masked in its' wake.

"What the fuck are you doing here?"

"Silence, boy. This is not the forum for explanation—I have but a moment. Rest assured that I told you of Mr. Kardi's discovery only to alert you to the danger of the situation—you were out the door before you could let me finish."

"You'd have turned me in yourself, you rat bastard."

"Such language, for a good boy. I'd have done no such thing! You know I value our…relationship, Mr. Fidler."

Were he capable, nerves *un*-frayed, he might offer a shudder; memories of a gnarled hand gripped tight over an equally gnarled member as he observed Tibor exacting a revenge he still doesn't quite understand.

"I'd have told you to return the money—or at least most of it—and secured your passage one at a time. Two families, vanishing at once, would draw far too much unwarranted attention for my liking. But no, you had to be a foolish young man and run directly to the one place in Budapest you shouldn't have."

"So you've come to gloat—*you told me so*, or some shit? I appreciate the sentiment, Sof, but it doesn't get me out of here."

"And it won't. So now, I've not come to gloat, you impertinent little bastard. You know, you're lucky that you're handsome Tibor—more handsome, even, than that quiet version of you over there—

His eyes leave Tibor's for the first time in the conversation, and linger—disturbingly so—on a still-silent Emil. Finally they retreat, focusing somewhat pitifully on pitiful Paul, before returning to their intended target.

"You and your motley crew will go before a judge in the morning. My cousin is a fairly high-ranking officer, you see, and has made it so."

Turning, he offers a disgusted look over his shoulder.

"Certainly higher ranking than *these* swine. I've pulled the appropriate strings—your misplaced guilt may curry you some favor, after all. I've come to tell you—and to promise you that, regardless of the outcome of tomorrow's events—you are never to step foot into my shop again, Mr. Fidler. My generosity, you'll learn, is nearly non-existent in the absence of compensation. Your...*assistance*...in previous matters is fortunate to have garnered you this; had if you handled yourself in other ways this morning, you may have been free of this country entirely. I hope you understand the gravity of your decision, young man."

He turns on his heels and leaves, his departure as sudden and unexpected as his arrival—as sudden and unexpected as his message. He knows he's backing from the bars of the cell only when his head and heels strike the wall opposite; slumping wearily back to his post on the cold cement floor, he feels the weight of his predicament bear on his shoulders a moment before Paul does.

Sentences about Sentences

The judge is looking down at him.

Reserved and stoic and unreadable, there upon his perch; from down below, Tibor can only assume that he's in the process of being judged, and does his best to look innocent. It's *hard*, he knows—he does his best to wet the corners of what have become two blackened eyes, gnaws aimlessly at the bottom lip he spent the better part of the night before chewing through. He hopes the dried blood helps to sell the horribly beaten angle he's visually presenting; from his vantage point, he has no way of measuring his success.

So he sighs, appears as humble as he humanly can, and awaits his fate. Somewhere beside him, Paul is crying—mercifully less so today than yesterday, still enough to help present the in-over-their-collective-heads vibe that they're going for. He doesn't need to turn to gauge Emil's countenance—surely he's stoic, reserved and defiant—not exactly the look he'd prefer. Amazing, he reckons, how two people sharing one face can employ it so differently.

They're gathered astride a bench; flanking them on either side are the humorless detectives, *Krantz* and *Chreschler,* maybe, and behind them, more uniformed and substantially armed officers. They stand in a painfully small courtroom—glancing from neutrally painted wall to neutrally-painted wall, he's not sure his new surroundings are much larger than those of his cell.

They're certainly no more comforting—he sighs heavily, the realization that the results of the next few minutes or hours could well determine the path his young life takes.

It's a funny thing, praying for the mercy of one's oppressors—as his heavy eyelids close, he exhales as calmly as he can, opening them with every modicum of strength he has left. The stone cold walls remain unchanged, some oppressive shade of grey. The stand the judge lords over is a similarly colorless podium, staring down at each of the accused with a methodical, deliberate stare. He takes his time, the judge does; in his head, above the quiet roar of Paul's continued cries, Tibor visualizes a series of increasingly unfortunate outcomes.

He hears

"20 years"

in his head first,

20 years

because it's all Paul's been pouting/promising, and

20 years is a terrifyingly suitable place to start.

When the words aren't spoken, and the judgement doesn't come, he assumes it must be because 20 years isn't sufficient punishment; after all, the theft in the stacks

and

stacks

and

stacks

of cash he's took part in, must be a fairly serious crime in a place where stacks

and

stacks

and

stacks of cash are decidedly hard to come by.

So he swears he hears

"Life"

next, and the thought almost makes him smile, because the

life

he's had to this point doesn't really count for much of one at all. And he knows the crushing oppression of Communism is to blame; as terrified as he is at the prospect of spending the rest of *his* where the bars aren't just proverbial, he's thinking of his poor mother and father, and wishing he just could have gotten away with it.

And gotten away from *here*, the courtroom he's drawn back from his tortured thoughts to when the judge *actually* opens his mouth…a half-second before the judgement comes, Tibor closes his eyes, wishing he could close his ears too, because

"I'm going to let the three of you go with a warning"

couldn't be coming out of those tyrannical lips…

…until it does.

…

He knows his ears are betraying him—for another, longer half-second he honestly believes he might now know how it feels to be clinically insane. And then all at once Paul's wailings have taken an entirely different tone and Emil is putting his arms around him and he feels his feet lifted from the courtroom floor a moment before the first of a thousand tears run from the corners of his swollen eyes.

He's crying and laughing and beside himself; over the combined laughter of his compatriots, he can't hear what must be calls for order from the police or the detectives or the judge himself; can't hear until what he assumes must be the gavel striking the surface of the tower the judge presides over.

"Order!!!! Or I'll throw you urchins away for disorderly conduct! My compassion does not equal a relief from the consequences associated with your crimes. By law, I can only enforce this upon two of you—that said, one of you Fidler boys, and the weakling, will be enlisting into military service early--

--*Monday morning* early."

The laughter dies as earnestly as it had come on. Even Paul, for once, is shocked into silence. The crushing oppression of Communism dictates that all young men of a certain age must enlist into military service upon reaching eighteen…Tibor figured he'd have escaped *long* before his next birthday.

Mandatory enlistment holds a strange caveat for twins—in the utter totality of likelihood that one should die during the various campaigns forced upon them, only one of a pair is permitted entry. Fear of grieving families rising up in outrage over the deaths of two potentially productive income earners must have informed such outdated ideas; still, the thought of separating from Emil wounds him (almost) deeper than any conviction the judge could place upon them.

So they listen in violent silence to the rest of the 'lenient' judge's commands—of how the two enlisting are to serve in different detachments and different bases outside of different towns and of how he's 'doing them a favor' by keeping their 'collective scheming minds apart.'

Resounding defeat and a sting of regret trail their collective wake as they leave the courtroom

single file!

the way the detectives mockingly instruct them to, this Friday afternoon, one weekend before their horrible existence is to compound tenfold.

Time, and Leaving the Way Time Tends to.

Tibor flies south for the winter.

His daughter, as fortune would have it, lives somewhere decidedly better than the wild North—come November, I long for summer the way I suspect every warm-blooded Canadian does. Tibor tells me of this magical place called Jupiter, Florida where it never ends—and though our conversations together outline the years of his life before said daughter and her fairy-tale home lived to spirit him away, I can't help but ask about it as our second fall together bleeds the way they tend to.

Can't help but be more than a little interested in his escape plan, too.

I'm becoming accustomed to this, now, pulling my sweater tighter around my weary, aggressively-anterior-rotated-writer shoulders as I fantasize about palm trees and oceans cold-but-still-warmer than the weather outside his living room window. I gather the particulars of his itinerary—how he'll be gone in two weeks, and for three to four months—and how we will meet with increasing frequency as those two weeks give way to his flight down South, hoping to capture as much magic on my page as I can.

Enough to last me the winter we won't be speaking, anyway—so that the book I'm failing to write will be closer to completion than the nowhere-close-to-complete that it is now, and two weeks before he vacations and I do not.

And I'm not saying that I've earned it the way he has—no, the more I spend hearing of the adventure of his life, the more that I realize I'm missing the *most* of mine. I think about this as I study the creases on his forehead, and somewhere to the left of me Emil argues in the patient way he argues something about the timeframe of his arrival—turns out, he and his wife Teala will be spending the holidays in this magical place somewhere South as well. I leave Tibor, and the wrinkles of his forehead just long enough to spot the admiration Emil has for his father—even in verbal battle, I find it readily apparent that a lifetime of listening to the stories I've spent falls, *plural*, listening to have left him somewhat in awe of this man.

It's the gravity of the man, and we're all within orbit—sensing I might be a touch too in touch with disclosing the magnitude of it, Tibor turns his warm eyes to me, and maybe I'm a little less cold for it.

He speaks softly—less softly than Emil speaks, or was speaking—and instantly we're off on a tangent, some previously-unrevealed miracle of a life just really, really lived distracting me from the fact that I need to do a much better job at living mine.

So I write

Move to Florida

in my notes right beside

So I was twenty, and living in—

and the rest of the sentence and the story he's started to tell me, and with urgency, because in two weeks' he's living in Florida and I'm here, cold and nowhere closer to living the life I'd like to, or chronicling the best of his.

Parallels Aren't Just for Parking.

I write in my notes and beside the notes I'm writing about the girl with black hair he's describing at least as eloquently as this writer could ever hope to.

And I'm seeing them,

parallels,

and I'm learning something, maybe, about how the more I listen to his story, the more I'm reliving mine, as well.

Because I've had love for girls attached to black hair too, and I'm thinking that while his story might have more wars in it than mine (well, depending on one's definition of the word war…I can think of Canadian Leos and Colombian Scorpios who have waged their fair share) maybe the commonalities are to be celebrated, the way that anyone who's ever had a heart or broken might identify with the broad strokes attached to words flowing from his weathered and well-versed lips.

I imagine that reading this will do for someone what it is doing, against my will, to me. I watch him, and the words become fuzzy the way they tend to when my introspection rides side-saddle to the great charging stallion that is his thought process, verbalized. And suddenly, it's less and less about the words themselves and more about the man breathing them.

I catch his eyes shine when he reflects on someone who, undoubtedly, was important at the time, yet here in context, is relegated to an afternoon some dozen-teen-afternoons in…I can't help but wonder how my own experiences will be ranked and cataloged. Can't help but daydream about the shine years-on and particulars forgotten or left hazy from days or months or years or decades will give insight to losses deemed catastrophic given my relative youth—wonder when time cauterizes bleeds still too fresh to reflect upon.

I try—and fail—to describe him as he sits across the table, etching aimlessly on the paper in front of me, still lulled by the cadences and rhythms of his seasoned storytelling voice. If I were to close my eyes—or blink long enough—I suppose I would write that Tibor sounds thirty years younger. The accent betrays him—a bit of what I would liken, to the ignorant like myself, as something from some Dracula movie; some Baltic undertones, maybe some slurring to words that would otherwise ring familiar.

No, maybe it's not the voice itself—it's the energy behind it that doubts the years attached; every tenth word is one that I'm familiar with in my thirty-something vernacular. That accent skews it foreign, somehow, and in earlier meetings I would suppress my smile, imagining Tibor studying pop culture programming on his television, and scribbling notes not unlike my own.

It's impressive and interesting and amusing the way everything about him is impressive and interesting and amusing. I tune back in to the notes of the song he's singing me, and I can tell from what-might-be mist under those glasses that, for whatever moment this particular one mattered in the span of his life, she mattered quite a bit.

Now, this is different than the unabashed admiration he exudes every time his wife enters the room or lingers on the periphery of our great revelations; that woman, it's clear to me, is the one, in capital letters—so much so that I tend to write

THE ONE

in capital letters each and every time I refer to her.

No, it's not like that, and about this other one with black hair, but it gives me great comfort to know that, even in reflection, what mattered years ago still matters, even if and only in songs like the one he sings.

My stories will have songs in them too, and I look forward to singing them to some handsome thirty-something sitting across some table from me someday; this book, however, is to be about Tibor.

So I play my role, sit handsomely and thirty-something across some table from him, and write about a life I'd be blessed to live some fraction of someday.

In the Army Now.

"Next."

And Tibor *is*—next after Emil, who, truly, is next…next in line, here in the heart of the crushing oppression of Communism, to enlist into the Hungarian army. They've come here, to the Dank Haus banquet hall that looks as though it has not seen an actual banquet in decades, because they have to…once a Hungarian boy reaches a certain age, it's conscription and mandatory enlistment. Shifting his weight in order to peer out at the dedicated enlisters currently beckoning his brother forth, Tibor admits to himself that the moment is not without a modicum of excitement.

Hell, had he not seen firsthand the atrocities of war, he might even be looking forward to his mandatory service.

Still, the hall he's herded in stinks, and no matter how precise and appealing the enlisting officer's haircut looks, there's little to entice him to soldier in the name of a country he's not crazy about.

"Next."

Well, besides Emil, who, despite his pleadings, was entirely too eager to join his countrymen…and so, here he stands, next in a long line of poor Hungarian bastards forced to entertain the idea of killing in the name of. His sigh does little to ease his doubts; over his left shoulder, a propaganda poster of a soldier with a similarly-sharp haircut winks and points at him the way the enlister with the haircut points at his twin, beckoning him forth. He shakes his head as subtly as the fire of his youth will allow him, and veers right, stepping dramatically in line with Emil, noting the subdued astonishment on the face connected to the haircut at the sight of two "*nexts*" instead of one.

"Name...*er*, names."

"Emil Fidler, sir. And this is my brother--

"Tibor."

"Sir."

"Tibor is my name. Sir."

"You're twins."

Tibor starts, drawing breath to illustrate

No fucking kidding

or something of the like, decides against it.

"According to law, only one of you is required to enlist. I encourage you to decide which of you that will be, and quickly."

The bastard looks bored, as though deciding the fate of lives not accustomed to separation is something beneath him, and, for his part, Tibor has to bite his tongue to avoid berating him. Emil, sensing the tension in the air, steps in front of his brother slightly, responds before Tibor has time to.

"I'm the one to go. Emil Fidler, sir."

"The fuck you are."

"*Tibor.*"

"Pardon me, sir?" The guard's face is three shades brighter; the *sir* comes through clenched teeth. He's rising from his chair…sensing the motion, Emil has to physically restrain his twin.

"I'm going too."

"Tibor!"

"I repeat,"

The guard, somewhat bemused now, takes his seat—all too eager, apparently, to accommodate the request.

"—I'm going too."

"As you wish, Mr. Fidler.

...

Three years.

As they enter the compound, huddled and hungry and herded with twenty-two or twenty-three year-old men—all significantly older, and all no doubt, equally hungry—Tibor tells himself that

no,

forcing that enlisting officer to take him in addition to Emil was not a bad idea, and

no,

three years

here

won't kill him.

Even though it looks like it might—the compound, isolated from the nearest town by a damn-near-impassable series of questionably-name roads snaking haphazardly alongside a mountain—is both gargantuan and impressive. Sitting atop a peak of the Bakony, the past three months of his life have been spent in preparation of this moment.

The fencing around the perimeter is suitably tall—taller than he had imagined—and, as the gate closes behind the truck filled with suddenly-not-so-eager young men, Tibor can't help but marvel at the sense of oppression washing over him.

Hell,

Communism would be proud.

...

Bootcamp in Szeged, as it happens, did little to prepare him for base life. Sure, the ninety days of brainwashing was nice—he never bought in the way the other boys, Emil included did, but he appreciated the sentiment. There were promises made, too—two week's holidays, they said, for every year spent here, nestled in the mountains of Bakony, making bullets, gunpowder and other military-industrial marvels, far away from the curious eyes and ears of the citizens they swore to protect.

Two week's holidays—judging by the looks on the faces of the despondent-looking soldiers as he steps off the back of the truck, that vacation isn't coming any time soon.

Fenced in now, appropriately trapped and feeling so, the boys are ushered

single file!

into a bleak bunker immediately to the right of the gated entrance. Once inside, Tibor discovers that

yes

the interior is equally depressing, and

yes

the drill sergeant yelling at the boys the moment they've all herded inside is appropriately domineering and depressing as well.

So far, army life isn't turning out to be the adventure that he hoped it would be…rather than providing the fantasy of helping to create a better Budapest, all his still-too-new tenure has done is reinforce his disdain for it.

"Find your bunks!"

So he finds his bunk,

"Stand tall!"

So he's standing tall

"Face front!"

And everyone is, and at this point, Tibor wonders, if his instructions will turn out to be anything other than common sense and already implemented, regardless of the bluster and enthusiasm with which they're delivered.

"March"

because, apparently, there's little time to spend actually settling into this hellhole—as Tibor

March-es back out onto the compound grounds, he wonders if this is to be the totality of his existence for the next three-years-minus-the-vacation.

...

Month two—plus the three months of training, far more East of Budapest than any self-respecting city boy would ever care to be—and that two weeks' vacation can't come fast enough.

His job is to patrol the perimeter of the compound. Each shift (--and those vary too, some days, some nights, some both, and always in two hour increments--) Tibor, Emil, and the rest of his regiment line up outside the bunkhouse and march

single file!

along the high-fenced wall, along a narrow trench he helped to dig, isolated from the activity of the center by rows of perfectly-placed pine trees.

Two hours walk.

Two hours sleep.

Two hours walk.

It is an important job, or so he tells himself during the monotony of seemingly endless patrolling; each day, workers are bused in from nearby Szeged to work one of four main buildings within the fence. Everything from bullet forging to small explosives testing occurs within the buildings, and Tibor would give one of his fingers—two of his brother's—to be counted among such workers (or guards for that matter) where the action is.

Still, he tells himself—often surrounding sighs of resignation—his job is important, if for no other reason than the civilian and military lives he protects are important.

And so, by extension, so is he—thus he patrols, endlessly, all the while dreaming of a scenario—an opportunity—where he could rise above his station. The way he tells himself—often surrounding sighs of resignation—he is destined to.

Another day, another patrol, another whimsical musing, and for the first time in the two months (plus three months of training) he tells himself that though his situation is unchanging, his outlook is about to.

...

Soldiers are required to sleep with their boots on.

"Just in case,"

the drill sergeant reasoned

"—the enemy was to attack; a soldier must be ready at all times."

Tibor secretly believed it had more to do with the ungodly patrol schedule—every two hours, he was violently awoken (--from a sleep he had usually just entered--) to return to the perimeter; God forbid he was two minutes late to stare at mountains for having to lace his boots.

No, it had more to do with the drill sergeant

single file!

being an asshole and establishing a modicum of dominance;

so

soldiers are required to sleep with their boots on—

soldiers, except *him*.

He sleeps better for it, there in between patrols, and he reasons that by keeping his boots *on* the bed and beside him, he's only moments behind the boys when they rise to march

single file!

along the trees, guarding the Bakony and the explosive treasures nestled safely within the compound walls.

He's enjoying a boots-off rest, there in his bunk on some Tuesday or Wednesday or Thursday, and he's dreaming of women, or glory in battle, or some other pre-programmed dream military men almost always dream, when

"Fidler!"

permeates his eardrums the way it has been lately.

So,

violently.

Communism, he's learned, struggling in a sea of tangled bed sheets, hates independent thinkers.

As light explodes violently into his instantaneously wide eyes, he realizes that Communism hates a smart-ass even more.

The drill sergeant is an asshole, and he's marching towards him at a pace that accentuates the air of violence. He scrambles to his (bare) feet as around him, his patrol-mates stand ready and at attention; ready because, unlike Tibor, they fell asleep with their combat boots *on*.

"Füdler!"

"Sir. Yes, Sir."

His voice cracks; his mind is still shaking the remnants of a dream about women or glory in battle or some other pre-programmed dream military men almost always dream when

"Fiiiidler!!!!"

a third time washes over him with the vigor of a bucket of ice water to the face.

There are only so many

"Sir. Yes, Sir's"

a just-woken man can muster, and so Tibor stops at two more, finishing enthusiastically just as the drill sergeant draws close enough to breathe his words in. Tibor blinks sleep from his aching eyes, alarmed at both the beady eyes of the bastard breathing back on him, and the aggressiveness of the bags under his eyes.

No wonder

"Sir. Yes, Sir"

is angry all of the time—he looks as though he hasn't slept for days, as well. So maybe he sympathizes, just a little, when the Sergeant begins his rant by enthusiastically spitting in his face. Judging by the garlic adorning both his lips and breath, the bastard eats better too; enduring his continued berating cements Tibor's disdain for military authority, and galvanizes his growing thirst for rebellion.

The vocal lashings continue unabated; Tibor allows his vision to focus past the beady, soulless eyes of his oppressor, noting the fear and resignation on the face of Emil some ten paces over the drill sergeant's shoulder. It's akin to looking into a mirror—a boots-on, buying in

Hoo-rah

version of himself staring blankly ahead; one in a seemingly endless line of pre-programmed drones waiting to march

single file!

to their postings.

Determined to never be the version of himself he allows his gaze to escape to, Tibor swallows hard and settles his focus back on the pock-marked and increasingly crimson face of the commanding officer currently giving him a dressing-down so earnestly.

His jowls are jiggling—jiggling because they are fat, fat like the rest of him, and because he gets to eat the kinds of rations Tibor and his bunkmates could only dream of. An eternity passes; finally, the beady-eyed jiggling-jowls pockmarked drill sergeant decides he has had enough. As the rest of his unit marches

single file!

to their pre-assigned and *not-at-all-repetitive* postings, Tibor vows in between pulls on his boot strings that this tiny revolution is only beginning.

Dirt Mounds, Things Worth Diamonds

A mound of dirt.

The scenery, compound-side – the object of his relentless and ever-dedicated patrolling; the totality of his existence here on base…it all amounts to a mound of dirt. The drill sergeant (--who, in the months that have unfolded since his now-infamous no-boots rebellion has managed to become an even bigger asshole) assured him that the twenty-two-foot high, consistently patrolled and ever important mound of dirt served an incredibly important tactical purpose.

Staring at it today, the way he has been both resigned and assigned to, daily— Tibor has no fucking clue what the tactical purpose could be. Secretly, he figures it must have something/everything to do with the amounts of explosive ordinance being constructed within the compound's high fenced walls. Tibor can't help but notice that the officer's barracks are shielded *behind* the safety of the mound—he can't help but notice that *his* barracks, as well as the ammunitions depot, the assembly building and the munitions testing facilities are not.

He spits on the mound for emphasis, returns to both his patrolling and spite, satisfied momentarily at his display, turning once over his shoulder to watch the spittle stain the otherwise-immaculate construct.

Lately, this will have to suffice, as rebellions go…after failing to salute three officers—and after being put in a military jail cell on three occasions as a result—Tibor is choosing his battles these days.

Besides,

he tells himself, the spit already dried on the surface thanks to the relentless heat of the midday sun

--it's not who wins the battle—

it's who wins the war.

…

It could be the lack of women soldiers on base

it could be the quality of the women shipped in to work from Szeged

it could be that he has not had sex in what feels like *ten* forevers

--but the girl getting off of the bus might just be the most beautiful woman Tibor has ever seen.

Her name is Erzsi, and he does not know it yet, and even if he did it wouldn't matter—for now, she's the raven haired beauty emerging from the back of the bus, there beside his bunker, just inside the compound fence—the latest in a seemingly inexhaustible supply of workers bused in from Szeged and parts nearby.

She's even more Jayne-Mansfield-like than the last Jayne-Mansfield-like beauty, resembling his favorite screen starlet the way they *all* do in his recollections, regardless of blonde hair or black hair like this particular angel has, and its swaying softly as she steps into the sunlight, and he swears

God Damn

softly

swearing that, one way or another, she will be his.

The problem is that twenty other soldiers are swearing

God Damn

softly and *less* softly

around him, and because every week the boys in the bunker crowd around a tiny window to witness the latest offerings to the compound; twenty boys offering at least twenty prays that one day, someone would step off that bus looking something like she does.

She shakes her hair loose, taking in the fresh air of the Bakony mountains, and twenty young men elbow and shove one another for the best view from the tiny window.

As she sways in a way that is decidedly *not*

single file!

from view, every soldier is standing at attention and suddenly silent—doubtless the energy spent catcalling and crowing moments ago is now reserved for silent contemplation.

Tibor, too, is dreaming of ways to bed her—as he begins to follow her, he's momentarily aware of a particular irony: the time not wasted lacing his boots is all at once a God-send, as he's among the first wave of horny young men to burst from behind the bunker doors.

He smiles to himself as his pre-laced boots trail her delicate footprints across the compound grounds, telling himself that this realization does nothing to quell his rebellion.

…

"Erzsi."

Her ladle drops hot soup into his bowl, her earnestness causing the overflow to splash haphazardly across the skin of his outstretched hands.

It burns like hell.

He doesn't notice.

"Ezra?"

"Erzsi."

"Erza."

He cocks his head, pretending at least as hard as he can that he doesn't hear her correctly.

"Erzsi."

He knows damn well her name is Erzsi.

"Erazsi?"

"No, listen to me—

He's listening.

Her lips quiver; she's working hard to suppress her giggles. They're full, her lips, and for the first time in the too-long it has taken him to be served his lunch, there in the line at the soup counter she has just started serving from, Tibor allows his eyes to fall from hers, and only to fall to the full lips she parts to tell him

"Err

--zee."

"Erzsi."

They're moist, her lips, and she spreads them to smile, and the smile is perfect too, and by the time his eyes rise to meet hers, he can feel her gaze lingering on him, as well.

So they enjoy the moment, and, maybe for a moment or two too long, because just as he's counting the eyelashes above her beautiful brown eyes, some asshole in line for soup behind him hollers something about moving on. This moment, hard-fought and long-planned—in the days since this angel's arrival at the compound some two weeks before—is not to be squandered by the next over-sexed cadet in line, so Tibor responds without leaving her gaze to turn. He figures his middle finger, raised defiantly and, more importantly, instantly, conveys his desire to remain just where he is.

The asshole in line behind him responds aggressively.

He hears it, but it doesn't register, because looking at her is much more fun than listening to whoever-the-hell is back there; no, the action is right in front of him and smiling, sheepishly, and he's opening his mouth to say something smooth when—

"Fiiiiidler!!!!"

It's not so much the recognition—no, the distinct and unforgettable ring of disdain in the voice is what snaps Tibor back to reality. Instantly, the surge he had been feeling somewhere south of his belly button is replaced with an electrical current of misery...so sure is he of the owner of the voice that beckons him, he takes at least as long as he can to turn and face him.

When he does, eyes already missing the decidedly more pleasing features of the Jayne-Mansfield-like soup angel, he's appropriately frustrated to find that his sinking suspicions were in fact correct.

Naturally, the man admonishing him—the man next in line—is the Goddamned drill sergeant.

"Fiiiiidler!!!!!"

The man's face is as red as the tomato-based soup still burning the hand it splashed on—the fingers on which almost fail to hold his lunch tray at the sight of the bastard's anger. He knows his punishment is coming and that it is destined to be both ridiculous and immediate...still, as the sergeant lays down the scathing course of action he is to follow, he can't help but smile.

(Which, it turns out, is not the way to avoid further reprimands.)

As Tibor slowly makes his way out of the mess hall—soup uneaten—on his way to begin the physical part of his torture—he catches the glances of his sneering and-yet-still-jealous comrades. Offering one last glance over his shoulder at Erzsi, and seeing her cheeks flush with both embarrassment and mirth, he knows it was worth it.

...

He's running up the damned hill, and as punishments go, this one isn't half bad.

Sure, he'd rather be hitting on Erzsi—or, at the very least, enjoying some of the soup she scalded him with; when the drill sergeant's goons gave him his marching orders, and pointed at the mountain just outside the compound fence, Tibor accepted his 'punishment' with a grin.

He was instructed to run to the top; stop a moment to contemplate his reckless behavior, and then return to his brethren in the barracks, solemn and somewhat starving, clearly having learned the lesson he has *not*, some quarter way to the top and already devising a more satisfying course of action.

His footsteps race the rebellions running across the terrain of his consciousness—terrain becoming less rugged with every step; as a plan formulates, his breathing increases, more from excitement than exertion.

He'll get to the top all right—

--and he'll make his way back down—

--but it will be the *other* side of this damn mountain, and he'll keep right on going.

Sure, Emil will miss him, and he's made an acquaintance or two in the months since his voluntary enslavement—but Szeged is only three miles away, and Erzsi can't serve soup all night. Which means the bus will be bringing her back to town just around the time he gets there.

If he hurries, and he does, playing out romantic scenarios in his mind and feeling his feet move faster for it; not once during his ascent pausing to wonder if the feelings he finds himself feeling are genuine, or just the by-product of being surrounded by too many other men.

...

He's still daydreaming as he reaches the summit; the breath comes slowly, and the heart beats wildly, but he's otherwise unscathed. Offering a disdainful glance over his shoulder, Tibor notes how decidedly small the compound seems; the man-made hill in the middle appears downright pathetic when compared to the majesty of the peak he pauses on.

It's been *hours*, and he's famished and he's angry and he's tired and he's exhilarated, really; army life, *clearly*, just isn't for him, and being a lady-killing refugee sounds infinitely more appealing than sleeping with his goddamned boots on.

They'll be angry, and *good*; Emil may have to do a pushup or two as punishment for his mirror's insolence, but the great thing about sharing a face with someone is that he'll still kind of be around in a way.

Besides, he tells himself, catching his breath and focusing back on the escape at hand—he technically volunteered for this. As his boots begin to race down the side of the mountain, eclipsing the compound from view, he reckons he will see Emil come the holidays—Erzsi, he hopes, he will see much sooner.

…

Communism, it turns out, has no sense of humor. As he races wildly through the undergrowth at the edge of the town of Szeged, he reckons he hadn't touched both boots down before the headlights of the military jeeps discovered him.

The forest edge looms painfully close—had he not just climbed a Goddamned mountain, he reckons he would be enveloped in its' sanctuary already. Instead, it's all blistered toes, and machine guns fired into the air, as behind him an army of humorless bastards gives pursuit.

He's touched that his latest insubordination warranted a platoon of his peers, funneled into jeeps and resplendent with both full stomachs and recently crafted ammunition; the latter of whom he hopes won't be scalding his skin the way the damned soup did.

He's moderately sure running down the wrong side of a mountain after flipping off a commanding officer is not punishable by death; then again, it has been a long day, and this is Hungary.

So he runs, the blood from aggressively stubbed toenails swirling in his *combat-not-mountain-climbing* boots as he presses on.

He's especially thankful he doesn't hear the dogs; those specially trained and aggressive-looking bastions of the perimeter patrol must have been deemed too important to base security to be wasted on one measly deserter.

Hell, right about now a Rottweiler sounds delicious, the rumble in his stomach both matching the revving of the engines behind him and reminding him that, as an unapologetic animal *lover*, he must be pretty damned hungry.

It's the forest and escaping that draws him back to his heightened reality; suddenly his latest-best-idea-ever seems anything but. As his legs fail him, tragically a stone's throw from the welcome foliage and limiting visibility of the forest's edge, the last thought across a troubled mind is the look *on* and proximity *of* his drill sergeants face when he's inevitably returned home.

And then, mercifully,

everything goes black.

Old Escapes, Fresh Consequences

Tibor scratches at his beard, damning the fact that both his face and fingertips hurt. He's gone, best guess, three weeks without a razor, and stuffing fuses into sticks of dynamite all day *everyday* has left every part of both hands raw.

It's not as though there is anything better to be doing with his time. He figures he spent about a week in a jail cell following his little escape attempt— a week with no sunlight and little food, a week that solidified his desire to escape this compound in the first place.

They let him out on 'good behavior;' more realistically, they let him out after he stopped singing at the top of his lungs, which turned out to be a surefire way to make the guards patrolling his cell as miserable as he was. He landed here; the remote building at the southern tip of the compound, far away from Emil and his particular patrolling perimeter, farther from Erzsi and her soup.

He'd take *either* at the moment; the rumbling where he imagines his stomach used to be tells him maybe one more than the other.

There is supposed to be a lesson in this, he knows, but as fuse number twenty-thousand-two-hundred and three finds a home in dynamite stick twenty-thousand-two-hundred and three, it's lost on him, like any hope of getting out of military life with his sense of pride seems to be.

...

Week seven

or something

and he's back—shaved and fresh and re-assigned to perimeter patrol.

The reunion was met with little fanfare—as it turns out, Tibor had attained a certain degree of notoriety in his isolation, and few of the men were eager to be associated with him upon his grand re-emergence. It mattered little—Tibor had his brother, and he had his flirtations with Erzsi to resume.

So today, a Tuesday or a Wednesday or a Thursday, Tibor steps into the sunshine

single file!

with his brethren, and for the first time since his return, feels himself formulating a plan—heralding both his return to sanity, and his bolstered desire to rebel against everything this ridiculous military institution stands for.

Emil mentions something about not trusting the smile written across his face, but it's hard to hear and it's inconsequential—the drill sergeant is marching directly beside Tibor and screaming marching orders in his ear, so despite the fact that he's only two soldiers behind his brother, he might as well be stationed somewhere else entirely.

He spends the duration of his two-hour patrol this way; biting his tongue and marching and collecting spit on the side of his face…despite his misery, the sergeant is unsatisfied and seems resigned to remain on pace directly *on top* of him. In between guessing what is staining his breath and shaking off march-rust, Tibor keeps his eye on the sun, knowing that when it is directly above him, the gallows give way to the mess hall, and the treasures within.

...

She's got *that* look on her face, seeing him march into the mess; having counted the moments until she noticed him (--and being pleased with the result—) Tibor stands as tall as he can, offers his very best shit-eating grin. She responds in kind, and suddenly his escape attempt (--and subsequent torture--) was well worth it. The crushing oppression of Communism can't dull the shine on his smile; he's dreamt of this moment for ten tiny forevers, and judging by the look on her face, it's crossed her mind a time or two as well.

He's a few back in line and fine with it; lunch is an hour in length and he figures he'll only need a fraction of it. The soup he can take or leave—it's good, as prison food goes; he hasn't the heart to tell her he's had better. It's not the type of satiation he's looking for anyway…the signals he sends her doubtless convey his intention. She's watching him, some four soldiers back, and her eyes smile when her lips can't; can't because the first person in line is the Goddamned drill sergeant.

He takes his soup and his time; naturally, he offers his best smile at Erzsi, who, sheepishly (--and entirely unnaturally--) smiles back, though the glint in her almond eyes never once leaves Tibor's sightline. He finds satisfaction in his discomfort—of course the bastard who lives to torment him would have an interest in the only beautiful girl on the compound.

Really, it's not competition, rather justification—more than once since arriving within the barracks walls, he's found his sanity questioned. Knowing that,

yes,

this woman is unquestionably attractive and

no,

it's not just isolation from all manner of women that fuels his desire, it's comforting. So, the wattage of his smile increases and exponentially, and, with three men to go, Tibor begins to formulate his pick-up line.

It's

hi

and it's not nearly as smooth as he spent three soldiers picturing it would be; still her

hi

back has enthusiasm and intention in it, too…and he read somewhere that a high percentage of communication is non-verbal, so he bites his tongue, smiles even bigger, and tries to flush the crimson collecting across his cheeks away.

…

She *tastes* better than he thought she would

so nothing at all like soup

when he tastes her the way he's been dying to, there in the empty bunkhouse he hangs his boots (feet still in, of course) between patrols.

Like the one he *should* be on now. It's the reason he's alone with her here and now, alone in the sense he's not surrounded by other like-minded (and somehow not as over-sexed) young men; looking at her and trying to breathe, his grateful *alone* isn't quite the alone of the jail cell he seems to spend half his time in.

Her company is better than any he's had in months, and though his fingers remind him

it's been that long

as he fumbles with the clasp on her bra, the heaven beneath assures him it was worth the wait.

Further north—when his eyes find the strength to rise from the goddamned miracle of her chest—Erzsi's gentle smile tells him (between bites of her decadently full lower lip) that his clumsiness isn't held against him.

Her body is, though, and Tibor takes the time both he needs and it takes, his mind so far removed from marching

single file!

and overbearing drill sergeants, that he's reasonably sure the entire Hungarian army could burst into the bunkhouse and he would not notice. Or care, the way he takes, and of the curves her body takes too when he traces them with the precision of a sculptor, outlining a familiar and still-nowhere-near-finished piece of art.

He is rewarded for his patience, the only urgency coming in the bites she bites *back* and in between enthusiastic lashings of her tongue.

Hot soup and harsh servitude can simultaneously wait and be damned, and for the duration of the patrol he's missing he's free and happy and Erzsi is too, simultaneously, and, *rusty-or-not*,

over

and

over

and

over again.

…

"No way."

Emil flashes him a lack of skepticism he, unfortunately, has seen a thousand-*thousand* times in the course of their young lives.

"I'm not kidding."

He's not kidding, and he has the *rawness* to prove it.

"You're lying, Tibor."

"I can show you the rash—

"I don't want to see it."

Despite being identical in almost every conceivable way, they are still violently individual in some respects. He had hoped, after years and *many-more-worth* of backing up every single

"Inconceivable"

seemingly tall tale with *proof*, that Emil would have learned to take his news with the proper respect it deserves.

"*I* want to see it."

Still, it takes the urgency of some soldier in his peripheral view to delve deeper into the cold hard facts of the situation.

So, as Tibor theatrically drops his pants in front of the (enraptured) congregation that has gathered here, in the bunkhouse, some ten minutes-and-plenty-of-time before patrol to hear his proclamation, he's somewhat satisfied that although his twin brother should doubt him, his fellow soldiers do not.

There's gasps and assorted cringes assailing his ears as he presents himself; assailed also (and more significantly) by the rawness a member can sustain only from the act of lovemaking, *and too much*.

"Six times."

"You lucky bastard."

and

"With Erzsi? God, what I wouldn't give for ten minutes with her."

and

"How did she look"

and

"Where did you sneak off to"

and

"It better not have been on my bunk"

and more, and not one of them are showering anything but praise and *deserve* upon him.

Except the one who matters most; Tibor sighs, because despite the need for respite he so desperately craves, he knows that, once again, he will simply have to show Emil his conquest in order for it to be appropriately registered.

...

She tastes even better on the seventh time

still nothing at all like soup

when he tastes her the way he's growing accustomed to

maybe even a little sweeter still

because this time, he knows all of his bunkmates—including and most especially his brother—are watching the whole damn thing.

From a tiny bathroom window; he can see them huddled against the tiny slit of an opening. He can't see their individual faces, but he can picture them—and it is more than enough motivation to make love to the beautiful woman somewhere underneath him.

Somewhere, because getting away with this little stunt (and in a very specific outdoor area nowhere near secluded enough) means making love next to (or, really, *in*) a shrub...and, as a particularly invasive branch obscures her face rhythmically, he reminds himself to keep each and every one of the promises he promised her to make this moment happen.

The thorn in his side might be metaphorical, might be literal—the anger at its' sudden intrusion makes him thrust harder; the sweat beading on his brow tells him his brethren surely must appreciate his performance. For her part, Erzsi is moaning enthusiastically, yet suddenly Tibor can't help but wonder how the hell he's going to sneak off the base in order to meet her mother the way he's promised to.

The diversions do well to sustain his endurance—the thorn is stabbing as rhythmically as the branch threatens to obscure her beautiful features. For a moment he's uncharacteristically mindful to shield the curves her body takes from the view of the window; blaming it on the racing of his mind, Tibor returns to his reveling, figuring the splendor of this scene will only cement his legend among his peers.

Better his superiors stay unaware of his rendezvous—the thought of the prison time he's sure to garner if discovered makes him work harder, and Erzsi, thankfully, is receptive. Following the deluge of sweat down her ample chest, he feels his heart racing—knowing his legend will only grow, he deliberately sets his mind back to the conversation that landed him here.

…

"No way."

Tibor sighs, tries his damndest to hold her gaze.

She really is beautiful—a black curl sweeps around her face, tickles lips far too full to be resistible. She moves it gently with hands he's come to find delicate—delicate like how he has to approach this situation, if he's to have any hope of success.

A month's worth of cigarettes—and, more importantly, his status as the biggest swinging dick on the base are at stake. He promised Emil he would prove to him that his relations (--seven, but who's counting--) are as real and vivid as his bunkhouse recountings have descriptively illustrated…he's even found the perfect place, well within view from the outhouse washroom on the southern-most border of the compound, well away from the perimeter patrol and any unwanted eyes.

He's planned everything perfectly—which is why, when those beautiful lips part to say

"No way"

again, he's fully committed to going deep.

"I want to marry you"

and he does, *kind of,* and at least every time he's inside of her. This part, he knows, is uncharted territory and the kind of reasoning it's bound to take to convince this goddess to take their coupling away from the relative sanctity of an abandoned bunkhouse, and to a series of bushes.

She's stunned

and

he's stunned

and he kind of can't believe he just said what he said;

but he'd really, really like to sleep with her again

and he'd really, really like all of his friends and his twin brother to watch.

She shakes a little, and smiles, or tries to—

Tibor can't tell because he's kind of shaking too, half-amazed that it's in him to go as far as, apparently, he just has.

Which makes the next part

--the part where he tells her, quickly and before she can fully stop reeling from the last statement

"I want to meet you mother"

slightly less astonishing,

and slightly less true.

He says it anyway and again,

and with conviction—knowing that he's fully in the moment and she's fully in the moment and that they're safe there…the other stuff, the stuff he just promised her, will wait because it has to, lingering long after she agrees to sleep with him in the bushes.

…

He's sleeping with her in the bushes, and he's moving both branches and buttocks, and, judging by the expression written across her porcelain-only-partially-obscured-by-shrubbery features, it's going well. The promises he promised her keep him from fully engaging in the experience; her increasingly voracious moans assure him she's unaware of his distractions.

Which include peering periodically across the bushes to the small outhouse building on the perimeter—Tibor, while appreciating the audience, by no means wants to be joined in his performance. He finds his focus increasingly diverted, half-swears he can hear muffled laughter where there should only be gasps of ecstasy.

His pace increases, deliberate now, and with the purpose of climax—he's close and she's close and then suddenly the light of the midday sun reflects off of the rock on her finger, and

just like that

he's lost in memory again.

...

It's weeks ago and he hasn't tasted her yet

but he's pretty sure she tastes nothing like the soup she serves

and so he's *trying* to—taste her the way he spent nights in a small cell dreaming of, removed from the bunkmates and mess halls and the mountains he scaled trying to escape.

Here, the perimeter he patrols closer and closer to the bus she pulls up in; he knows another minute or ten and she'll arrive from Szeged, all raven-haired and doe-eyed and increasingly receptive to his ever-stronger advances.

He nods to Piotr, the patrolman who *should* be patrolling the position he's been patrolling, and every day, since his release from the brig—turns out the twelve cigarettes a day to trade positions was well worth it.

He's reminded of his good fortune moments later, when the bus appears over the hillside, its engine rumbling low with the promises of what's to come.

He's the first thing she sees when she glides effortlessly from her iron chariot—her hair sways gently and it affects him; the surge somewhere south tells him that, of all the overly-eligible bachelors on this goddamned base, he has to be the one to claim her.

So it's

"Hello"

and sheepishly,

and her

"Hello"

back is laced with both recognition, and more importantly, intrigue—making the next words from his lips, though a little less full, just as sweet as he hopes/prays hers will be upon the tasting.

...

It's moments like this, *now*, that keep him from finishing as he lays with her the way he imagines one should while being observed—recounting the details and minutiae of their whirlwind romance in efforts to both embolden his passions and keep them from overtaking his performance. His eyes dance from hers; which, he notes, have not fallen from his since their coupling began—and he is thankful for this, given the dangers both real and imagined, should they be discovered...discovered *more*. Still, the ring adorning her ring finger bewitches him the way the gentle bouncing of her ample breasts *should*; it's almost all that he can focus on and part of him is glad it rests firmly on her ring finger.

As firmly as the day, two days ago

--when he placed it there.

...

"It's beautiful"

she says between breaths that come faster than they should

and he is breathing just as heavily if not more

because he just proposed to Erzsi

--and he just successfully broke back into base after his first also-successful break *out*.

She said she would want a ring—or at least indicated really hard that this would be the case, right around the time he progressed from kissing behind the mess hall to what he would describe as heavy petting—and the smile pressed against those heavy-breathing lips tells him he may finally have done enough to get her to sleep with him.

All it took, really, was a daring nighttime escape; lying on the bed of a supply truck as it left the way it tends to twice weekly to restock materials in the conveniently located nearby town. Another twelve cigarettes assured the poor bastard two bunks over would patrol for him the duration of the night and subsequent morning he was to miss—catching the bus back with Erzsi was the easiest part of the plan.

Having been the patrolling soldier closest to the arrival point, Tibor realized weeks ago that his brethren really paid no mind to the workers piling from the bus anymore…creating the perfect camouflage for his plain-clothed, low brim and wholly unnoticed arrival back at base.

No, the hard part was finding a suitable ring in an industrial mountain town on a soldier's pay. He figured it would work out the way it clearly has—the pawn shop he found some ten shops in had a suitable bauble, and cash and cigarettes and two handfuls of appropriated rounds from the munitions pile proved just enough to secure it.

It being the ring he nervously secures around what-he-prays is the appropriate finger. Despite himself, Tibor finds the courage to raise his eyes to hers. This proves to be more challenging than breaking out of the compound and then breaking back into the compound to give it to her—still, he manages to match her gaze.

The look written across her pristine features is worth enduring ten drill sergeants; she's *humming* and the energy radiating from her excited-terrified body fills him too, huddled as they are by the back door of the washroom compound he plans to sneak through.

(Emerging wet, with a towel wrapped tightly around his waist, for the short jog from the showers to the barracks will be far more easily explained if discovered than should he be noticed in the decidedly *not* military garb he snuck onto the bus with.)

His plan has worked perfectly, and there is satisfaction in that—satisfaction and *sugar*,

sugar

because he's suddenly kissing her and the lipstick attached to those lips,

and the lipstick tastes like sugar.

Or the adrenaline does—the can't tell/care because he's telling himself that this is what he wanted and he's pretending hard that those aren't tears rolling down her cheeks and staining his, there in the night and the compound he realizes he's found another way to trap himself in.

…

It's an *odd* thing

the excitement that comes with danger

and Tibor is feeling it now the way he is feeling a great many things, on top of Erzsi and *still*.

There's the warmth of her

and it's urging him onward, and were he a lesser man, he knows it would be enough.

Furthermore, to occupy his every thought--still, he's no lesser man and as a result and maybe because of it—there is also the (literal) thorn in his side and the audience watching him semi-secretly and wholly attentively and although time has passed sufficiently to cement his dominance, the act of looking into her eyes distracts him the way it always seems to.

The way it seems to *lately*

because lately her eyes have the forever he promised her written in them,

and although Tibor likes the idea of it,

he's not entirely sure that this—his ridiculous pursuit and conquest of her—wasn't meditated *more* of necessity and need…and maybe a little *less* of love.

He swore that—one way or the other—she would be his; now that she is and totally, Tibor can't help but feel the sadness that comes with knowing a particular goal has been attained, and nothing more remains.

So when she looks into his eyes and sees maybe a little deeper than she has any God given right to, Tibor finds holding her gaze increasingly impossible, fearing that she may discover an awful and ugly truth hiding just behind his cornea.

The danger intoxicates him the way it always does and he pushes harder for it; suddenly Erzsi's cries are growing and although they possess the pitch to attract attentions unwarranted, he half-convinces himself he doesn't care and pushes harder.

She moans something that sounds a lot like

"Yes"

and he's thinking

no,

and suddenly the projections dancing wildly on his conscience—

meeting her mother

and

actually going through with the proposal he maybe even tricked *himself* into believing he wanted

are replaced by the gnawing inside of him to escape this Goddamned base

and

this oppressive Communism

and

everything that makes his life the hell that it is.

So there's danger and it excites him and it is more than the thought of being caught mating in the bushes behind the base and it is more than the thought of being caught by his fiancé for having all of his bunkmates watch and it is more, mercilessly, than the thought of being caught for treating this entire ordeal as a game of sorts—no, the danger that grips him so relentlessly—the danger that forces him to feel as though he's being smothered—comes from the thought that all of this has been manifested of his own design.

The crushing totality of such a realization forces the breath from his lungs; a particularly angry vein running the length of his forehead beats in ever-increasing rhythms and encourages him to climax the way he abruptly and magnificently *does;* as he falls, spent, into her warm and waiting arms he hears her tell him

"I love you"

and he tricks himself into thinking it is the exhaustion that prevents him from replying.

…

They lie together for what he hopes is an appropriate length of time—

time for her to feel suitably cared for and comforted

and

time for each and every one of his bunkmates to, filled with images of his new fiancé being ravaged, leave the bathroom building.

He lies uncaring amongst the thorns, blanketed by the bushes and the warmest half of her body and he cannot decide if he waits because he wants to—hold her as tightly as he is and can—or if he waits because he needs to, and shower alone, thoughts of the adulation and praise to be bestowed upon him suddenly lacking in luster.

She rests her head on his chest and speaks softly, and Tibor wonders if shooting horses for food and living in squalor and sleeping with mothers and daughters hasn't served to create a monster; the horrors surrounding his existence no longer a justification for his behaviors—rather a form of sustenance for the growth of something such atrocities could be proud of.

The Trouble with Trees

He's running and away; and this time the running is both literal and metaphorical, and he can't tell which haunts him more. He knows he's tired—tired of running, yes, because he's at a good pace and he's weaving in and out of the trees that line the interior of the perimeter he's supposed to be patrolling…but it's more so that he's tired of

all of this,

the base that encompasses both his peripheral view and the totality of his existence.

It's dark out and that will help—help with the plan and the solution he's devised in moments and executed moments later…the plan that has him running the length of the interior, intending to meet his brethren on the other side of the trees as they patrol the side he hopes he runs to.

It began a couple of weeks ago—*then*, he couldn't have known that it would end up like it is *about to*, but, in reflection, maybe the seeds were sowed on the day that he witnessed one of his bunkmates writhing on the floor of the bunkhouse, hands fixed around one of his legs as though gripped by some imaginary demon.

The incident in-and-of itself wasn't the memorable part—it turned out the poor bastard was suffering from varicose veins that had begun to irritate him…something about backing up of the blood, he'd later find out. No, it is what happened next that stayed so vividly on his mind.

The soldier was taken, that night—instantly and without pause—

--to a hospital in Budapest.

Weeks since, spent half-hoping some grievous injury would befall him, had Tibor picturing the various ways calamity could visit one on base, requiring a similar extraction. The thoughts stayed, churning violently in the pit of his soul with continued promises to Erzsi—promises he realized that, sooner or later, he would be required to keep.

Hence, the running away, and literally and metaphorically, and as fast as he can. It's dark enough—the way dusk sees the sun hide behind the Bakony mountains, he knows it's only going to get darker…making the calculations of his movements more difficult as he negotiates the trees. His brothers should be rounding the southwest corner of the perimeter any moment; Tibor accelerates in the dying light, knowing that if he's going to make something happen, it has to happen now.

The pictures flashing across his mind are of Erzsi and often; the thought of hurting her the way he's about to; force his feet to beat in tandem with his heart. Spotting his target—the last tree, an oak, on the edge of the path the patrol has just passed, he closes his eyes, draws the biggest breath that he can—

--and runs headfirst into it.

…

She's looking down at him

and

she's kissing him

and

although she doesn't taste like soup

she kind of really tastes like *wood*.

For a moment he realizes that she's not there at all

and

that he's just run himself into a tree the way he planned to

and

the voices rising in pitch and echoing both urgency and tragedy tell him that he's accomplished his goal of running into that damned oak. He feels warmth crawling down his face and hopes feverishly—because feverishly is how he feels—that the crawling is blood, and that it is *sufficient*.

And then he's gone again, surrounded by images of her and happy in the abyss he finds himself slipped to; happy because he's not on base and everything is just black, and he's fairly sure, from the ringing in his ears that used to be the voices of his concerned friends, that he's hurt himself enough to escape this hell for good.

…

He wakes slowly

because slowly is the only way his tired eyes can open

and the fluorescent lights invading his rest and pupils could very well double for heaven, given their brightness. Heaven also, he notes, grunting as he shifts his weight, because he knows damn well that no lights on base burn quite so brilliantly.

So it's a good mood he wakes up in—rising steadily in the bed he finds himself in, the respite lasts two precious seconds.

And then the pain hits, pounding at consciousness and temples and anything, really, that it can get hands on--like he tries to--and anything around him that can ease the pain. Thrashing at the glass of water on the bedside table proves futile; the ringing in his ears disorients him just enough to prevent his fingers from closing around it, and he settles for watching the contents splash haphazardly on what appears to be an overly-sanitized hospital floor.

Despite the throbbing, he forces a smile—no floors on base were nearly as sanitized. Realizing—between hammer strikes to the base of this brain—that his escape must be fully realized, he closes his tired eyes, allowing the darkness to overtake him once more.

...

He awakes only because he wants to, more out of curiosity than necessity. There's hunger, sure, but it's gnawing at him the way it only *always* does; more of an annoyance than an outright urge. Communism compounded with military life seems to have a way of quieting even the basest needs of humanity, Tibor knows, opening his eyes to the welcome burn of florescent lights.

The wrestling in his bed does little to satisfy his mind, however. A feeling decidedly close to regret tickles his frontal lobes where only elation should be—again, his mind is on her, and although he could not be happier to have escaped the hell he seemed destined to remain in, *too much of him* wishes she was with him here and now. Double-checking to ensure that he is not restrained takes his mind from such things, and the interruption is welcome—more so, once he realizes that nothing is tethering him to the bed.

Meaning, really—there is little reason to remain in it.

His feet embrace the cold of the overly sanitized hospital floor; he's well on his way to weight-bearing when

"That's quite a nasty bump you took"

--coming from the only corner of the room he hasn't surveyed—stops him dead in his tracks.

Turning as fast as his concussion will allow, Tibor is relieved instantly to learn that the face attached to the voice is one he does not recognize. The military uniform he's wearing, however, is depressingly familiar. Familiar, he notes, save for a few more stars, and a couple more medallions. His elation has retreated to apprehension by the time he's standing, knowing full well that he's doing so in the presence of the highest-ranking officer he has ever seen.

"Tibor Fidler."

He's managed to maneuver his once-intended escape into a decidedly impressive salute—the vigor with which he brings his hand to his forehead reminds him instantly that his injury—and the effects—remain.

He speaks, this man now emerging from hospital-room-corners-unseen, and his voice rumbles low like thunder.

That, or the concussion is just aggravated by the tenor in his tone. Either way, what follows isn't nearly as important as the inflections placed in and around the words—words he can't quite seem to focus on. At least, the ones *after*

"Colonel"

The hairs on the back of his neck are standing long before the electricity coursing through his veins upon meeting the man's gaze, this

Colonel

looking into his still-cloudy eyes with an intensity he's never felt before.

They're blue, his eyes, and not the kind of pleasant blue he usually seeks out in the kind of women he usually seeks out—no, the man's eyes are the color of the sea following a violent storm; a kind of blue beyond comprehension and, suddenly, impossible to investigate further. Tibor's eyes fall to the floor—he knows the impressive bastard is still talking, somewhere close to him, but suddenly it all seems a little much, and he knows he would rather return to the comforts of the bed, saving any berating for times when the thunder isn't beating at the base of his brain.

He winces, but remains vertical—he's resigned to the fact that, although the military has decided against sending patrols after him *this* time, he's pissed off the institution enough to send the big guns. So he's swaying there—because standing would truly be inaccurate—and he's waiting for words like

"jail"

and

"disgrace"

and

"insubordination;"

he's entirely surprised when the next words he hears are

"I want you to rest here awhile, son."

Son being the key word—the swaying is suddenly exaggerated, and he feels downright feverish, until, violently, the swaying stops.

Because this man, this

Colonel

has his hand resting firmly on Tibor's shoulder, and for the first time in what feels like two forevers, the look on the face of the military commander in front of him is lined with sympathy, and not disgust.

"I understand you've had something of a hard road lately, Tibor."

Understatement.

But he appreciates the sentiment.

"So I want you to take some time, let that nasty bump on your head recover, and evaluate just what your service means to you. I'm not ready to give up on my soldiers, and although you've had some…

colorful…

field reports, I'd like to believe that there is a good soldier in there somewhere."

Picturing Erszi's face, hearing words like

good

send the remaining blood in his body rushing to his forehead. The throbbing threatens to topple him, but the hand remains, the resolution in the voice he half-hears keeping him conscious.

"Rest, son."

"Yes, sir."

He's guided back into the bed he wholly regrets leaving, and just before the warmth of the black takes him back, he lingers on the latest and last surprise coming from the Colonel.

"I understand you're something of an artist, Fidler. I'll have the room stocked with some canvas—hell, the appropriate medium you request. Your service isn't over…let's call it a re-assignment, of sorts."

"Sir?"

"Consider it a commission, Fidler. You're going to come up with a portrait of Stalin for the field office—and, if you're any good, you're then going to come up with *more*. Congratulations, son, you're now an official artisan for the Hungarian forces."

Tibor half-grins, falls into bed, and then unconsciousness saves him from what could only be the lunacy of a head wound.

…

Two weeks and two thousand seven hundred forty-three brush strokes later; Tibor is starting to love the military.

The Colonel—Adrojan, it turns out—joins him periodically, making the commute from a nearby base in Budapest to see how the commissioned works are turning out. He's a good man, broad and stern but fair and surprisingly mirthful, given a whiskey or two.

Or *three*, lately, Tibor pausing between pours only to navigate the length of what was once his hospital room…now it would be more accurately described as his quite-comfortable studio. Canvases of various sizes rest against a bed he no longer needs and rarely retreats to; the pounding in his head has ceded to the pounding of *inspiration* in his head, and his whiskey-free hand races deliriously across the canvas.

Stalin was the first, resplendent in his ridiculous moustache and deep-set coal-pitch eyes; he illustrated him in half-jest, with those eyes set a touch too-close together—when Adrojan saw the portrait, the whiskey in him prevented proper scrutiny, and so he was commissioned again.

Hence the stroking and the drinking and the laughing, when the Colonel drops by to lament on the ineptitude of his battalions, or the cooking of his hapless wife, burdened with three equally-strong sons, or whatever brings him to room 2028 next.

The conversation and the illustration and the inebriation prevent the appropriate sadness from visiting in the moments his new friend does not; for this he's eternally grateful, and thoughts of Emil on base and Erzsi on base and *himself*, and back on base are buried like rejected munitions behind whatever hill they've taken to burying them.

No, he saves his service thoughts for the various commanders and aircraft he's resigned to replicating in oils and acrylics—concussion and commitment are behind him and fading, just as the new are bleeding color by brushstroke before him.

"The color is wrong, Fidler."

He's drunk, and particularly mirthful this evening—so, when he opens his mouth to respond

"You're drunk"

it is without the abject terror that any other military man would feel when addressing his superior's superior. His comment is greeted with a snort, and something similar to a laugh, and then a healthy sipping of appropriately expensive scotch. In the time since his hospitalization, this unlikeliest of men has become the closest thing to a friend he's had.

"And still…the color remains incorrect."

"It is called 'artistic license, *sir*."

It is—called artistic license—and in this case it is not being used. The photograph he uses for reference—that of an American Douglas F4D Skyray clearly shows the detailing of the stripes adorning her tail to be red, then white, then navy blue…just as in his rendition.

"The red is something akin to tomato, Fidler…"

"The red is deeper; crimson, maybe. The lighting in the photo—

"Bah! The lighting, my ass!!! Paint it correctly, damn you. Military intelligence may mean nothing to you, but the ranks above demand excellence!"

At this, Tibor offers a hearty laugh; so infectious is it, that Adrojan's façade is forced to crumble, and laughter once again drowns out the bustle of the hospital hallway. Why he's relegated to painting aircraft that have never seen combat—and most likely will not—he'll never understand…his patience persists, safe in the knowledge that it still beats marching

single file!

around some goddamned munitions depot.

It's not Stalin, again, at least; so he returns to the brush once the laughter has ceased the shaking of his fingers, his back to his commander once more as behind him, Adrojan breaks into song the way he only does when his inebriation is approaching shut-down levels.

…

This behavior continues the duration of his superior's-superior-approved medical stay; Tibor paints daily, joined by Adrojan when he is able. They share more than they should—or at least Tibor tells himself in the moments his painting is uninterrupted by the clanging of whiskey on some glass behind him: despite these self-imposed warnings, he's a half-glass from spilling his guts when Adrojan pries.

So he tells him of Emil and Erzsi and of all of his concerns with military life…Adrojan listens and offers advice unburdened by his title. *Colored*, perhaps, the way military life has consumed the totality of his adulthood—still, Tibor finds the man reasonable to a fault, and, truth told, appreciates the insight.

The whiskey yields to fresh coffee and fruit on days when the Colonel is required elsewhere, and Tibor's artistic output benefits for it; as the days bleed into weeks, he becomes increasingly accustomed to the luxuries afforded him.

The area alongside his hospital bed is littered with canvases depicting dictators and war planes and glorious renditions of battles long-since fought; Tibor retires to the confines of his bedding only when his arms will no longer effectively hold the brush, knowing first light can't come fast enough to hold the latest masterpiece emblazoned across his mind while he sleeps.

...

He awakes to the aroma of freshly brewed coffee; reaches unconsciously for the baguette he knows will be waiting for him on the table beside his bed. He navigates the myriad assortment of brushes, knowing by the touch of a fingertip their place in his creative hierarchy. Two of lesser-import fall to the floor, but it is of no concern; as his hand bites deeply into the still-warm bread, he's grateful that the totality of his misery is now relegated to cleaning his own mess.

Sometimes—on days when the nurses are occupied with really, really injured soldiers.... although there is no active combat in the area, Tibor is always amused at the number of horrifying accidents that can befall a sleep-deprived soldier on patrol. Hell, he has a tiny scar on his forehead to prove it; he smiles, the taste of the fresh breakfast assuring him his self-destruction was well worth it.

He watches the brushes roll lazily along the beautifully lit floor, thankful for both the painting-friendly hospital lighting, and the somewhat sudden, if-slightly-calculated reversal of fortune that has befallen him. Soon, he knows, his required enlistment time will be up—as he raises a particularly plentiful piece of baguette to his mouth, the whiskers tickling the corners of his lips tell him that the past few weeks free of oversight and oppression and regularly-mandated shaves have passed far too quickly. He thinks of Emil, as always—he thinks of Erzsi, *as always and as well*, and with a mouthful and a sigh, ponders the events of the day to come.

Far too soon, he'll be leaving this place—Adrojan assures him that his remaining time to be served on base will be uneventful and perhaps even tolerable. He wishes he could serve the totality of his remaining detail here, amongst his canvases and his creations and his friend...still, he knows that eventually he will have to face those he left behind, and perhaps the sooner, the better.

The gnawing at him—the resignation and regret that he supposes hinders all men—comes in waves, ebbing when his creativity flows. So he stays occupied, the act of picking up his brushes a welcome distraction. He returns to his breakfast, and then returns to the canvas, hoping today's illustration—a lone wolf surveying his kingdom from atop a mountain perch—settles his mind the way the baguette settles his stomach. Adrojan isn't overly fond of wildlife paintings, but they're Tibor's favorites…in between Communist overlords and F-84F Thunderstreak fighter jets, his need for rebellion is satisfied by such quiet escapes.

And so he remains, satisfied and yet somehow still yearning, and as the days that pass draw inevitably towards conclusion, he relegates himself to the thought that his next adventure will somehow be as grand as this one has been.

…

Six days later, his boots touch the familiar ground of the base nestled in the Bakony Mountains. Where there should be resignation, there is nothing—as Tibor breathes the fresh mountain air, he tells himself that, *this time*, things will be different.

Hell, he's sure of it—as commanding officers and peers witness his return, he is pleased to see their collective gaze quickly fall from his. Colonel Adrojan's voice must have travelled down from on high, meaning that the man has kept his word; the remainder of his (short) mandated stay here would be pleasant.

He sighs, grateful for the powers his new friend possesses, and feels the familiar surge of adrenaline course through his body when he rounds the corner to his bunkhouse. The boys are on patrol—somethings he recognizes, never changes. The place is appropriately empty of testosterone filled, hapless worker drones—leaving the only breathing soul there in the bunkhouse with him…the only one he agreed to come back for, at all.

…

"It's a dog."

Adrojan laughs heartily, there in Tibor's memory and at his bedside those six days earlier, having finished his breakfast and not his painting before the man barged into the room, shouting declarations of war against, as habit would dictate, threats both real and inherently imagined.

The painting he had *been* painting—the painting of the wolf—resplendent in his glory alone on the mountainside—had the effect his paintings always do; meaning instantly the conversation changed from

"Goddamned American dogs"

to

"It's a dog"

and leaving him to reply that,

"No"

the painting of the wolf is, in fact

"A painting of a wolf."

"Bah! I had such a dog, you know, before my second wife put the notion into my head that it would eat the children…I should have let him, for the way my son turned out, Fidler!"

"So you owned a wolf."

"A German Shepard, you bastard! The finest bred, and a proper soldier, I'll have you know. He patrolled by my side for years. We still breed them to be soldiers; I'll have you know. Even now, we're raising pups to be proper guards—

It must have been the look in his eyes, as they fell from the canvas, to the man sitting on the chair painting the canvas.

…

Six days later, and the eyes looking back at him are equally filled with mischief.

Tibor recognizes both the look, and the intentions behind it.

As the beautiful German Shepard recognizes kinship in the returning soldier standing overtop him, he wags his tail in excitement.

As Tibor gazes down at his new assignment, he silently thanks the Colonel for keeping his word, and despite his best efforts, forces a grin equal-and-perhaps-passing-in-magnitude to any grin he's offered any girl on this base.

"Hello my friend."

The dog answers back, his tail wags a little harder.

"I will call you Blascka."

…

Blascka patrols furiously, a whirlwind of movement backed by intent and purpose. His beautiful auburn mane sways violently in the mountain breeze, masking only some of the powerful contractions his hind legs create. His fur dances as though trying to keep up with the chaos his powerful, lithe footfalls wreak upon the rain-softened path.

Despite his resolute, contained fury, he does not stray far from his master; on most days, Tibor would appreciate this with a pat or a scratch behind the itchiest of his two ears. Today, however, Blascka is left to his own devices, as some four yards behind Tibor is reminded that, despite his best efforts, the world continues to turn.

Tibor shifts his weight, coming to an abrupt and somewhat jarring stop. Yards ahead, it takes his new best friend a moment to sense the pause in his movement, and he waits, quietly, for Blascka to follow suit.

Emil stops too, sharply, and—were he counting—perhaps a half-foot before—as if recognizing the weight of the information he had been saving to reveal merits at least a momentary pause.

In the three weeks since his glorious return to base—the twenty-one days filled with reunions and training dogs and patrols exactly like this one—his twin brother had been constantly by his side. Regaling him with tales of the news, the events, and the moments he had missed in his six-week sabbatical.

He had assumed, foolishly, that his brother had told him *everything*.

Erzsi, broken-hearted, had left the kitchen and the base, and—word has it—Szeged.

The drill sergeant, (--having received correspondence from some high-ranking officer that Tibor and Emil Fidler were to be relieved of patrol duty in favor of spearheading the new dog breeding program on base) was himself close to being removed from his station, after physically assaulting the poor bastard charged with bringing him said correspondence.

Some kid named Peter fell into the hole, spent munition rounds were disposed of and shattered his femur.

Some had hit him harder than others, he remembers...still, he appreciated the update, and, some two weeks ago, assumed that he had been appropriately updated in regards to current events.

"I'm going to be a father, Tibor."

Apparently, not.

He finds that he thinks of Erzsi, for some reason—if and only for the split-second it takes him to process the news; he swallows hard, as if hoping to digest it.

He reads the look on his twin's face—so his own—searching for validity in the words that he knows he doesn't need, but appreciates just the same.

A breath comes, and then another, less labored than the first, and finally, he moves to embrace him, discovering the warmth that consumes him strange and yet somehow comforting. Some five yards in front of him, he hears Blascka bellow his approval.

This takes him more time to digest than it *should*; he knows that he is excited, he accepts the smile threatening to take over his face. He's quick to embrace his twin, half-hoping that the act of burying his face in his shoulder will hide the emotion written across his features. After months of seemingly nothing but military life, the news represents the passing of time. A symbol, really, for the ending of servitude, and the life waiting for him—for both of them—once the time on base comes to an official end.

Which, he notes, remembering Adrojan's promise to him—is happening sooner than later.

"Say something Tibor."

Ahead, Blascka snorts in solidarity.

"Congratulations, brother."

He shakes Emil violently for added effect, hoping that the physicality the roughhousing prompts hides the distinctness of the water pooling at the corners of his eyes. He gets away with it, as moments later; he has his twin brother in a headlock, wrestling him to the ground before the pools race the length of his cheeks. Their laughter is echoed by the roaring of his pet, the three of them entangled in an alarming cloud of dust and identical limbs.

A pair of foolhardy patrolmen, undeniably alarmed by the disturbance in an otherwise serene afternoon walk, fumbles hastily towards the sound of commotion. No doubt drunk on the thought of something actually exciting happening within the perimeter, the younger of the two even manages to raise his rifle…upon realizing that there are *two* of the *one* soldier on base that is exempt from the verbal thrashings of the drill sergeant he retreats as hastily as he approached.

Leaving the twins to their dog and their play, reunited and invigorated in the knowledge that soon their mandatory enslavement will be replaced by the trappings of a better life…or, *damn Communism*, better than the one they've spent the last *however-long* living.

…

Chicken wire.

It's genius, really—as Tibor explains his plan to Emil, he can barely contain his excitement. He recognizes the look on his twin's face, if for no other reason than it is the look on *his* face when he believes something is completely full of shit.

This, ultimately, is the disadvantage of sharing a face. He sighs, recognizing that, lately, this particular face—screwed up lip, squinted eye and *not-entirely-secretly full of disdain sneer* isn't going away until he executes said plan.

So he grabs his boots—off, the way they should never be—and, with a brisk command to Blascka, sets off into the dead of night.

The patrol—the patrol that, ordinarily, he would be a part of—is along the northern ridge, and about as far from eyesight as a patrol could possibly be. In the time since his return, Tibor's friendship with Adrojan—not to mention his nocturnal penchant for running head-first into trees—has afforded the twins a laxer patrol schedule…after all, training dog soldiers is a time-consuming endeavor.

Judging by Blascka's steadfast pace alongside him, said endeavor has proved fruitful, the way his new plan is sure to, should he manage to avoid detection.

He reaches the southernmost tip of the compound, huddles briefly against a tree, his eyes straining in the night for any semblance of movement. Blascka is indifferent, his nose in the dirt somewhere beside him, a sure indication that nothing is approaching to interrupt them. As carefully as three a.m. will allow, he removes the spool of chicken wire he recently...*obtained*...from the munitions warehouse, securing one end around the base of the tree he stands to distance himself from. Gingerly, he lays the cable along the soil adjacent to the path the perimeter patrols; he works in tandem and opposite the positioning of the guardsmen making their rounds, always about as far from them as possible. Momentary lapses in tension—even from a wire as thin and as close to the ground as his—are sure to draw the eyes, the way movement does...and he'd prefer his plan to be executed properly before invited scrutiny.

He stops periodically and *only*, and only to secure one of ten tin cans recently pierced (--just enough to allow an entry, and an exit for his wire to run through--) along reasonably equal spaces the course of the base perimeter. Each can is pierced once more, and just enough to drop a single iron washer inside. He leaves just enough slack to allow a quick pull of the wire—at any point along the perimeter—to force the wire to dance, and the washer to rattle in the tin can.

A practice pull—just enough to discern vested interest from his canine companion—tells Tibor that his plan...this makeshift, incredibly effective alarm system—is fully operational.

A moment to appreciate his underappreciated ingenuity, and he's off; racing the rising sun back to the comfort of his bunk, and he knows, the smug satisfaction he'll wear on *his* face when he sees the reaction he's sure to get on Emil's.

...

"Chicken wire?"

"Chicken wire."

"Of all the god-damned, hair-brained schemes you've concocted—"

Tibor interrupts his twin with a stern finger pressed against still-moving lips. They're on patrol, the two of them, and trailing within earshot of the rest of the company they patrol with. Tibor expected a tiny resistance to his latest, *most-definitely-ingenious* plan—this was calculated, and to be tolerated. However, if Emil thinks he's going to blow the proverbial whistle on his whistle-blowing-like invention, he's sadly mistaken.

"Shhh…wait and see, brother. Wait and see. You stay here, I'll follow the boys down the line. When they round the corner, I'll give you the signal."

"What signal? How the hell is chicken wire supposed to tell me anything? And what the hell am I supposed to pretend to be doing, when I should be falling in line, like the rest? Tibor, I swear that bump to the head has affected you."

"Blascka will stay with you. Pretend you're tending to his paws, or some shit. And wait for the signal!"

He's off down the path before his twin can continue the protest. He catches the usual look of disdain, grins in response, and is turned before the venom of the words that follow can penetrate his sensitive ears.

He catches the patrol rather easily, and is comforted when absolutely no one turns to admonish him for his delayed march. Being friends with Adrojan has instilled a perception of invincibility in him—one his bunkmates have picked up on. As a result, he's left with the latitude to spirit away the way he does once again, moments after falling in-step with the patrol—when they round the corner on the southeast edge, far beyond earshot of his twin, Tibor slips two feet down the embankment parallel to the stamped patrol path.

Nestled against the root of a particularly angry pine, he gently removes the debris of leaves and twigs covering a thin post with wire spooled hastily around it, and with the precision of a boy tearing into a new gift on Christmas morning, pulls upward twice on the wire.

Midway between his position and where he can make out Emil playing with Blascka in the distance, the tin can with the bearing inside rattles; just significantly enough to cause the dog's ears to whip to attention…the only indication that the sound has in fact travelled the appropriate distance.

Satisfied, he conceals the post, at least twice as well as he fights to conceal the grin written across his face, and sprints up the embankment, eager to join his patrol once more. He knows that, once they round the remaining three corners lining the perimeter of the base, his reunion with Emil will bear him the victory he's waiting for.

...

"You're—

Wait for it.

"You're—

He knows it's hard for him, so he's patient. He studies *his* face—so his twin's face—and he recognizes the discomfort the forthcoming admission must cause him. He fights to hide the grin he's been fighting to hide for moments, chokes down a laugh.

"—you're a goddamned genius, Tibor."

The boys cheer, laugh, and generally relax, huddled as they are around Tibor's bed. The bunkhouse was quiet tonight, moments after concluding patrol, the rest of the lads doubtless sensing the tension between the twins once they reconnected with Emil during the final lap.

Eager to be let in on the source of said tension—and the following adulation—Tibor is instantly absorbed by the din of their questions and sporadic embraces. He silences them sternly as he rises to stand—boots off—on his mattress, shooing an over-stimulated Blascka as she climbs the bed in pursuit. Confident in his command of the room, he lowers his gaze to meet each of their waiting eyes in turn, and, once assured none among them will rat him out to a particular drill sergeant, he begins his explanation.

"We work hard, boys."

Muffled cheers and assorted nods. Satisfied, he draws breath, presses.

"And what do we get for it? Limited rations, constant patrols....Sugasz over there looks like he hasn't slept a full night in five years."

Sugasz, looking like he hasn't slept a full night in five years, nods. And then immediately looks as though he's fallen asleep on his feet.

"Bastards like the Drill Sergeant bellow and bark and order us up every two hours…and then what? Retreat to the comforts of the officers' lounge, the sanctity of their warm beds?"

Scattered responses, the odd hushed "yeah." Momentum building, Tibor raises the tenor in his voice an octave.

"So while they're sleeping soundly, confident that young, able bodied men are looking out for them, we're out here freezing our balls off, marching a dirt path that will never see an invader."

The responses, louder now.

"Well, boys, I can't do anything about the patrols. We will continue to be rousted from sleep—whatever sleep we can manage with these damned boots on."

The noise stifles a touch—so as not to lose the room, Tibor decides he best reach his point. Stamping a bootless foot on the bed, he pauses dramatically, before drawing an anxious breath to continue.

"However…"

Silence, now.

"I've devised a way for us to know if a supervisor approaches. So that we can actually try to enjoy patrol; rather than be separated, rank-and-file, we'll be free to engage in conversation, to play the odd game of cards. Hell, to be able to lean against a tree and close our eyes, even."

"As long as we don't bump our heads, Fidler."

Emil makes the moment his—the laughter fades quickly, the proposal pressed from Tibor's lips too tantalizing to disregard.

"I've lined the perimeter with a thin line of chicken wire. In the middle of each section, I've fastened an alarm system, of sorts…if any man sees someone unwelcome approaching, he simply pulls twice on the wire, and a tiny rattle will indicate their presence. Two pulls, for a superior…let's say three pulls if the coast is clear."

"What if they see the wire, Tibor?"

"It's off the path—two feet or so, below the grade we're constantly slaving away on. I wanted it hidden, somewhat, but still easily in reach, should some sorry bastard walk up on us in the dead of night."

"And what if they hear the rattle? What then?"

Tibor sighs, as if accepting the fact that a self-appointed superior intellect means having to explain the minutiae of his masterful inventions.

"A tiny rattle, against the still of night, Private Stokhanz? Tell me, do you jump at every sound the dark makes?"

The laughter of his comrades forces the diminutive Private to silence his protests—having voiced the first, as well, Tibor is thankful for his lack of further interruption.

"In closing, fellas, I'd like to encourage you to *relax*. Here, for the next hour and fifty-odd minutes before we are roused from sleep to march—and some ten minutes from that point, when the officers return to their beds, and we stop pacing like fools, guarding a series of shitty bunkers that no one cares about, in the middle of a mountain no one will invade."

The boys cheer so hard, that for a moment Tibor fears they may wake the guards. His dread lasts but that single moment, if and for no other reason than the moment that follows has him hoisted from his perch atop the bed by a sea of clearly appreciative—and, like Sugasz, probably sleep-deprived—soldiers eager to show him their appreciation by not-un-violently carrying him the length of the bunkhouse they proceed to revel in.

From his vantage point, elevated and lateral and upside-down to the floor—the floor Emil broods just-slightly-less-than-usual on-- Tibor catches the ghost of a smile across his twin's face.

...

It's a night later, or maybe two—and he's down, *literally*, from the heights he watched his brother from, lifted high above the heads of his adopted brethren; he's not down, metaphorically, having become something of a makeshift savior to the disenfranchised among them.

Patrols have been infinitely easier, in the dozen or so since he revealed his chicken wire alarm system. He marches slowly now, observing comrades sleeping soundly with backs against trees, and basks in the fruits of his ingenuity. Emil is beside him, and even he appears at ease—having positioned a single watchman (with, democratically, one-hour shift rotations) conveniently at sightlines, which could present the best views of approaching commanders, he's confident that they'll have plenty of time to snap to attention should the situation change.

For now, it's afternoon strolls and nighttime games—cards and dice and the impromptu boxing matches they tend to create…he never once doubted the abilities of the men he bunks with, should a situation with actual gravity arise. For the life of him, he couldn't understand the benefits of constant, mind-killing patrols laced with anxiety-induced over watches from fat, boisterous blowhards.

This—admiring his handiwork, just one in a herd of indescribably happier soldiers—*this* is how base life should be. The downtime continues for almost an hour—a rare occasion, and one savored by every man attached to every smiling face he sees—until the now-telltale ringing of the bell snaps the boys immediately to attention.

Tibor, snapping to attention from his 'post' underneath the shade of a tree, is amongst the last to march

single file!

a half-step out of sync with his still-overly-jubilant brothers as they round a corner. He is abruptly stopped, stepping awkwardly into Emil's suddenly stone-stiff back. Still somewhat leery of head-on collisions, he momentarily feels his vision blur—as it returns, he sees the proverbial waves of soldiers parting, given way to the approaching, oppressive marching tenor of what could-only-be…and is…

his least-favorite commanding officer.

"Füddleer!"

The Sergeant, looking appropriately evil--all pock-marked and puffy--bellows in a familiar tone, replacing the klaxon of the makeshift alarm system. This presents a sense of concern for multiple reasons—ever since his return to the base following his hospital stay, he's been left alone…the fury in the bastard's voice can only mean one thing.

Discovery.

"Fiiidlleerrrrr!"

It's comical, at this point—the pock-marked features stained an alarming shade of red, the beads of his already-overly-beady eyes shining some shade of bloodshot…discerning their exact color is interrupted by the sudden need to dodge saliva, flying as it does and *is* from his stretched lips.

He stands at attention as impressively as he can, biting hard on his lip to suppress laughter. He knows he knows that he's nigh untouchable following his friendship with Adrojan; this chastising no doubt intended to be more ceremonial than anything else. Still, he goes through the motions, and, satisfied that no more spit is likely to garnish his face as he stands, he swallows a final laugh, meets his accuser/oppressor's gaze.

"What the fuck is this??"

He leaves his eyes firmly where they've fallen, directly and more-than-a-little aggressively registered on the bulbous patch of pockmarked skin dancing between his wildly contorting eyes. He does not need to look down to recognize one of the tin alarms clenched firmly in the Sergeant's meaty hand.

"Sir, it's an alarm, Sir."

"You smug little bastard. I realize that it's an alarm, Fidler. What, pray tell, is it doing along the perimeter of my patrol path?"

His beady little eyes convey a sense of smug satisfaction, all

I've got you this time

written across no-more-room-to-write-anything-across features.

"I'll have your head for this, you little shit. Intent on ignoring your responsibilities, devising this Goddamned ridiculous system just to avoid duty…your level of insubordination appalls me. You're a disgrace to—

Tibor hears the rest—catalogues it even—but he's otherwise engaged, rationalizing his explanation even as he makes out the shape of his favorite military official approaching in the distance. Upon his arrival, the rest of the patrol stands *more* at attention; if such a thing were possible...Tibor simply sighs, moves his gaze from the Drill Sergeant to the Colonel, and offers a smile.

This, appropriately, enrages the already-enraged Sergeant, and once more Tibor is forced to subtly dodge a trail of saliva.

"Tibor."

"Adrojan."

"Care to explain?"

The Colonel appears to be having trouble hiding his smile, as well.

"Sir, yes, sir."

"I'll explain, Sir. This son-of-a-bitch—

"Language, Sergeant."

"On my patrols, Sir—

Tibor begins earnestly, failing to hide the corner of a grin too-long suppressed.

"—I've noticed that, despite the dogs, the perimeter yields glaring lapses in visibility. Blind spots, if you will. I've taken it upon myself to remedy this, by installing a thin perimeter of chicken wire, invisible to the naked eyes of those not looking for it."

"Intruders?"

"Yes, Sir. Intruders. Furthermore, I've taken it upon myself to fasten a tiny, makeshift alarm to the center of each of the perimeter posts. Regretfully, the craftsmanship is lacking, however I believe it yields the appropriate results."

Adrojan, grabbing the tiny tin rattle from the Drill Sergeant, has abandoned all attempt to disguise his grin.

"Rudimentary, yet clever. Continue, soldier."

"Yes, Sir. Should any party breach the outer fence of the compound; one tiny pull on said wire would alert any on patrol, regardless of their positioning along the path. Far subtler than the braying of a dog, yet, to the trained ears of my patrolmen, just as clear an indication of approaching danger."

He flashes his best *'I'm-a-Goddamned-Genius'* grin directly in the direction of the Drill Sergeant's bulging nose.

"Genius, Soldier. Genius."

The Drill Sergeant looks as though he may explode. Tibor rocks his weight to his heels, preparing to dodge the brain matter should such a situation unfold.

"Sergeant, this man is to be commended. Draft a report, at once, and send an emissary to the Commissionaire's office. I want to be on hand to present this man a medal by the time Thursday's annual inspection rolls around."

"Yes...Sir."

The Sergeant chokes out his acknowledgement admirably, however he admirably cannot meet Tibor's gaze. Still, he takes his victory the same.

"Follow me, Soldier. I'd love to hear more of your ingenuities over lunch. Carry on, Sergeant."

A half step behind Adrojan, Tibor's march has more than a little saunter to it. Breaking stride to look over his shoulder, he's half-surprised to see the Drill Sergeant still standing; notes the lack of shouted orders emanating from his lips as he tucks tail, turns to follow some twelve

single file!

steps behind.

Leaving the Army.

He stands as straight as someone decidedly-not can.

His brother stands straighter beside him, his dog sits straighter in front and below. He's standing, rank and file and the way he has been, for the better part of far-too-long, for the last time. It's worth celebration; celebration kind of like what this is intended to be, as he stands waiting to receive a medal for coming up with a way to slack off at work.

He smiles because there are more reasons *to* than *not*; eyes forward and fixed the way he was taught, he's watching a reel of highlights in his mind, settling on faces attached to memories and friends-met…pausing only and painfully on one hurt more than should have been.

So he's on to moments not attached to marriage and the intent, daydreaming of boots off in bed and foot-chases and paintings from hospital rooms, reflecting only on the experiences that haven't scarred him as he stands ready to rid himself of all of them.

Were he able, he might scan the perimeter of the munitions warehouses one last time—might fix his gaze on the bunkers and the men's rooms and the bushes behind them he had come to know so intimately. He might acknowledge that, in leaving this place, he's closing the proverbial chapter in the book of his life someone will sit across from some table and chronicle someday.

He might take the moment in, digest it the depths of some soul he knows he's supposed to have, save it for the times in his life he will want to dig up memories of moments that shaped him; moments, he supposes, just like this one.

As his friend and superior, Colonel Adrojan, pins some important medal to the breast of his meticulously kept soldier's jacket, one solitary thought beats at the base of his brain, quieting the revolutions his deeper self should be struggling to throw.

...

It's about fucking time.

...

He takes the hand Adrojan, his friend, extends, accepts it as such, knowing the salute he follows with one of his own is merely formality. He removes the hat his fellow soldiers in line still wear, holds it in his only free hand, and finishes the handshake with a decidedly informal but no less important hug.

Before the Colonel can finish the ceremony—before the Colonel can move on to shake the hand of his twin brother beside him, the hat is on the ground and, his enlistment officially over, one Tibor

Fiiidleeerrr!

is running, as fast as he can, alongside the dog he is stealing, as far away from the base in the mountains as his combat booted feet will allow.

Time is Slipping Away.

I write at the top of the page, the way I have been lately, and on at least every page I begin to write on.

I've been meeting with Tibor for well over a year now, and despite the regularity of our afternoons together—despite my growing familiarity with the story of his life—I'm not writing at the pace I should be.

So,

time is slipping away

and it is reflected, subtly, by the look on Tibor's face today, as he struggles to remember the particulars of the story he's telling me.

It has been happening with increasing regularity, and I've taken to scrawling reminders like

time is slipping away

to fill the pregnant pauses between the start of a story, and its' conclusion.

It weighs on me, there across the table from Tibor as he apologizes, and as I realize that

I'm sorry

should be escaping my lips instead of his, I think of the promises I made to this man and his son, and how little I'm doing to fulfill them.

Tibor's concentration allows the room to fill with comfortable silence—I've been made to feel as though I'm a part of this family, and as I wait, I allow my doubts to beat me black and blue.

Tibor is not a young man.

I watch him wrestle with the words, reflecting on my own recollections of the story I secretly admit I've heard most of before, and I think of the full life he has lived. I watch the lines bite into his weathered forehead as he marvels at his inability to remember. I glance around the dining room for the ten-thousandth time; still impressed at the luxury of the home Emil has built, but find no solace in the fact that his golden years have been spent in relative comfort.

No, I wallow in my own inadequacy (the way, I assume, any good writer should) praying to whomever-will-listen that I'm able to hold up my end of the bargain, and complete this damned book while Tibor has the ability to *hold* it.

I picture it, scrawling

time is slipping away

absently, musing the look on his face *then*, when he feels the tangible weight of his life's adventures in his liver-spotted hands, dreaming of a look of satisfaction written across his features, on the afternoon I sit across the dining room table to celebrate a mission, accomplished. A story finished, the way Tibor wants to, *today*, and the one he was in the middle of telling—just before his mind slipped away—the way it has been, lately.

Ganz Vallalatok.

Money and education were rare; Emil had managed to secure employment as a welder for Ganz-- the largest producer and manufacturer of ships, locomotives and streetcars—in all of Europe.

Ravenous at the prospect of joining his brother, Tibor accepted Emil's suggestion he come to work as well with no hesitation. Productivity at the factory was legendary—hammering out massive steel frames, engineering railroad tracks…to be a part of progress, of industrialization…

Nothing was going to deter him from his goal of a better life—

--not the fact that he did not know the first thing about welding

--or the fact that he would never be considered for hire in the first place—

he merely recognized the mischievous glint in his brother's eye when he suggested it, shrugged his shoulders, and began devising the plan that would pave the way for the next great adventure in a life already brimming with such.

Security at Ganz Electric Works—even in those days—was decidedly strict. Each employee was given a photographic identification card, and was checked both in and out of the factory by armed guards daily. The benefit to being a twin, however, is that Tibor shared his face—and Emil, his card. By showing up to work early, and claiming he had simply forgotten his ID back home, the 'correct' Fidler was able to arrive at work on time, and make it past the stringent security check post…and, a couple of hours –and a guard shift—later, so was Tibor, flashing the card that bared his face, if not his name.

Avoiding discovery once inside became a task in and of itself. By hiding in the work bays underneath locomotives, Tibor secluded himself away until after hours, amusing himself with bits of scrap iron and whatever tools Emil could sneak to him. Here, in the darkened factory's midnight hours, he gradually came to understand the technique, and after a time, became a passable welder himself.

Hired on to Ganz as a Level 3 (--3, being the lowest level) welder, and finally having achieved his vision of gainful employment, Tibor set his sights—quite literally—to the heavens above.

And the woman working diligently, amongst them.

…

She's beautiful, of course—Tibor's eyes grow wild with excitement when he describes her…a ringer for Jayne Mansfield's face; those big brown eyes surrounded by raven hair, an exotic contrast to the platinum blonde of the star bearing her likeness. The kind of body, he breathes, recalling fondly—the kind of body that would make a set of Hungarian laborers toil vigorously and diligently below, hoping for an approving gaze from the Goddess on the crane (--literally and metaphorically—) high above them.

He recounts the curves her body takes, and he takes his time. His breath comes longer now, concentrated, as he describes her legs—a kind of romanticism born, doubtless, of the enhancement the senses must take when surrounded by danger and uncertainty…as though beauty and moments of such are savored like the finest wine, so certain that they'll come infrequently and without cost.

Of the nineteen or twenty laborers laboring below her, he tells me,

nineteen

or

twenty

wanted to date her.

So daily he toils in her shadow, one of nineteen or twenty watching her and her crane as her crane lifts whole train cars and moves them down the assembly line; dancing amongst the hydraulically-induced dancing shadows, dancing to steal gazes from underneath the twisted steel and pulsing rivets of her literal and metaphorical protector…the moving manifestation of the separation between.

"Needless to say—"

He begins without really needing to;

"—my frustrations grew exponentially as the days passed. In a way, it was another example of the divide in my life—the things I wanted, ever out of reach."

He smiles, just a sliver.

"Of course…I was never one to accept circumstance for circumstance-sake."

By now, one of the

nineteen

or

twenty

had finally built up the courage to ask her to dinner.

"A real Rock-Hudson looking bastard" he snorts, shaking his head.

"I was sure it was over for me, this guy was so handsome—but she turned him down. I told myself, perhaps the direct approach wasn't the best, so I bided my time."

Bided his time with lingering glances,

"Lustful glances."

--*lustful* glances and non-verbal communications. (I'm to learn that non-verbal cues, like the kind he was laying down on Jayne-Mansfield-Two were in fact a secret weapon that afforded him many such luxuries initially deemed 'above his station.' As he describes them to me, I'm sure to write '*throw more lustful glances*' in the side column of the page I'm writing on.)

These pay off, the way they always do, some weeks after Rock Hudson's crash-and-burn. He's in the lunchroom, and he's shirtless--because it's hot in there--and he's minding his business about-as-much-as-one-can mind their business in the presence of both testosterone and beauty. Having one outweigh the other, he's in the midst of pouring his fourth cup of tar (to call it coffee, he assures me, would be doing coffee everywhere a great disservice) when he's alarmed by the touch of a decidedly un-calloused hand upon his shoulder.

Turning, it takes everything in his power not to drop his freshly-poured sustenance.

"Hello."

Jayne-Mansfield-Two is looking directly into his eyes with her eyes, and her eyes are, matter-of-fact, among the most beautiful he's seen. Her cheekbones go on for days, or at least appear to; locks of loose raven-tinged ringlets are doing their damnedest to obscure the angles her face takes when she smiles at him.

Which she is, and brilliantly, and the sudden hush in the lunch room might be the collective grieving of every other male in eyesight, or it may be a vacuum caused by even the oxygen being caught breathless by her beauty; either way, Tibor concentrates at least as hard as he can on not dropping the coffee all over himself when she repeats

"Hello"

softly, and

"Hello"

softly

is all he can softly speak back.

...

"Well?"

This, she asks, after an eternity-in-a-moment-or-two of staring at her, Jayne Mansfield Two—staring at her and taking in the beauty of her smile and the shine in those big dark eyes and imagining the curves her body must be taking under a blouse blissfully two buttons too-tight.

Tibor knows she's expecting an answer, and he can't remember her asking a question and in his mind he's questioning why the hell this goddess would be questioning him about anything, and out of the anything he could possibly say, all he can possibly say is

"Hello"

again, and more softly, if possibly, than the

"Hello"

he remembers/hopes he softly offered an eternity-in-a-moment-or-two ago.

So he gives it a shot, there in the lunchroom, and God-Bless-Her, she seems to be enjoying it, or him—he's flustered and failing and moderately sure he's making a fool of himself. She's smiling still, and when her lips part once more, she mercifully ends the silence with,

"Well?"

again and it takes him just as long as it just took him, the first time, to realize this beautiful woman has been asking him a question.

"Uh, well...what?"

The smile graduates to laughter, and she really, really seems to be enjoying herself, and surrounded by his peers in the lunchroom, Tibor makes a mental note to enjoy himself as well. Really, this is about the farthest any of the boys have gotten with this goddess—and as the realization that he's in a relatively-tight space with each and every *all* of them, he prays he doesn't look as befuddled as he certainly feels.

And just as he dares to believe he may be doing okay, there in the lunchroom, she asks him,

"Aren't you going to ask me out on a date?"

and it's all one Tibor Fidler can do to remain on his two feet.

Every little thing inside of him is working overtime to push the words that follow somewhat gracefully from his mouth, but for every

"Would you like to "

There are at least a half-dozen

"Umm's"

And

"Uhhh's"

and he figures that, in the time it takes to ask this woman out on a date, they could have had at least *two*.

…

She's forgiving, Jayne-Mansfield-Two, and before he can finish what he hopes he was trying to say, she's saying,

"I would like that very much,"

and he hopes harder that everyone around him heard her say it.

…

He takes her to the movies, he recalls, and he's shirted for the duration of the date and the dinner that follows, but not, he assures me, for the duration of the rest-of-the-night they spend together. Time and time again, he entwines with her in ways he can only partially recount, all these years on, but his eyes never fail to glimmer when he remembers the curves her body takes.

"So the next day, I'm at work, and nobody believes me. They know we went out, sure, but after months of watching her shoot down every handsome bastard who bothered to ask her to dinner, you have to appreciate their hesitance to accept my word."

I'm about to interject—Tibor, no doubt sensing my forthcoming query, hits me with

"So, you see, I had to prove it to them..."

and I know I'm about to be privy to another wonderful dissertation on what I have come to dub 'The Tao of Tibor.'

The lunchroom, it turns out, is the heartbeat of Ganz. Gossip, cigarettes, alcohol—the currencies of the day filter through poorly-insulated walls. Gambling is a daily distraction; all of the aforementioned are traded religiously, under clouds of both smoke and colorful language.

Armed with this knowledge—and the foresight to recognize he would have to prove his conquest—Tibor wastes no time in implementing his latest scheme.

"So I made a bet."

"What kind of bet?"

The laughter returns, and he leans in, the way I imagine he would have on that day, surrounded by what he describes as a doubting brother and an overly-skeptical mob.

"My boy—the kind that would see me not only elevated amongst my peers, but make me a good deal of money in the process."

...

"We're on this crane..."

For what it's worth, I smile, and my pen moves a little faster on the page below. I know that whatever is going to come out of his mouth next is bound to be good.

"...and we're making love, the way we tend to..."

He pauses; lowers his voice, and his grin threaten to overtake the entirety of his proud features. His eyes dance, scrambling to ensure his beautiful wife isn't within earshot, and once satisfied, he regales me with the most intimate of details.

"So, we're fucking, and she's loving it. I've got her pressed against the side of the crane, and it's rocking back and forth, and we're rocking back and forth, and she's making the kinds of noises a woman only makes when she believes everyone has gone home for the evening."

The mischief is practically bleeding from the corners of his mouth. He speaks faster now, the loudening of his voice illustrating the assorted climaxes they must make together, suspended in the air of a

'wink'

abandoned warehouse.

"Fucking for an audience—write this down—

I write it down.

Fucking for an audience

"—changes your mentality somewhat."

The bet, as it happens, requires that—in exchange for a great deal of lunchroom currency—Tibor must provide proof of said relations with one Jayne-Mansfield-Two. Imagining that, *no*, suggesting Jayne-Mansfield-Two allow more than Tibor to witness their lovemaking in her bedroom (—where, up until right there, on the crane, the majority of the lovemaking was happening--) he was left to alternate measures to ensure his payday and reputation be solidified.

So the bet stated that a small core contingent of the boys, captained by Emil, hide from the masters upon the end-of-day whistle, steeling themselves away in the bays Tibor had once used to hide his employment. From their sub terrain-in vantage point, they would be able to witness the debauchery to follow.

Looking back, Tibor recalls that convincing the gang to take the bet was met with a great deal less resistance than convincing the star herself to make love in her proverbial office. Knowing she would balk at the very thought of an audience, he presented the adventure as a sort of controlled voyeurism; she could enjoy the excitement at the possibility of discovery, without the threat of *actual* discovery.

"So we're up on the crane, and it's dark, but not too dark—

My pen races to keep up as his tone changes; the wattage of his smile doubles.

"—and I'm doing my best to be considerate of the boys down below…you know, ensuring the angles and positions I'm putting her in are best for their viewing consumption. There could be no doubts as to my conquest, you see, and I knew Emil, above all others, would be skeptical."

"Were the boys discovered?"

"No, gratefully—at one point, I was sure I heard some muffled laughter, but she was so lost in the moment—

He pauses for dramatic effect.

"—someone could have driven a truck through the front entrance and she wouldn't have noticed."

…

The romance continued, he tells me, for some time. Occasionally--and only in the interest of being a good brother, Tibor tells me—he would pull the old 'Twin-Switch' and allow Emil, disguised as himself, the opportunity to bed Jayne-Mansfield-Two.

Noting my head shaking at this particular revelation, Tibor assures me that it was, in fact, in her best interest.

"It kept it fresh and exciting for her, you see. After a time, she would get used to my style of love-making; I consider her fortunate that, at times, to her, it may have felt as though she was with another man entirely."

His charm belies his sincerity, and despite the logic, I'm forced to agree with him. Tibor, if nothing else, presents himself as a very caring lover—one who, despite his mischiefs, loves women and would never do anything malicious to something he values so dearly.

I ask him how long it continued, this torrid love affair, and he appears remorseful. Gazing into some imagined distance, head bowed, he searches his mind for an appropriate answer, and finally, comes back with

"For a little while…and only."

My pen hits the page below, rolls with a degree of certainty towards the floor of the living room we sit in on this, another countless afternoon in afternoon's worth of regaling. We track its path together, a welcome break for both my weary wrist and his weary heart.

He sighs, pauses for a moment.

"My God, that ass, though."

And there it is.

A moment, passed, and then--much the way it has been for the totality of his existence—we're on to the next adventure.

Interludes and Architects.

He spends the bulk of his early twenties working on the Konti Utca, or, following a shortened yet *distinguished* military career, the Ganz. Menial, blue collar jobs, his evenings spent in the class rooms of a trade school, studying architecture with Emil. Although he often wishes only *one* of them had enrolled—so that he could have nights off when needed, and vice versa, the virtues of a shared face—he appreciates the details in the draftsmanship, a perfect application of his more artistic talents.

There's a beauty to the structure, the process—one that lends itself to his growing obsession with artistic interpretation—and soon, despite the mischievous underachievement of his previous academic career, he's a recognized talent and reputable student. He still finds time for trouble, but for the most part, he's focused-- and for the first time—on something other than escape from the crushing oppression of Communism.

His days give him license for the foolishness that comes with the death of his teenage years; his adventures continue somewhat vigorously, and with a frequency that satisfies the more primal of his ambitions. After months of continuous study he's presented with an Architect's Certificate; should he choose, he's able to leave the comfort of the Ganz and the Utca in favor of work at one of Hungary's many design houses.

He's contemplating this—telling himself he's leaving anyway, and that a man with his skills is easily and readily employed—his certificate would virtually guarantee employment anywhere in Europe--when a walk to work one cold winter morning changes the course of his young life once again.

...

"I'm walking Blascka, the way I always do—on the same route I always walk. It's funny, really...I'm just thinking about the quiet my life has somehow become; how I'm settling into life here. Emil is soon to be a father, I have an education and a relatively good job—maybe the desperation of escape is fading."

"And then?"

I ask, knowing him well enough to recognize this peace must be temporary.

"And then, I'm a half-block from home, and I'm bending down to wrestle a stick from my dog's mouth, when I feel a gun pressed against the back of my head. I'm frozen, fearing the worst—my neighborhood was relatively safe, you see, but not without the odd robbery or assault. Naturally, I didn't have any money on me—and I conveyed it to the man, as I slowly turned to face him..."

The look he gives me conveys a great sadness.

"It was a soldier. Behind him, hanging from a military truck, are three more. They may have had their guns drawn on me, they may not have; once the bastard with the gun at my head spoke, I lost sight of everything else."

"What did he say?"

"He said I had stolen government property. He said I could be charged, that I was getting off lucky. And then, right from my hand, they grabbed the leash and took my Blascka from me."

"Needless to say—

--I was settled in Hungary no longer. The government, the military—I would no longer be their slave."

That Hospital Story.

There are, truth is told, a great many things that stand out in my mind, when I reflect on my bi-weekly visits with Tibor. Tales of adventure, both grand and not; stories of heroism and honor and friendship and love, all spoken about so casually—so liberally—by a man fascinating in both presence and his recounting of such stories. I often think of his bravery; of his cunning and determination, of his zeal and the childish grin on his face when he gets to the 'good stuff' entertaining me with tales of a life unimaginable and yet somehow, terrifyingly real.

There is, among the adventures, one that stands out in my mind as I collect and catalogue his story. One so wild, so captivating, so encapsulating that I reflect upon it every time I think of Tibor Fidler.

This, without further hesitation, that story.

"I'm twenty-three years old" he begins, and, simply by hearing his age, Emil's face lights up beside me. This—apparently—is a good one.

"I'd been at Ganz for about two years, and I was starting to make something of myself. I'm making a little bit of money, I'm dressing well, I'm taking care of my family—

"This is the one." Emil can't help but interject, his own grin a shadow of his father's as Tibor draws breath to paint the picture.

"So, I have this girlfriend."

Of course he does. Renowned for his love of women—and their love of him—I realized the moment Emil told me 'The Hospital Story,'

"This is the one."

--was a particularly juicy one, that it must have something to do with a beautiful woman.

"So beautiful." His accent has a way of deepening, somehow, when he speaks of women—the Hungarian drawl is decidedly overpowering now.

"Her parents were very well-to-do, as they say…he was a doctor, of something and she was a beautiful woman herself. They were away a lot, vacationing in the countryside—their daughter was frequently staying home, to watch the house in their stead."

His eyes do the devilish thing-that-they-do, and he continues, well aware that he has a captive audience. He tells me that a maximum of two weeks holidays were allowed at Ganz—Communism, it seems, had a way of being overly vigilant…missing extra time could result in incarceration.

"Her parents had gone away, and I had spent the better part of two weeks off of work, alone with her in her parent's house, basically just—"

He stops, as if suddenly remembering that his beautiful wife, present as she always is during our sessions, is well within earshot.

"Oh, Tibor—it's nothing I've not heard before." Her voice washes over his, revitalizing him, the positivity radiating from a beautiful woman is all he needs to center him, continue the tale. Emil grins across the table—I too, am getting the hang of their relationship, and, to be honest I'm entirely envious.

"So, I'm just back to work, both refreshed and exhausted, from all of the—

"Sex. From all of the sex."

"Yes…so I'm not back to work, but two days, before my friends tell me of plans to vacation themselves, in the mountains to the North. Of course, I want to go—swimming, camping, relaxing…but, I can't take any more time off of work, lest they throw me in jail."

Communism, I'm quickly realizing, was a hell of a thing. Regardless—as Tibor assures me, he's never been one to miss a good time on account of a pesky little thing like oppression—so he devised a rather ingenious, if dangerous, plan to accompany his brethren.

...

The foreman blows the whistle, heralding a commencement of the day's work.

Tibor Fidler falls from his chair, writhing in agony, as if on cue. His screams, bellows louder than machinations of locomotive engineering devices and, at once, a crowd surrounds him, concerned and entirely helpless at the sight of their writhing, foaming peer. Even Tibor's twin brother Emil is baffled—just two days before, he had returned positively radiant from a two week work reprieve, filled to the brim with stories of debauchery and adventure.

A stark contrast to the pained, contorted figure laid out before him; in a frenzy, Emil scrambles for the commandant's office, and a desperate phone call is made.

Tibor moans and bellows, confident his ruse is having the desired effect. Surely, his co-workers and superiors have seen him fall ill; surely they'll understand if he's away from work long enough to recover. Impressed by his own commitment to the role—let alone the desired effect—he increases the frequency of his agonized wailings…as he hears the sirens approaching from the gates to Ganz, he figures he may even come away with a Doctor's note excusing him from duties.

His plan, it seems, coming to fruition beautifully.

The accompanying ambulance feverishly maneuvers Tibor to the hospital; their steady hands and fast work have him medicated and unconscious before he hits the Emergency room door.

"This—

Tibor laments

--may have been a *bad* thing."

"You see, the whole scene was a ruse—I knew that I was not to be granted more time off from work, and I really—

--really—

wanted to vacation in the mountains…"

"So you faked an illness?!"

Emil laughs beside me, shoots one of those Told-You-So looks, and instantly, I'm in agreement…

This is the one.

…

Tibor awakens, delirious, as though still enthralled in the fever of some half-remembered dream. The stiff hospital gown is entirely unwelcome, as is the tether seemingly restraining him to a small bed in a small room. Bathed in fluorescent light, his reality comes to him in patches…the tether is an IV drip presenting itself furiously from some throbbing vein below his blanket, which is suddenly entangling him as he rises to—

--nearly fall to the floor, instantly doubled-over from a sharp, searing pain along his lower right abdomen. He fumbles aimlessly at the source of the pain, and is shocked to feel sensitivity and wetness beneath his gown. A heat washes over him as he realizes something is not right…something is missing…

…

"My appendix."

I'm astounded, enthralled and baffled as I listen to him. Beside me, Emil is in hysterics.

Did he really--

"They took out my appendix."

And it hits me, as Tibor and Emil laugh together, there in the living room where we recount and record these adventures, that Tibor Fidler is the kind of man who would have his appendix removed in order to go on vacation. I'm in awe, and hysterics myself, as he struggles to continue amidst the laughter.

"Rest assured, I went on vacation. But first, as it turns out my ruse had worked, there was the small matter of recovery."

...

He's barely coherent before the deluge of co-workers, well-wishers and particularly-concerned-twin-brother surround him in the tiny room. Much to Tibor's delight, his nurse is...

"Astonishingly"

beautiful, and as it turns out, very concerned for the handsome young man, tending to his handsomely stitched lower abdomen. Days pass, and they are not without delight, save for the at-times blinding reminder of the lengths he will go to, radiating up from the hole in his side where an organ used to live.

"They brought me cake, fruit—I'd never eaten so well in my life, you see. I was in no hurry to leave that bed—until, of course, I tired of my beautiful girlfriend coming to see me in between bouts of care from my (astonishingly) beautiful nurse—and then watching her leave to worry about me, alone in her parent's house."

...

"One thing about having a twin—

His smile is a mile wide.

"—you can be two places at once."

...

Emil was nothing if not the concerned brother. As such, Tibor formulates his words carefully, ensuring Emil that he's fit enough for his plan to work, assuring him that the ruse must be exact if he's to avoid detection. The ever-looming threat of detention for his deception weighs on Tibor—Communist policemen kind of look down on faking appendicitis to extend one's holidays—however, the thought of his beautiful girlfriend wasting her nights in a home alone weighs more.

And so, carefully, in between rotations from (astonishingly) beautiful nurses, Emil slips into Tibor's bloodstained hospital gown and takes his place the way he has before, and Tibor slips into the Budapest night, searching for something he's spent operations and nights without.

He's careful to avoid detection, dancing at first down hospital halls, his brother's cap pulled tightly over his eyes. He pauses only to catch breath when the pain reminds him to do so, slinking through cobblestone streets on the way to that familiar backdoor. Her light is on, and relief comes between waves of pain—really, the thought of climbing through her second story window isn't nearly the fun he remembers it being.

She looks as though she's seen a ghost—and bathed under her porch light, features drawn and weary—maybe she has, the efforts of his adventure leaving Tibor taxed and ready for bed in a decidedly different way than originally intended.

She takes him in, knowing

"—only by the glint in my eye—"

which brother it was, and as Tibor so gracefully puts it, there across the table from me…

"—tended to all of my needs."

Several (somewhat) restful hours later, feeling the energy to pull himself from the warmth of both her embrace and bed, Tibor steels himself to the streets. Careening somewhat blindly down back alleys, the familiar tread of cobblestone underfoot, he guides himself home, eager to pay one final visit before his hospital bed claims him once more.

…

"Emil!"

The ruse is on—as the heavy door to his parent's humble abode opens, and as Racz Anna throws her arms around her son, Tibor grins, eager to continue this charade.

"How is Tibor? Is he okay? Are the sutures binding—I was so worried that they would burst, and he would be in great trouble—oh, Emil, tell me, has his color returned?"

Her concern masking her ability to distinguish the decidedly pale skin tone 'Emil' has returned wearing, Racz Anna ushers her son into the living room, stirring Tibor Ference from his rest with the concerned pleadings.

"Ference—wake yourself—Emil has returned from the hospital…Tell him, Emil, tell him Tibor is okay! Tell him—

"Mother, Tibor, unfortunately, has run into trouble."

Her face, immediately, goes three shades lighter than Tibor's, though Emil's cap successfully masks his visage as he snickers beneath its brim. He allows the anguish to wash over his mother's delicate features for but a moment before he can no longer stand the sight of it—removing the cap, he lets out a laugh that nearly doubles him over, the pain shooting from his side chases the laughter escaping his lips.

"Tibor????"

"Yes, mother. Do not worry—as you can plainly see, I'm fine."

In truth, he may not be, the agony of his boisterous laughter coupled with Racz Anna's palm across his cheek serves to remind Tibor to take it easy.

His father shares in the bewilderment for but a moment, before embracing his son heartily, the family rejoicing. An eternity in their arms, Tibor pulls himself away, laughter still cascading across his body, radiating against the stitches of his wound.

"If you're here….in those clothes…"

"Yes, father. Emil is in the hospital—in my bed, even now—so as not to arouse suspicion as to the severity of my injury."

"Severity—son, you've had major surgery. You should be bedridden, not out playing such horrible games with your mother."

"Father, I'm fine. You see, I need—"

"What you need—no, what you must do—is return at once. Your poor brother, Tibor—this ruse will not go on a moment longer. You'll be back in that bed by the hour's end, and I'll hear nothing to the contrary."

"But, Father—"

...

Tibor sighs, here in the present, across the table from me. Mischief, as he explains to me, is the perfect (and, at times, only) escape from the oppression of a life somehow seemingly pre-determined. Finding joy amongst the struggle to become something greater fueled his exploits…his father's stern tone and steeled gaze served to remind him, on many occasions, that mirth and merriment could potentially have serious consequences.

...

That look—seen countless times over the span of his young years, forces Tibor back into the night-time streets, leaving Ference and Racz Anna shaking their heads as he careens wildly towards the warmth of his currently-occupied bed.

Breathless, exasperated, and somewhat reeling from admitted over-exertion, Tibor swears under his breath as he approaches the hospital gate. He had assumed—clearly incorrectly—that the nighttime guard would long-since have abandoned his post, allowing him entry hours past the doors closed to visitors. Attempting to sneak past him in his current state would surely lead to discovery; perhaps the only crime worse than the one he's already committed, he muses, mind racing as he surveys the scene from around a nearby corner.

His options are decidedly limited. His wound pulsing, echoing the beating of his heart, Tibor swears the rhythm is shaking the very ground beneath him. Deciding that honesty could very well be the best policy, he shambles onto the cobblestone path leading towards the massive gates, praying his grim visage bears proof enough to gain him access to the bed now screaming his name.

He steadies himself as best he can, the wound and its fresh stitches biting sharply into his side with every feverish step. The guard, some thirty feet away now, tenses immediately, hand reaching for the rifle no doubt hiding behind the arch of the simple doorway he emerges from.

"Halt! Visiting hours is over."

The man's tone is stern, his eyes unwavering. From his vantage point, Tibor ascertains the rigidity of the man's stature, the proud cleft of his chin, the cords of muscle buckling against the restraints of his perfectly-pressed uniform. Instantly, he's assured that his plan to be brutally honest is the correct course of action.

"I'm not a visitor…I'm a patient here."

"Nonsense." The guard's tenor, a few octaves lower, resonates against the still of the Hungarian night.

"My name is Tibor Fidler, and I merely went for a walk--

"Your name is of no consequence to me. You couldn't possibly be a patient, as the only way in or out of this ward is directly behind me. And you couldn't possibly have eluded my eyes during my posting, Tibor Fidler, so unless your walk began before my shift seven hours ago, you need to turn around and return to your home."

His breath measured, his posture as rigid as the calamity of his wound will allow, Tibor meets the guard's gaze, attempting to appear undaunted as he readies his response.

"I assure you, sir—in fact, I can prove to you that I need in that building."

He reaches for the bottom of his shirt, but decides against it, as the guard's hand shoots to his hip, preparing to release the leather clasp tethering his pistol.

"Don't move!"

"I merely intend, sir, to prove to you that I am indeed expected here—I've had a procedure done within these walls, not even two days ago…"

His hand remains firmly around the handle of his Walam .48M pistol, but the steel in the guard's voice recedes as he sighs.

"Show me, Tibor Fidler—and then I will check with patient registry—if you're lying to me sir, you'll be spending nights in prison…these walls will be nothing but a well-remembered dream."

Tibor is uncertain if his hand trembles from the fear, or the pain, or the exhaustion; he is labored nonetheless, fingers grasping wildly at the base of his brother's shirt, revealing himself deliberately, as delicately as the tiny tremors in his fingers will allow.

The guard's demeanor changes instantly, and violently enough that Tibor races his gaze with uncertainty…as his eyes behold the state of the wound and the scar surrounding it, he instantly regrets his decision.

The stitches remain, certainly—he is confident, even in his semi-delirious state, he would have felt them give way—infinitely more alarming is the purplish-green sheen his cold, clammy skin has taken. The sweat is back, tracing the contours of his face as he raises his eyes to meet those of his juror's.

"Tibor Fidler looks at the guard, sir…I can assure you, I need that bed in there. To answer your question, yes, I left the hospital, and apparently, far earlier than I should have."

"Of that, I agree—my God, Tibor, no doctor would release you in such a state…how in the hell did you get out?"

Sensing the sympathy in his tone—and remembering his commitment to truth telling—Tibor manages a rakish smile.

"Well, funny story there…"

…

Four minutes later, the very same guard—Zsigmond, it turns out—escorts/carries a bewildered and decidedly semi-conscious Tibor to the bed occupied by Emil. His concern is genuine—if not exacerbated by the curiosity of beholding a pair of identical twins, and the appreciation for the benefits having a carbon copy of one-self must afford.

Rounding the final darkened corridor to Room 321—the one, it turns out, listed in the patient registry as housing *one* Tibor Fidler; the guard imagines the look on his face must be somewhat similar to that of the Fidler twin rising from the bed to greet him.

So *astonished*, seeing Tibor slung over the smaller of his not-small-at-all shoulders.

"Oh shit—Tibor—

"Is fine, I assure you."

The nurse—Anna, if Zsigmond recalls correctly—rises from what-she-believed-to-be Tibor's bedside with a shriek. Instantly, she looks as though she may pass out herself, the duplicate visage surely wreaking havoc on her senses. Moments before—from the looks of the hospital-grade applesauce now adorning the wall beside the bed—she was confident that the patient she was checking in on (--and flirting with, no doubt, if the rumors about her among the guards are true--) was *one* Tibor Fidler. Now, ghastly, grandiose, and bathed in the dull moonlight seeping from an applesauce-stained window, Zsigmond ingloriously presents her with *another*.

Seeing the exasperation in the twin—Emil, if Zsigmond remembers correctly—he is astonished at the similarities in the brother's faces…Tibor's expression, before he passed out on the stairwell minutes ago—was identical in every respect. The coloring is off, of course—Zsigmond both allows for blood loss and appreciates Tibor's insistence on seeing his woman—but the real Tibor Fidler needs the comforts (and confinement) of the hospital bed more than the fake Tibor currently scrambling from it.

Zsigmond assures Emil of his discretion, beckons him to assist in the transition of brothers. They share a laugh, tucking Tibor gently into the confines of the small, rigid bedding, avoiding and ensuring that Anna stay conscious and maneuvering amongst the applesauce riddled floor to the bed. With a final semi-astonished glance, he resigns himself to his post at the main gate, confident he will have no adventure similar to this one in many, many nights.

…

Tibor awakens with a grunt, the fire in his side magnified by the uncomfortable feeling of being watched. He labors to rise from the confines of the hospital bed he has no recollection of entering, his weary eyes straining against the sunlight assaulting him from a somehow-stained window.

His heart skips *at least* a beat, pupils dilating wildly as they absorb the image of a stern-faced doctor towering over the foot of his bed. To his right, Emil looks appropriately concerned…beside him, a curvy nurse appears to be somewhat cross with him. His mind is dancing, and he's feverish, but to the best of his recollection, he doesn't recall sleeping with her, so, he assumes, she's upset about something else.

The doctor's anger, however, appears to be focused directly on him.

"Fidler."

"Yes?"

"Tibor Fidler."

"The same."

"*The* Tibor Fidler?"

"Unfortunately."

Emil snickers, probably against his better judgment. For a moment, the doctor directs his laser-like intensity toward the Fidler-decidedly-not-Tibor's way. Tibor appreciates the moment's respite, clamoring to collect his wits as the doctor's head slowly pivots back towards its primary target.

"Your appendix…

"Hurts, doctor, I assure you."

"Was in complete health. Which leads me to believe, Tibor Fidler, that this…farce…has been nothing but a reckless, ill-advised ruse from the very beginning."

"Correct."

The doctor's granite features soften, for an instant. Clearly, he wasn't expecting a confession…however, following the exhaustion of last night's adventures, and the success with the guard, Tibor figures that this whole 'telling-the-truth-thing' may have advantages.

That, and he's tired and he's sore and he really would appreciate a little peace and quiet.

"So, why in the seven hells would you do such a thing? The penalty for such stupidity, I assure you, is severe. If I inform the Ganz—"

"All due respect, doctor…"

Emil shifts wildly in his chair, as if silently urging Tibor to remain silent. He steels his gaze, sets his jaw, ignoring the color draining from his brother's face as he parts his lips.

"…Ganz is quite rigid; cruel even, with their allowance of holidays for established workers. More than the allotted—even for a missed day, a death in the family—is punishable by jail time."

"I know doctor."

"Then explain to me why you would risk such a thing? Why in God's name take the chance? You could develop an infection, sepsis, heart failure."

"I needed a vacation."

The words stop the doctor instantly. He stands, dumbfounded, not a crack of emotion in the granite veneer stretched across his features. The room is silent, save for the restless hand wringing of the *now-ninety-percent-sure-he-didn't-sleep-with-her* nurse.

Moments crawl; Tibor can't be sure he's conscious. The doctor's visage, after an eternity of condescending and overtly critical looks, appears to change ever-so-slightly. Finally, terribly, he opens his mouth—Tibor sighs, realizing his sentence rides on the lips parting to announce it.

"Heh."

He cranes his neck, there in his hospital bed. Surely, he couldn't have heard the good doctor correctly…for a moment, it sounded as if he almost—

"Heh, heh,"

Laughed.

Miraculously, he continues, his howling, now, unrepentant, and echoed by Emil's nervous chuckle from his seat somewhere beside him. Beside him, he *assumes*…truth be told, Tibor has no idea where his brother is—or if any of this overtly surreal theatricality is nothing more than the by-product of his blood loss and exhaustion.

Still, it continues, and the nurse is laughing, and despite himself, Tibor is laughing as well.

Eventually, the absurdity of the situation subsided; the doctor wipes tears from his eyes, shakes his head, and pats Tibor on his shoulder.

"You're a crazy man."

"Yes sir."

"Ah, God—"

He stops himself, needing a moment to collect his thoughts, the laughter threatening to overtake him once more. Tibor heaves another sigh, resigns himself to whatever fate he's earned.

"—but you deserve that vacation, Tibor. I will inform the Ganz that you will be needing a full two weeks reprieve from duty, in order to fully convalesce."

"Thank you, sir."

"You've certainly earned it. Take two days to rest—for real, this time, please—and then enjoy your vacation Tibor."

"Yes sir. Thank you, sir."

"However—

Tibor swallows hard, feeling his guts tense and writhe.

"—no more stunts, Mr. Fidler. No more holidays."

"Yes sir."

"You're going to be needing every organ you have left, son."

...

For my part, chronicling Tibor's many adventures, I'm confident that this must be the extent of the fantastic as well. He finishes the story with a grin, and, as I labor to recount the totality of his mad tale before closing my worn notebook, I reckon that now—surely—I've heard the wildest and most extraordinary of his tales.

Naturally, as Tibor heaves a sigh, beginning to tell me the next—I'm completely wrong in my assumption.

Passions Enflamed (Or, painting shit for kids).

Working the floor at Ganz proved easy enough; in time, Tibor became so proficient at his job that he began to pass his increasingly free time constructing small toys from scrap.

He worked diligently, to be sure, and there were never questions as to the integrity of his welds or the quality of welding. No, his hobby came to fruition more out of boredom than anything else—Communism, naturally, dictated that more hours than humanly tolerable be spent within factory walls; Tibor simply began to harness his free-time into something decidedly more productive than the usual mindless conversation.

Small model planes were his first endeavor—followed earnestly by tiny houses and tin horses. Hidden from the ever-watchful eyes of his oppressors/employers, Tibor's minute creations proved increasingly popular amongst his co-workers, eager to trade cigarettes or lunch items for toys to take home to their impoverished families and tiny children.

Emil, as always, seemed to take umbrage with the

…*liberties*

Tibor was taking during work hours, and was becoming increasingly animated in his urgings that such operations cease.

Tibor, drunk with the accolades his tiny treasures were earning, simply increased production.

Never,

he told himself,

at the expense of his commitment to quality in his position proper. Before long, he was pleased at his manufacturing process; still, he felt his productions lacking in aesthetic prowess.

Sure, the feedback was positive enough, and his clientele was growing appropriately, given the 'hush-hush' nature of his newfound enterprise—looking at a particularly masterful interpretation of a World War II German Luftwaffe Fi103R Reichenberg one day, Tibor decided he needed to do *more*.

...

Schneider works the gate at Ganz, and God Bless him, he's manning his post the very morning after Tibor concocted his latest scheme.

It's a Tuesday, by virtue of some small miracle; small miracle if and for no other reason than *The-Powers-That-Be*—middle management and staunch Communism-enthusiasts the Brackt Brothers—always arrive *after* 10am on Tuesdays.

This is of note for two reasons; the gatemen—*like Schneider*—are much more liberal in both the comings-and-goings of employees otherwise chastised for being late, and the gatemen—*like Schneider*—are much more liberal in their comings-and-goings as well.

Watching him carefully from his position in line, latest in a sea of ever-miserable worker drones, Tibor is eternally grateful for his fortune.

His fortune *and*—gripping the plethora of cigarettes he'd spent the previous night bartering for—Schneider's unfillable Tuesday penchant for smoke breaks.

Normally, attempting to bribe a gate operator at the Ganz has more to do with arriving late; Tibor has had his share of attempts at this as well, thankful his ever-responsible twin would punch his timecard in case of his (momentary) absence.

Inching closer to his prey with every shuffle of tired, zombie-like feet, Tibor realizes that this time is entirely different. Different, not only in the fact that Schneider had earned something of a reputation as a staunch, unflinching Jew—and, generally, a last-resort in terms of potentially-bribable gatemen—no, different in the sense that the bastard *only has one arm.*

Tibor swears under his breath, careful to avoid detection from the ever-closer gatemen—his reconnaissance had gathered that, yes, Schneider works Tuesdays and, yes, Schneider loves cigarettes…he bites his lip at the mental anguish flooding his brain, steels his gaze to the limp coat limb swaying in the harsh winter breeze.

How the fuck

he asks himself as delicately as the situation will allow

did he fail to notice the bastard is missing an arm??

Meaning, of course, that although the bastard may be appropriately swayed by means of cigarette-suggestion, his hopefully acquired aid in transporting small toy contraband out of the Ganz is suddenly a one-handed job, where he was set on at least two.

The seeming futility of his latest, best-laid plan encourages whatever trembling the wind hasn't forced; Tibor takes a pregnant moment to consider the possible punishment for toy-making during work hours, should Schneider not be swayed.

Communism has had men arrested for taking an extra sick day; surely, using scrap from authorized assembly endeavors in order to create toys for profit must carry as steep a penalty. A lesser man may abandon the entire operation, he reasons—hell, a brave man might consider another route.

Tibor considers himself the latter, and at *least* foolishly-so; and so he steps forward, chin up, and meets Schneider's oppressive gaze with the largest grin he can muster.

"Yes?"

His eyes are cold—grey almost, and a little too close together.

Or it's the nose—a beakish thing, curved aggressively and aggressively red from a Tuesday morning ushering in miscreants such as him, exposed and raw in the wind and sleet. Tibor finds diverting his gaze from the bulb of it difficult, curses himself for standing, slack-jawed, before his intended, and having difficulty forming a reply.

"Move along, then."

"Hello."

"Yes? Be quick, damn you—I've a half-day of you poor bastards to push through this morning."

"I brought something for you--

Sensing the irritation growing exponentially, Tibor is quick to produce a fistful of cigarettes from the restraints of his not-nearly-insulated-enough jacket; in the process, he spills an errant few onto the snow-covered pavement at his feet.

"—thought you might like these."

"Is this some pity thing, you little bastard? Bring the guy with one-arm sympathy smokes? Boy, you taking the piss outta me?

He hasn't time to find the question peculiar; above him, Schneider and his beak are rising from the confines of the small wooden chair he lords from. The man grabs the collection from his half-extended arm in a flash...had he the time, Tibor might appreciate the dexterity the remaining arm seems to possess.

Stunned, the communication to his brain *does* notice that his bait seems to curry favor; he fumbles over his apology, and quickly, gets to the good part of his proposal.

Schneider stares at him for what seems to be a (cold) eternity; finally, he motions to the guard standing opposite the drone line, and with a nod back, traffic begins flowing to the right of him. More eternity passes, and when

Schneider and Tibor mercifully find a modicum of privacy, the man opens the mouth under the beak once more.

"I assume you've got some kind of proposal for me boy? Hmm—something you need? Or, is this merely a 'kindness-of-your-heart' gesture?"

Tibor is amazed at the agility the one-armed man possesses; as those cold, wolf-like eyes remain transfixed upon his, he deftly withdraws a single cigarette from Tibor's outstretched hand, and, with the kind of reflexes that could only be honed by years of compensation, lights the cigarette instantly pressed to his just-closed lips with a lighter that seems to function as an extension of the isolated appendage.

"I do, actually."

"*Do actually*, what boy?"

"I—I have a favor to ask of you."

"Bah!"

The eyes never waver, despite the sudden increase in inflection. Tibor stands astounded, baffled at how a man's mouth could open so wide, and yet still hold a cigarette against a bottom lip.

"Favor, he says. Tell me boy, what is this favor, that you'd seek to bribe poor Schneider with shitty menthol cigarettes?"

Tibor retracts his hand, taking the chastisement as indication that his purported offering has been rejected—with a violence to this tenor, he's made aware of his apparent success.

"Hell, not so fast boy. Not so fast—they're better than nothing, goddamn you. Now tell me, with what have you come to propose to me? Tell me fast, lest the other gatemen wonder what we're conspiring out here in the cold."

Handing the sole appendage all of the menthols, Tibor uses his lucky second arm to reach into his coat pocket. Schneider's eyes widen, doubtless anticipating another mound of partially crushed cigarettes, to add to his overburdened hand. Instead, he appears perplexed when Tibor's palm returns—presented in it, a tiny tin model of a German airplane.

He eyes it quizzically, Schneider does—takes it in the outstretched hand that, until moments ago, was ravenously gripping shitty menthols; menthols which have since retreated into some dusty pocket in one of the seemingly countless layers adorning his near-emaciated frame. His sunken cheeks twitch, the beak wrinkles somehow, and, after a small eternity, Schneider does something distinctly—to this point, leastways—uncharacteristic.

He smiles.

"Toys, boy?"

Tibor nods, feeling his characteristic charisma come ebbing back.

"You're making toys in there?"

"Yes, sir."

"Humph. Quality toys, too. Quality toys, when you ought to be working."

"That's right."

He does his best to match the gateman's thousand-yard stare—those close-set, wolf like eyes are bearing down on him even *more* intensely, if possible, than they have been for the duration of this increasingly uncomfortable exchange. Still, Tibor knows that his plan is sound and that his bait has been accepted and that once he feels the confidence he's currently feeling that there is no *un*-feeling it, so

"Yep. And I'm going to make more."

Schneider smiles a second time.

"Bigger ones, too. And I'm going to need someone to help me get them out of here."

"And, boy…

Tibor offers a smile back, just in case.

"…you're going to need to learn how to *paint* them, as well."

…

Schneider the one-armed gateman is a painter.

One hell of a painter, as it turns out—and soon Tibor's toy-making enterprise is reaping considerable financial gain. Tibor, the craftsman—still somehow, impossibly, keeping up with his welding duties at Ganz, spends his days filling the orders of other workers eager to bestow impoverished children with the kinds of toys they would otherwise be unable to purchase…while Schneider takes them home with him and paints them masterfully in the evenings.

This is serendipitous, Tibor reasons, as his initial prospecting of the guard was for distribution purposes alone; now, he's gained an important ally and, as it turns out, a mentor of sorts. Soon Tibor is following Schneider home, spending evenings revisiting the virtues of acrylic and water-based paints, of oils and pencils with vibrant colors and the canvases they enliven. His model planes and tin homes and tiny automobiles are now brought to life in the most elegant of ways, and the prices and exchanges the workers at Ganz are willing to pay/trade increase exponentially as well.

Still, the rewarding part—aside from being able to treat his mother and father to fresh fruit from the market, and to ensure his twin has two lunches to eat everyday—is turning out to be Tibor's discovered love of painting. He's crude, at first—clumsy with the brushes, his hands more accustomed to the intricacies of the welding torch than the brush—but he reckons he's making strides, and his one-armed, beak-nosed master is quick to tell him so as well.

"Bah! Not as pathetic"

and

"That one looks like a bear with antlers"

are inspiring and encouraging, and, sooner than later, his airplanes are recognized by true-to-life marking emblazoned in vibrant reds and blues, and his deer begin resembling…deer, more than bears with antlers.

He finds it relaxing, this work-after-work never quite feeling like *work*, and he's more than content to filter the pessimism from Schneider's tales of world travels and states-of-affairs. Within a month of their joint venture, Tibor would daresay call them unlikely friends; partners in profit and paint, the elder seemingly more than willing to impart knowledge on someone willing to listen.

The money isn't much; in Communist Budapest, it never is, and so the two of them continue, more for the love of painting and company than to substitute salary at Ganz—the money goes to food, more often than not, and the prices of their works never rise, despite size increases or trickier fabrications. He's resolute in that he will never lose sight of who the model airplanes and tanks and tiny towns are for—he remembers a time when he was shooting horses to feed his family…a time he would have much rather been playing with toys such as these.

Revolution!

We dance around this, Tibor and I, for the first couple of meetings. Emil pushes harder than I do, eager to hear his father regale me on the intricacies of the event that changed his life, and tore him from the man who shared his namesake.

It's our third encounter before his tone shifts, his shoulders sink slightly, and he submits to his son's relentless urges to tell this particular story.

...

It begins, like so many of his adventures, as the boys step into the security alcove at Ganz, weary and wild-eyed and somehow still enthused at the prospect of another day's labor, and the pay that day's labor will provide.

It's early—the kind of ridiculously early Eastern Europeans called normal; the kind I honestly don't remember seeing for years. The sun, he recounts, is up or well on its way; there is a chill to the air entirely uncommon for the time of year. Emil reaches the security checkpoint first, ever the leader—if he's as tired as Tibor, he's not letting on. Two steps and ten thoughts later, Tibor reaches the first checkpoint; he's half in dream before colliding into his brother, who, for some ungodly reason, has stopped the daily dread to the gate.

Instantly, Tibor is jarred from his half-daze. His eyes snap to attention, focusing on a most unusual site.

The maw of the factory, hellish and mountainous and covered in the kind of soot and black only locomotives and broken souls can produce, is at once familiar in iron-crowned visage…and chillingly *different.*

For the first time in World Wars and time-drunk memories, the gates at Ganz are closed.

It is October 23, 1956.

Standing there, exhausted—and, thanks to the onslaught of adrenaline—entirely and uncomfortably awake, Tibor Fidler first hears the word--spoken in the hushed tones of terrified co-workers—that would alter the course of his life irrevocably.

Revolution.

It is February -*something*, 2014, and Tibor pauses, the word and its passing and its meaning and its weight weighing just the way it must have, every time he's spoken it, for the past fifty-eight years.

"It was as though the very air had been…electrified."

His breath is slightly slower…under the dim light, I swear I catch his pupils dilate violently. He sighs, and sighs the kind of sigh only a man weary of this particular tale, and it's telling, can; and then, when *he* can, he gets back to telling me the kind of tale I know will stay with me long past *his* telling.

…

The guards say something, and it's a lot like

"We're closed"

and the mob collected at the mouth of the mighty industrial giant react en masse. There's confusion, at first, and then the din of the mob rises in both protest and profanity, but, as Tibor quickly realizes, to no fruition. Over his shoulder, *left,* Emil is whispering to some guy somewhat recognizable from some station—over shoulder *right,* however, that word

Revolution

and about one hundred different interpretations from about one hundred different lips. Some are crying, some are steadfast and stoic, some—somewhat like himself, are curious.

Call it a life already brimming with death and near death and the kind of morbid fascination of a world filled with nothing but…regardless, once a symphony of shouting through a megaphone penetrates the eardrum reserved for the crowd still buzzing around shoulder right, the electricity in the air overtakes him, and Tibor violently pulls Emil from conversations and crowds, hurriedly recounting a plan, a half-second after he plans it.

"It's only a student demonstration," Emil assures, recognizing both the mad gaze and its meaning stretched across Tibor's wildly contorted features.

As the broadcast, projected now from what must be loudspeakers somewhere attests; the chaos is something much greater. With their backs to the crowd at Ganz, the message is overhead and increasingly everywhere, and in *stereo*—this, as if to answer Emil's assertion—as if to feed Tibor's ever-growing madness—is something much more.

Weaving through maze-like streets, on fire now, from the deluge presented in the noise around them, the brothers learn of the origins, straining their ears to hear the messages from the radio. They're on the way—along with thousands, if the voices buzzing all around them are to be taken at face value—to the Parliament Building at the very heart of Central Budapest.

It began with students—tired of the oppressions of Soviet control, they had managed to infiltrate and accost the radio broadcast building. Cries of freedom and uprising continue to fill Tibor's ears as he nears Parliament, crisscrossing the cobblestone amidst the petrified, gentrified and outright stupefied.

His footsteps echo cadences of revolution, pounding asphalt underneath worn and broke soles, pushing alongside such worn and broken souls, all energized by the commands presented in the airwaves above, until….

A scream—

--and then silence.

Some seven paces behind, Emil has to catch himself from crashing into Tibor, who, following the cues of the broadcast, has stopped as suddenly and as violently and as *totally*.

"Did you hear, Emil?"

"I hear, Tibor, I—

Breath comes harder for Emil, while, crazed and panting, and somehow nowhere near spent, Tibor interrupts

"Something about the scream…"

Footsteps are becoming labored, and the crowd thickens beside the boys as they approach the Parliament Building at the heart of Budapest. Hearts pounding, ears buzzing, they're eventually forced to a dead stop blocks out. Voices assail them from all sides now…as Tibor strains to listen; one in particular is decidedly absent.

The radio is silent.

Dead silent.

Confirmation comes in waves, as hurried whispers dance amongst the gathered throng. The news is universal, and overtly troubling. A delegation of students, storming the radio live building, were fired upon by the State Security Police—killing one student in the process. Incensed, the deceased was wrapped in a flag and held high above the crowd—the gruesome effigy sending both peers and countrymen racing through the streets, stopping only now, on the foot of Parliament Square…

…in the direct path of Russian T-34 tanks.

What happens next happens, Tibor says,

--too fast—

--and yet, somehow, in slow motion.

Emil falls, somewhere beside Tibor, and, somewhere else, a flash. Too fast to catch, and somehow, stuck in a moment—a moment forever between the flash, and the thunder that follows, echoing and reverberating throughout the square—too slow to be bearable.

Emil's weight suddenly falls on him, and together they topple to the cobblestone. Debris cascades him as he twists, shielding his brother amid a clamoring of screams and then

BOOM
BOOM

and he would focus on the noise, if he could, but he's wet somehow, and it's not raining and then he looks down at Emil and sees…

The blood—the blood from holes in his chest, just now racing to darken the dark of his tattered shirt, tells Tibor a half-heartbeat before the

BOOM

of the tank tells him that his twin brother is dying in his arms.

A moment of clarity would tell Tibor that the tanks littering the square they've stumbled upon have opened fire; a volley of shots intended to dissipate the gathering throng, their ensuing volley decidedly deadlier.

…

He pauses when he recounts this, and his eyes turn taking on a different shade as he draws breath to tell me the rest. I listen, more to the half-breaths he takes between telling than the telling of it, and I begin writing gingerly only when he lowers his head, closes his eyes, and takes me grudgingly back to the square.

…

Emil says something—says something or *tries*, and Tibor can't tell, if not for the

BOOM
BOOM

of the tanks, than for the ringing of screams and chaos reverberating in his ears. He's frantic now, pooling the blood in his hands as if to put it back, to fill Emil with the vitality draining from him. The tanks, the mob, the shouts, the shells are inconsequential now, as he works to erase the visage of his twin in pain and entangled in his arms.

There's movement now, everywhere and all around him, as dozens of terrified protesters trample and trash one another in efforts of escape. Holding Emil, Tibor's eyes leave his brother's only to scan the remainder of the crowd, desperate pleas for assistance reflected in his never-lingering gaze. Base, guttural self-preservation has gripped the rabble, and Tibor realizes, he's alone in his efforts to save Emil.

A frenzied glance provides him with an opportunity; a toppled wheelbarrow rests against a concrete wall some dozen feet away. It takes every reserve of strength in his exhausted, electrified body to separate himself from Emil long enough to dash towards it, oblivious to the

BOOM
BOOM

of the guns seemingly above and all around him.

A courtyard and a forever later, he's crossed the square, somehow still alive—and yet not—he can't tell as he half-collapses against the wheelbarrow, toppling it—and himself—as he struggles to regain breath long absent.

Scrambling frantically, a rush of adrenaline grips him as his fingers encircle the familiar wood of the handles—he's diligent, wide-eyed and desperate as he reaches Emil's side once more. Blood splashes in puddles as the wheels careen to a stop. Emil speaks—speaks or seems to, but the

BOOM
BOOM

of the gunfire makes discerning his quiet words impossible.

Not that Tibor would stop to listen, his mind feverishly reminding his hands to work as he reaches desperately underneath his brother's frame. Fingers fail, in the way they wouldn't with the wheelbarrow—as though his body recognizes the importance of his cargo. Lost there, a hail of cannons and the echo they create intertwines with the cannon-like pounding of his heart, steeling him to the task at hand.

His fingers find one another, opposite hands locked now, under one-hundred-sixty-five pounds that feel disconcertingly familiar as he lifts with all his might.

"Leave me,"

Emil states, or tries to—the blood escaping his mouth does much to muffle his pleas.

It is no deterrent.

Neither is the debris that cascades his cheeks and stabs his eyes as he strains under his brother's weight, the

BOOM
BOOM

of the guns little more than a rhythm for which to encourage his diligence, a chant ebbing him on as he nearly buckles, tired feet slipping under crimson puddles.

At once the weight is weightless, the urgency of the moment forcing tired limbs to task, and with as much care and finesse as a siege will accommodate, Emil is unceremoniously draped into the wheelbarrow.

A moment, a breath, and then

BOOM
BOOM

Tibor is off again, careening madly through a labyrinth of blood soaked cobblestone streets, the smoke and stench of gunpowder assaulting his nostrils a constant reminder of the danger overhead and all around him.

The route to the hospital—the same hospital that kept his appendix, when all he needed was a holiday—is a million million miles away, and yet somehow cruelly just from reach. Tibor isn't reminded of such times as much as assailed by them, memories of a life so wholly dependent on the face reflected back on him from the bottom of a bloody wheelbarrow battering him as routinely as the screams filling his ears, reminding him to

Please, save the life

he races so desperately to save.

Every muscle fiber in his body is screaming now, urging him to stop, to rest—his body racked past the point of exhaustion, he carries on, ignoring Emil's urgings to leave him, ignoring the frenzy and chaos and pandemonium around him, pressing onward until he has the all-too-familiar gates of the hospital in his sight.

He's close now, and pressing, footsteps burdened as though dragging through increasingly hardening concrete…the gates of the hospital are swung wide, without a doubt full of panicked and injured Hungarians seeking refuge.

He looks down at his brother…

…he's so very close—

"Emil, we're here—we've made it…"

But Emil is silent. His brother is gone, submerged in the blood pooled there in the wheelbarrow, his grim visage visibly only as footsteps vibrate the wheels to his makeshift tomb, sending crimson waves cascading across ethereal features.

…

"Needless to say—"

Tibor strains, there across the table from me, his icy blue eyes welling as they meet mine. I'm frozen, there, unable to write as he lowers his voice.

"—part of me died in that wheelbarrow."

Getting Out.

"I remember walking home."

There's a melancholy in his tone now, describing the events following Emil's death. I don't press; I write when he speaks, and it's in bursts—as though the courage to formulate word one gives momentum to word two and the one or two that follow…

"The States are involved, at this point."

And then the pause, again, as though his mind is editing his mouth. I give him time, keeping my eyes low and my scribbling to a minimum. When he's ready, he sighs, and the grip tightens on my pen once more.

"I'm walking by this cemetery, and its rows—rows and rows and rows—and I'm thinking it's never going to end. My eyes are down, and I'm deeply saddened by the death and the hunger and the misery—and then, for whatever reason, I look up."

A bit of the pain, even in the recollection, lifts from his voice.

"I look up, and the sky is beautiful. Reds, blues—there's a tone to the sky, when it's wounded; smoke and debris. Smoke and gunpowder and metal—it does something to the air, you see."

I nod, and as his tone accelerates, my writing follows.

"So I'm walking along the edge of the cemetery, and my eyes are on the sky, and I notice there's a man lying on his back just along the fence line, and wouldn't you know it—

He waits for my reaction; disappointed when I offer none, he returns to the telling.

"He's looking up at the sky too. He doesn't notice me, he's just kind of staring, and I'm about to say hello when—

BOOM

BOOM

I scribble this down before he can even say it. After hearing him tell of the Revolution, I know better than to assume this particular tale will continue without the omnipresent sound of gunfire.

"I dive into the ditch beside this guy, just as I realize the Germans are hiding amongst the tombstones. They've got a goddamned anti-aircraft gun set up and they've spotted some sort of American plane. From my vantage point, I can't tell if it's a bi-plane or a bomber, but even overtop of their incessant

BOOM

BOOM-ing,

I can hear the roar of the engines getting louder…"

My pen moves. His mouth moves in tandem.

We may be getting good at this stuff—both in the telling and the transcribing.

"So I crawl over to this guy, just as I spot a tiny little two-prop circle the area above us. He's too small to be making that much noise, I say to the poor bastard…"

He pauses.

I pause.

"…about a half-second before I realize he's dead."

My pen stops dead now, as I catch the look in his eye. He's tired of even speaking this; I can't, for the well-insulated life of me, imagine how weary he must have been *living* it.

"He's just lying there, so peaceful looking. I can't imagine he'd been there long, but I'm thinking, as the roaring grows in my ears, that I'm sad that no one has come to claim him, and I'm sad that no one else had noticed, and I'm—I'm just sad, you know?"

I shake my head yes, and we both know that no, I do not.

"The Germans are yelling and the roar above me and in my ears is growing and I'm thinking that I'm tired of it all…and then I'm not listening to the yelling of the Germans and the roaring above me, and wouldn't you know it…"

I shake my head no, and at this, he smiles once more.

"…through the smoke I spot the biggest goddamned plane I'd ever seen. I remember thinking that it was beautiful; I could spot the American flag along the side, and it's as though I was fixated on it as it rumbled lower towards us."

He sighs, and the smile stays a little.

"I'm just staring, slack-jawed…frozen; and my buddy lying beside me is staring, slack-jawed and frozen—because he's dead—and as I see the hatch door open on the underside of that big bitch, I'm thinking that maybe I'm dead, too."

I'm writing and I'm realizing that, even though I know the end to this particular story—namely because the alleged deceased is the one crafting the tale across the table from me—that I'm absorbed nonetheless. His eyes betray a certain banality towards death.

"And I'm thinking that maybe it's not so bad. I'm tired, you see—tired of losing things, tired of being told how and when to live. Tired of losing Radors and friends. I'm thinking, as I see some distant sunlight kissing the surface of the bomb that beautiful plane opens its hatch to drop, that maybe I should just lie beside this poor bastard and let it all go away."

And let it all go away

scribbled violently on the page below me, and for all the zest and zeal this man before me has, I'm beginning to understand the quiet despair his existence must have held.

"And then—

The smile grows.

"—I remind myself that the beautiful sunlight is kissing a big fucking bomb, and I run as fast as I can."

BOOM

"Boom—

BOOM

"—boom! Smoke and fire everywhere! The blast must have pushed me some dozen feet through the air…I'm lucky I didn't break my back landing on some damn tombstone. Once the ringing goes away, I'm assaulted by both the sound of screaming Germans and the smell of unearthed, re-charred corpses. That damn bomb blew the cemetery all to hell—tombstones and bodies and body parts and dying Germans on fire…it was like something out of a movie, I tell you."

He's speaking quickly now; my hand is starting to burn as I struggle to keep pace. His inflections are distinct, and are distinctly careening around the room we sit in—or more accurately, the room I sit in—Tibor is out of his chair re-enacting the chaos.

"It looked like—like—one of those zombie movies! The Apocalypse! Fucking arms flying around me like rain drops, in between chunks of dirt and mud and God-knows-what-else. I tell you—I'm dodging bodies and flaming heaps of tombstone and flaming bits of bodies, and I'm almost laughing at the absurdity of it all."

As he's dancing around the living room, and imaginary bodies and flaming heaps of tombstone and flaming bits of bodies, I'm right there with him—I absolutely can picture a grin on his face.

"It's so macabre and ridiculous, I'm thinking to myself—promising myself—that if I somehow live through this…I'm not wasting another night in this hellhole."

Knowing the ending to this particular story, with the man himself standing before me, I find that I wholeheartedly agree with his decision.

"Remember, I was walking home—after I checked myself to ensure I wasn't missing any toes or ears—and after the roar of the plane passed, I found myself running—

--in the other direction."

So, away.

"Look, Emil was gone—my family was gone. You have to understand, I associated Budapest with nothing more than death. Communism was a hell of a thing; after surviving under its tenets and structures, I was desperate for a change."

He looks at me with resignation; scanning my eyes as if to see a trace of disdain across my features—as though I would secretly shame him for his decision to leave.

He finds only empathy.

"I wasn't overly willing to stick around to see the promised 'changes' any willing regime would instill—I'd heard promises all of my life, you see."

He sighs, and it's the kind that, despite decades of a relatively royal Canadian existence, tells me the scars of his formative years still burn fresh patterns across the skin of his soul.

"I had friends—I—I didn't mention them, until now, not because they were not important to me in those times; I simple choose to dedicate the majority of my memories and recollections during the years of Emil's existence to recollections and musings of him, and our life—if you could call it such—together."

"I understand."

His look softens,

No,

He tells me without needing to tell me at all;

You most certainly do not.

"It's poetic in a sense that they were sets of brothers, as well. Tibor Hackel shared more than just a name, you see. He always had that sense of zeal—do you use that word anymore?"

"Yes

I assure him;

"We most certainly do."

He smiles at this—the years and atrocities have done very little to dull his sense of humor.

"We had been friends for some time; the Tibors, and Emil, and the other Hackel boy, Marton."

"*Radors.*"

"Brothers?"

My Hungarian is nowhere close to respectable; all said, I've come to appreciate my ability to discern even the smallest of terms.

"Brothers."

I underline the word in my journal; doubtless a term and a theme I'll return to in our times together.

"The Jugovics were Radors as well—Pal and Laszlo; before—before Emil, we were inseparable. Ganz, the fighting, the death—we had one another, and at times, *only*—and it was always enough.

Another sigh.

He's searching for the words, and I've learned to give him all the time he needs.

A moment passes, and then another, and it's just the two of us, alone today in his son's home, and a name and a home his son shares—shares because family is synonymous with brothers, far and away the most and important and oft-writ of the words I will write.

It's what we're writing about today, when the moment he needs is taken, and the breath he draws is to continue.

"Hackel Tibor had, like myself, had enough of Budapest, albeit for different reasons. He had labored for years to buy his first automobile, and after surviving the horrors of the Revolution he was so proud to be able to buy the damn thing."

His smile has returned, and it is admittedly infectious.

Despite myself—normally as reserved as possible, so as not to project my emotions onto his storytelling sensibilities--I'm smiling as well.

Praying that the tale is not about to turn dark again—but smiling.

I note in my journal…

It has been some time since Tibor smiled this way.

"He'd had it, like, a week—two tops—and wouldn't you know it—

The smile becomes laughter.

"—the damn thing died."

We laugh now, together, in the house of the son who bears his uncle's name, tears coming at the absurdity of it all.

"So you can see, the writing was on the wall for us all."

The laughter doesn't feel forced, and so we let it linger, unabated, well past any natural duration.

"That poor bastard walked five miles to tell us he was done. We Tibor's were leaders, if you will, and it took no more than a conversation with colorful language to determine the time to leave was now. The five of us made a pact, that night, that we were going to run, and we were going to run together."

Radors.

"We promised that, no matter what, we would never be separated. Ever."

Pause for dramatic effect.

"This, you will come to understand, was not always the ideal situation—

A smirk.

"—but it was our declaration, and we swore it to the memory of Emil, and I would be goddamned if I was to be the one to break it."

My pen races to match his inflection.

"I'm twenty-four, and I'm devastated—and, maybe, in some ways, I'm a little naïve. I know of a man—a farmer—who agrees to take us to the Austrian border. He feeds us, he houses us; we wait until nightfall and we head out, huddled together under a tattered blanket in the bed of his truck."

"I remember shaking—and its nerves or its excitement or it's both—regardless, the drive is long and we're exhausted. We reach what the farmer tells us is the border—

Another pause, more dramatic effect.

"—only it was not."

…

The truck rumbles over a bump in the road, and Tibor is wrestled violently from what has been the first semblance of solace he's felt in days.

Fittingly, it is torn from him, there on the road out of hell—as though the very dirt itself is desperate to drag and keep its sons down in the mire. The night surrounds him, engulfing him in the totality of the unknown, and Tibor shifts his weight to dismiss it.

Beside him, around him, Radors stir, but sleep still; doubtless comforted by the promise of escape. A promise sold by the man behind the wheel of the truck they escape in—a friend of a friend of a family friend—one who, when spoken of in certain circles, is the sort of man who facilitates said miracles.

It's both comforting and welcoming, sure—as Tibor catches the driver's eye in the rear-view mirror, he's increasingly aware of the chill racing the man's gaze down the base of his spine.

BOOM

Another bump in the road and shifting his attentions out from under the blanket, there in the bed of the truck, the night offers no certainty.

BOOM

and the memories wash over him and they're bad; he's half-dreaming of body parts raining down on him in cemeteries under beautiful skies as he feels the truck lull softly to a halt.

The piece of some soldier's arm hits him in his half-sleep, and he's instantly miles from the debris and chaos that has taken over his subconscious, but the feeling of dread is the same, because the driver's eyes are fixed on him in the rearview mirror, and Tibor senses a malice behind the gaze that simply was not there when the journey began.

"We're here."

Here is supposed to be the border, and yes, there are the faintest hints of light ahead of them, on the road somewhere, but from his vantage point half submerged in half destroyed blankets there in the bed of the truck, Tibor isn't buying it.

Before he opens his mouth to protest, the truck lurches forward once more. It's crawling, steadfast—certainly not at the cantor one would expect when making a mad dash for a borderline. Struggling in vain to see out the driver's windshield, Tibor knows he may only have a moment or two to react, and decides to trust the gnawing at the core of him.

He rustles the sets of Radors from their slumber—a task herculean in nature; the boys, under the assumption a better life awaits upon waking—are in no hurry to comply. It takes a half-shout from Tibor to violently wrestle them to cohesion; one by one they wake, struggling to open tired eyes.

Tibor whispers to them in piercing tones, doing his absolute best to avoid detection from the now-ever-watchful driver. The pace of the truck is deliberate, yes, but the pounding of his heart tells him to escape, and he's certain the jump to the roadside would be far from fatal.

Realizing he will have to lead by example—and that there may not be time to explain—Tibor slaps the last half-dozing Marton boy, and, a finger from a still-stinging hand covering his mouth, motions the foursome to the back of the truck bed.

The driver shouts something, and he can feel the lurching of the truck as he, without question steps on the throttle, but in a moment the wind and the rush of the dirt racing up to embrace him is forefront on his troubled mind—because he has jumped clear of the moving vehicle.

A moment and a warmth, and then the half-welcomed haze the mind takes when it's been rattled, and then there is only the sharp, lingering pain of dirt and rocks—and the taste of dirt and rocks—as Tibor rolls somewhat safely down the embankment at the side of the road.

Firing his gaze northward to the still-moving (and very much still-occupied) bed of the truck, his heart jumps into his throat.

The border is there, sure.

But so is the Border Patrol Station, and a half-dozen waiting and well-armed Border Patrol guards. They're on the truck before it crawls to a stop; a swarm of garish tan and green colored uniforms instantly infecting the truck. Over the din and roar, Tibor can hear the driver attempting to point out their location, pressed against the still-Hungarian dirt—instantly he is grateful the man's arms are restrained as he's pressed violently onto the ground himself.

He swears at him at least as violently as he can, albeit under bated breath, and motions the *Radors* farther down the dusty embankment they've landed so unceremoniously upon. Tibor realizes it will be only a matter of time before the Communist bastards realize the truck is empty, and perhaps the traitor with the knee pressed firmly onto his back will be able to breathe long enough to explain himself.

Should that happen, he realizes, it's best for the five of them to be on the other side of the border they've come so very close to. He's under the assumption that the rattle of free-falling from the bed of a moving truck has everyone's faculties sufficiently stimulated...as such, he begins to crawl, belly planted firmly in the not-welcoming dirt, praying-to-whoever-he-prays-to that the boys are following his lead.

He knows he can't chance a telling glance behind him; no, his eyes must remain fixed on the small of the driver's back, and the knee pressed firmly into it—should they begin to allow him up off of the ground, the crawl will have to turn into a mad dash, and the stones biting into his flesh may well turn into bullets.

He figures, based on the makeshift chicken-wire evoking 'fence' running the length of the flatlands some hundred, hundred-fifty feet south, that the border is close enough to taste. From the driver's position, a haphazardly constructed guard station—erected hastily, no doubt, and with both suspect concrete and architectural prowess—houses the immediate threat some fifty yards west of their current location.

He counts the six guards—the leader, with the loud voice and omnipresent knee-to-the-back; a pair of young-ish looking troopers doing their best to appear menacing behind their crouched master; the fat bastard perched behind the spotlight at the apex of the withered tower, and a roaming patrolman to both locations east and west of the decaying building.

The sole spotlight, despite the menace of its' just-illuminated shaft, is unmanned, and thankfully, focused solely on the truck they *used* to be secreted away in.

This information he collects in a moment, and in said moment he's crawling and still-thankful and kind of wishing he was crawling faster—because the driver is still swearing and as loud as he can that he had five defectors in his illuminated truck, and that he was bringing them to justice, rather than the border some seven steps south.

All of this tells Tibor his crawling had better continue, and quickly. A stifled cough behind him sounds close enough to be a Hackel, and unfortunately, loud enough to potentially cause trouble. He risks removing his eyes from the ever-evolving scene at the command post to shoot the Radors his most-menacing gaze, urging them with bright blue eyes against a Hungarian sky backdrop to

Shut the hell up

and

Crawl faster

lest this Hungarian night just be the Hungarian night before the *next....next* because they didn't escape.

He can sense them behind him, moving as if in unison—bellies pressed at least as firmly as possible into the dirt, each movement deliberate, calculated, and cautious. He knows that the fog of sleep, sweetened with half-dreams of the impending better life, has long since burned away, replaced by the vicious light piercing the night sky from the watchtower.

One hundred paces—so two hundred, two-fifty at a crawl—and they're into a new country.

A new life.

He feels his pace increase, racing now to match the rhythm his heart pounds into his ears. In the distance, he can see the commander begin to shift his weight off of the traitor's back....

Cough.

Somewhere behind him, in the night, from some Rador, some fingernail lengths away, pierces the night like a gunshot. He freezes, feels the tips of the fingers against his heel freeze, feels the night itself stop abruptly.

The searchlight swings violently, as though reacting to the sound he's almost certain—or at least he hopes he's certain—the guards couldn't have heard. His gaze lingers on the commanding guard, who, it seems, is in the midst of ordering his soldiers to canvas the surrounding areas—meaning the bastard driver must have convinced him of their presence.

Time is a luxury, and luxuries certainly have no place in Hungary, and so Tibor knows that if he's going to escape, he better goddamn do it now.

…

"Crawling."

An hour has passed, maybe an hour and a half. My fingers hurt, and it's the only comprehension of the passing of said time—the more they hurt, the more I'm invested in the tale he's recounting, the longer it must have been that I've been writing while he recounts it.

"It's all I remember, really."

I stop, my pen stops. I watch him for a moment, and it's more than the usual glance I give him in between furiously inscribing his furiously spoken sonnets. It's not that I don't believe him—no, I learned long ago to trust implicitly every word from the man's mouth, no matter how fantastical—it's that I worry why he can't recall something so monumental in his life.

I press; hoping the rest of the story will come to him.

"Did they chase you?"

"No—I don't believe they did. My heart was pounding, you see—the beating in my ears echoed the drumbeats of marching soldiers."

He pauses to laugh, cutting the tension gloriously, and in the fashion I've become accustomed to.

"Hell, it was the only way I knew we weren't pursued."

"How so?"

"Well, they wouldn't have been marching after us, would they?"

My smile brightens.

"I suppose not."

"So I remember crawling…and crawling…

…and crawling…"

He's mimicking the motion his hands must have taken, the table we sit at suddenly Hungarian dirt. I feel as though I'm crawling with him, both of us searching the fog of his subconscious for the next events in what was surely one of the most pivotal nights of his life.

As I pick up the pen to continue, I am acutely aware, and for the first time….despite all evidence to the contrary, this man across from me—the one crawling across the smooth polish of a mahogany dinner table—is mortal.

Mortal, and in his later years, and has charged me with the task of completing this vision—this chronicle of his life—before…

I stop, mid-thought.

Save the darkness for the pages that need it,

I tell myself

and maybe I write what follows a little faster than I used to.

I know the ending to this particular tale—I know that Tibor and the *Radors* make it, I know that the next story he parts his lips to tell me will be of the voyage here to Canada—so I don't press.

Tibor is crawling, literally and metaphorically, across both the dinner table and Hungarian badlands, and as his fingertips scratch the surface of the polished mahogany, I can't help but wonder if he's crawling through the fog of memories momentarily (I hope) forgotten.

Trains and Boats and Dubious Travels.

"The crawling stopped, at some point."

He pauses, scanning my eyes for answers that just aren't there. I put on my sympathetic face, and satisfied, he moves on.

"Or at least it picked up speed. We found ourselves on a train headed west—for the coast. I remember vaguely that we spent two—maybe three—

--two—

--damn it, we spent a couple of nights just across the Austrian border, in a building that must have housed a hundred Hungarians, all of the same mindset."

"Freedom."

His smile becomes a grin, no doubt welcoming the interjection. He savors it for a moment, his fingers no longer crawling across the tabletop.

"Freedom."

"So we're hiding, and we're recovering, and we're shaking—those goddamned foot soldiers must have almost had us, you know.

I nod and encourage him to continue, not wanting him to focus on the fact that he can't seem to remember.

"So after these...couple...of days, we're planning on just where the hell we should go. We had been so focused on just escaping Budapest, you see, that we didn't put a second's thought on anything else. And, now that we had escaped..."

"It must have been odd, in a way—had you ever left before?"

His laugh, again, erases any tension his stories had been mounting.

"Never—hell, I had no idea what the outside world would look like. *Smell* like. Those days in that building; all adrenaline and half-eaten stew, just coming around to the idea that I was away from it all...and coming to terms that, despite the *Radors*, I was away and alone."

The laughter fades, setting as suddenly as it rose. Even now, decades on, the loss is scarred deeply across his weathered features. That the man smiles *half* as much as he does is a damned miracle.

"Leslie and Paul—the Yugovitch brothers—had their hearts set on Australia. Something about beaches and surfing and women...their reasons, if I can't remember specifically, were sound. Martin and Tibor—the Hackel brothers—were suggesting Canada. Their argument was for the relative youth of the country, and of freedom and opportunity. Naturally, I represented the swing vote."

"And you chose Canada."

"And I chose Canada...but for none of the reasons put forth in their particular argument."

"Then why?"

Another smile.

"The women."

The women, I write in bold lettering on the page below.

"Someone had told me, in passing, that Canadian women were renowned for their beauty. I was young and full of testosterone and adrenaline—and the things that testosterone and adrenaline bring—and I convinced myself that the best way to get over the pain of my old life was to distract myself in beautiful things."

"And your decision was the tie-breaker…"

"The odd man out, yes."

He shakes his head, some memory flashing and fading before his eyes, the imprint burned across his veneer.

"The only stipulation to the whole endeavor remained—we could not—would not—be separated. This was the steadfast agreement we had made to one another, and I had absolutely every intention of honoring it. Pieces of my family were gone—in the boys, I had forged a new family, of sorts—and I would do anything to keep us together."

"That's very honorable."

He draws a breath to respond, stops, as though contemplating how best to verbalize the next.

"Well, that's not to say there were moments I did not regret it. Remind me to tell you the 'boat story.'"

"Tell me the boat story."

I fire back immediately, before my hand can echo the sentiment in the writing journal below and before me.

"I'll get there. But first—you need to hear the train story."

Trains, and Boats, and Sick and Such.

Tibor fidgets wildly as the train rumbles down the tracks. The destination is exciting, sure—he reminds himself a new life awaits him and his Radors, and that they'll be living a better life soon—still, he finds the fabric of unfamiliar comfort anything *but*.

So he leaves the warmth of his reclining seat, and the task force of oppressively snoring ex-pats curled comfortably-chaotically around him. He's careful not to wake them, mind tiptoeing patterns his feet follows, musing the last time he awoke the bunch, it was to order them to jump from a moving vehicle.

He hopes no such fate awaits him as he pulls the cabin door, listlessly lurching as the

click

click

click

click-ing of the tracks causes a dimly lit hallway to stutter in soft light as it presents itself.

There's a whiskey somewhere with his name on it, and the night can wait until he's appeased before attempting to claim him.

…

They boarded sometime before, the still sanctuary of the bunker replaced by the rambling sanctuary of the travel. Canada, it was decided, would be the paradise they staked a future upon—now, bound for a freighter bound for places with funny names like

Newfoundland

and

Alberta.

Tibor finds his thoughts set upon Emil, and hauntingly, the look on Emil's face as he bled out in a wheelbarrow.

So,

whiskey.

…

Two carts down, he stumbles upon some semblance of a bar, and therefore, at this hour, some semblance of solace. The soft-faced and soft-stomached barkeep is welcoming enough—at this hour, the three liberal looking women clinging to the stools before him, even more so. One in particular matches his gaze as he shifts his from the cabinet containing his salvation…watching her watching him, Tibor feels the

click

click

click

click-*ing* of the tracks whisper encouraging depravities in his ear.

It's all

Hello

Hello

Hello

"Hello"

from his lips at least as practiced, as rhythmic, as smooth as the track song.

She says

"Hello"

back and her

Hello

back has a little more whiskey and a little more sex in it. Knowing he needs more of the former and always the latter, he flashes her a smile and the barkeep a twenty, content to drink whatever said twenty will buy them.

The

"So where are you from?"

he offers *doesn't*, that he knows it's not from Hungary…the lines lining her porcelain features don't have enough hurt in them.

She's pretty enough to take away the pain, for a moment; knowing the scotch the soft-stomached barman will pour can't hurt either, he bites his lip, offers his best

I'm vulnerable

smile back, and moves gracefully onto the barstool beside her.

She says her name is

Yvonna

or

Yolanda

or something equally difficult to pronounce and nowhere near important enough to matter. He responds kindly and quietly, and he tells her the truth, because he desperately needs both the escape from and the anchor to the reality he finds himself running from.

She bites, God bless her, and they spend the next twenty dollars of watered down whiskey washing away memories by pretending what lies on the tracks ahead is anything better than what's

click

click

click

clicking away behind them. Her blonde-enough hair sways gently when she laughs—which is often, God bless her—and it's engaging enough and she's engaging enough that when she suggests they leave her two slightly-less attractive friends to the significantly less attractive barman, he agrees with decidedly less hesitation than he sat down with twenty minutes and three drinks before.

...

The bed goes

click

click

click

the way the tracks do, and Tibor thinks that fucking

Yvonna

or

Yolanda

is infinitely more appealing than lying between Radors and wishing his brother and his sister and his mother and his father and everything he's ever known wasn't miles and miles behind him. *She's* not—this girl—no, she's bent over in front of him--and he takes it all out on her, sweating watered down whiskey and ignoring the scent of failure that mixes with the vanilla of her perfume.

She moans something softly, and he bites his lip again, the banality of the dance enough to distract him. The pushing does something for the violence sitting on his soul, but his heart's not in it, and ten pumps or twenty pumps later she's catching on.

He fights her position change the way he figures he must fight everything, and as she bites his lip the only thing he's thinking is that he wishes she had it in her to bite half as hard as he does.

There's blood, or there isn't—he can't tell and doesn't care; and for her thrashings she seems not to care either. She fucks like she's running from something as well, and her efforts, God bless her, do just enough to coerce him to finish desperately inside of her.

She heaves, and lies somewhere in the ether beside him and for a moment Tibor figures he must be having a heart attack. Surely, feeling nothing must mean he's dying or dead and maybe for the first time, he's sure it doesn't really matter.

The smoke from the cigarette she lights invades his senses, and his heart rate calms considerably, so in this he knows he must not be having a heart attack, or dying, and he supposes this must be some kind of relief. He feels again, momentarily; his tongue traces the wet corners of his mouth, and the blood from his bitten lip tastes sweet.

She's saying something,

Yvonna

or

Yolanda

and it's sweet the way she tastes, but he knows her words are empty and he's empty and all of the vanilla perfume and hope for the future can't take away what they roll the other direction from.

So it's all dead brothers and Communism, and no matter the promises she promises him, of a life together a world away and how she's got a sense of these things and about how he's the one she's meant to find—one fuck in—can't sway him the way the lurching of the cabin car can.

She says something softly, something that sounds like

"Don't lie to me,"

and

he can't help himself from looking at her and saying

"I won't lie to you,"

knowing he's lying to her and he's hurting her, a half-second before she follows that up with,

"Don't hurt me,"

the way, sadly, he knew he was about to.

He waits until the gently swaying and the

click

click

click

click-ing of the railroad lullaby sets her to sleep, and, unsetting his transfixed gaze, he quietly collects his clothes and his composure, and leaves her to the night.

…

The boys are still asleep the way he can't, anymore, and so he fixes his gaze on something somewhere in the distance disappearing out the window, and simply waits, content knowing that the sum of his remaining train ride will include avoiding a beautiful woman he's already struggling to remember.

He fights the darkness that struggles to take him, telling himself that the person he will become in this New-Found-Land is better than the one he will leave on this trek.

As the blinks come longer and faster than they have any right to, the last thing on his mind is a valiant attempt to discern the name of the woman he just shared his misery with.

The. Boat. Ride.

"That damn boat."

That damn boat.

It looks good on paper; I underline it, thinking it's at *least* a great subtitle for the book. I've been waiting to hear this one—Emil has a grin on his face every time Tibor brings it up; for weeks he's been dancing around it. Every time we come close he conveniently finds another aspect of Budapest or Ganz or the things that came after Budapest or Ganz to disclose instead.

"That damn boat."

 "How long?"

I ask tentatively, hoping by fooling him into discussing logistics. I'm hoping to break into the tale gently, guiding him with imagined and sometimes real notations along the pen-stained ledger before me. I curse both my penmanship and my damned left-handed disadvantage, the smear my clumsy knuckles leave across works like

How long

and

Why is this tale, in particular, so damned difficult to discuss

and then, after crawling across imaginary borderlines on the table surface before him, Tibor sighs a mighty sigh and offers…

"6 days."

6 days

I write, wondering silently to myself what could possibly have been so difficult about….

"It was *supposed* to be 6 days."

I find containing my excitement difficult, staring down at a half-finished thought in my notebook. This man hasn't blinked an eye when it comes to recounting boyhood atrocities and teenage revolutions…yet the very thought of his journey to Canada has him visibly disconcerted.

"We were leaving from Lehovre, France, headed to St. John's Newfoundland. And just the sound of it—*New.Found.Land*—is appealing as all hell to me, because it just sounds kind of free, you know?"

I do know. Anything aside from the Old World must have seemed like a dream; no communism, no oppression, no tanks in town squares.

"All it would take to get there…to my new life….was 6 days…"

…

Tibor feels comforted as his boots hit the steel mesh of the barge deck; the resounding clang of metal echoes off of the titanium, and it does a small wonder for his confidence. This Canada thing sounds appealing, sure—the fact that he has to cross an enormous body of water to get there decidedly less. He feels a familiar hand compress his shoulder; of the traveling party, only Marton understands his reservations in regards to travel…and, in particular, to travel in this fashion.

Still, communism dictates escape is a ridiculous notion, and therefore, well worth the effort. He matches the Rador's gaze, grits his teeth, and makes his way somewhat hesitantly across the deck. Eyeing the doors for the quarters, he joins the herd at the mouth of the barge, latest in a line of similarly minded refugees hoping for something simply better.

The boys are together, and it does wonders for wavering resolve. He can hear the brothers arguing somewhere in the masses behind him, however his gaze remains transfixed upon the small wrought iron portal he's meant to traverse.

He's told their quarters are somewhere below—and, as unappealing as spending any of the duration across the water above deck sounds—the very thought of spending a second below seems infinitely worse. Yet still he stands, simply one amongst one-too-many resigned to whatever fate awaits them in the steel slabs beneath troubled soles and souls.

He remembers the throngs of children stewarded haphazardly through classroom halls, and for the briefest of moments, recalls Hadja and his schoolyard hustle; bribing the boy for protection from threats real and manifested. Sighing, he almost longs for the days where carefully-constructed sandwiches were his primary objective…this—crossing the world on a glorified tugboat in seasons decidedly un-ideal for such travel—seems infinitely more arduous than punching bullies in the face.

…

He's herding down darkened hallways, soft red light bulbs radiating around him, presenting narrow hallways in buzzing tones. He feels the breath of the next unfortunate bastard on his neck; half-hoping said breath belongs to a man decidedly familiar to him.

It's unsettling, sure—the proximity and the pulse, really, of the iron walls as they sway with the will of the ocean—more so are the minute portals sailors haplessly lead travelers to, and disappear behind. He tells himself these can't be the resting quarters…no, they must have hallways to larger sections of the barge undiscovered…certainly the size of the vessel would not betray such fantasies. Still, it's one of many burdens beat across his brow—the breath of the man behind him is hot and most certainly unwelcome on the back of his neck. He feels his temperature rising to match the inferno of the overclocked light bulbs beside him—beside him, and not above, because he's continually forced to duck to avoid clanging his head off of the damned ceiling.

He vows his journey had best be ending soon—and at the foot of a warm and welcoming bed—lest he turn his frame awkwardly in the slightly-wider-than-shoulder-width portal and clock the proverbial bully breathing on him in this, his descent into hell.

Heaven, allegedly, awaits in this New-found-land, and it sounds glorious, and it had better-damn-well-be glorious, for the frustrations and the water and the way the water makes this damn boat move in a way it looks like it shouldn't.

His boots whisper

Communism

every time he moves them to walk away from it, so he grits his teeth, gives a sailor the least welcoming look he can manage as he's steered towards what must be *his* tiny portal.

Engineers are marvelous people, he's heard and believed; as his shoulders contract and crack against metal moorings, he surveys his 'home' for the next six days, and curses each and every one of them to hell.

To call it

Small

would insult the very definition of the term…before him—so, beneath him, as there is virtually nothing except for a titanium wall in front of his nose—is what he assumes is supposed to suffice as his bedding. That the thin wire framing runs wall-to-wall ought to be something of a luxury—would that the walls themselves extend past the breadth of his shoulders.

He heaves his latest heavy breath; attempts to roll said weary shoulders, only to be interrupted by both the biting of the rivets lining the walls into the flesh of his left arm, and a stern hand slapping the right. The sailor conducting the macabre tour has apparently decided that his resting period is over, and ushers him back into the not-much-wider hallway, and unabated and entirely irritated, the masses continue to pour and crash down the depressing and depressingly lit hallways.

He hears a Hackel behind him, and it does small wonders for his confidence—surely this goddamned boat and its goddamned complicated layout must be coming to conclusion soon. He braces, gritting his teeth against the pushing and pulsing of the mob, hearing absolutely nothing the bastard conducting this bizarre symphony has to say. Resigning himself to his fate, Tibor reminds himself that, for the rest of his life, he will never travel by water again.

6 Days

he tells himself.

How bad could it get?

...

The swell crashes against the side of the barge, and could Tibor move, he would undoubtedly be very, very upset.

Day Seven began with

The.

Storm.

—the way Day Six ended—the only difference being that, rather than continuing on a trajectory towards Newfoundland, the goddamned boat started travelling backwards, towards Communism. Waves crash continuously over the deck—at times the nose of the barge seems to disappear into the swell.

From his distinct vantage, Tibor is positive he is going to die.

Being tied to the mast of said barge

--helpless in the maelstrom

--one could hardly blame him.

...

It started with the best of intentions, he assures himself.

He could see their point—even as the three of them, his Radors—plus the captain of the very ship he finds himself tethered to—dragged him kicking and screaming to the foredeck. Marton argues that he had a knife, and that he was brandishing it wildly...now, his recollections are affected by the flotsam and spray of the sea he struggles to stay out of—but he's moderately sure he wasn't *really* going to cut anyone.

He just really wanted off the damn boat, and was tired of just *saying* so.

They had assured him the voyage would end soon, and Goddamn them, it took three of them to get the knife off of him—so sure was he that threatening the captain could produce a faster end to this foolishness. He kicked and punched and bit, by the time the fourth bastard jumped him from behind, the mob was able to lash his torso to the great mast of the very ship he had longed to be free from—now, he finds himself literally and figuratively a part of the prison he loathes.

He's sure that the boys would have untethered him, had they known the storm would hit as lightning fast as it did; he tells himself they're not to blame for being hunkered down below deck while he alone braves the elements. Could he move the muscles of his face against the bracing cold of the freezing water assaulting his features, he would almost smile…the literal essence of 'going down with the ship.'

He wants this boat ride to be over—if the ending involves being dragged into the mouth of hell, well, the dragging had best begin. Tibor knows his patience for being assaulted by spray and salt and is beyond tested, and would just as soon spend the rest of his afternoon dead.

At least, he tells himself, he'd be done with the damn boat.

…

Tibor finds his prayers have gone unanswered, as, hours later, the storm mercifully—or not, depending on the point of view—begins to relent. Curiously, crewmembers and concerned passengers have been spotted sporadically venturing out onto the debris-strewn foredeck, and Tibor notes, have been eyeing him with amazement.

Perhaps, he ventures, he is simply too stubborn to die—he certainly would prefer to live, he knows, straining his body against his increasingly uncomfortable bonds. A wary sailor approaches, hints of apologies and astonishment reflected in his gaze, and Tibor does his best to snarl. The man retreats, a look of acceptable fear strewn across his features, and Tibor laughs as heartily as his bonds will allow.

Damn them,

he tells himself…

If I'm the devil, and not even the sea herself can stop me, than they had better keep me tied up.

He tells himself—because it makes the duration of the voyage—the duration of the voyage he spends tethered to the same damned mast, on the same damned boat—tolerable.

…

9 days

9. Damned. Days.

And the boat pulls into the harbor—this New.Found.Land—under a canopy of blinding sun. From his lofty perch, Tibor is beyond thrilled to see land.

And people.

And people who aren't the people who tied him to the mast.

Said people look somewhat puzzled, as the boat glides towards the dock, to see what must be the first *live* masthead, in the decades upon decades this relatively New.Found.Land has been accepting boats to its' shores.

Yeah, they're puzzled, he reckons, at the sight of him—moments later, they're repulsed, such vitriol he finds escaping his lips, admonishing them even as they turn their collective back to him, shrinking from the wrath of the vengeful Sea-God bound to the barge. His thrashings keep the wary crew from approaching him as well, and it soothes him—should it be anyone except his Radors that reaches to unbind him, they will probably be missing fingertips, the gnashing of his teeth relentless there upon his perch.

It comforts him, the way it has for nine damned days—although he has reached—in relative safety—his destination, Tibor knows he still has his role to play…and should a member of such a ship's crew ever attempt to spirit his back to Communism, he's assured his reputation will precede him.

He laughs once more—a great, hearty bellow, carried by all of the madness and mirth he can muster. From the corner of a wind-burned and wet eye he spots Marton, no doubt the bravest or loser of the bet as to who would attempt to free him from bondage. The man approaches cautiously, apologetically, and Tibor is both amused and pleased.

"T—T—

--Tibor?"

3 consonants—he welcomes his friend's hesitation. It is well deserved, he knows; Marton and the others may have had the best intentions—they may even have saved him from jumping to a watery grave…but days late and a damned storm means they'll owe him for years to come.

The thought comforts him as the man pulls tentatively at his bonds. His wrists burn, undeniably the blood circulation causing the new discomfort; discomfort that simply races to replace the old. He'll take it, he knows—anything better than the restrictions forced upon him. Rubbing his sore hands, attempting to feel some semblance of any emotion short of rage, he steps tentatively from his prison post, squinting his eyes in defiance of the sun, tracing the outline of his new home across his troubled mind.

"T—T—

--Tibor?"

It comes again, this squeaky, timid voice, reverberating softly over the crashing of the water against both barge and land; and, of the two, Tibor knows he'd best never find himself on the former. So he ignores the call, accepting only the resignation it has been vocalized with, and leaves the Rador speaking it to his fears. He steps assuredly, ignoring the pain and burning in legs circulation only now struggles to remember; he strides at least as rapidly as he can in the direction of this New.Found.Land. positively singing to him.

Tibor feels comforted as his boots hit the steel mesh of goddamned land; the resounding clang of metal he'd become so unfortunately accustomed to does not echo off of the sand, and it does a small wonder for his confidence.

For the first time in ten forevers, Tibor Fidler is home.

Labour (--with a 'u,' because he's in Canada now—and as he's learning, Canadians do it different).

Railroading *sucks*.

Worse than being an alien in an alien land, worse than not speaking—or even remotely comprehending—the native tongue, worse than the ache of the blisters on the bottoms of his tar-stained feet.

This 'Edmonton' isn't without charm; the lack of civil war and death in the streets is nice—but the whole working-for-a-living thing is going to take some getting used to. Particularly when the bosses shout obscenities in foreign tongues…the meaning is understood, the reasons why, not so much. Obscenities, and the shouting of them, are surely what landed Tibor and his Radors *here*, on the ass-end of nowhere, stopping every five or ten kilometers (---whatever the hell *they* are--) to hop off of a pushcart to lie down railway ties.

He would have preferred to work on the steam engines themselves—monstrous creations, bristling with engineering genius and the kind of sophistication more suited to the talents he'd developed at Ganz—but a wayward comment or two, about a rail master's daughter, must have drifted to another Hungarian's ear, and subsequently, up the proper channels—hence, here, laying railway ties in the blistering heat of some bush.

Tibor curses the presence of hidden countrymen and their questionable allegiances, offers a steady gaze down a seemingly endless strip of rail, and sets about his work. He spits the tobacco he's become so fond of chewing for emphasis, yet reminds himself that this work is still miles more fun than both Communism and boat rides. And so he labors, unabated, under the mid-day sun, middling in both memories and malaise and enjoying the melancholy of both. He's in the middle of some-such thought when the bellowing of a yardmaster, somewhere down the rail line, interrupts his warmth.

He squints hard, fighting the glare of the sun off of the tracks, and the mirages the heat can create—but he'll be damned if he can't see what looks to be a box car, unhitched and abandoned, just beyond the grade. The bellowing seems to be rising, a crescendo to match his pace as he drops his shovel, making his way towards the commotion. Edging closer, he realizes he wasn't—thankfully—hallucinating…some ten yards over the ridge he runs past what appears to be a single, unconnected box car sitting, dead center in the middle of the railroad tracks. Approaching the foreman—whom he recognizes as Jon, a Magnificent Ukrainian Bastard—he struggles to gain his breath, so eager was he to be a part of whatever excitement has thankfully disrupted his grueling manual labor.

"Sonofa whore—"

Tibor understands little Ukrainian, but colorful language is colorful language in any tongue, and Jon, the Magnificent Ukrainian Bastard, didn't earn his nickname by being selective with his verbiage. Still, in the oppressive heat—tempered only by the occasional stirring of dust and dirt—Tibor can't help but admire the man's dedication to diction. He cranes his neck as he approaches, hoping to steal a glance at the interior of the surprisingly-not-dilapidated car before Jon turns his attentions to his intrusion.

He's not entirely successful—behind him, he can make out new vulgarities, half-reasons-half-understands that they're intended for his ears. Abruptly, however, they no longer matter…so all consuming is the ghastly display unfolding before his eyes. They are not the only senses to be assaulted—something about being a mother-lover enters his eardrums, only to leave, replaced by a clamor of screeching decidedly two octaves too high to come from any man.

What must be a mirage reveals itself to him, and, although the desire to rub his eyes is overpowering, Tibor fights the urge with at least all of the strength he can muster. The dust particles assault his cornea relentlessly, and yet he refuses to relent himself—so terrified is he that the splendor before him will disappear should he close his eyes, if even only for a moment.

Bathed before him, naked and resplendent and shrieking and scattering—is an assortment of beautiful dark-skinned and wild-eyed women.

Railroading, suddenly, sucks a lot *less*.

These…*Indians* (his mind struggles to translate the term the other railroaders have used for such tanned people) are full and voluptuous and thick, in a decidedly un-Eastern-European way. They move chaotically, the four or five of them that shriek and squeal and attempt to gather some semblance of garment before scrambling down the side of the open cart, and before disappearing into the bushes that line the dusty railroad, Tibor is momentarily uncertain his eyes do not deceive him.

He climbs the cart from the other side, straining his neck to catch a glimpse of the nymph-like creatures disappearing before him, angered that his eyes fail to adjust to the oppressive rays of the mid-day sun. Around him, Jon the Magnificent Ukrainian Bastard continues his relentless sonic assault, and having positioned a foot inside the makeshift whorehouse, Tibor comes to at last spot the source of his vitriol.

Two men are scrambling to collect themselves as well, although decidedly less timidly in their respective reaches for clothing to cover their genitals. Which- -Tibor notes with an at once puzzled and disdainful gaze—look positively raw. This, partnered with the fact that both men move lazily about the box car—despite Jon, the Magnificent Ukrainian Bastard's dictatorial lashings— leads him to deduce that both have been whoring, magnificently, for quite some time.

And who could blame them? The women—all of them—possessed a kind of beauty Tibor was unaccustomed to beholding. The kind of beauty that fogs his thoughts, images of luxurious hair cascading over full breasts keeps the scene before him dulled, the excitement of two stark naked railroaders trumpeting with a fuming-mad foreman somehow *less* than it has any right to be.

"Tibor!"

His name resonates above the din. The naked men seem to calm their retorts, though Tibor knows nothing will calm Jon's.

"TIBOR!!"

His fury misdirected, Tibor whirls on his heels, confronting the Magnificent Ukrainian Bastard.

"Tell me you knew nothing of this—this—debauchery!"

Jon's English is patchwork, and horrible—and yet, despite his admitted ignorance to the tongue, Tibor is certain he gets the gist of his accusations.

"No,"

He offers back, shaking his head as passionately as he can, all the while keeping a wary eye on the amassed nudity whirling madly behind him.

"You knew??"

"NO,"

Empathically, this time, seeing the crimson veil painted on Jon's features deepen. Surely the two who had indeed been whoring sense this as well, as, abruptly, Tibor senses *less* nudity behind him.

Jon, the Magnificent Ukrainian Bastard's incredibly—oddly—deep set eyes scan Tibor's for signs of deceit; straining against the fury in his gaze, he imagines he must be holding his own. The pockmark's upon Jon's skin dance as his puffy, soot-blackened cheeks dance and twitch in agony. Locked there, engaged in a battle of wills with a positively seething and not-quite-tall-enough-to-be-intimidating man, Tibor finds himself counting the too-few remaining hairs atop his steam-producing head while waiting for his anger to dissipate.

Eventually—and undoubtedly seeing absolutely no resignation across his features—Jon removes his invasive gaze, re-focusing (with laser-like intensity) upon the two now-semi-dressed bastards worthy of his ire. Tibor heaves a sigh of relief, does his best to follow the broken English, secretly hoping it will reveal the mystery of the dark-haired beauties, and perhaps give indication when and where he might join such festivities.

...

The words "Sex" and "Train" give credibility to the musk permeating both the air and the conversation; put together, "Sex Train" sounds like a perfectly reasonable and engaging way to spend an afternoon on this, a railroad in the middle of nowhere. This makes it difficult to understand the rationale behind Jon, the Magnificent Ukrainian Bastard's magnificent ranting's. Which continues, unabated, under the mid-day sun up until the point in which the sun itself decides it has heard enough, and begins to relent the sky to the stars.

The sex-culprits—Sex Culprit Mikel and Sex Culprit Esteban, it turns out—are positively drained from both sex and the chastisement of such activity when Jon finally succumbs to a much-earned desire to fill his mouth with anything other than scornful words. After agreeing to return to the camp in which they all railroad out of, Jon beckons Tibor to join him on the trek back, doubtless more contempt and scorn to fill his ears as they travel together. Gritting his teeth at the very thought of it, Tibor is disappointed he had endured the entirety of the dressing-down without as much as a moment to converse with either weary man.

He sure would have liked to learn where those boys found the Indians.

Changes

He cleans the floors, not because he *has* to; hell, he knows the railroad would take him back in a second, should he desire a nomadic existence—no, he cleans the floors because it's *quiet*.

He told Jon, the Magnificent Ukrainian Bastard he could take his job and shove it about a month ago—time has a funny way of running away from him in this new land—but he figures he's been set up here

Edmonton

for about that long.

His apartment isn't much—four walls and a pull-down bed—but its home, and it's his, and it's his alone; alone unless the Radors stop over from wherever-the-hell they're staying to stay with him. So he comes here-- to the architecture firm he works at during the hours when the architecture firm isn't open—to maintain the sense of self he hasn't been quite able to since his brother died and his journey began. He loves the nights alone for this—hours spent by himself, occupying his time with both menial tasks and the freedom menial tasks can bring—during the days he paints, thinking often of Schneider and Emil and those who have shaped him into the man he's working on becoming. Although his Architectural education and certificate may not guarantee him work in Canada, he figures he's a hell of a lot closer working *here* than a building that does not employ architects.

He knows the job may be beneath him, but for now, it's enough—enough to allow him the time needed to study this culture, the language and the slang, days spent dreaming and reading between acrylic and oil paint dreams, telling himself that he's *here* and not *there*, and that—for now—this will do *just fine*.

…

Doing *just fine* in a foreign country can go on for longer than it has any right to. Year three, and he's still cleaning and still cleaning the same architectural firm; his grip on the language is slightly better, but the whole 'reading English' thing is for shit—he's contemplating taking night classes tonight, wondering where he'd get the rent money for the tiny apartment he's tragically still living in, when

"You there"

interrupts the night in the way it shouldn't.

Shouldn't, because he should be the only one in the building—working the night shift means working alone, alone in a way that just isn't the fun it was all those years ago when he started working. He turns on a dime, thanks entirely to the efficiency of his wet mopping on the tiled floor, to face a weary looking man in a finely tailored suit. Instantly, he's reminded of Sof Pupos' shop on the Konti Utca, and the hairs on the back of his neck jump for it. Somewhere in the distance, a faint

ding

tells him his guest has arrived by elevator; elevator indicating he's arrived from a floor decidedly higher than this one, labelled

Ground.

"You're the night custodian?"

finely-tailored suit-man asks rhetorically, and though Tibor's grip of the language may not yet allow for mastery of such complicated terms, his real-life experience tells him that this man ought to be addressed with respect.

So it's

"Yes, sir,"

in his finest years-in-the-military voice; he's standing stick straight and looking the suit in the eyes by the time his expensive shoes carry him across the immaculate floor. He takes the measure of the man, meeting him with an extended hand and his warmest handshake; the strength of his grip indicates to the well-dressed stranger that although he may be the night custodian, he's no less the man. The crushing oppression of Communism will mold a man this way, and it's as though the suit can sense it because his handshake back is equally as firm, and his smile equally as warm.

"What's your name, son?"

"Fidler, sir. Tibor Fidler."

The man has airs of authority about him; Tibor prays his cleaning has been to standard.

"Tibor? Ah, wonderful. Hungarian, no?"

"Yes, sir."

"Hard workers, Hungarians. One of my best men is Hungarian. Roman Vesziki—you know him?"

"No, sir."

He laughs, pats his shoulder. His tone indicates sincerity; Tibor does his best to relax.

"My name is Samuel—Robert Samuel. My friends call me Bob."

"Pleased to meet you, Mr. Samuel."

He roars, rocking back on expensive shoes; for a moment, Tibor dreads that his immaculate floors may be about to claim Mr. Samuel's life. He recovers, thankfully; the cut of his suit indicates that he is a man of station, and not one he needs taking a fall on his watch. Tibor doesn't quite see the humor in the moment, but offers a nervous laugh nonetheless; Samuel composes himself as quickly as he initially lost it, and, placing an arm around his shoulder, continues his introduction.

"That's why I love Euros—so polite! Call me Bob, Tibor."

"Yes, sir, Mr.-err, Bob."

"Tibor, I own this firm. And I have it on good authority that the artwork that's mysteriously showing up on the walls of my building might have something to do with you."

He *had* taken to hanging some of his artwork on the hallways; only where he felt it would accentuate the otherwise sterile colors of the admittedly magnificent design; the building itself may be a marvel—the decorations adorning it, not so much. All at once he's regretting it; hell, had he any room left on the tiny four walls of his makeshift apartment, he may not require the space to showcase it. Still, he'd felt as though the works—collectively more structures than animals, line works in charcoals and oils, cityscapes and such—would do well to cheer the worker drones otherwise ambling through immaculately-cleaned hallways on their way to and from the various offices of the mammoth building. The fact that many of the works displayed architectural significance was no accident either.

"I'm sorry, Bob—I—I thought that they might add a little something—

"So, you hung 'em…did you paint them, too?"

"Yes, sir."

Bob bellows; another hearty roar, equally as surprising as the first. Tibor, at least as unsure of his intent as the first, offers a hesitant chuckle of his own, taking the man's clap on his shoulder with the hope that he's *not* about to be fired for defacing private property.

"The balls on you, boy! I love it! You're a talented artist, Fidler—what's more, you've got a keen eye…you ever do any formal draft work?"

"I have my architectural certificate, from Budapest—

"Certificate? That like a degree, son? You Europeans, I tell ya. So you're telling me you've studied architectural design in some semblance of formal education?"

"Yes, sir—Bob."

"Ha! Perfect! We'll figure out the details, I'm sure. Grab your mop, Tibor, you're officially on your last cleaning shift."

"I'm sorry, Bob, honestly—I'll take the paintings down…I just really need this job."

"This job—

Bob throws his arm around him, begins what Tibor assumes is a walk towards the front door and the unemployment beyond.

"—this job is beneath you, son. As of tomorrow, you're officially an architect. Oh, and Tibor?"

"Yes, Bob?"

"The art stays."

…

"That's how it worked back then"

Tibor tells me, stopping to sip from a freshly poured mug of coffee. I'm earnestly scribbling, trying to catch up on the afternoon's worth of stories. I've heard that things were different back in the day—that one could pretty much fall into a career—this, however, incites more than a modicum of jealousy.

"These days, you need a degree, and then another degree, and then another damned degree—I have no idea how anyone makes a living when the first half of their life is spent paying for Goddamned education!"

"I agree,"

I tell him,

because I *do*,

and because as someone in the process of paying back years and years of education, I'd have loved a Bob Samuel character to put his proverbial arm around me.

"Back then, we went right to work—and, if we worked hard, we could make something of ourselves and gain employment based on the merits of that work—not just the worth of a damned piece of paper."

We vent, for maybe a little longer than we should—I offer my two cents as though my just-plus-thirty years allows me any perspective on the way things *are* versus the way they were in the *good-old-days*; Emil joins us and the afternoon disappears. Days like this I don't mind; we speak of life and family and love, and I feel closer to him for it. I capture insight into the man in meetings like this—his wild inflections, the passion with which he speaks on a myriad—really, *any*, subject—and by the time he urges me to pick up the pen again, the afternoon has bled well into the evening.

Emil disappears into the kitchen, and over the rumbling of my stomach, I strain to hear the rest of the story, grateful for both the opportunity and the food destined to arrive once it's been suitably told.

…

Bob—after one final stop to the tiny janitorial closet Tibor had called his work home for the better part of the past three years—takes him up the elevator to the fourth floor; the fourth floor, Tibor knows, belongs exclusively to the draftsmen.

"This is Vesziki's desk—

Bob says, pointing to a particularly-cluttered draft table; Tibor, still bewildered nods appreciatively.

"—and this one beside it is *yours*."

He tries to stop the welling of tears in his tired eyes; three years of relative stagnation beat against his sub-conscious, and ultimately, three years of relative stagnation win out. Bob, hand still resting on his shoulder, simply pats him a couple of times, offers a

"See you tomorrow morning, son"

and disappears as quietly as he appeared. Alone again, in the same building but suddenly with an entirely different perspective, Tibor stares at the empty surface of the modest draft table, wondering if Bob Samuel is an angel and musing that if Edmonton *isn't* heaven, then it's pretty damn close.

Views from the Top Floor

He shows up early the next morning—so early, he had debated simply staying the night. Tact, however, demanded he wear his very best suit—and while he knows the quality is nowhere close to that of his new boss, he figures he'll earn points for decorum. He cleans a little, entering his new workspace—habits, he figures, die-hard. By the time his new co-workers arrive, not only is his draft table immaculate, but the majority of theirs are as well. He nods at them, catching their thinly veiled curiosities; given the amount of whispered conversations, Tibor assumes Bob is not in the habit of hiring new architects in the middle of the night.

He is growing increasingly uncomfortable, staring at the surface of his table and wondering when Bob will arrive to quell the growing disdain amongst his ever-amassing peers, when a well-fed figure slumps into the previously-painfully empty chair beside him.

"Roman Vesziki?"

"The fuck? Who are you?"

He offers a

"Hello"

in Hungarian, hoping the commonality will come off as endearing; Roman Vesziki, appearing appropriately startled, turns to study him.

"You're Hungarian!! What's your name, brother?"

He sighs, instantly relieved. Since his horrifying exodus from his homeland, he's felt disconnected from most everyone in this strange land. Aside from his Radors—themselves now scattered and working or married—he's had little exposure to his native tongue; admittedly, it feels good to hear it once again.

"Tibor Fidler—Bob tells me I'm to work here, beside you."

"Ha! Bob loves Europeans, doesn't he? I'll show you the ropes, Tibor. You've some draft experience?"

"A certificate from Budapest."

"Ganz?"

"Two years—with my brother, Emil."

"Is he here?"

He pauses, unintentionally. Roman Vesziki, apparently, is particularly observant.

"The Revolution?"

He nods, fighting back both tears and the pain of memories attached to them.

"I lost two of my cousins; got out right after. Been here ever since."

Relieved, Tibor spends the remainder of the day attached to Roman's side. He learns the history of the business—how Bob started the company with *his* brother, the successes and failures in the years that followed—as well as the particulars of the position he's been hired to work.

When Bob shows up, it's late—apparently, common practice—and Tibor is introduced to the remainder of what he's learning to be a tight-knit group. Had he not spent the bulk of his time since the railroad alone, perhaps he wouldn't be as quick to appreciate the attention—regardless, he's basking in the adulations of his new workplace associates. He learns that he's not the only immigrant-come-architect amongst the group—Bob, apparently, has a knack for gathering talent and influence from all over the world. As a result, the firm is one of the most respected and cutting edge in all of Canada—a title yielding a scope that Tibor can't pretend to understand, his exposure to this strange country reduced to the limited geography along rail side. He shares his story with his co-workers, and takes time to listen to the advice they offer; all the while, Roman Vesziki remains tethered to his side, compass and navigator on this strange journey.

...

He spends the majority of the weeks that follow working alongside Roman—and proves to be a quick study. The differences in architectural design prove minor, Canadian regulations and policies, however, anything *but*. The work he can't accomplish during the days he either takes home or stays late to complete; habit, he figures, from his previous, nocturnal employment. He appreciates the balance the night creates—though he's relishing the conversations and...*human* presence of his days, he's used to the relative solitude of the night. Regardless, he's a fast study, and his voracious appetites are quickly noticed.

 Within a month, he's advanced himself farther than the previous three years combined; working a respected career amongst the upper echelon of Edmonton's brightest minds. Dinners with Bob and weekends spent with Roman and his family is beginning to erode the sense of yearning for his travelling companions—when they do communicate, Tibor feels as though he's finally achieved their previously envied successes in assimilation to Canadian culture.

There's an art to the work as well—he relishes in the opportunity to create, a combination of his creative and mathematical inclinations. He labours diligently, and before long Roman is asking *him* for advice on matters architectural. Architectural, and—as of one particularly spirited afternoon—matters *not*.

"I'm building a boat, Tibor."

Clearly, Tibor reckons, Roman wasn't listening intently when he described the horrors of his voyage to Canada.

"And I want you to help."

More Fun with Boats

Helping Roman Vesziki means toiling relentlessly in his tiny basement, light filtering in through the smallest windows Tibor has ever seen. His increasingly acute architectural sense tells him this is a design flaw—a fact he finds ironic, given Roman's profession. Upstairs, Roman's wife Ingrid—a robust, boisterous and not-particularly-warm woman, interrupts only to call them to dinner. Though she may not be warming to Tibor—claiming in broken Hungarian that he's taking all of her husband's free time from her—her cooking is both warm and one-hundred percent traditional—and the closest he's had to home since his arrival.

Having been hesitant to undertake the project under the implications that *crafting* said boat could result in the expectation to co-captain it, Tibor's eagerness to acclimate to the culture of the office forced his hand. And so the cooking is a welcome intrusion; the wine that flows at the supper table may not be aiding in the workmanship—it surely helps his ease with the concept behind the construction.

The work continues, unabated aside from the respites that both the architectural firm and Ingrid's suppers provide, until—at last—Tibor and Roman stand over their perfectly constructed, nine-by-six foot paddleboat.

Meticulously crafted, it is not without a sense of pride that Tibor looks upon his latest project—he's reminded of his early days working alongside Schneider, and the beautiful toys they would produce. He runs his hand across the surface lovingly; behind him, he hears the familiar release of a bottle-cap.

Turning to receive his celebratory beer, he's taken aback by the look of horror written across Roman's features. The look is sobering—even following *this*, the latest and numberless of beverages consumed during tonight's particularly vigorous construction; instantly—furiously--the elation from the completion of the task is dashed.

"What—are the dimensions off?"

He turns on his heels, straining his eyes against the dying light filtered into the tiny room from decidedly tinier windows. He remains dumbfounded; surely, two of the brightest minds working at one of Edmonton's most prestigious design firms couldn't have made a mistake—

"No, Tibor; the goddamn dimensions are *perfect*."

"Ha! I thought so! I must say, Roman, although I hate boats, this one might actually be worth a test."

Slowly, Tibor realizes that the man was not jesting; his expression remains grim and pale. Roman was never known for his sense of humor anyway—he knows that he was foolish to assume the elation of completion—coupled with perhaps one too many beers—could instill the man with levity.

"Tibor—

"Yes, friend?"

"—the dimensions are perfect, the boat is beautiful. Look around you—how the hell are we supposed to get it *out* of here?"

The horror washes over him once more; this time, mercilessly, it lingers.

The boat assembled and completed. The basement the project has been housed in. The lack of any semblance of usable windows—the narrowness of the staircase they've climbed down, countless times. To work on a boat nine feet by six feet, in a basement that can't be twelve by twelve.

A beautiful, fully realized project constructed by two reasonably intelligent men, employed and renowned for their architectural ingenuity.

In a basement.

With absolutely no way of removing it.

...

They curse in unity, and with such voracity that Ingrid stomps her feet against the floor—violent response and universally-acknowledged signal to quiet down. More associated with the fact that they've built a goddamn boat in a goddamn basement with no way of getting it out—they swear again. Loudly. Ingrid, annoyed, must be employing a broom for assistance—her strikes increasing in volume and frequency.

Months of labor, delicate planning, and questionable implementation—for neither man had claimed to have any prior boat-building experience—release in frenzied tandem. Tibor has mind to hurl his beer bottle against a tiny, twelve-by-twelve wall; it is only his fear of Ingrid's reckoning that stays his arm.

Admittedly, all of the cleverness associated with his previous exploits—sneaking toys out of Ganz, running chicken wire along military base perimeters—seems nothing but distant memory if the face of the debacle staring back at him in this damned basement. It's a blow to egos better left inflated; one admittedly alien to Tibor, having had a knack for turning ludicrous concepts to skin-of-his-teeth successes. He takes this one on the chin, swilling the remainder of a now-warm beer and offering a chuckle under his breath.

Roman, having turned several shades of scarlet in the moments since the astute observation, looks as though he may strike his suddenly-mirthful collaborator; thankfully, the laughter proves infectious, and it isn't long before the both of them have replaced cries of agony with tandem bellows. Ingrid remains the same—hammering the butt of whatever-object-she's-secured-for-hammering against the floor, a clear indication that the enthusiasm of their laughter hasn't dissipated their collaborate pitch. They rest against their ridiculous construct in the time it takes for the ridiculousness of the moment to cause them to fall to the basement floor; by the time a furious Mrs. Vesziki comes down to quiet the chaos, they have rolled the length of the twelve-by-twelve, bellies sore from mirthful cries.

Less About Boats, More About Art

They commiserate over bowls of warm Hungarian stew, removed from the basement and the boat trapped in it. Laughter comes between mouthfuls and only when Ingrid turns her back to them—having taken time to corral them off of the basement floor, her temper is decidedly short, and neither man has the fight left to challenge her.

They make a pact to never mention their error publicly; amongst their coworkers, the story is to be that the boat was not only constructed magnificently, but a trial run on the water proved successful. Discussions over stew as to the efficiency of *de*-and-*re*-constructing the boat are tempered by both the beer in their bellies and Ingrid's insistence that no further projects are to take place...resigned to their fate, they agree.

Fatefully, Tibor's second experience with watercraft proves as disastrous as the first; between mouthfuls of homeland stew he vows that both boats and the element they travel upon are best avoided entirely. Above him, Ingrid is swearing and yet slamming heaping spoonfuls of delicious home cooking into his bowl; Roman is silently swallowing and, having observed the interactions steadily worsening between friend and wife, decides to offer solution.

"Tibor, I have a favor to ask of you."

Ingrid snorts violently; for a moment, Tibor is concerned that some of the resulting debris has landed in his food.

"Ha! I'm sorry; I'm not the guy for your projects, apparently."

"No, no—this one is destined for success! You're a hell of a painter—Ingrid, you should see his cityscapes…the office is filled with them!! The colors, Tibor; tell me, do you paint portraits as well?"

He smiles, thoughts drifting back to the crushing oppression of Communism, lying in a hospital room with Androjan and painting commissioned works of its patriarch.

"I've been known to, on occasion."

"Brilliant. Tell me Tibor, would you be so kind as to paint a portrait of my lovely wife?"

They gasp in tandem—Tibor and Ingrid equally taken aback by the request. In the time since the boat-building project began, a mutual uncertainty has bloomed into outright disdain—although Tibor can find no fault in her delicious cooking, he's decided that the two of them need never become friends.

"Hear me out—Ingrid, you stay out of this. This man is a genius with a canvas, and I've been promising you something for that anniversary I…*may*…have missed—Tibor, tell her, tell her how you paint."

"I paint, a little."

"Bah! A little! Honey, the office is full of this stuff—a piece of art on every wall! And no, as a gesture of my love—and appreciation for you putting up with our…experiments…in the basement, let me commission this good man to do you justice."

Nearly choking on, regrettably, the last spoonful, Tibor clears his throat as best he can, raising his eyes to meet those of his friend's wife, who, he realizes, has been studying him with her usual degree of scrutiny.

He takes measure of her in a way he hasn't since their first meeting—her being his friend's wife, he's taken care not to scrutinize her image with the hunger he usually affords women—which is not to say that she isn't …*pretty*…in her own way. Still, from day one she was distinctly off limits, and his respect for his closest Canadian work associate prevented his imagination from running wild the way it tends to when he spends a degree of time with a member of the opposite sex.

Her features are passably soft; reasonably beautiful, he supposes, particularly for one whose first dozen winters were spent under the crushing oppression of Communism. He can't tell if her nose is a touch too large, or her eyes oddly set; either way, she strikes him as the kind of woman who landed five degrees west of being stunningly beautiful. The fat of her lower lip, however, he finds enticing—the jut of her proud chin would take away from those perhaps-too-far-apart eyes if not for their attractive hazel-*esque* hue.

Hazel-*esque*, because he never could discern their true color; most times he's caught her gaze he's been distracted by the contortions her visage takes when she's yelling at him. Still, he supposes it's an entity he can work with; her hair, slightly matted yet thick and suitably curly, frames her face in a way that he supposes is enticing, given certain light. He sighs as in-audibly as he can, more a result of the alcohol than the proposal, and agrees with a nod. Across the table, Roman says

"Splendid!"

or something similar; he can't quite hear because his attentions are focused solely on Ingrid, who looks as taken aback as he is. So it's

splendid

for Roman, undoubtedly assuming that this latest endeavor will service both the end of the silent feud between the painter and the subject, *and* create a lovely if-not-slightly-late anniversary present at the same time.

For the first time in two forevers Tibor believes he spots Ingrid blush; first of a pair of decidedly alien expressions that crack her eternally stone-faced veneer. He's amazed, frankly, by the second; a look of embarrassment, perhaps, replaces the usual shade of cross—her features soften, revealing the beauty beneath—and Tibor realizes that *this* is the Ingrid he will capture for them.

A heaping bowl of fresh stew is offered where disdainful comments would normally be; he takes a moment to appreciate the sudden change in her behaviors towards him. He vows to begin immediately—Roman assures he will facilitate the project with offerings of canvas and brush, no doubt eager to erase the memory of their previous collaborative failure.

He's agreeing to mediums--oils over acrylics--and debating canvas size, when the bare wall opposite Ingrid and her stovetop of stew give him the latest of his infinitely good ideas.

...

He hears the lock on the front door turn, and increases his brush stroke in response. A bead of sweat trickles the length of his forehead, threatening to enter his eye—he acknowledges it with a series of strong blinks, refusing to interrupt his work. He knows he has a moment—two, tops—before he's discovered.

Counting the footsteps, he weighs them against his memory of the length of the hallway; he figures he has seven, eight more footfalls before the intruder rounds the corner *here*, to the kitchen, and his hard work is exposed.

He'd begun the painting first thing in the morning—the last to leave the home, Roman had left the front door unlocked, granting him access to the empty abode. He had promised he could complete the work before Ingrid arrived at six—were he to glance at the wall opposite, he might learn she's twenty minutes early. He's two, three strokes from some semblance of completion—he'd have preferred to have packed away his brushes—he's left hoping the magnificence of the display isn't detracted from by their scattered presence.

He paints furiously, accenting the cut of her cheekbone, until, snorting with relative displeasure; he's forced to step away from the wall. Ingrid rounds the corner to the kitchen as planned, stops dead upon seeing Tibor standing proudly in the center of her kitchen. Her gasp, however, is reserved for a split-second later, when she turns her head to face the kitchen wall.

The wall now covered with a mural depicting her resplendent face.

His homage to the Greek frescoes he'd studied under Schneider's watchful eye; a masterpiece—if he does say so himself—depicting her natural radiance, augmented ever-so-slightly by the oils he chose to adorn the wall.

Her mouth hangs agape, no sound escapes.

Tibor glances at her—and then back at the wall with her face all over it—and then back at her again. He reckons her slack jawed expression and parted lips are almost the size of those he spent the last seven hours and forty minutes creating. He sees tears welling in her eyes, and for a moment, wonders if—by some previously unimaginable slight—she could be unhappy with his artistic interpretation. She looks from the wall to the canvas strewn on the floor amidst the paints and he understands.

"Really, Ingrid—how could you expect your magnificence to be contained on a crude piece of canvas?"

Across the kitchen, she looks as though she may burst into sobbing hysterics; hesitantly, she begins to move across the floor. She stops just short of the image; raising a trembling hand to the wall's surface, she delicately strokes the freshly dried section under her right eye. Tibor detects the trace of a smile, offers one of his own.

"Do you like it?"

She turns suddenly; the smile is ear-to-ear by the time she's facing him. She throws her arms around him; Tibor wraps her in his embrace as laughter escapes her lips. The sound is admittedly alien to him, but he welcomes her affections just the same.

"Thank you, Tibor."

He pulls her closer, hugs her as earnestly as he can, relieved that she supports his decision to paint directly onto the kitchen wall, and hopeful that her display of positive emotion heralds the end of their squabbles regarding the usage of Roman's free time.

They dance, there in the kitchen, laughter drowning out the music she separates herself from him to play, until Roman arrives home from work, himself overjoyed by the work Tibor leaves to dry on the wall adjacent from the stove and the stew Ingrid now *happily* cooks atop it.

…

The months that follow are relatively uneventful; Tibor spends his days mastering his craft alongside Roman at the firm, his evenings painting or venturing out to the city's various dance clubs. He joins Roman and Ingrid more often—his apartment feels decidedly lonely on the nights he chooses to stay there. So it's dinners underneath the mural of a woman who now offers both stew and comradery—and both he and Roman are less stressed for it, despite the still-assembled boat lingering one floor below their feet.

Doing Better.

Oh, Canada

Tibor tells himself as he adjusts the collar on *this*, his latest and most-expensive suit, stepping down onto the sidewalk in front of the tailor's shop he just spent a small fortune in.

And *on*, like the suit he's walking away with, feeling like the kind of man he imagines successful men feel like. He thinks of Emil, momentarily, as he squints in the sunlight of a far-too-fresh Edmonton afternoon, the sadness reminding him the way it tends to that the cost of this suit was decidedly more than the funny-colored paper he put down to pay for it.

Still, his sacrifices haunt him only the way he reasons sacrifices should, and so Tibor smiles the way Emil used to as he unlocks the door of the brand new automobile he paid even more for, climbing behind the wheel and onto a rich leather seat.

Cadillac sounds good in any tongue; his own doubtless as exotic as he finds them to be *here*, this frequently-snow-covered-but-not-today paradise his tears have earned him. He inhales deeply, appreciating the new car scent, tells himself that of all the frivolous luxuries his new life has afforded, this one is by far the greatest.

The wheel still feels foreign when he grips it; cold in a different kind of way then the air around him, even now as he shuts the far-too-fresh Edmonton afternoon outside. He shifts his weight, and the rich leather seat reminds him with a sound just how rich and how leather his seat really is…and maybe he needs it, gripping the cold wheel back and reminding himself for the latest in a half-dozen times that this is real, and that he really, really deserves it.

The ignition roars the way it should when he turns it over, and while he assumes he's slowly getting used to the sound, he reminds himself to never really get used to it. This must be the immigrant story, he assumes, catching eyes with the man in the *not*-Cadillac beside him as he pulls out of the parking space and heads the opposite direction down the first in a series of streets he hasn't learned the names of. The immigrant story, success in some far away land, placating the sorrow of things left behind with toys called Cadillac and feelings called *freedom*.

His calloused hands bite into the supple leather of the wheel, and the wheel bites back as he glides his favorite new toy left on some street, heading in the direction instinct calls home. And he's not used to *that* term either, his apartment some seven stories higher than any homestead has any right to be…just another thing to get used to here, this magnificent city in this magnificent land, another thing he tells Emil of when he speaks to him every night before he closes his eyes.

He'll get used to it, he knows, this paradise that he doesn't quite yet feel tethered to; used to it when the dust settles on the westward journey he's had across this land, Canada already filling a void in his soul he hadn't fully realized Communism and the homeland had wrought. The days keep him busy enough—the days like today, securing work when he can to pay for distractions like the one he currently sits in, accelerating hard on a stretch of pavement uncovered by the gentle, now-falling snow, racing towards a still-beaming sun and telling himself that he can outrun and out-busy the best of his sorrows.

…

Outrunning sorrows has a lot to do with moonlighting at places like the place he pulls up to, parking the Cadillac at least as carefully as his relatively-new driving experience will allow. 124th St, the European Health Spa, was, at first, a place to come and relax. Endy Vince, another Hungarian at the Architecture firm he spends his days in, told him of the place, and Tibor figured why not? Exercise couldn't hurt, given his constant need to attract members of the opposite sex-- and he was told things don't hang the same in one's thirties--so the dawn of a new decade prompted a few changes.

Hell, it has 'European' in the title, and Endy promised many Hungarians frequented the spot, so Tibor and his spotty-at-best English wandered in the front door some weeks ago, walked out with a membership—and only because the job he received came with it.

So he works nights here, and the working nights means a second income, which means not only gas in the Cadillac, but also that the shoes he steps out of the Cadillac in are the finest leather an immigrant with two great jobs can afford.

So pretty damn fine, and he avoids the residue of some snowfall as he steps onto the street, home at 124th the way home is, really, only six blocks away, so working until almost dawn and going to his real job slightly after sun up isn't as bad as it may sound.

He hears Lucile Ball is a co-owner, and he loves movie stars, so working every waking hour, plus ones he shouldn't be, doesn't bother him one bit. He reminds himself he's not shooting horses or patrolling munitions piles, and so the 'work'—running pampered rich debutantes through their aerobic workouts—doesn't really feel like work at all.

Tonight's first client is Mrs. Weatherspoon, and Mrs. Weatherspoon prefers to be touched when she does her step exercises, and though Mrs. Weatherspoon may be a little…weathered, she's a paying customer, and mercifully, a hilarious woman.

It's groping and it's squeezing and it's inappropriate and it's all things she does to him, and he wouldn't have it any other way. Her flirtations are both good-natured and welcomed, the way an immigrant with a…finite grip on the English language welcomes the warmth of any positive human interaction. They end the session with a dance, the way they always do, and Mr. Weatherspoon comes five minutes early the way he always does, too, and tonight he joins in the laughter.

It continues, the dancing and the touching, and most importantly, the riotous and infectious laughter. Even Endy, late for his shift—and shift, because he's now working there too—is far more jovial within the walls of the European Health Spa than he is during his days at the firm. This, too is a relief—were it not for Endy being the only other Hungarian-born architect at his day job, Tibor would have a hard time relating to his tempestuous nature.

Watching him spank the bottom of Mrs. Schmidt—spank it with those chubby fingers attached to the obscenely hairy palm of an obscenely hairy man, Tibor knows that although Endy may have introduced him to the Spa, *his* employment is a direct result of the owner, Mrs. Schmidt, taking a liking to Tibor and his chiseled good looks, and understanding that Endy Vince and his pockmark faced, half-foot-shorter-than-a-man-should-be was simply part of the deal.

So she grimaces as the short, poor-skinned man spanks her bottom once more; grimaces because Tibor howls every time he does it, and Tibor has the good sense to suspect Mrs. Schmidt would howl too, should *his* hand be the one grazing her shapely bottom.

For his part, Endy Vince howls and sweats in equal parts, the comb-over adorning his glistening brow fighting as furiously to escape as one Mrs. Schmidt, and Tibor can't help himself but double over at the sight, knowing first-hand and full well that the top of his head and Mrs. Schmidt are the only two places near poor Endy not completely covered in sweaty fur.

He dances like a handsome man, the bastard, and his confidence is the second most infectious thing resonating within the walls of the European Health Spa tonight for it—a new song comes on the radio and although he would be Goddamned if he could understand a single word of it, Endy moves like the beat has been bottled inside of his hairy little body.

...

Mrs. Schmidt's office is next to the canteen, and for the better part of the last two nights, Tibor is spending the majority of his free time there. Mrs. Schmidt seems to sincerely appreciate this—although English is her second language as well, and his German is spotty at best, lately he's finding he doesn't need a translator to decipher her intent. The way her body moves when he makes her laugh; the way her body doesn't when Endy tries twice as hard to draw half the smile.

This—making friends in what still feels like a foreign land—is important to his sense of fulfillment; watching her ample breasts sway under the fabric of the little-too-tight dress she chose tonight—only slightly tighter than the little-too-tight dress she wore yesterday—Tibor is certain making Mrs. Schmidt a friend is suddenly even *more* so.

She bellows hard enough—at one of his tamer jokes—to snap him from the daze of analyzing her hips; deciding the medium-sized language barrier worth crossing, he grabs the hand without the wedding ring in his, looks her in those big emerald eyes, and asks in his best English

"Would you like to go to the dance with me?"

but it comes out more like

"Whooood yhou lyyke thwo—

and although it's a mess and he knows it,

Mrs. Schmidt gives him the universal sign for

"I thought you would never ask"

a half-second before her *more-robust-every-night* lips part to mouth

"I thought you would never ask."

...

There are maybe two, three locations in all of Edmonton that Tibor knows how to drive to. Forget street names…he uses buildings to judge where he's going. His latent Architect's eye delineating height and concrete grade and equating this to the areas he's entering or leaving, the way the office and the European Health Spa are in decidedly better socio-economic areas than the area he drives to now, Mrs. Schmidt riding beside him and resplendent in a dress Mr. Schmidt paid for, God Rest His Soul.

He passed some years ago, Endy tells him, and the money from his estate helped pay for her share in the club she used to just go to exercise in. Following his death, Mrs. Schmidt found the gym to be the only place she felt distracted from the hole his absence tore in her heart...Tibor respects her for wearing his ring, finding that her loyalty to family only adds to his desire for her.

Wearing that dress, it sure-as-hell isn't enough to deter him, and as the Cadillac pulls up to the one place on the wrong side of town he loves the most, Tibor and his newly-expensive shoes touch pavement outside of the Hungarian Club.

So, *home*, and tonight—like every Saturday night—home of the decadent Hungarian Dance Hall. Mrs. Schmidt is positively trembling with excitement (--and maybe a slight bit of utter horror...they really are on the wrong side of town) as Tibor takes her tiny hand.

He's new in town, but not new enough to have missed a single weekend here, and so he's grateful that Horst is working the door, and that Horst gives him the

right this way

invitation that makes him feel like a movie star escorting some ravishing starlet down the red carpet, opening night of the film he's starring in.

And he's not far off, because the beautiful woman on his arm is whispering in his ear, and Horst is ushering him through a crowded, smoke-filled room as horns blare, trumpeted from players on some stage barely visible through the din.

The table is waiting,

and he keeps it that way,

because the chairs surrounding it are just decorative stands for the coats they drape on them, in passing and on the way to the dance floor.

They start with something fast, and it's fitting because the night's just kind of going that way, and he's moving this way and she's following, and, for-and-befitting a widow, she's dancing like she's got demons to exorcise.

Problems tend to disappear in dance halls—including the problems *started* in dance halls, but there's none of those tonight; at least not for Tibor, because while the beautiful woman he's dancing with may be spoken for, the man doing the speaking won't come calling tonight.

So it's the tango, and the foxtrot, and the night—and she's moving and laughing the way he's guessing she hasn't in a long, long time. She looks at him with wide eyes, and they're green and they're beautiful and maybe they're watering a little…the window to the soul telling him both

thank you

and

I'm just really, really lonely.

She catches him catching on, and her laughter becomes the laughter of a woman possessed, and so she moves like one, and both welcome the distraction, though the significance behind it is not lost on either party.

Which means that when Mrs. Schmidt goes in for the kiss, Tibor does the right thing for once, and takes it on the cheek. The water escapes the corner of her eye, and she just laughs, burying both her beautiful gaze and the face attached into his shoulder.

Some horn player, or some aspect of fate, notices the change in pace and belts out the saddest note Tibor has ever heard. A second horn echoes the lament, and they're playing in unison and somehow sadder still, and its' a

one-two-step

left, and maybe Mrs. Schmidt doesn't mind the change in tune, because the sudden and growing wet spot on his shoulder tells Tibor she's not ready to move her head yet. They dance like they've lost someone, and it's a dance they both know not everyone can dance, and it makes the moment that much more.

When the bar lights come on to signal the end of the night, Tibor holds her close on the way to the Cadillac, and the kiss he gives her lands on her forehead, right before the lips that kissed her move just west of her left ear, whisper

"Same time next week?"

...

"I'm impressed,"

I tell Tibor, putting my pen down and catching some sentiment of sadness in his eyes, reminiscing on Mrs. Schmidt and his adventures at the European Health Spa.

To this point, Tibor was something of a *cad*, and stories with women in them usually ended one way—my face blushing as my pen scrawled his debaucheries. I had assumed, at the start of this particular adventure, that it would end much the same—with Mrs. Schmidt a victim of his beautiful features and sharp tongue.

"She was married."

"Yes, but you said—

The look he gives stops me mid-sentence. Understanding, my eyes fall to the paper below me, and in bold letters, I note

Thirties=new maturity

thinking,

finally,

before remembering that, at thirty-five, I'm no wiser.

...

Tibor takes Mrs. Schmidt dancing every Saturday, and every Saturday the Cadillac is as immaculate as her makeup, flawless as they speed through Edmonton's bad side towards the one place they can bury their problems in.

Dead things wait at dancehall doors, and though they wait patiently, the fervor with which Tibor and Mrs. Schmidt dance suggests they have no place *here*, on Saturday night.

It isn't long before eligible bachelors, drunk on wine and whiskey, muster the courage to request Tibor separate from the ravishing widow long enough for a dance of their own, and suddenly, they're time together is growing apart.

Watching her smile from the newly brave's vantage, there at a table beside the dance floor, Tibor is gratified knowing that his work is almost done. Her laughter comes faster and faster, and though his shoulder is the only one her head retreats to when the sad songs play, he knows it won't be long before some lucky bastard makes her smile hard enough to make Mr. Schmidt less a ghost and more a pleasant series of periodically-devastating memories.

The whiskey whispers lustful thoughts in his mind, and she's at least as ravishing on the tenth Saturday as she was the very first. Still, he's proud of both his restraint and his role; protective older brother now, watching that red dress move and silently approving of the latest Hungarian to twirl it around the dance floor.

Fresh continents and thirties are having pleasing results on his journey into manhood—Tibor salutes the ghosts of his past and future, watching Mrs. Schmidt dance her way out of his romantic life and drowning out the whispers with the roaring of devils in bottles named tequila.

Time, and the Things Time Takes

"What happened to them? Your Radors?"

Tibor breaks eye contact for the very first time this afternoon, his gaze and thoughts drifting to the storm outside the window. I'm still wet, having just escaped the weather long enough to sit across the table and a fresh cup of coffee; since Tibor's tales of his time in Canada, they've yet to come up in story. I figure I'm doing my part as chronicler, tying up loose ends—ends that amount to plot points in the notebook still drying on the table before me.

Tibor's sigh tells me that they're much more to him.

"What happened to them? Time, you might say. We had the best intentions, the four of us…we meant to stay close together here, and after everything we'd gone through back home. We were young, and you might say we were over our collective heads; the country was new and exciting, and we were all so eager to make a mark on it."

"You'd promised to always stay together."

He sighs, his gaze returns to mine.

"We did. All of us were so…heightened…after what happened to my brother; all of us just wanted out. We made the trip together, and then we tried…we really did…but life has a funny way of making other plans."

I decide not to press; seeing the look on his face, I ask him of Lilia instead. We talk for a coffee or two of her family, of a trip to meet them in the Philippines—just as Tibor stands to make a fresh pot, he turns to me and says

"Pal Jugovics died last month."

I stop writing whatever trivial thing I was writing; setting my pen down, I look him in the eyes. He's smiling, but there's a sadness to it—as though he's reliving some memory from some time decidedly better than this one.

"I'd meant to see him, you know."

"He was still in Edmonton?"

"He was. Hell, he lived two blocks from the first shitty apartment building he moved to when we got there. Pal loved that city—maybe more than I did."

"Did you stay in touch?"

"Not as much as I'd have liked to. Pal was the only one who didn't join the railroad; he followed us to Edmonton, but got work as a stock boy at a grocery store. He was fast to learn English—faster than the rest of us, that's for sure. He was always a bright boy."

"So you had stayed friends?"

"We...tried. The rest of us—his brother Laszlo, and that Hackel brothers—were laying rail for months at a time, and he was pretty much in one place. He met a girl, and we didn't see much of him. However—

Sensing a story, I pick up my pen.

"—he came to me for money once. Something about buying a car...turns out the Canadian Pacific Railroad paid more than the mom-and-pop shop he'd decided to join. So he asks me for nine hundred dollars—you have to understand, back then, it was a helluva lot of money."

"Nine hundred dollars is *always* a lot of money."

He chuckles a little, having poured the latest round, and returns to the table, slightly more mirthful than when he'd left.

"True. But back then, my boy, nine hundred dollars could get you just about *anything*. I barely had it, but we'd made a promise to always be there for one another, and maybe I felt a little guilty for not forcing him to come with us. So, like a fool, I lent him the money."

"He never paid you back."

"He paid me one hundred dollars…maybe two times. I knew it was hard for him; hell, I wouldn't have asked for more…but he lied to me."

"Lied?"

"He told me—told his brother—that he'd paid me back. In full."

Moments like this present a particular hardship for me. My job is to recount his adventures in their totality—to put pen to paper just about every time the man opens his mouth to recount them. Times like this, I feel hesitant—part of me just wants to be there for him, a friend as he shares the more painful parts of his story. At his behest, I continue to write as he tells me of the hurt this caused him, the disconnect that grew between the Radors in the months to follow.

"Tibor Hackel was an alcoholic, unfortunately, and had a habit of borrowing money, too. I think we all knew he'd never pay it back—but, after what happened with Pal, maybe none of us had the heart to say it. Hell, when you come from where we came from, you learn to try to look the other way for your brothers…at least, when it came to the *small* amounts, anyways."

He stops to adjust his glasses, the way he tends to when an uncomfortable story is coming.

"The final straw came less than six months after swearing off Pal; Tibor begged me for two hundred dollars to bet on a horse. We'd been down this road, you see, and back then—as you say, *even today*—two hundred bucks—"

"Is two hundred bucks."

"—exactly. I lent him the money, of course; for once, the bastard was actually right."

"He won?"

"He won. Big. Moreover, if he had an inside line on that damned horse, you'd think he'd have told us. No, he won *twenty thousand* dollars at the track, and do you think I saw my two hundred?"

"And you forgave him?"

"Of course I forgave him. We'd been through so much together; maybe I was tired of losing Pal this way, maybe I figured he'd just had a tougher time adjusting than the rest of us. That…"

His smile betrays the warmth of his memories associated with the man.

"…and he kept me on that damned boat, didn't he?"

I smile, picturing Tibor thrashing against the restraints that tethered him on his journey to Canada.

"Besides,"

he tells me with a grin

"I was making new friends anyway."

Criminals, Curiosities

Tibor had been working alongside Roman Vesziki for the better part of a year, toiling diligently at his work and earning praise—from Bob Samuel and others—for his efforts. Before long, his renown had grown, and the hard working Hungarian duo became a hard working Hungarian foursome.

Pifko Jula, having learned of the accolades Roman and Tibor were quickly receiving, left a high-paying job at a rival architectural firm to join them; Bob, increasingly believing that Eastern European immigrants had magic in their blood, hired him without hesitation. Bakor Zoltan—a prodigy of sorts in architectural circles, shared an office with them not two months later. Together, they began design work on a four-story apartment, with eyes towards claiming Edmonton's prestigious 'Engineering Marvel' award.

The symbolism of 'four' not lost on him, Tibor spends evenings—evenings not spent at Roman's, eating Ingrid's increasingly plentiful portions—lamenting the distance between his first three Radors, and appreciating the ever-increasing bond between the *new*. Knowing he's nothing if not a survivor, he balances the distance by the act of putting one foot directly in front of the other, head filled with the promises of prestige and the satisfaction that comes with work well done.

And so he does, days without contact from his Radors steadily increasing, until he admits a modicum of surprise when the phone rings and a familiar voice is on the other end.

All the while, his brotherhood with his fellow Hungarians at the office continues; their apartment complex project is proving to be an unparalleled success.

Tibor, contented by the distractions his burgeoning career is presenting, is so intent on the aforementioned act of one-foot-in-front-of-the-other on his way to work one Tuesday morning, that he fails to notice the police officer standing at the entrance way to the firm until he runs headlong into him.

"Sorry, my friend—I wasn't paying attention…"

His words bear the honesty of a man who has yet to realize the station of the man he's careened into—having collected the myriad of drafting papers that escaped his overflowing satchel on impact, he raises his gaze for the first time to discover the identity of his makeshift roadblock.

"…sorry, *officer.*"

The country—the continent—may be only three-plus years old…*that* uniform, he's learned, is pretty much universal.

"Accidents happen, Mr.….Zoltan?"

He's reaching; the steel in his eyes tells Tibor that the question belies the identity of the *reason* for an early morning visit. Still, he can't help but feel a touch insulted—had the officer any photograph of Bakor Zoltan, surely he would realize that the diminutive, pock-marked countenance—the rapidly receding hairline accented by the never-before-tweezed eyebrows and omnipresent hairs escaping from seemingly oversized nostrils—bear no similarities to his own chiseled features.

"Sadly, no, sir. Tibor Fidler. Pleasure to meet you, Mr.?"

"Sergeant Gaines. Timothy Gaines."

"Sergeant Gaines. A pleasure."

He smiles warmly, all the while amused at Canadian police rankings; when he thinks of the title of Sergeant, he thinks of the military, the authoritarian airs of those who held the rank. Why such a peaceful, welcoming country would adopt rankings with historically tyrannical associations escapes him. Still, it's

"What can I do for you this morning, officer?"

politely,

knowing that he's undoubtedly first to the office this morning, and that his Rador will not be arriving for at least another hour.

For once, it seems Bakor's perennial tardiness will serve him well; this officer—this Sergeant—apparently has questions to ask of him.

"May I be so bold as to ask why you would like to speak to him?"

"I'm afraid that's private, Mr. Fidler. If you see Mr. Zoltan—when you see Mr. Zoltan—could you please have him give me a call? I'll be expecting to hear from him this afternoon."

He presents his card with the authority of someone used to getting his way—Tibor is reminded of his stay in the Bakony mountains as he takes it in his left, right shaking an extended hand, eyes all the while fixed on those of the *latest* Sergeant attempting to make life difficult.

…

He's at his desk and working—and not as much as he should be, mind racing with thoughts of what his compatriot could *possibly* be up to—when a hand on his shoulder wrests him violently from the inner conspiracies of a troubled self-conscious.

"Jesus, Tibor! You nearly jumped from your seat!"

Tibor notes that Bakor Zoltan's stoic countenance is undisturbed. He hastily produces Sgt. Gaines' card, half-expecting the façade to crumble as he presents the small piece of paper. More alarming than a sudden hand on his shoulder is the fact that it does not; with a half-smile, Zoltan takes the card, setting down the coffee he so courteously picked up for his co-worker with his free hand, turns slowly to hang up a rain-splashed coat.

"I see you met my friend, Gaines."

"What sort of trouble are you into?"

"Trouble? Ha! It's no trouble, Fidler—simply a misunderstanding."

"Bah! He seemed serious, Bakor; care to explain?"

He sits at his desk across the room; Tibor can see his eyes scan the remainder of a still-quiet office. Surely he knows that the others are tied up in a meeting downstairs—something about Bob planning one of his lavish team-building jaunts—yet still he seems to be scanning the darker nooks of their tiny domicile for activity. Once satisfied that they are indeed alone, he spins on his chair, and, with a sip of his own still-warm coffee, opens his mouth to offer an explanation.

"Do you remember the two-story I was working on last fall?

Tibor nods—a brownstone, if he recalls correctly—one that Zoltan had been commissioned to design previous to his transfer to the office.

"Yeah—Augustine St."

"That's the one. Turns out that, in ordering supplies for the build, I may have been a touch…what's the word in English…

"Overzealous?"

He laughs, loud enough to draw the attention of anyone who would be hiding in one of Zoltan's just-checked darkened corners.

"*Overzealous*. That's just the word, Tibor."

"How overzealous?"

"You've been to my house, no?"

Tibor, nodding once more, feels a bead of perspiration at his temple. Swallowing hard, he knows the coffee isn't *that* hot. Suddenly the pieces fit—Tibor recalls the ornate finishes in Bakor's home the night he, Roman and Pifko had stolen away from one of Bob's late-night bar crawling adventures. Zoltan had been bragging about the lavishness of his just-renovated home; the imported fixtures, the granite-and-limestone countertops, the elaborate flooring designs. He'd meant to ask Bakor where he'd come up with the capital for such an expensive remodeling, but the liquor and the conversation had escaped him.

"Christ, Bakor—the government paid for that brownstone!"

"Right you are—it was a housing project for the underprivileged, or some bullshit. I figured, hey, no one is as underprivileged as us Hungarian immigrants, right?"

"So you remodeled your entire house using materials meant for the brownstone?"

"Ah, Tibor, don't be so dramatic. The two-story received everything it was supposed to. I just…ordered a little *more* on the government dime, is all."

"*All of it?*"

Tibor's mind is racing, recounting—as best he can, given the amount of alcohol consumed on the night of his visit to the opulent home—every single faucet, floor, and fixture he had marveled at.

Unassuming, Bakor simply takes another sip of his coffee, fixing his gaze directly upon Tibor before offering reassurance that

"All of it"

was paid for by the Canadian government.

"You could go to jail!"

"Ah, you're being dramatic. This Gaines bastard has asked me twice now where the rest of the materials ordered went; I've told him—and I'll tell him again—they must have buggered up the delivery. It's not on *my* end."

"Surely they're smart enough to realize it had nothing to do with delivery—Jesus, Bakor, what are you going to do?"

"I'll tell you exactly what I'm going to do…

He smiles in between generous sips of coffee.

"…I'm going on vacation."

…

"And he did, the bastard."

"Did he ever get caught?"

I put the pen down; hoping the conclusion to the story is as exciting as the beginning. Silently, I marvel at how many times one man can be close to danger—or close to those who are close to danger—and manage to escape unscathed. As Tibor opens his mouth to respond, I have a feeling I already know the answer.

"Oh, he got away with it. Eventually, the government took possession of his place; didn't matter, he hadn't lived there for about a year before that happened."

"So what happened?"

"He just finished his coffee, stood up, and walked out of the office. He didn't tell anyone where he was going—not Bob, not Roman—not anyone. He must have went home and gathered his belongings; I went over to his place that very night to reason with him, and he was gone."

"And this was the last you heard of him?"

I ask, half-expecting to close the book on the character of Bakor Zoltan.

Tibor simply smiles, gesturing with a nod of his head that I had better pick up my pen.

"God no."

Peace River

Tibor sits at his desk, fumbling over the specific dimensions of a load-bearing wall on the page before him. He's thinking of many things as he thumbs aimlessly at the design--the relation of the wall to the structural integrity of the wall opposite, his plans to go dancing on the last Saturday night before Christmas; Emil.

When the phone rings somewhere down the office hall, the last thing he's thinking about is his old teammate, Bakor Zoltan.

It's

"Tibor! Phone!"

just the same; by the time he saunters down the hallway to take the phone from the looking-good-today receptionist, the last

"Hello"

he could have expected on the other line is the

"Hello"

he receives.

"Tibor!!!"

"Oh God—Bakor Zoltan?"

He'd not heard the voice—or *anything* from the man attached to it—in the year since that fateful rain-and-coffee morning. Bob had blamed Tibor, in a way, for 'scaring him off' all that time ago; the man was so distraught, he refused to clear his desk. Glancing down the hall at the desk still strewn with drafting paper and coffee cups, he realizes the bastard might never be replaced.

"How have you been, brother?"

"Ha! Great Tibor! Great!"

He half expected to hear that the call was coming from prison; instead it's

"Peace River!"

when he asks; and about a year—or, to be more specific, the year *minus the time* it took to drive there that day following Sergeant Gaines.

He says that he's calling because it's the holidays—Tibor, glancing at the Christmas tree blinking frenetically next to the unfortunately oblivious receptionist, knows there's something more.

So when he boasts

"there's something more"

there's no surprise; Tibor can't help but smile, realizing between Christmas light blinks just how much he's missed the man.

"I'm married, Tibor."

The lights seem to blink differently—he's reasonably sure he misheard him.

"I said I'm married, you bastard!"

He thinks many things, the various words associated with them. Manages

"Congratulations"

just the same.

It's not that Bakor Zoltan was the ugliest Hungarian in the world—hell, he reckons, he wasn't even the ugliest Hungarian in a four-Hungarian office—it's just that hearing from him for the first time in a year, after essentially running from the government and the law—the last thing he figured he'd hear when he picked up the phone was that Bakor Zoltan was

"Married!!! To a beautiful woman, you ought to know!"

"I'm happy for you, Bakor."

He laughs on the other end of the line; he's comforted to learn it is the same laugh, one year removed.

He's about to ask him what the hell is so funny, when

"You're probably wondering what the hell is so funny, Fidler."

"It crossed my mind."

He sighs; Tibor can practically hear him wipe the tears from his eyes.

"You said that you're happy for me, Tibor—but you have no idea how happy you should be!"

"Zoltie, please—it's been a long time. That bastard Gaines came by the office every day for *two months* after you disappeared—you have any idea how many times he threatened to throw me in jail?"

"That sonuvabitch—he had nothing, Fidler. Nothing! And it all worked out, trust me. My wife—Maria—she was married before, you know. To a very rich—very old—man. When he died, guess who he left his fortune to?"

The lights on the Christmas tree blink in a way that makes sense again.

"Ha! Speechless, Fidler?! I knew you might be. This is the part where I pay you back for helping me out last year. You didn't think I'd forgotten about my Hungarian brother, did you?"

In truth, he had. Hell, they all had—Bob was downright distraught; Roman, having grown increasingly disinterested with boating following the basement incident, allowed an increase in duration between invitations to enjoy Ingrid's cooking…Pifko refused to speak to him for two days after seeing Gaines in the office for the first time. Still, they'd gotten by—absent one Rador, they even won that damned award.

He thinks of mentioning it all—the award, the strife his absence caused—but he's admittedly interested in just *how* Bakor Zoltan's disappearance and subsequent marriage could possibly benefit him.

He offers a

"No"

instead, and, allowing a breath and then another, figures his long-lost brother is expecting more before he comes back with

"*She has a sister*, Tibor."

The lights on the Christmas tree blink in celebration.

…

Peace River, as it turns out, is roughly five hours straight north from the comforts of Edmonton and the office. Tibor makes the drive in his Cadillac, half pleased to be spending the holidays away from his tiny apartment, Christmas dinner at Roman's notwithstanding. He'd lied only a little when he told them he'd heard from a Rador—figuring they didn't ask if it was Radors *volume one* or *volume two* justified his omission of details. Bob, for one, would have been devastated—he'd been saving a bottle of champagne for what he called the 'eventuality' that Bakor would be back to celebrate his part in winning the Engineering Marvel award.

So he makes the drive alone, and only partly because Zoltan insisted he do so.

Turns out that Maria only has one sister.

The plan, according to Bakor, is to woo her, thus becoming part of the family, and a direct line to the fortune Maria's dearly departed first husband entrusted entirely to her. Seeing as how Maria only had one living relative—her beautiful

"—trust me, Tibor—"

sister Esther, she was left with only one other person—new husband aside—to share in the spoils of a

"ten *million* dollar"

inheritance.

And so, the drive.

As the Caddy grips the ice and sleet covered roads, Tibor tells himself that this is just the latest in a series of adventures. Hell, he'll have to lay eyes on Esther before he can say with any certainty that she'd be worth millions—and, more importantly—giving up the comforts of bachelor life for. He knows that putting a dollar amount on Saturday nights at the Hungarian dance hall will prove difficult; she'll have to be the rare beauty Bakor proclaims her to be to convince him that single life is for the birds.

Still, the excitement of seeing an old friend—the added element of danger, what with his…*complications*…with the Canadian government, and the added bonus of a mega-rich, potentially beautiful woman? Tibor reckons it was worth the drive. The road begs to differ, occasionally reminding the Cadillac just how powerful prairie winters can be—but he's motivated, and he's hungry, and he's as curious as always.

Besides,

he tells himself—

his track record with adventures such as this is impeccable, no?

Winter Number Two (Many)

It's winter-*two* since my first encounter with Tibor; at eighty-five, I know that there are more winters in his past than his future. He flies south for the winter the way he tends to, and I tell myself I've got months *and four* to finish this book before he's back and ready to read it.

I intend to and I suppose I try, but life for a starving writer has a way of placing necessities on *not* starving, and so the day job takes precedent in a way that keeps the stories from flowing the way they should. They are excuses and they're poor ones—and though I have recordings of our times together to listen to, and my hand-written notes to refer to, I miss the meetings with Tibor and the way his stories inspire me to hold up my end of the bargain, the way I'm not, week seven into winter-*two*.

I miss the theatricality of his presentation, the wild in his eyes that tells me that haunting memories do not have to fade when the fresh ones threaten to replace them. I miss the way he dances in his favorite chair across that dining room table, miss the way Emil watches with silent reverence, shaking his head when the tales spin too raw.

I tell myself that these are just the musings of the lazy--and this writer is—and then I get word that Tibor, in addition to having fallen twice in Florida, has been relegated to a hospital bed with pneumonia, and maybe I write a little more than I'm used to.

Spending time with this man has a way of buying into the air of the invincibility his tales are tinged with—in truth, his exuberance has lulled a sense of security into me, a feeling that we'll have years to chronicle some eighty-five worth. Of course, it's just as realistic that I don't want the stories to end, and so I delay under the auspices that I'll need just one more conversation with Tibor in order to go home and finish my writings.

In any case, I'm writing and Tibor is in some hospital bed somewhere south—and again, I'm struck with the concept some thirty-something's are immune to…the concept that, if I don't hurry, the most important reader may not have the chance.

Whiskey, and the Self-Realization that comes with too much…

The view from the laneway is certainly promising.

Mainly because he can't see the house at the end of it—and it has nothing to do with the measure of snowfall masquerading as a blizzard and doing its best to obscure his vision. The gate he pulls up to is certainly opulent; instantly, he's reminded of the lavishness of Bakor's former residence.

Some guys,

he figures

have all the luck.

Knowing that he's one of them, he blasts his horn, presses the button on the intercom, and waits for the whirring and clunking of impressively hidden mechanisms. Moments later—after the weight of the semi-oppressive snow has given way—the gates begin to slide open, and for the first time, Tibor spots the lights at the end of a long, long

long

laneway.

The drive *up* is painful in duration—he's chastising Bakor's lack of adequate snow removal, half hanging out the window of the Caddy, so concerned is he that he not leave what-he-hopes are the confines of an invisible driveway. He's mid-curse when the completion of a particularly-difficult-to-discern bend reveals the manor in all its' snow-masked resplendence.

Tibor only realizes his jaw is hanging open when a blast of snow explodes upon his tongue.

It's taller than the four-story they won that damn award for—his discerning eye for architecture appreciates the post-colonial design elements, subdued as the snow attempts to make them. He reckons he's seen wealth in Canada—hell, he's been responsible for designing the types of buildings that seem to revel in showcasing it—but he's never seen anything like *this*.

He spends a minute, climbing from the relative sanctity of the Caddy, gazing at the finishes. The snow is invasive, crashing against the rims of the glasses he puts on to inspect the marble pillars, but he pays it no mind. The numbing at the tips of his fingers does little to stop his slack-jawed gazing—the ones he can still feel trace the groves in the granite adorning a twelve-foot front door. He reaches for a brass knocker, admiring the weight—the heft of it in his hand—before crashing it against the stop. He feels almost guilty for doing so, fearing he may mar the perfection of its surface. He's relieved to hear the echo ring clearly from inside what he imagines to be an opulent foyer—half-hoping the clarion takes a moment to be answered, he backs up, staring at the beautiful millwork placed atop intricate latticework just above the frame.

He's wondering many things, straining to hear footfalls on what must be marble floors over the roar of the wind; chief among them is how a fool like Bakor Zoltan could have escaped the pursuits of government, only to end up *here*.

The door glides on what must be well oiled and perfectly engineered hinges; against the din of the storm he strains to make out the figure on the other side.

A voice calls to him, beckoning him forth; as he steps in from the storm, he's still struggling to hear over the ever-increasing wailings of prairie wind. Despite the fog of his glasses, the figure just behind him—the one now closing the massive door—is unmistakably female. As the voice attached to the shape welcomes him to her home, Tibor hopes that, should this be the sister Bakor urged him to meet, she's as lovely as her voice seems to be.

He hastily removes his glasses, cursing his still-frozen fingertips, and offers his warmest

"Hello"

back; pivoting—snow covered boots on marble floor—he's greeted with an embrace by a woman perhaps even more breathtaking than the foyer he finds himself *thawing* in.

She says something, this blonde goddess—something about taking his coat—but he's focused on holding her—and tightly—and hoping with everything he has that this is

"Thank you—*Esther*?"

"Ha! Tibor, come in, dry off—we've been hearing so much about you…"

He lets go long enough to study her, his half-hearted attempt at removing a heavy, snow-soaked jacket lending much appreciated time to his observations.

Her golden hair seems to go on forever, glowing almost under the overhead and no doubt priceless chandelier. Her eyes radiate a warmth he's doubly appreciating, given the environment he's just escaped from—he reckons only his and Emil's have ever burned more blue. Still, her cheekbones threaten to swallow them when she smiles—which she is—no doubt amused by his assumption that she's his…intended. He's caught up in counting the magnificence of each individual tooth—white as the driven snow melting against the rich grey of the marble beneath his boots—when she mouths something that sounds a hell of a lot like

"Esther is my sister—I'm Maria. Pleased to finally meet you."

He's appropriately devastated; he takes her warm, delicate hand in his and the parts of him that aren't numb appreciate the contact. She seems to be standing across the room, yet her breasts are still touching him too, so round and voluptuous that Tibor has to remind himself to keep his eyes respectfully *north*.

He smiles back, his perfect-if-he-does-say-so-himself smile seeming suddenly inadequate. He's crushed, left to the hope that her sister is half the beauty she is—he's both anxious to discover the truth and resigned to be anywhere but *here* and with *her* when Bakor Zoltan's familiar voice rings down the hallway and ruins the moment.

"Tibor! You son of a bitch, you made it through the storm!"

"Ha! Zoltie!"

His eyes, he's noticed, haven't left Maria's.

Mercilessly, Zoltan sets upon them in a flash, wrapping Tibor in a less-welcome embrace and urging the pair of them down what seems an impossibly long and equally opulent front hallway.

He's talking all the while, breaking only to draw breath or indulge in belly-deep laughter—Tibor joins him, seemingly shaken from the spell Maria put him under, happy to see his friend.

"I've been telling the girls all about you—Esther's dying to meet you Tibor."

As if on cue, Maria disappears through a doorway, carrying Tibor's still-soaked jacket—in part, no doubt, to allow the Radors to catch up on lost time.

As Bakor leads him into a cinnamon-scented study, they do—Tibor is barely handed the first of what he knows will be many glasses of scotch before he's questioning Bakor as to how the hell he escaped Edmonton and landed *here*.

"Bah! That bastard had *nothing* Tibor—someone must have been studying the manifests, figured out we were getting two of everything. Shit, for all they knew, someone from the warehouse requisitioned double—how they figured it landed on me, I'll never know."

"They saw your place, Zoltie—the renos…hell, the exterior remodeling alone was what, a half-million?"

"I told him I didn't keep the receipts; that I liked the materials we were using on the four-story, that I got them at cost through the developer. That kind of shit happens all the time."

"Then why leave?"

Bakor takes a long draw from his whiskey, smiles the smile that must have won Maria.

"It was a big order, Tibor…the kind of money that went into my place? Hell, you keep those receipts. Besides, Gaines wasn't gonna let it go—figured it best to leave it to his imagination."

"You just up and left, Bakor—no call, nothing. They seized that house, you know. Claimed it was government property."

"Ha! Bet they got a pretty penny for it, no?"

"They turned it into a banquet hall for students."

They laugh in tandem, stopping only to sip the expensive scotch. By the time it subsides, they're both doubled over and sore; Bakor takes this, the only moment absent levity blessed by alcohol, to offer serious commentary.

"I couldn't have handled prison, Tibor."

He wipes a tear from his eye—for a moment, masked under the influence of the whisky, Tibor believes its origin may not have been the laughter.

"I'd have had a sex change, come out and killed somebody."

The moment passes; clearly, the origin of the tear not some deep introspection. They laugh once more, happy to be back in one another's company. As Bakor wrests the glass from his grip on the way back to the bar, Tibor takes time to study the proverbial study.

Books line the walls surrounding them—a great many tomes, leather-bound and magnificent—placing his glasses on once more, Tibor leans closer to inspect them, marveling on unsteady feet just how quickly the liquor seems to have hit him.

He knows he's nowhere near drunk enough to mistake his findings.

"The books—they're written in German."

"Good eye, Fidler. Maria's first husband—he was a professor of some sorts. Richest man in Peace River, too."

"You speak German?"

"Nah. I just like the looks of them."

"What happened? To him—Maria's first husband, I mean."

"He was like, eighty years old, Tibor. The old bastard had a heart attack. Left everything to Maria—some ten mill—she and her sister had been the only ones close to him at the end."

"And you started seeing her, what—after she got over his death?"

"You've seen her, right?"

"She's a beautiful woman, yes."

"And not a day over forty. Let's just say she wasn't with the old man for love."

His fingertips can feel again; they appreciate the warmth from the whiskey as much as the rest of him as he takes the second glass, settles into a rich leather sofa alongside his friend.

He tells him of his escape and subsequent lading here; how he met Maria by chance in the aisle of a department store. How they'd struck up a conversation over coffee—how she'd introduced him to her husband, an ailing German investment banker come professor who could help him land architectural design work for the township.

It takes another scotch before he gets to the *good* stuff; how they'd started an affair in the very office her husband had secured for him, how they'd talked about starting a life together once the old man kicked.

Turns out they got their wish—the poor bastard hadn't survived the last winter; gazing outside the window at the horror outside, Tibor isn't surprised.

"—and we were married this fall."

"I wasn't invited."

He's half-joking, half-bewildered; settled away here, in the middle of a cavernous mansion, in the eye of a storm, he's more interested in the details than any omissions.

"I apologize, friend; it happened fast—had to, you understand…no way I was going to let this slip between my fingers."

"*This,* love?"

The sound of the voice over his shoulder is electric. He cranes his neck, already recognizing the honey in her tone—so sweet is Maria, that he relishes any opportunity to gaze upon her beauty.

"Ha! All of—

He gestures with his hands as she sways lazily into the room, outlining the curves her body takes as she's presented magnificently in the candlelight.

--this…and who could blame me?"

"Certainly not I."

"Ha, Tibor, we're getting to the good part!"

She takes his place at his side—running her fingers through Bakor's hair, Tibor is embarrassingly aware of the fact that her eyes have discovered his chasing the length of her.

He moves his whiskey glass to his lips in apology; hope the offering is enough to return her attentions to her doting new husband.

"Maria and her darling sister, Esther, have been inseparable forever—lately, it seems, Maria's been…pre-occupied."

She giggles; Bakor's hand, he notices, has disappeared somewhere south of her low back.

"And I remember you telling me how close you were with Emil…I thought, hey, you're a handsome bastard…good job, decent man…"

"Hey!"

"Ha, I'm joking, I'm joking. Seriously, it hit me one night, in between…talks… in bed…

She giggles again, as infectious as the first.

"…you two would be *great* together!"

"Tibor"

He reckons he could listen to her call his name all night.

"—we're so happy you've come to see us. Esther, I know, was very excited to make your acquaintance."

"*Trust* me, Fidler. She'd be quite the catch."

There's something to the inflection—could be the whiskey, coupled with anticipation—but it feels strangely as though something was implied by the *trust me* part. He's half-pondering this, half straining to hear down cavernous hallways, when he catches the echo of heels on marble.

He notices a presence from the corner of his eye; a silhouette, yet to be illuminated by the muted lighting of the study's candles.

He swallows his whiskey, attentions drawn immediately to the lazy sway of hips down infinitely long hallways. He feels his heart rate increase, knowing—in part at least, that he really did want to see his old friend—that he braved a five-hour drive and the rage of winter to discover this beauty.

He's torn by the urge to steal a glance at her sister, to absorb and try to process Maria's ethereal gorgeousness, perhaps to project an imagined realization of what features her younger sibling could share.

But he's mesmerized, lost in a string of promises made, exuberant and thought-disappeared friends claiming that, in addition to wealth unimagined, he's about to enter a courtship that would capture him as rare a beauty.

She's painstakingly moments from appearing at the threshold of both the lounge and realization; he's already imagined her a thousand magnificent ways, reflections of her sister's reported and later justified claims of goddess-ness.

He takes one last shallow breath, removes his glasses from eager eyes, not wanting his first impression to be diluted by quarter-inch frames.

"Ah—

Bakor starts from somewhere over his shoulder

"—the woman of the hour! Welcome, Esther, please, meet my good friend—

He's out of the chair before his friend can finish,

ensuring

"Tibor Fidler"

escapes *his* lips, hand already extended and anticipating contact as—

Esther enters the study and the light cast upon the stature of the study by the instantly far

far

too effective candles.

She's soul-crushingly plain.

As she takes his hand in hers, offering a smile that Tibor reasons even her mother would have a tough time appreciating, he blinks twice, hoping the act of removing his bifocals has played some cruel trick on his vision.

Immediately, Bakor's insistence on violent, repeated glasses of expensive scotch are realized; the woman before him, all lopsided angles and aggressive features is mouthing something like

"Hello"

but he can't hear/tell—he's suddenly reeling and only *partly* from the whiskey.

"Dashing, isn't he Esther?"

"Quite."

He cringes, feeling the hunger in her eyes as they assault him; still, a compliment is a compliment, and he's a guest—decorum dictates he be civil. And so, with a smile and the forced laughter that follows, he spins her there in the study, dancing painfully and without music, thankful the whiskey provides a song in his head—for music he desperately needs in moments like these.

In between effortless steps, he wonders how the hell he gets into these situations; at least

he tells himself mid-step

the storm outside is sure to provide adequate reason for an early—and alone—retreat to whatever grand guest room he's sure to be spending the remaining of a road-weary night in.

"Ha! Tibor, dancing is a grand idea! What do you say, ladies?"

Esther responds with a shrill laugh; reminiscent of nails on a chalkboard. Maria's soft voice is barely audible over the wailings—Tibor can't help but hate the bastard for both the idea *and* the better part of the deal.

"Trust me, Bakor, the roads are impassable—I barely made it up the laneway."

"Bah! It's Saturday night, Fidler. Trust me, the dance hall in town may be modest in size, but the talent trumps anything at that Hungarian Hall we used to frequent."

"I'm sure it does; but the storm appears to be worsening."

"For that Cadillac, maybe. Baby, fetch the keys to the Rolls—weather makes little matter when you're riding in luxury!"

"Come, Tibor--"

Esther is positively cooing in his ear—he knows, after a lifetime of nimble escapes from dire situations, that tonight will not number among them.

"—Bakor tells me you're *full* of adventure."

"Take your sister with you—and no, you won't need to freshen up. They *look* dazzling already, am I right, old friend?"

Half of them do, Tibor notes, eyes falling far more often and longer than they should on the sister that was *not* promised to him; clearing his throat he offers his best

"Perfection, Bakor"

as he twirls Esther from his grip, at least as forcefully as the parameters of a dance allow.

She's laughing all the way down that goddamn hall, dancing still, and falling in and out of the arms of an equally enraptured and eternally more beautiful Marie.

Handing him a fresh glass of whiskey, Bakor places his hand firmly on the shoulder Esther just let go of. Together they watch the sisters disappear from view, still walking straight, so long is the passage they travel down.

"I fuck both of them, Tibor."

He nearly spits a mouthful of scotch.

"I just want to be honest with you, my friend. They're both so…*alluring*, yes? I tried to behave; Esther has a…*way*…about her."

"I don't know what to say, Bakor."

Truer words, he knows, he has never spoken.

"Full disclosure, Tibor. As always."

Full disclosure. Tibor scoffs, takes a stiffer-than-usual swig from his glass. Full disclosure, he wishes he was anywhere but *here*—hell, had he all of the pertinent and later-disclosed facts, he might well have left the Caddy in the garage, saved himself both the five hour drive and the headache the whiskey tells him he'll have tomorrow.

Still, he's happy to see his friend, and as always, his curiosity outweighs his penchant for rational thought—and so he's to the bottom of another glass, soon trekking down ridiculously long hallways, headed toward whatever the remainder of the night has in store.

…

Dancing, as it turns out

and *furiously*.

Bakor moves somewhere beside him, here on the floor of the dance floor they dance on, twirling his beautiful bride and resigning him to the less enviable task of twirling Esther.

He does, and with abandon; too much the gentleman to give the admittedly lovely-on-the-inside lady anything other than a great night out. Hell, he'd have preferred the comforts of the mansion their last dance was danced in—still, the Hall is nice and reasonably filled, given the horrors of winter outside.

The drive over—less than five kilometers, he was promised—was terrifying and illuminating in equal measure; Bakor's driver (a decidedly not Hungarian fellow from some faraway place called Tuscaloosa) seemed to have very little respect for the ice coating the roads on the way.

As they passed through the sleepy community of Peace River (surely waking the totality of the town and treating them to visions of a Rolls Royce screaming sideways through mercifully desolate intersections) Maria provided welcome distraction by pointing out the storefronts, apothecaries, split-level walk-ups and banking institutions she—and Bakor, now, by proxy—own.

He's weighing this—the ridiculousness of the wealth he too could share in, the admitted envy regarding the casual ease with which Bakor Zoltan seems to be settling to his new circumstances—against the refrigerator-sized hands she moves to hold both his.

His feet, on instinct, move faster—a blend of intoxication, adrenaline, and anxiety in regards to his latest predicament powers him across the dance floor.

Mercifully, the dance requires a changing of partners—he's a half-step early in the exchange, trading Esther's south travelling mitts and whisperings of

"I'll fix you good, my hot Hungarian champion"

for Maria's lavender-and-cinnamon perfume.

She breathes heavily/beautifully against his chest; the music demands they slow and he *does*, wishing Bakor Zoltan (--who, it's worth noting, looks equally as comfortable gyrating with Esther--) had good news of *this* nature when the phone rang and this ridiculous adventure began.

Maria rests her head on his shoulder; he prays she doesn't pick up the frenzied beating of his heart over the rhythm from well-tested speakers. Seven beats and three lyrics before the music stops, he comes to a powerful realization, lost in the middle of some dance floor, holding tightly onto a beautiful woman.

Should he ever be in this situation again—in some dance hall somewhere, half-promised a forever with someone—he knows that his heart had damn well better be beating like it is right now.

Problems…

Seven weeks later, he's back in the office, staring at the desk once inhabited by architectural prodigy Bakor Zoltan.

He's reflecting on the madness of a freshly concluded holiday season, remembering more of the *good* to come of his journey to Peace River, time gently erasing the stain of uncomfortable memory the way it tends to.

He was happy to see his friend doing so well—and told him so, several times, over the course of his alcohol-fueled visit. He reckons he's still recovering from the hangover—despite the pounding on his brain, he's grateful too for his lapsed inhibitions regarding moderate consumption.

They had saved him, he knows, later that night after the dance Hall—having survived the equally-perilous drive back to the mansion, he'd found himself alone in an apartment-sized (and still entirely too small to escape) bedroom with the *wrong* sister.

Esther had done everything in her power to seduce him—careless application of school bus sized hands over wilting appendages, cat calls and cooing's into eternally retreating ears.

For the first time in a legendary lifetime, Tibor felt himself unable to perform the task he took the most pride in performing, citing an abundance of whiskey as chief culprit.

He hadn't the heart to hurt her—hell, he hadn't the heart to let her hurt him in the way she surely would have should her carnal inclinations be consummated. She took it on the chin and talked all night—Tibor slowly learning that a lack of beauty on the outside has little reflection as to the beauty within.

Still, he was too kind a man to settle or marry for anything other than love—and so, again relying on the effects of alcohol for escape, he claimed the hangover so severe that he must return immediately the next morning.

So subtle was his deception that the poor girl felt as though she still had a chance—hence, his lack of surprise when his phone rings *now*, snapping him from wistful remembering as he sits in the office, staring at the desk that once belonged to the man who got him into this mess.

He knows who is calling

Esther

and he knows why

I'll fix you good, my hot Hungarian champion

and so he lets it ring, doubtless to end in an overtly sexual voicemail the way they *tend* to. She'll call again, he knows, and she *does*—so relentless is her assault that he retreats; before he can breathe

"Hello"

it's

"I miss you, my hot Hungarian champion"

and other madness.

He knows he has to think fast—she's already offering to come up and see him, promises of carnal adventures sending chills up his spine, memories of refrigerator sized hands in places better suited for delicate caresses.

So he feeds her half-truths; how he has to complete a large architectural presentation by week's end—how he's to present said project the very day she's selected for her arrival.

The project is real—the dates perhaps accelerated, and to the point that, should she enlighten Bakor to his rebuttal, surely the lies of presentations on weekends would be exposed. Still, it's worth the risk—should she see him again, he knows he would be expected to complete the task better left unspoken.

So its chills again, amidst gentle assurances that

yes,

"I'd love to see you again"

and

"have to come and see me, *real* soon"

all the while scanning the world outside the office window, praying a solution presents itself.

He's eight assurances from hanging up the phone when, mercifully, one does.

...and Solutions (Or, Near Misses)

"His name was Joe. Joe Geve'b."

Tibor removes his glasses, rubbing doubtlessly weary eyes. We've been talking for hours now, the excitement of potentially completing our collaboration urging us on past reasonable hours. Emil sleeps peacefully in his chair, having successfully absorbed a small lifetime worth of storytelling. I look at him and smile, realizing that these are all adventures he's been privy too—some, many times—before. He's always game to hear them again; I make a mental note to thank him once more for the opportunity he's brokered me, powered by caffeine and bolstered by the fact that I'm hearing them for the very first time.

I scan Tibor's face for a tale; though difficult to read, he has certain facial cues that let me know when he's internalized the coming story appropriately. I pick up my pen once I realize he's ready to go again; as he repositions his glasses, I surmise by the drawing of his breath that this one may not have a happy ending.

"Joe was a taxi driver—Bob, ever a man of sophisticated nuances, had decided it beneath him to drive to work. So Joe came by the office twice a day, *every* day—Bob swore he'd let no one else ferry him about the city—for the better part of a year. Of course, we all got to know him quite well. Joe was a widow, recently, and had been out with us to the dance Hall a couple of times."

He clears his throat, offers a wry smile.

"Joe was looking for love, you see."

I'm writing and putting the pieces together—one benefit of countless hours together, I've learned, is a sort of symbiotic ability to discern where a particular story is headed.

"Let me guess—looking out the window, that day on the phone…"

The smile widens, pushing the frames of his glasses up over his eyes.

"One thing about Joe—

He rests his elbows on the table, leaning forward over a freshly poured coffee—sure sign that it could be awhile before we stop again.

"—he was a handsome bastard."

…

He was a handsome bastard

I write

as Emil sleeps across the table; between sips of coffee, Tibor sets in to tell me the rest.

"He went down to Peace River to see her that weekend; Bakor recognized him from the office, but the bastard kept his mouth shut. They met at a coffee shop, 'by chance' and by design; a coffee shop I'd told Esther I would meet her at, you see. So it was Joe Geve'b to the rescue…they fell in love straightaway. He had access to the fortune once they'd married that summer…from what I'd heard, he was blowing it with abandon."

"Do you ever regret it? Giving up the money?"

"The money was never my motivation, you see. It's not like I was escaping Budapest—money had since ceased to be anything more than a byproduct of doing work I loved. I went up that winter for adventure; I went up to see and old friend…hell, I suppose I went up under the auspices of falling in love. When that wasn't to be, I felt no regret for moving on."

"I'm happy to hear that, Tibor. Besides--

I motion to Emil, snoring, now, and slumped over the table.

"—things worked out in the end."

"My only regret in the matter is how it all worked out for *them*."

I was right—here comes the *sad* part.

"They had a baby girl; from the pictures I've seen, she was blessed to have more of *Joe* in her than Esther. I assume he figured that, once they had a child together, he'd have cemented his claim to the fortune—so he bore down, spent it *faster*."

"Bad investments, gambling…it wasn't long before Esther had enough and ran him out of Peace River. So now poor Joe had an ugly wife, a child to care for, and no access to the money he'd gotten married for in the first place."

"What happened to him?"

"He was back to driving Bob to work—from the front of the cab, to the back, and right back to the front. He saved—scrounged—for another year or so, finally got enough money to buy a plot of land. He told me he wanted to build a little house, with a room for his baby girl to come stay with him every now and then."

He pauses for dramatic effect, or a sip of coffee—I can't quite tell. Beside him, Emil stirs.

"Poor bastard. The land he bought? Was a layer of peat moss on top of clay. He killed himself that spring."

"Jesus."

"Life, my son—

He reaches over to wake Emil, patting him softly on the shoulder as he studies him with near-watering eyes.

"—is a series of near-misses."

I put the pen down, thank the both of them for the time and the coffee, and begin to make my way home. As the speakers sing to me, I stare at a muted sky, wondering with each passing intersection just how many near misses one is allowed in a lifetime of such magnificent adventure. Weighing the odds in my mind, I decide that the time for interview is both over and better suited for transcribing the tales already told; Tibor Fidler, having seen more winters than those to come, deserves to have a collection of his stories to *read*, rather than *tell*.

My foot falls heavier on the accelerator; the significance and the symbolism are not lost on me.

Love. Also, Moose.

Love at first sight is a funny thing, Tibor reckons, sitting atop his throne at the dance hall. His eyes scan the crowd, falling and in love *on* and *with* every attractive female within the walls as he surveys his kingdom,

latest in a line of

because this isn't the Hungarian hall he's used to. No, his tastes are changing, he reckons, and as such he's grown accustomed to expanding his horizons, the search for love taking him to new and decidedly exotic destinations.

Like this, the Moose Temple; a dance club in a nicer area of town; nice enough that the drive over saw the Cadillac windows all the way down and the radio station speakers all the way up. Horst whined a bit, the way Horst tends to when the Saturday night drive is to anywhere but the usual hangout. Still, five minutes after pulling into the packed parking lot and two minutes after seeing his first of five tight floral-printed miniskirts--first in an ever-louder series of colors—Horst stopped whining entirely.

So now it's dancing and feverishly, in between bouts of sitting and surveying, and trying not to fall in love with each and every beautiful thing that salsas past his throne.

And he's failing at this, the excitement of new faces and the bodies attached to them, gyrations in time with beats from better speakers than he's accustomed to; all the while scanning the throngs of tight-waisted dance partners, searching for someone worth *sharing* with.

He's heard that love happens when one isn't looking for it—to Tibor, the expression is the latest in a line of bullshit this decidedly difficult English diction seems so fixated upon.

No, love is all around him, adorned with loud and form-fitting fabrics, writhing to the beat of unfamiliar—but not unwelcomed—music. For every sip of his whiskey, a half-dozen more beautiful, beautifully liberated women enter the well-lined wall of the Moose Temple, latest in a line of potential lovers lounging under the smoke-filled half-light. He strains to see through it, eyes drifting occasionally to the only source of natural light, presented in flashes each and every time the door to the great hall opens, admitting another bevy of potential suitors.

For every ravishingly delightful woman on the dance floor, there's always the anticipation of the *next*, and his eyes drift the way they tend to until…

…they're forced to stop.

A shape darkens the light emanating from the doorway; Tibor is enamored instantly by the way said shape moves, hips swaying gently and yet with purpose as the presence attached enters the hall. He tells himself it's simple curiosity that keeps his eyes fixated on what is still only a shadow, the growing restlessness in the pit of his stomach hinting at something else entirely.

Mercilessly, beats from foreign music settle their tempo, eliminating the last bastion of potential distraction. His senses now otherwise unburdened, Tibor strains his eyes to make out the details of this exotic beauty's face.

And when he does, her features revealed to him under the soft lights of an overcrowded dance hall, abruptly everyone else within its walls simply ceases to exist.

It's not so much the smile that intoxicates him, although surely the flawless veneer of teeth too perfect for the seventies holds a certain and distinct appeal within the recesses of his mind. It's not the struggle her very-much-in-fashion tight floral-printed miniskirt has holding the magnificence of her hips at bay...not the effort her sheer silk blouse makes—and fails—to smother the resplendence of her breasts.

No, it's more the color of her skin, tanned and exotic and something akin to caramel; both shade and ethnicity attached wholly foreign to even him, foreigner in a distinctly foreign land. It has enraptured him in a way he instantly and terrifyingly recognizes no other has before—Jayne Mansfield look-a-likes and would-be army-base brides be damned. No doubt sensing the danger this presents, his body betrays him and breath becomes labored, the now-subtle music from better speakers doing little to sooth him, cascading and presenting sonic support to the sheer pandemonium he finds himself unable to draw his eyes from.

Eyes, like hers, yet decidedly *not*—for the first time in two forevers, counting the each-and-every-day both he and Emil heard that the blue of their blue eyes was superior in shade to all others—he stands humbled by the beauty of almond-*brown* eyes, slightly slanted and standing, still, leagues above the beauty of his on their very best day.

So after some rain sometime, sunlight from soaked asphalt reflecting off of corneas he figured would always just kind of be superior—standing here, dumbfounded, Tibor recognizes that it could have been raining inside the hall for the last tiny forever, and he would not have noticed.

They catch his gaze, those almond-brown, slightly slanted eyes, and the warmth emanating from them damn near doubles him over. Could he feel anything, Tibor might appreciate the single strand of sweat that races the length of his temple, latest in an utterly-failing series of attempts to draw his attention anywhere but the hypnotic centre of her dark pupils and the features surrounding them.

Bewildered, he makes note of the fact that he hasn't bothered to breathe since she glided into the room. When they return, they come labored—harder than they should. Between fitful gasps of air, attempting to power a clearly-overworked heart, Tibor strains his now-humbly-inferior eyes to catalog the curves her body takes as she throws her head back in laughter, attentive to the friends he only now recognizes she's walked in with. Naturally, they're beautiful too, but Tibor forgets the details of their faces instantaneously, focusing instead on her hips and the way they kiss the fabric of her painfully tight skirt.

She moves in circles when she moves—or maybe those hips move in circles and the rest of the body follows…he can't tell the way he's lost in the study of her. She moves within the circle of her friends as well—all laughing together, all probably attractive, though he knows there is no way that any two of them could equal her beauty. He can't hear the music over the pounding of rushing blood to his temples and areas south, but he figures that she's probably swaying her body to the rhythm of whatever notes are permeating the hall.

Were he able to decide anything at all, Tibor would doubtlessly decide that he has to have her; were he able to move he may begin to, and in the direction of her dimly-lit table. He wants to—really wants to—but he's decidedly unable to function. He's thankful that, from his vantage point in the smoke-filled room, she has yet to spot him; he's reasonably sure that, should she discover him leering at her from the northern most corner of the Moose Temple, any further pursuit would be dashed.

Tibor doesn't doubt his own irresistibility—could he feel his face, he's reasonably sure that his mouth is currently agape, and the amount he's perspiring at the very sight of her has him questioning his inevitable forthcoming introduction. He resigns himself to his fate just the same—he knows the thought of not approaching her is the only thing potentially more terrifying than the approach itself.

Somewhere behind him, Horst begins to question where he's headed—this he makes out, barely, over the din buzzing in his brain. She's up from the table and dancing, the sound on the speakers decidedly pleasing to her and her cohorts. Her body moves with a fluidity that attacks him—he's aware of both, his friend's hand on his shoulder, and the fact that he's almost tripped over a table leg only because his determination tells him that he needs to appear somewhat coherent should he have a hope of speaking to her.

She laughs, and he's nearly close enough to hear it, hear it over the pounding of his heart. Her laugh is infectious, clearly, as her circle laughs too—dancing and writhing together on the floor. He's close enough to make out their individual features, these four women; he can't tell if discerning their looks is impossible because they're *less* beautiful or because he simply doesn't care.

He approaches the edge of the dance floor, a lion on some African plain—his proverbial water buffalo takes no notice. He chides himself for the poor analogy, fails to think of an animal worthy of comparison. At this he fails too, stumbling in both mind and body and wishing at once that the copious amount of liquor in his system were decidedly *more*. He needs courage in a way he's never needed it before, strangely…this isn't shooting horses or surviving the crushing oppression of Communism, yet still he finds the sensation unfamiliar. So he moves as best as he can, dancing and breathing harder than he has any right to, moving methodically and as-coolly-as-he-can towards this ravishing beauty and her circle of friends.

Painfully, he's in front of her far faster than he's prepared to be, and any breath he'd managed to collect on the dance over is torn from him.

And she's even more beautiful, cruelly, closer than she was from afar. The soft light hits her impossibly high cheekbones at angles he'd not realized exist, his time as an architect be damned. He's grateful that his feet don't fail him as her almond eyes descend from the lights on the dance floor to fall upon him, and in the instant it takes for her to acknowledge him, his confidence tells him that she's equally enamored.

She hesitates for a moment, misses a beat in the music. Or at least Tibor perceives this to be true, his anxiety appreciating the momentary respite. Appreciates it, until he realizes that she's studying the surely-troubled features of his face at least as intently as he's studying hers…as if painfully hoping for a flaw that isn't there, a mar on the façade to somehow make her *real*.

Her gaze is both intimidating and enticing—feeling deliriously inadequate, he tells himself to turn away, is something less than surprised to discover he can't. The music stops, maybe, or he just stops listening, counting the colors in her eyes as she dances, all the while hers remain locked until—

--Horst's hand explodes violently across the small of his back, ushering in a return to the music on the speakers and the movement of the dance floor and everything, cruelly, that had stopped mattering the moment she laid eyes on him. Freed from his beautiful captivity, Tibor whirls and is about to chastise his clearly-inebriated comrade, when from the corner of his still-somewhat-paying-attention eye he spots her laughing, moving in tandem with her friends and away from the dance floor.

He panics the way he *has* been; the only thing more intimidating than the thought of her close to him is she not close to him.

And so he follows, explaining in his best shouting-voice to a clearly inebriated Horst that the pursuit is of paramount and all-consuming importance. He seems to understand, Horst does, because all at once his urgings to retreat back to their previously-established vantage point is replaced with his urgings to stop at the mini-bar on the way to her table, somewhere in the dark of the far wall she retreats to.

The mini-bar be damned, Tibor powers past, brushing off Horst's latest and alcohol-fuelled back slap on the way to her. His heart starts thumping in tandem with the

thump

thump

*thump*ing of the music, and driven in a way usually reserved for escaping the crushing oppression of Communism, he soldiers past the drunken hordes and dancing peasants on his way to her. He appreciates the jungle analogy he pictures himself in as he moves, ducking writhing shapes and masses under the now-flashing lights, somewhat aware of them, foliage under the canopy of stars as he closes on his elusive prey.

He spots her in the distance, his eyes chasing hers as they scan the dance floor he approaches from, settled as she is at the back of a particularly intimidating booth full of not-quite-equal beauties. Mercifully, Horst notices this as well, and his backslapping is replaced by impressively audible panting, somehow heard over the din of the jungle. He's breathing something about being in love with

"that one"

but

that one

isn't the one he's enamoured with, and so he brushes it off with disdain usually reserved for back-slapping.

The music keeps

thump

thump

*thump*ing, and his heart is following suit and *louder*, now, and all of a sudden he's at the edge of their booth and barely breathing.

She locks eyes with his, and in between counting the colors of her eyes, he opens his lips to say

"Hello"

in his *deepest* voice, but she beats him to it, and her

"Hello"

first has more sex in it.

So he stammers his reply, unable to remove his eyes from her eyes, and the rumbling in his stomach and somewhere south tells him he's fucked far before he stops to think, and about how much he'd really *like to*.

…

There are words they share, after the

"Hello"

and although they matter, he's reasonably sure they don't matter as much as the word they exchanged to land him *here*, in the booth he stalked to approach her, while somewhere to his left, Horst does his best to entertain the four friends that surround them.

And the four friends are nurses, and he's learned, so is she, and her name is Lilia, and instantly, Lilia is his favorite name.

He's always liked the name Tibor, but in the telling of it, he has decided it is as insignificant as the rest of him, beside her in the booth. They order drinks—drinks to break ice that has already melted, and by the time the second round comes around, he's feeling as intoxicated as Horst clearly is.

They talk in hurried, hushed tones, about the kinds of things that two people violently invested in one another talk about. She tells him she's from the Philippines, and instantly, the Philippines is his favorite place. She speaks of how she came here to become a nurse, and they share stories of their experiences in this strange land, the commonality of being decidedly alien only serving to attract them to one another more. Tibor tells himself its fate, meeting her here tonight, a half-second before he leans into what is quickly becoming his favorite ear, whispers

"It's fate, meeting here tonight"

and lingering the way he knows she wants him to. His good ear tells him that there's laughter, somewhere in the booth around him—doubtless Horst is charming her friends, nurses all, the way he miraculously seems to when necessity demands; Tibor can't really tell and can't really care, because Lilia is leaning into him, and her breathing is matching his breathing.

They breathe together for a moment or maybe twelve, and he recognizes that it's the first silence between them since he braved the jungle of the dance floor to sit in the booth beside her, and he's realizing that the silence is entirely comfortable and is about to be comforted by the realization when her lips explode across his, and he realizes he can't think anything, at all.

He's kissed before…hell, he's been told that, in no uncertain terms; he's relatively good at it. Still, his heart beats as though this is his very first time, and the time he takes to trace the corners of her lips with his does little to lessen his fear that his kiss is nowhere near good enough for the mouth he's kissing.

He buckles down and gives it his all, there in the booth at the Moose Temple, while beside him, the laughter and the music and the-everything-other-than-this melts away, lost as he is in the tasting of her. He stops only when breathing demands it, and his face doesn't move far from hers and their eyes not at all, and Tibor knows a half-second before the music makes sense again that he's not having his way with *this* one.

Marriage. (Or, the Beginning of a Brand-New Book.)

Marriage is a funny thing, Tibor thinks, looking at the woman who is now Mrs. Tibor. Hell, he thinks many things, standing at the periphery of the stairs, basking in the adulation from the few people in this strange land he knew to invite, and feeling at ease with absolutely *none* of them. Save the one he stands beside; the one who is now his bride and *for real*—and although he's promised things and purchased the rings to promise them with before, he's never really invested the way he realizes he's invested now.

He looks at her, his bride, and any-all-other thoughts melt away the way they tend to when he catches her eye; instantly he's reassured and revitalized and ready—ready for all of the adventures to follow the somewhat grandiose adventures of his life so far. They take their first steps as husband and wife; behind him the church bells may-or-may-not be ringing, and what he can't-hear-doesn't-care. The church and the bells are behind him—behind him the way the crushing oppression of Communism and the life he left on the other side of the damned water he crossed to get here is, the life and *new* and *better* he starts now, each sure-footed step telling him the pain it took to get here was worth it.

Flower petals fall around them, received and recognized and strewn by and from the friends he thought would fill the void of the family that couldn't; seeing hers—now, technically, his—the elation of his new life recedes just enough to allow him the longing to have any surviving on the Fidler side there to see him on his big day. Horst does his best, two steps down and to his left—Tibor stops staring at his wife just long enough to catch him crying as he bombards them with an unceremoniously large array of confetti. Still, the sadness falls akin to the petals, and by the bottom step he's focused solely on sweeping Lilia Fidler off her feet, literally, and into the waiting and warm leather of the Cadillac he calls home.

And in a turn of the key, they're off to the next, *home* and the new one that waits the way his life does; speeding down a street on a better side of town, Tibor's glance travels from her to the road ahead and back to her again. He's already thinking of names for the son or sons he's sure to have—he smiles when he thinks of the twin that should have been here today with him, and how *Emil* is one hell of a good strong name. The road curves, and he takes the turn with a grace and fluidity he's spent the first thirty years of his life honing—when the pavement straightens again, he offers his new bride a grin, knowing that, should his story ever be told, the next chapter will be a hell of a lot more exciting than the ones that came before.

Too Many Winters, but--

I close the book I write in when I write, and I offer Tibor a smile of my own.

I could spend the next one hundred afternoons listening to his stories—I'm sure he has hundreds more to tell. Part of being a writer means knowing when to finish a story—to leave the reader wanting more. I tell him this, and he just nods, smiling that megawatt smile and telling me

"I trust your judgement,"

both of us realizing that this man knows far more regarding the Art of Storytelling than I could ever hope to.

I stand from the table we sit at when I write, there in the living room, and Emil rises to join me. We shake hands, Emil and I—and then I offer Tibor an embrace and a

"Thank you"

and his

"Thank *you*"

back is better too. As I walk out the front door, my mind is racing, already assimilating the days' worth of information, plugging in time frames and telling myself to elaborate *here* and pull back *there*. I'm reaching for the door handle of my car, and as I turn back to wave at this great man, who, as always, is waving goodbye from the doorway—a simple kindness not readily practiced in today's world—I'm gripped by one distinct, recurring thought.

A thought that dances in between concerns regarding pacing and phrasing, a thought that gives me pause as I study the lines on Tibor's cheeks as his smile continues unabated, hand waving furiously.

A thought that, really, has been attacking my consciousness ever since I met the man in that diner some two years and two-thousand-two-hundred-twenty-four stories prior.

I linger, offering a wave of my own, and then I retreat to my car, power it on, and drive all the way home.

The thought stays with me.

It's there when I brush my teeth; I see it when I study my own face in the mirror, the last thing I see reflected on the glass before I turn off the light.

I've typed it on this page two-thousand-two-hundred-twenty-four times; it's buried in between every single line on every single page of this book.

--I hope I do your life justice—

Tibor Fidler;

it has been an honor and a privilege.

Photo Gallery

Emil (left) Tibor (right) approx. 19 years' old

Passion for painting

Emil (left) Tibor (right) serving in the army.

Tibor and Blascka.

Tibor & Lilia Valleramos, Married Jan 30. 1971

Tibor's Father, Tibor Ference   Tibor's Mother, Racz Anna

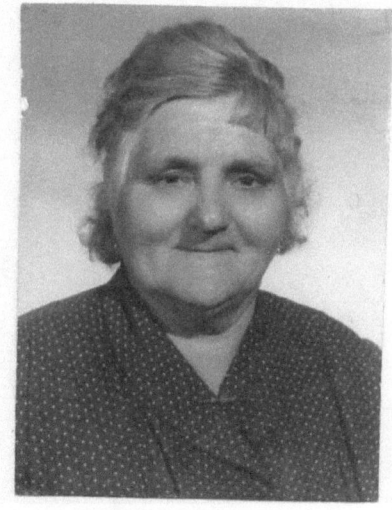

Tibor's Sister, Piroska Fidler

Piroska Fidler

Tibor (left) Emil (right) approx. 2 years' old

Tibor (left) Emil (right) approx. 18 years' old

www.ingramcontent.com/pod-product-compliance
Lightning Source LLC
Chambersburg PA
CBHW030433300426
44112CB00009B/986

NEGATIVE THEOLOGY AS JEWISH MODERNITY

EDITED BY MICHAEL FAGENBLAT

Indiana University Press
Bloomington and Indianapolis

This book is a publication of

Indiana University Press
Office of Scholarly Publishing
Herman B Wells Library 350
1320 East 10th Street
Bloomington, Indiana 47405 USA

iupress.indiana.edu

© 2017 by Indiana University Press
All rights reserved

No part of this book may be reproduced or utilized in any form or by any means, electronic or mechanical, including photocopying and recording, or by any information storage and retrieval system, without permission in writing from the publisher. The Association of American University Presses' Resolution on Permissions constitutes the only exception to this prohibition.

⊚ The paper used in this publication meets the minimum requirements of the American National Standard for Information Sciences—Permanence of Paper for Printed Library Materials, ANSI Z39.48-1992.

Manufactured in the United States of America

Cataloging information is available from the Library of Congress.

ISBN 978-0-253-02472-5 (cloth)
ISBN 978-0-253-02487-9 (pbk.)
ISBN 978-0-253-02504-3 (e-bk.)

1 2 3 4 5   22 21 20 19 18 17

CONTENTS

Introduction. Delineations: Negative Theology as Jewish Modernity — 1

1. The Limits of Negative Theology in Medieval Kabbalah and Jewish Philosophy — 30
   SANDRA VALABREGUE

2. "No One Can See My Face and Live" — 48
   KENNETH SEESKIN

3. What Is Positive in Negative Theology? — 62
   LENN E. GOODMAN

4. Negative Theology as Illuminating and/or Therapeutic Falsehood — 85
   SAM LEBENS

5. "My Aid Will Come from Nothingness": The Practice of Negative Theology in *Maggid Devarav Le-Ya'akov* — 109
   JAMES JACOBSON-MAISELS

6. Secrecy, Apophasis, and Atheistic Faith in the Teachings of Rav Kook — 131
   ELLIOT R. WOLFSON

7. Two Types of Negative Theology; Or, What Does Negative Theology Negate? — 161
   SHIRA WOLOSKY

8. Khoric Apophasis: Matter and Messianicity in Islamo-Judeo-Greek Neoplatonism — 180
   SARAH PESSIN

9. *Negative Dialectics, Sive* Secular Jewish Theology: Adorno on the Prohibition on Graven Images and Imperative of Historical Critique — 198
   IDIT DOBBS-WEINSTEIN

Contents

10. The Passion of Nonknowing True Oneness: Derrida and Maimonides on God—and Jew, Perhaps   213
MICHAEL FAGENBLAT

11. Jewish Negative Theology: A Phenomenological Perspective   238
DAVID NOVAK

12. Mysteries of the Promise: Negative Theology in Benjamin and Scholem   258
AGATA BIELIK-ROBSON

13. Can Halakhah Survive Negative Theology?   282
DAVID SHATZ

14. The Stylus and the Almond: Negative Literary Theologies in Paul Celan   304
ADAM LIPSZYC

15. "Gods Change": The Deconstruction of the Transcendent God and the Reconstruction of the Mythical Godhead in Yehuda Amichai's *Open Closed Open*   323
TZAHI WEISS

16. The Politics of Negative Theology   335
MARTIN KAVKA

Contributors   357
Index   361
Citation Index   377

NEGATIVE THEOLOGY AS
JEWISH MODERNITY

INTRODUCTION

Delineations: Negative Theology as Jewish Modernity

The idea that God has essential attributes or predicates—such as existence, life, knowledge, power, goodness, or mercy—is implied throughout the Bible, embraced by the Talmudic rabbis, and problematized in medieval Jewish thought. In the modern period, denial of essential divine attributes increases dramatically among Jewish thinkers, especially throughout the twentieth century, when it spreads from theology to secular forms and contexts such as philosophy, ethics, aesthetics, literature, politics, and history. The marked increase in prominence, rigor, and intensity of Jewish negative theology in recent decades has modified the very topography of Jewish thought, reshaping its theological contours and enabling it to grow on secular, even atheist ground. Influential theologians such as Rav Kook, Yeshayahu Leibowitz, and Franz Rosenzweig made very different versions of Jewish negative theology central to their views. But so too the Jewishness of the work of secular and even atheist writers, artists, critics, and philosophers has been frequently associated—by the individuals themselves or by others—with a conception of Judaism as a *via negativa*.

The modern association of Judaism with a *via negativa* regards the distinctively Jewish features of a thought or work as involving the negation, denial, or refusal of its own ultimate grounds and thereby the discovery of mysterious ruptures constitutive of its own legitimacy, authority, and even "identity." *To the extent* that Jewishness and Judaism play a significant role in their respective work, a conception of Judaism as negative theology is often detected in major writers such as Kafka, Celan, and Jabes; abstract expressionists such as Barnett Newman and Mark Rothko; philosophers such as Cohen, Adorno, and Levinas; and literary critics such as Bloom and Benjamin.[1] The purpose of this volume is to investigate how the perception and self-understanding of Jewish thought in recent times has been determined by this alliance with negative theology. What historical and conceptual reasons gave rise to radicalized and sometimes secularized forms of negative theology as a distinctive marker of modern Jewish intellectual history? Do radical forms of negation still allow for compelling articulations of Jewish thought? Or has the modern pairing of Judaism and negativity reached a point of exhaustion? And if so, what comes after Jewish negative theology?

1.

A word, first, on what is called negative theology, which, following the Latin tradition, conventionally renders the Greek *apophasis*, meaning "unsaying" or more simply "denial" or "negation" (as for Aristotle, *On Interpretation* 17a25). Modern scholarship on medieval Jewish philosophy speaks of the "negative descriptions" or "negative attributes" that are used by an author to challenge positive theological assertions, though the medieval authors do not themselves use the phrase *tᵊārīm šlīlīyim*. Derrida thought it significant to acknowledge that "negative theology" comes to us predominantly in a Greco-Latin idiom and therefore that one should be wary of assuming that all forms of negation of divine attributes share common structures, goals, and methods.[2] Such caution is prudent, though it goes without saying that Greek thought influenced medieval Jewish and Islamic thinkers no less than their Christian counterparts, especially in instances where they verge negative under the influence of the Arabic Neoplatonic tradition.[3] The attempt to distinguish Jewish negative descriptions from Greco-Latin negative theology is therefore a complex matter, making all the more welcome attempts to unfold this distinction in various ways.[4]

What is usually called negative theology can be parsed into ontological and epistemological variants. In denying affirmative theological attributes, theologians of the *via negativa* argue that descriptive characteristics such as living, loving, good, or wise are not essentially constitutive of God's nature; or else they deny that the essential divine nature can be known to us as such.

In the ontological version, negative theology involves the discursive practice of denying divine attributes *in order to speak more truthfully* about God, either by unsaying (apophasis) untruths about God or by deploying forms of theological speech that eschew predication. Aristotle suggested that prayer was an example of a nonpropositional logos, as happens in "rhetoric or poetry," since prayer is "neither true nor false" (*On Interpretation* 17a5). Recent phenomenology of religion has attempted to develop the thought by emphasizing the difference between prayer as a form of *address* (speaking *to* God) and prayer as a descriptive or representational discourse (speaking *of* or *about* God).[5] It is questionable, however, whether theology can be entirely reduced to forms of discourse such as prayer and poetry that supposedly suspend referentially descriptive language. It can be objected that prayer *implies* predication, even when it is reduced a pure form of address, and therefore quickly surrenders its theological advantage over representational discourse. Yeshayahu Leibowitz, a prominent exponent of radical Jewish negative theology, argued that even the implied predications of prayer should not be understood as informatively representing God's nature but as theologically warranted on account of being *instituted* forms of theological language whose significance is *entirely* normative and nondescriptive.⁶ This move, however, slides into theological noncognitivism, thereby landing the negative theologian not closer to truth but outside the entire domain of possible truths. The significance of religious language and the motivational basis of religious praxis risk collapsing into conventionalism or even behaviorism. This is an ironic result, since negative theology begins as a radically critical form of theological praxis but here ends up in a dogmatic form of traditionalism.

More often, austere ontological versions of negative theology veer toward skepticism as a form of religious life, for they demand an active mental and linguistic iconoclasm that persistently rules out predicating essential attributes of God. The internalization of skepticism into the heart of theological conviction has sometimes wrongly been confused with atheism, since atheism also denies everything that can be predicated of God. The comparison is crude, however, for conventional atheism treats the existence of God as a predicate that can be denied ("God is nonexistent"), whereas negative theology denies that God has predicates.⁷ Alternatively, conventional atheism affirms a determined concept of God in order to deny its instantiation; as Blanchot says, "we carry on about atheism, which has always been a privileged way of talking of God."⁸ By contrast, the negative theologian denies the concept of God, creating space within the discourse of theology for internal critique, an incessant displacement of meanings, and a range of skeptical praxes oriented by religious fidelity to the truth of God.

If the skepticism associated with the ontological version of negative theology differs in the respect noted from conventional, conceptual atheism, it nevertheless resembles a rarer form of *nonconceptual* atheism.⁹ Nonconceptual atheisms deny not merely the existence of the Divine but the divinization of existence; they deny all absolute conceptions of ultimate reality and for that reason converge on ontological versions of negative theology, sometimes to a hair's breadth, for they become likewise implicated in skeptical praxes and discourses that incessantly contest their own grounds.¹⁰ It is surely for this reason that negative theology has played a crucial role in recent continental philosophy, whereas in the analytic tradition, "negative theology has been no more than a minor strand."¹¹ But if negative theology resembles a certain nonconceptual atheism, it steers clear of naturalism by refusing to identify the divine Will with natural causes or with the totality of causal relations that naturalists believe can explain the entire realm of intelligibility. Yet it does not resort to supernaturalism, for it denies the analogy of God with an immaterial cause operating externally on the world. Negative theology calls for alternative strategies for understanding the relation between faith and scientific knowledge.

In contrast to ontological versions, epistemological accounts of negative theology do not deny that God "has" essential attributes but that such qualities can be known to human beings through usual modes of acquaintance. Divine reality exceeds the capacities of cognition. But if knowledge falls short, this does not exclude the possibility of approach or even contact with modes of divinity that cannot be captured in discursive or cognitive form. Accordingly, whereas ontological versions of negative theology incorporate radical skepticism, epistemological versions tend toward mysticism. Thus Maimonides, the most influential medieval Jewish exponent of the *via negativa*, says that one comes "nearer to the apprehension of Him, may He be exalted, with every increase in the negations regarding Him," leaving the question open as to whether this acquired proximity involves some contact with, or illumination of, the divine presence; whereas Gikatilla, in his thirteenth-century Kabbalistic classic, compares the positive descriptions implied by the divine names to garments that must be disrobed in order to behold the truth of God, thereby suggesting an intimate, erotic encounter stripped of all descriptive embellishments.[12] The two versions of negative theology are often entwined within one author, however, as the reception history of Maimonides's negative theology makes plain.[13]

2.

As a mode of skepticism or critique of the possibility of a logos appropriate to the truth of divine oneness, negative theology is as old as philosophy itself: the "unwritten doctrines" of Plato's middle period, like the later *Parmenides*, already suggest as much, while Neoplatonic, Gnostic, and influential early Christian thinkers likewise attest to theology as a form of auto-critique.[14] A Jewish predilection for the *via negativa* can be detected in Philo of Alexandria, who has even been called "the Father of negative theology."[15] This overstates the case, however. Philo's immense confidence in the power of the Logos attenuates his incidental discussions of the incomprehensibility of God.[16] In light of the motivating assumption of this volume, namely that negative theology becomes a shibboleth for Jewish thought only in the modern period on account of specific historical developments, Carabine's view of Philo's role in the emergence of the *via negativa* is of particular interest. Not only does Philo provide "no developed theory of the unknowability of God," but he is inhibited from adopting such a theory precisely because of his Jewish theological convictions: "it would have been but a short step for him to take, but his Jewish faith would have made it almost unthinkable."[17] This is a judicious view of the incongruity between ancient Judaism and the negative theology of late Hellenistic philosophy.

If there is almost no Jewish negative theology in antiquity, it is commonly supposed that there is an eruption of negativity in the medieval period. Two forces are often regarded as decisive. The first is the philosophical pressure exerted on the pervasive anthropomorphic language of the Tanakh, which the educated elite of the medieval period finds at odds with the appeal of abstract conceptions of divinity.

Metaphorical and allegorical interpretations of biblical anthropomorphism indeed constitute a type of negation of biblical literalism, abstracting from the plain meaning by negating its ostensible descriptions in order to reconcile the text with scientific or philosophical conceptions of divinity. Moreover, in some authors, such as Ibn Paquda and Maimonides, the negation of biblical anthropomorphism seems to lead inexorably to further, more radical negations. When this happens, more abstract conceptions of God such as "first," "wise," or "powerful" come to be regarded, or discovered as, in truth, no less anthropomorphic than biblical images of God's walking, speaking, or outstretched arm.[18] Negative theology here emerges as a type of immanent critique of rational theology, as a theological critique of a rational conception of God.

A critique of biblical literalism does not, however, amount to, or even demand, the negation of divine attributes.[19] More often than not, the critique of positive descriptions of God found in Scripture lead to rational or mythic accounts of the divine, as in Saadia Gaon or the Zohar, both of which heartily affirm the eminent attributes of God and our capacity to understand the divine nature through intellect or symbols. Philosophical or folk-philosophical critiques of biblical anthropomorphism are perhaps necessary conditions for negative theology, but they are far from sufficient.

A second, more precise way that negative theology was introduced into medieval Jewish thought involved the transmission of Neoplatonic thought to Jews via the *Arabic Plotinus*.[20] This medieval Neoplatonism played a pivotal role in reshaping numerous theological concepts such as those of a Creator or the immortality of the soul. For our purposes, the decisive factor is the contribution of medieval Neoplatonism to Jewish conceptions of *divine unity* and thus to the very notion of Jewish monotheism. By virtue of Neoplatonic views of the "One beyond being," the notion of God's oneness becomes both a philosophical conundrum of the highest order *and* an opportunity to distance Jewish theology from the speculative and scientific dominance of neo-Aristotelian thought. The Neoplatonic elevation of the One beyond being, beyond intellect, soul, and nature, introduced *a critical distance* between, on the one hand, the source of intellect, the foundations of knowledge, and the grounds of being and, on the other hand, medieval metaphysics and a literal understanding of sacred Jewish texts, both of which were seen to contravene the monotheistic truth of divine oneness.

The Neoplatonic conception of divine unity yields numerous interpretations, but we can identify two models, namely, oneness as wholeness and oneness as uniqueness. Both models generated discourses and praxes of negation as a means of fidelity to the divine One. The notion of a whole implies component parts and therefore contradicts the principle of God's indivisibility. And since language divides reality into items or entities, there can be no language of the whole and no language adequate to the whole. Moreover, the absolute whole, by definition, is not an entity within reality but an ever-expanding concept, since *qua* whole it must include all that is *not yet* revealed or created. The whole therefore eludes affirmation by virtue of identifying "one" with "all," including the still to come, and can accordingly be approached only by negating what has already been affirmed of it.[21] On the other hand, stipulating that God's oneness means uniqueness rather than wholeness raises its own problems. The unique is by definition inaccessible through concepts and words whose intelligibility depends on their common currency. Every concept or descriptive representation of the unique betrays its uniqueness, a paradox that goes back to the *Parmenides* but became central to Jewish thought through its assimilation of the Neoplatonic One beyond being to the mono of Jewish monotheism. A fundamental shift in understanding the nature and purpose of religious language and, arguably, in religious experience, can be detected wherever the Neoplatonic One beyond being is invoked in the guise of God's "unity," "indivisibility," or "oneness." This shift consists of critical and skeptical reflection on the powers of language and cognition, leading to various modes of unsaying everything said in the name of God.

Two main avenues are open to a thinker in the face of cognitive and linguistic limits imposed by the One beyond being: the ineffable, with its silent intuitions, contemplations, and inexpressible illuminations; and skeptical critique, with its strategic failures to face up to the ultimate term of its own faithfulness. We thus come upon two types of medieval Jewish negative theology, a unitive-intuitive type that involves silent contact with the ineffable and a critical-skeptical type whose purpose is to draw attention to the constraints of theological language and religious experience.[22] Most medieval Jewish Neoplatonists, like their Christian and Islamic counterparts, belong in the first camp (Isaac Israeli, Ibn Paquda, Ibn Gabirol, the Kabbalists), while Maimonides is often, if controversially, held up as the champion of the latter.[23] Whereas the first, predominant type of negative theology served to *supplement* positive theological assertions, augmenting faith and the presence of God with mystery and incomprehensibility, the second type aims to *separate* God from all positive predication.[24] A reading of Maimonides as articulating this second, radical type of negative theology has an illustrious pedigree, from Aquinas and Eckhart to modern Jewish advocates such as Shlomo Pines, Yeshayahu Leibowitz, Kenneth Seeskin, and, most recently, Josef Stern. Stern's systematically skeptical interpretation argues that for Maimonides, intellectual abstraction suffers from the anthropomorphic structures of a subject/predicate syntax that belies the truth of divine unity. The view of Maimonides as a radical or skeptical negative theologian is contestable, however, and Lenn E. Goodman offers an important criticism of it in this volume. Moreover, if the Latin reception supports it, the Judeo-Arabic reception presses Maimonides closer to an account of negative theology as the achievement of ineffable knowledge attained, or at least envisaged, through contemplative-unitive intellection.

Some, often Catholics, claim that the "radicalization" of negative theology is in fact a degradation that fails to account for the distinction between the *via negativa* and the *via eminentiae*.[25] The latter view proposes that there are "supereminent" senses to descriptions such as "first," "cause," "good," "exists," and so forth that are at once incommensurable with the ordinary meanings of such predicates and at the same time apposite for theological purposes, for they orient thought toward more perfect ideas than do lesser predicates and thereby draw us closer to the strictly inconceivable truth of divine perfection. Critics reply that the notion of a supereminent sense equivocates. Either such concepts share their meanings with worldly instantiations and have therefore not been sufficiently negated, or else they differ categorically from the worldly sense of such concepts and therefore forfeit their claim to a reserve of supereminent meaning.[26] Whether Maimonides himself articulates or else inspires the radical view, he clearly sets the tone for a Jewish negative theology in which fidelity to true oneness introduces skepticism into the heart of philosophical monotheism. As mentioned, the shift from negations that supplement to negations that separate God from all positive predicates can even blur the boundary between faith and faithlessness, or theology and atheism, since faith shaped by radical negation denies that there is any adequate way to refer to God with any certainty at all. Most modern Jewish thinkers who have entered this debate (Derrida, Elliot Wolfson) belong to this radicalized camp. Like Leibowitz and Stern, and despite major differences in their methods, goals and formulations, these thinkers reject the prospect of a supereminent theology in favor of a skeptical bracketing of all attributions.

3.

As Sandra Valabregue demonstrates in the first chapter of this volume, the overwhelming uses of negation in medieval Jewish thought serve a higher theological purpose in which nonknowledge is integrated into affirmations regarding the nature of God. This bids us to view the modern penchant for critical and skeptical forms of Jewish negative theology as a distinctly recent development. Why does the radical version of negative theology become the mark of a distinctly Jewish sensibility not only within the field of theology and the philosophy of religion but throughout modern Western culture? We can point to three conspicuous developments.

The first involves a generalization of the central problem of negative theology in the form of the modern epistemological problematic. Whereas negative theology arises for the ancients and medievals in view of the desire and difficulties of conceiving the One, the transcendent source of reality (the Platonic Good, the

Neoplatonic One, the Christian Father, the Islamic Allah, the Jewish Yhwh), for the moderns, an analogous problem plagues *all* objects individuated by virtue of being representations in the mind of a subject. For the medievals, negative theology is a way of articulating the failure of language and thought with respect to the one ultimate source of reality, and representation is a problem only in so far as it lays claim to represent God as One. For the moderns, each (and therefore every) act of representation is implicated in a problematic relation with the unique object to which it refers (or seems to refer, wants to refer, etc.). In modern times, each mental act presents the possibility of failing to refer to the very object it intends. The unity of the object divides in the modern period into its presentation and representation, its reference and sense, its noesis and noema, and so forth. The object divides into itself and its representation, an epistemological gesture that unwittingly draws all the problems of theological reference into the heart of philosophy, for it now becomes questionable whether language and thought refer, and are able to refer, to the very things they claim to be *about*.[27] The medievals found the relation between thought and the transcendent reality of divine oneness uniquely problematic. Modern thinkers, however, often doubt the relation between any representation and any individual bit of reality, with each object presenting itself doubtfully, as amenable both to knowledge and the vagaries of mental representation.[28] As Derrida observed, the impossibility of definitively closing this gap for *any* object gives the modern problem of representation an audible if not always heard echo of negative theology. Where representation and reality come apart and positive discourse falters in securing its referential claims, one finds echoes, traces, or analogues of negative theology.

The crisis of representation in the modern age is intricately, if somewhat accidentally, related to the perception and self-understanding of Judaism in the same period. Problems of representation and its referents are fundamental to modern *philosophy* from Descartes through German Idealism, as to phenomenology through analytic philosophy and cognitive science. During the same period, however, new and austere *theological* interpretations of the biblical ban on representation become increasingly associated with Judaism and indeed frequently embraced by Jews themselves.[29] The obvious equivocation here between mental representations, on the one hand, and idolatrous representations, on the other, hardly matters, for among philosophical theologians in the modern period, especially Jews and Protestants, there is widespread agreement that idolatry is a mental state. For modern Maimonideans, for example, mental representation is precisely idolatrous representation.[30] The prohibition on representation is thus a second element in the newly forged alliance between Judaism and negative theology in the modern period. The widespread, general philosophical problem of representation that saturates modern Western intellectual culture intersects with the prohibition on representation construed belatedly as a problem of theological cognition. The ground thereby becomes prepared for a notionally Jewish prohibition on representation to characterize every discourse—literature, art, history, psychoanalysis, ethics, theory of translation, etc.—where representation is at once necessary and ineffectual in attaining its object, and for the latter reason prohibited. In this way, Jews and non-Jews alike came to associate Judaism, Jewish culture, and sometimes even Jews themselves, with the prohibition on representation, interpreted as a principled iconoclasm motivated by an impossible fidelity to the unique referent of their faith and desire.

Finally, we should recall the influential German philosophical construction of this Jewish prohibition on representation, for it sets the stage for what will become, in the twentieth century, a decisive transvaluation of the uses of Jewish negative theology. Protestant philosophers, most famously Kant and Hegel, had correlated the positivism of Jewish law—a dubious conception emphasized by Luther, Spinoza, and Wellhausen, among others—with their perception of the insurmountable discord and distance they perceived between the Jews and God. In their view, the irrational positivism of Jewish law, its brute givenness and opacity to reason, expresses the Jewish conception of God as an alien, opaque Will. This generally derogatory view of the Jewish religion as wholly heteronomous stood in conflict with Kant's project in the First and Second Critiques. Almost grudgingly, however, Kant acknowledges that this very theology anticipates the account of the sublime presented in the Third Critique. "Perhaps there is no more sublime passage in the Jewish Book of the Law than the commandment: Thou shalt not make unto thyself any graven image," he wrote, because this proscription attests to "a presentation of the infinite" which, though "merely negative" with respect to the true idea of the infinite, affects the imagination by saturating it with sensibility and thereby "expands the soul."[31] Tension and displeasure, awe and respect, and above all the nonpurposiveness of nature characterize both the Kantian sublime and Kant's view of Judaism. This marks a crucial moment in the transvaluation of Jewish negativity, for on this view—which is far from laudatory, given the desideratum of a religion of reason—Judaism is founded, through the prohibition on representation, on the impossibility of unifying the understanding.

In developing his account of the sublime, and of the Hebraic prohibition on representation as a negative response to the sublime, Kant drew heavily on Mendelssohn. The latter had illustrated Burke's idea of the sublime through the example of biblical poetry, arguing that many Psalms arouse an intuition of realities that "cannot be adequately intimated by means of any sign and cannot be presented as they are by any image."[32] Hegel, however, bypasses Mendelssohn's sympathetic construal of the Jewish sublime while intensifying Kant's emphasis on the Jews' failure to conceive the God they worship. Judaism thereby becomes a religion of self-alienation. For Hegel, failure to understand God, expressed in enslavement to the Law, casts the Jews into a "fatal unholy void" where Spirit cannot be reconciled with Reason or mediated in the historical form of the State.[33] For most philosophers and historians of the immensely influential modern German Protestant tradition, Jewish negativity was *rigid*, a theological dogma whose sublime specter was confined to the form of brute, positivist law that cannot be realized in historical forms, for these require mediation and representation.

In the course of the twentieth century, however, Hegel's account of the inexorable reconciliation of the real and the rational looked increasingly malignant and was met with widespread resistance and repudiation. The "unholy void" of Jewish theology that found no place in the dialectic of historical reason was slowly transformed into something of a holy void. Mendelssohn had described the appropriate response to the sublime as "a holy shudder," and if this was elicited in response to an idea of perfection more perfect than any representation, in the twentieth century it was not perfection but the unrepresentable that aroused a shudder. Here is the third development contributing to the prominence of modern Jewish negative theology. Whereas nineteenth-century thinkers understood the Second Commandment as warrant for a rationalization of Judaism, as Spirit appeared in ever more violent and oppressive historical forms in the course of the twentieth century, influential thinkers and writers embraced the negativity of Judaism as an elusive mode of spiritual critique that resists representation, refuses reconciliation, and defies communication.

The unsympathetic construction of Judaism as a religion of sublime but nonintegratable negativity was thereby resignified. A holy shudder before the unholy void of history became a characteristically Jewish way of resisting the violent optimism of the modern European imagination. The perceived shortcomings of Jewish thought in the long nineteenth century came to be viewed in the twentieth century as a major source of the power of postmodern critique, the Jewish refusal of representation dialectically becoming an affirmation of the claims of the unrepresentable in the midst of modernity. This is how Levinas regarded Judaism, as a way out of the violence of historical reason, a way "backwards, through the very door by which Hegel thinks we enter it."[34] So too, as Dobbs-Weinstein argues in this volume, Adorno's sense of historical critique emerges directly out of this commitment to a transvalued affirmation of the impossibility of reconciling spirit with history.[35] The German-Jewish negative theologies of Scholem and Benjamin, Celan and Kafka, are variants of the same trajectory, as other chapters in this volume show. Moreover, modern Jewish theologians such as Rosenzweig and Michael Wyschogrod embraced Jewish negativity for similar reasons, though to quite different purposes. In rejecting the Protestant-Idealist view of Judaism as a religion in which God is distant and transcendent, they emphasized the presence of God *as* the negativity that nurtures Jewish life. The prohibition on representation becomes, in their view, not a prohibition on representing the transcendent exteriority of the divine but the normative impossibility of reflecting the absolute immanence and excruciating intimacy of God in the midst of Jewish life. For Rosenzweig, negative theology involves a coming to terms with the divine Nothing that circulates among us, as that which we cannot know except through living.[36] David Novak's phenomenological account of Jewish negative theology in chapter 11 makes a comparable argument.

The transvaluation of the sublime discord of Jewish existence was adopted not only by an array of Jewish thinkers, many of whom are examined in this volume, but also by thinkers such as Blanchot and Lyotard.[37] The criticism that the likes of Kant and Hegel directed at Judaism was thereby converted from a modern deficit to a postmodern surplus. Jewish and non-Jewish thinkers alike grasped the core contribution of Jewish thought in terms of transcendence, unrepresentability, and otherness that correlated, more faithfully than reason or understanding, to the excesses of the twentieth century. A complex history entwining the generalized crisis of representation in the modern epistemological tradition, the association of the failures of representation with the Jewish prohibition on images, and the deployment of the unrepresentable for the sake of critiques of historical reason thereby fashioned negative theology into a fulcrum around which Jewish thought was transvaluated from derision to respect in the course of postmodernity.[38]

4.

Can we specify modern Jewish negative theology further? Are there ways of distinguishing Jewish negative theology from its proximate rivals, such as the Neoplatonic One beyond being, Christian mystical theology, Hegel's dialectical negativity, or the nothing of which Heidegger speaks? It is unlikely that Jewish negative theology could be systematized or brought in line with a paradigm through which examples could be classified. But perhaps there is something approaching what Agata Bielik-Robson calls a swerve or clinamen of thought.[39] Harold Bloom, no friend of Adorno or Levinas, agrees that Jewish negation is non-Hegelian in the sense that it offers no redemptive prospect of reconciling the rational with the real or reason with history. He further suggests that Jewish negativity cannot be put to "destructive use" for the sake of the disclosures of being-as-a-whole, as is the case for Heidegger. Even less likely will Jewish negation yield silent disclosures of divine being, as Thomistic negation avers, or saturate us with pure gifts to which the only proper response is "Eucharist" (that is, "thanksgiving"), as is the case for Jean-Luc Marion. Rather, Bloom argues, and in so doing perhaps unhappily comes close to rivals such as Adorno, Benjamin, and Levinas, Jewish negation "always . . . reenacts the ambiguities of the Second Commandment" by supposing a thorough "dualism" between experience and truth.[40]

This is a helpful start to speculating on a distinctively Jewish amalgam of the prohibition on representation and negative theology, though it must be further distinguished from the unsurprisingly gnostic cast of Bloom's account. This can be done by observing that the "dualism" of Jewish negative theology transpires entirely *within* the phenomenal realm. It is not a dualism of spirit and matter, still less of mind and body; it is a dualism within the world, an elusiveness within the concrete. Mobilizing the abstract negations of Greek and medieval metaphysics, modern Jewish thought finds divine uniquenesses amid creation, prohibiting not only representation, which reifies, but also the *reductio ad unum*, which culminates in intuitive comprehension or rapture.

A Jewish mode of negativity would be, in this view, concrete but fluid, incarnate yet elusive.[41] These are near-contraries that are difficult to combine, and yet it seems that not only does much modern Jewish thought attempt to do so, but in so doing it reiterates, in a negative idiom, something of the incarnational monotheism of the Bible.[42] Jewish negation is not abstract, and tropes such as those of "transcendence" do not conjure an ultimate reality that stands over and against, or above and beyond, the immanence of the world, in another realm.[43] Rather, Jewish negativity is at work *within* the immanent order, as *aniconic immanence*, *olam ha-bah* not as another world but as this world becoming other, different from the given one, "nonbeing as not-yet-being," as Martin Kavka says of Hermann Cohen's messianic negative theology.[44]

As many of the chapters in this volume argue, modern Jewish negative theology is consistently carnal *and* aniconic. Rosenzweig is perhaps the boldest inflection of such a view. In his view, Jewish nonknowing encompasses the distance between the Jewish people and God; Jews cannot see God because God is too close, dwelling amid the people in their not knowing and thereby becoming expressed in the course of life without becoming an object of knowledge. But Scholem's interpretation of the Lurianic account of the divine contracting and fragmenting is another, more anarchistic inflection of a similar conviction. The shapes of Jewish negation mark neither absence nor abstraction but the incessant displacement of the divine amid creation, liberating creation by renewing the exile of God from Godself into the world. This is "God's absolute mobility," as Scholem calls it.[45] This is a negative theology different from both the epistemological version that fosters mystical intuition and the ontological version that induces skepticism. We might call it a "negative panentheism." It is a Jewish negative theology entirely different from the rigid conception of Jewish negation propagated by the Protestant German tradition.[46] Celan's poem attests to the "dualism" to which Bloom vaguely gestures.

ONCE
I heard him,
he was washing the world,
unseen, nightlong,
real.

One and Infinite,
annihilated,
ied.

Light was. Salvation.

"One and Infinite" are not disclosed, not beheld, not grasped, and not even skeptically suspended, but undergo a *tsimtsum* into the world, contracting into the real like silence contracted into a stutter. The contraction of silence into language *communicates* the One and Infinite itself, its *I* (*ich*) as annihilated (*vernichtet*). This is not a contraction into what *is* or even *was* but into what must have "once" become without settling into being, thus in a sense without ever having been: it was annihilated before it was *ied* (*ichten*).[47] It is a becoming once, a becoming unique, through which the whole, the world, becomes washed, lustered. And yet this washing is only "heard," its luster remains "unseen." How can this negation of One and Infinite result in *Rettung*, Salvation, Rescue, or Recovery? Perhaps by fostering the belief that "Light was"—the way a blind man's belief in vision might foster more sensitivity in his touch, hearing, smell, and taste. This is not the salvation of sight but a salvation born from the intensification of blindness illuminated by the vision of another.

In the same vein, the theme of negative theology affords a wider, more fluid conception of "Jewish thought" than might often be presumed. Moses de Leon, one of the great masters, understood "the superiority of the human over the beast is nothing [*'ayin*]" (Ecclesiastes 3:19), to mean that the human soul is distinguished from that of a beast because of the *'ayin* it alone shares with God.[48] In the Zohar, he attributes the highest part of the human soul to the divine aspect called *Who?* (*Bina*=*Mi?*=*Who?*), and so implies that selfhood is an enigmatic questioning that cannot be resolved. For negative theologians, to be in the image of God is to expose oneself to one's own unrepresentable, shape-shifting uniqueness, to put oneself in question and thus become *Who?* to what one knows oneself to be. Seen through the mobile shapes of negation, a different history of "modern Jewish thought" comes into view as a community of those who have *'ayin* in common. Kafka's famous quip, "What have I in common with Jews? I have hardly anything in common with myself," is emblematic of the unbounded relations that Jewish negative theology can yield.[49] That is why in this volume the Maggid of Mezerich stands alongside Theodor Adorno and Rav Kook alongside Jacques Derrida. Negative theology as Jewish modernity calls for the negation of identity in accounting for Jewish intellectual history.

5.

The volume opens with a chapter by Sandra Valabregue that describes a major theological fault line marking the passage from the medieval to the modern. Valabregue tells a cautionary tale of the Jewish passion for negativity and transcendence. Discerning a range of negative theologies in the medieval period, when Jewish thinkers first begin to think theologically with the help and hindrance of philosophical concepts, Valabregue proposes that a "comprehensive" or "uncompromising" negative theology demanding the total negation of human knowledge is marginal within the medieval landscape. It emerges in a certain interpretation of Maimonides—and by no means the most prevalent one—and in the Kabbalistic thought of Nachmanides, for whom concealment (*ha-ne'elam*) becomes the principle appellation of God's essence. But on the whole, as Valabregue shows, Jewish philosophers and mystics, including those writing under the sway of medieval Neoplatonism, describe their experiences and interpret the Torah with reference to a modest mode of negativity that is "integrated" into the positive program of knowing, understanding, and cleaving to God. Rather than standing against or undermining theosophical commitment, medieval Jewish negative theology for the most part complements and completes the cataphatic. As many of the contributors to this volume demonstrate, the same is not the case in the modern period, where tropes of negativity such as otherness and transcendence overwhelm the positive commitments many Jews are prepared to make to an ultimate term of knowledge and desire.

Since this volume takes seriously the hypothesis that negative theology affords something of a mobile paradigm for Jewish modernity, it opens with conceptual arguments that can help us understand this swerve. Kenneth Seeskin (chapter 2) argues that the disjunction between divine reality and human concepts has its first formulation in the biblical idea that no one can see the face of God and live. Why should a benevolent God destroy someone who looks at him? Seeskin's answer is that the destruction at issue here involves the devastation of thought in the face of the uncontainable, overwhelming reality of God. The biblical idea is philosophically articulated by Maimonides, Descartes, and Levinas, all of whom explain how it is that thought runs into ruin on the shore of divine reality. Seeskin's argument prompts one to think that biblical monotheism is distinguished from paganism not simply by the substitution of one god for many but by the introduction of a type of autoimmune condition into thought. Monotheism introduces a stimulus that precipitates thought's turning against itself, eating itself up, and attacking itself. No one can see the face of God and live because the face of God is a catalyst for thought destroying itself, for consciousness breaking apart, the way direct vision of the sun is blinding. The core of monotheism narrated in the Bible in metaphors of concrete, physical destruction is philosophically elaborated as the devastation of consciousness's capacity to conceptualize. Seeskin thereby offers an original way of understanding the distinct contribution of Jewish monotheism, germinating in the Torah and mushrooming in philosophies that describe the human experience of autoimmunized abnegation. Monotheism is not a view of divine isolation, but of a divine desolation of the power of consciousness. Yet as Seeskin explains, this admission does not imply that God "really is" destructive or malicious but only that our conception of divine reality is essentially unreliable. We should, he therefore urges, adopt a stance of humility when speaking of God, as did Moses and Job in light of their respective near-death experiences of divine reality. Institutional religion can then be reclaimed on the basis of a positive vision of society founded on fragile foundations that correct against fundamentalism.

Lenn E. Goodman (chapter 3) offers a clear alternative to Seeskin's account of the destructive value of negative theology. According to Goodman, there is far more positivity to Jewish negative theology than Seeskin implies. Goodman argues for an important corrective to the dominant reception of Maimonides's account of negative attributes. Whereas the Rambam is famously said to deny all predications of God, including "relation," as Shlomo Pines translates the term *nisba*, Goodman proposes that relation is far too broad a concept and even a misleading one. If there were no "relation" between God and the world, as Pines and his followers suggest, Maimonides would seem to contradict himself within a matter of sentences and, worse, would undermine his own persistent affirmation of God as Creator, of there being purpose to the Torah, and of the intelligibility of the created order—all of which imply a "relation" between God and the world. Offering alternative translations of *nisba* as kinship, link, connection, or comparison, Goodman argues that these narrower yet more precise concepts suggest a very different account of "the scope of his [Maimonides's] apophasis," which allows for positive approximations to knowledge of God's wisdom and purpose. Even so, Goodman proposes that a corrected account of what is positive in Maimonidean negative theology still requires "a new ontology and axiology" that overcomes the excessive intellectualism of the Rambam's approach. Spinoza, he suggests, paves the way toward this new ontology and axiology, because he sees both intellect and matter as equally significant aspects of the one substance while proposing that even these are but two of God's infinite aspects.

Samuel Lebens (chapter 4) provides an analytic philosophical perspective on the viability of Jewish negative theology. Agreeing with Alvin Plantinger's rejection of negative theology for violating its own constrains by describing God as indescribable, Lebens argues that there is nevertheless room to make conceptual sense of what he calls "the apophaticism of experience." He offers three ways of exploring the analytically viable space that remains. The first draws on Graham Priest's account of dialethism, the idea that noncontradiction is not quite the sacrosanct law of logic it is usually taken to be and that, rather, sentences or propositions can be simultaneously true and false. The second introduces a distinction between the ascription of fundamental properties to God and the ascription of nonfundamental properties, arguing that if we preserve this distinction we can have our apophatic cake (at the nonfundamental level) and eat it too. But it is in a third sense that Lebens offers an original contribution. Building on Wittgenstein's idea of falsehoods that are capable of illuminating something, he argues that apophatic experience, the experience of an indefinable presence in everyday life, disturbs religious life and unsettles the knowledge of God that believers tacitly assume. As a way of speaking *about* God, he concedes that negative theology cannot be true on pain of contradiction, or even useful to certain ways of thinking of philosophical theology. Even so, if apophatic experience fails to convey truths it nevertheless illuminates and makes salient the tacit ineffable knowledge religious people have of God. In Lebens's view, this does not compel us to accept absurd conclusions or reject the premises that led us to the illuminating falsehood; rather, it leads us to a place of epistemological and theological humility. The position allows for a more sympathetic rereading of Maimonides and Saadya, among others. A plausible reading of Maimonides, for example, could maintain that negative theology is patently false if formulated propositionally and discursively, even as apophatic experiences illuminate the limits of our knowledge and thereby imply epistemological and theological humility.

The three previous essays defend the viability of Jewish negative theology today, even if they characterize it in interestingly different ways: Seeskin's radical view of monotheism as negation, Goodman's view of negativity as admitting of relation, Lebens's almost Popperian view of negativity as the infinite horizon of theological falsifiability. It is reasonable, I think, to conclude that negative theology plays a *rationalist role* for these philosophers, one that enables Jewish theology to enter the blazing lights of modernity—dispelling superstition, anthropomorphism, fantasy and so forth—without lapsing into the false achievements of atheism. They are historically informed essays, but their purpose is less to explicate than to point to reasons for defending, and ways of articulating, a Jewish theology in which negativity is the traction enabling travel in the desert of the modern theological imaginary. And yet they were not the first to sense this exigency. As James Jacobson-Maisels (chapter 5) shows, at the dawn of the modern period, and perhaps not by chance, the Hasidic movement was nurtured by a font of theological negativity that still today quenches the souls of traditional and neo-Hasidic devotees. This font is the Maggid of Mezericz, disciple of the founder of the Hasidic movement, the Baal Shem Tov, and the principal transmitter of Hasidic mysticism to the "holy fraternity" (*hevra kadisha*) of Rebbes who would spread and develop the Hasidic way. Bearing the centrality of the Maggid in mind, it quickly becomes apparent that negative theology has been immensely attractive to a wide array of modern Jewish theologians, including many who never read Descartes, Kant, or Hegel. Jacobson-Maisels offers a close reading of a sample of the Maggid's influential work, *Maggid Devar le-Yaacov*, which exposes the systematic and pragmatic role of negativity at the very origins of Hasidic theology. As he shows, not only does the Maggid provide novel midrashim that have abiding pertinence for the practice of not-knowing-God and not-being-God, but this practice is particularly suited to the experience of alienation and disenchantment that marks modern life. Here we find precedent, from traditional quarters, for viewing negative theology as an essential tool in cultivating a Jewish response to modernity by embracing God's own negativity.

If the Maggid of Mezericz opened the Hasidic font of mystical negativity, Rav Abraham Isaac Kook, the first Ashkenazi chief rabbi of Israel and an immensely influential figure in twentieth-century Israeli mysticism, widened its channels. As Elliot R. Wolfson (chapter 6) shows, for Kook the experience of not-knowing God becomes entwined with mystical historicity, the acknowledgment that ultimate religious experience is riven by the concrete entanglements that become inescapable in the modern world, of faith entwined with heresy and truth with unbelief. Wolfson delves into Rav Kook's mystical writings and discloses his Kabbalistic meontology, a clandestine Torah or revelation of the nonbeing of all that is. One of Kook's innovations, as Wolfson shows, is to divulge this secret to a wider public than is commonly supposed to know it, a disclosure based on the conviction that in modern times there is theological truth in atheism and a margin of heresy within the experience of faith. The secret that inheres in the world can no longer be kept within the confines of the law—though it is found there abundantly, which leads Kook to his distinct form of ethnomysticism—just as the divine mysteries of the natural world can no longer be cordoned off from athiests and heretics. Rather, in the modern period, as Rav Kook sees it, the world itself betrays the clandestine traces of divinity, manifesting the *complexio oppositorum* that in the medieval period remained beyond the world. Accordingly, as Wolfson shows, the limits between faith and heresy, truth and unbelief, are transformed by Kook in the modern period from antitheses to potentially mutually enriching experiences. Dissidents and heretics such as Spinoza, Jacob Frank, and Ernst Bloch hover in the wings of this transmigration of the divine secret, even as it makes historically viable the sort of Ultra-Orthodox theology of Zionism that Rav Kook's son, Rav Tzvi Yehuda, politicized with such success.

A persistent thought and a common approach taken by several of the contributors in this volume suggests that there are two prevalent ways of thinking of negative theology, but that only one is compatible with the project of Jewish philosophical theology, especially as it is thought of in the modern period. The distinction between "Two Types of Negative Theology," as Shira Wolosky calls it in chapter 7 of this volume, turns on the difference between negating the world for the sake of a higher Being or the One beyond being, and negating the prospect of attaining to the One for the sake of the world in which differences are glorified as "particularized" by the divine Will, as the medieval put it, and thus inherent in the created order. Wolosky elucidates these two versions of negative theology, one that longs to return back to the One beyond being and thereby negates the world, and another that negates the attempts to unify being by desiring and relating to differences within the world. This useful distinction allows her to get a foothold where angels might have feared to tread. Despite the unquestionably syncretistic developments in Platonic and Neoplatonic monotheism, the distinction outlined by Wolosky is of great explanatory value in accounting for major differences among writers who employ the tropes of negative theology for rival purposes. Levinas's work is an exemplary case of the second, "ethical" type of negative theology that negates the unity of metaphysical concepts in order to embrace—to desire, love, and respect—the multiplicities of difference presented in human relations. In contrast to the vertical negative theology of the ontological tradition that seeks to ascend the hierarchy of being by retracing the grades of emanation from the Many to the One and thereby overcome difference, Levinas's work proposes to release thought from the violent fantasy of transcending the world by turning to the multiplicity inherent in the goodness of creation. By negating the illusion of unity, Levinas answers Nietzsche's call to discard the mask of a metaphysical world behind this one and develops a nonhierarchical negative theology that addresses the demands of postmodern ethics and—or through—the Judaic legacy.

Sarah Pessin (chapter 8) endorses a similar distinction to the one Wolosky develops. For Pessin, however, the distinction manifests when the exigency of negation runs up against positive religious doctrines that enjoin us to imitate the truth to which they refer, as for example in core Christian beliefs about the presence of God, be it as hypostatic Person of the Trinity or as historically incarnate flesh on the cross. Such limits, she argues, do not constrain all varieties of negative theology. The case of the medieval Jewish poet and theologian, Solomon Ibn Gabirol, offers a characteristically Jewish way, she thinks, of releasing thought from the grip of presence by imitating the unlikeness of God, becoming unlike oneself in a practice oriented toward transcendent goodness that never settles into being itself. Idit Dobbs-Weinstein (chapter 9) extends this line of thinking as it manifests in what she calls the secular Jewish negative theology of Theodor Adorno. She offers a reading of *Negative Dialectics* in which Adorno's antitheology is construed as a rejection of the Christian *via negativa*, which she argues aims at consolation and salvation, and she find in its place an iconoclastic refusal of all concepts that naturalize and dehistoricize injustice. Jewish negative theology is the praxis of iconoclastically liberating the singular demands of the historical hour from generic concepts that dampen them, demands heard by secular Jewish theology in the singular voices of the oppressed and the suffering. These chapters thus provide a far-ranging interpretation of the ban on images as a prohibition on *unio mystica*, and are thus starkly at odds with much Christian negative theology.

David Novak (chapter 11) argues that Jewish negative theology emerges only in relation to the concrete historical experience of revelation that the Jewish people underwent, for the only way to speak of God, whether positively *or* negatively, is in relation to direct experience. This is reflected in the phenomenology of Jewish life that supplicates to God on the basis of recollections of God's past redemptive action for the sake of the Jewish people. The crucial point, he suggests, is that the limitations of Jewish knowledge concerning God already suppose a great deal about God, for example what God has done in the past and, more importantly, what God promises to do. Like G. E. Moore's answer to the philosophical skeptic, Novak answers the theological skeptic by holding up his hand; his left hand, no doubt, with tefillin wrapped around it. Liturgy is an elaborate ostensive demonstration of what a Jew believes on the basis of direct historical experience; it allows for the endless play of negativity but always only in a supporting role that confirms the liturgical covenant of Israel. Even so, what is that supporting role? Novak proposes that negative theology pushes liturgical thought beyond the only admissible evidence there is, that of historical experience, toward experiences not yet given, the God no eye has seen. Within the liturgical parameters that Novak proposes for a phenomenological approach to Jewish thought, the role of negative theology is to orient prayer toward the fulfilment of the eschatological promises that have been given but not yet realized. Liturgical negative theology is experienced in eschatological prayer.

The liturgical sense of Jewish negative theology that Novak brings to the fore makes one less surprised than one might otherwise have been in reading Agata Bielik-Robson's reconsideration of the famous correspondence between Scholem and Benjamin concerning the negativity of Kafka's world. Bielik-Robson (chapter 12) offers a completely fresh approach to this highpoint in Jewish modernity. Rising to the formidable challenge of contesting Moshe Idel's characterization of this German Jewish theology as but a veiled Protestantization of God as *deus absconditus*, she demonstrates that Benjamin's misunderstanding of Scholem is based on his failure to distinguish between the prospects of God's absence and God's promise. In her view, Scholem's celebrated notion of "the nothingness of revelation" is not the reflex of Judeo-Protestantism, as Idel alleges, but articulates a messianic promise of the abiding antinomianism of revelation. Kafka's works are like scripture for the moderns, thought Scholem, but not because God is entirely concealed or absent in them but because we find there traces of God's antinomian promises, sparks of laws that still bear promises of overcoming the natural and political orders of the world, even if these sparks remain dormant in modern life. Whereas Benjamin, she suggests, rejects the idea that the law might be reactivated by the fulfilment of its dormant promises. For Benjamin, all that remains is to reconfigure the fragments of revelation in ways that allow for new narratives of exodus that do not congeal into yet another form of law. The disagreement between Scholem and Benjamin is thus marked, but without collapsing Jewish negativity into the Protestant *deus absconditus*, for in neither case is it a matter of a leap into the holy terror of an absent God that leaves room for nothing but grace. Like Novak, Scholem and Benjamin understand Jewish negativity as an eschatological spark that promises to illuminate our historical coexistence in this world, even as this spark is cast among the grave shadows of modern life.

The crucial question raised by Bielik-Robson's account of Jewish negativity as the antinomian promise of a different world concerns the role of Jewish law: does it guard or obstruct the promise of mystery that jolts the world through the nothingness of revelation? David Shatz (chapter 13) and Adam Lipszyc (chapter 14) offer divergent answers to this question. In Shatz's view, "the attempt to undermine Halakhah via the alleged inscrutability of God's reasons" involves a grave misdiagnosis of the Halakhic process. Shatz's strategy is sophisticated. Rather than argue against a strong account of negative theology, Shatz maintains that Halakhic commitment does not depend on an antecedent understanding of the nature of God. But is not Halakhic practice the hubris of cleaving to the Will of God, and therefore bound up in strong positive theological commitment? No, says Shatz, who then proceeds to argue that even without the pretense of knowing God's Will one can justify not only Halakhic practice but even reflective Halakhic decision making, for the teleological knowledge of God implied in the latter can either be substituted by formal Halakhic exegesis or else, in the relatively small number of cases where formalism falls short, the divine Will can be constructed on the basis of a virtuosic view of authoritative Halakhic expertise. The authority of Halakha does not derive from putative knowledge of God's Will but from a type of virtuoso familiarity with the Halakhic system as a whole and an ad hoc commitment to the teleology of the particular law at hand. If a penetrating negative theology runs the risk of reducing Halakhic practice to a form of behavioristic habit, in fact the risk is slight because negative theology hovers over the Halakhic system without ever quite penetrating it, leaving the Halakhic practitioner with a sufficient margin of rationality, experience, and teleology to justify his or her existing ways and maneuver through new challenges.

Shatz's answer to Bielik-Robson, then, is to deny that the nothingness of revelation penetrates Halakhic life, a move that also explains the immunity of Halakha to the antinomian negativity of revelation. In stark contrast, Adam Lipszyc argues that the negativity of revelation penetrates not only to law, but also throughout the secular discourses of modernity. For Lipszyc, there is no immunity from the negations of intelligibility, purpose, trust, and morality that the Holocaust brought upon us, and therefore, as Paul Celan showed, our lot is to bear these negations as rigorously as we can. By carefully analyzing two poems by Celan, Lipszyc shows how literature distorts our experience of language in such a way that presents us with our enduring losses, losses concealed amid the familiar, assured, everyday language in which we traffic with ease. In Celan's poems we find a breaking of our linguistic vessels, God defaced among fractured symbols, distended into the poem and transformed into a shadowy communication that prizes faith over understanding. Tzahi Weiss (chapter 15), however, suggests a very different way to think of how negative theology transforms into secular literature. In Yehuda Amichai's *Open Closed Opens*, he finds an impetus that is commonly called apophatic, for it unsays the positive predicates attributed to God such as power and wisdom. But Weiss discerns in Amichai's poems the contestation of a distinctly rationalist Maimonideanism, one with which the poet would have been familiar from his Modern Orthodox German upbringing. This opens a new way of understanding negation. Recalling medieval Kabbalists such as de Leon who were also unsatisfied with the rational God of Maimonides, Amichai's passage beyond philosophy eschews rarefaction. In his work, the falsehood of a powerful God is negated not in the name of an abstract orientation to a God beyond power but to the concrete truth of God's powerlessness, "a god who is seen but doesn't see so I can lead him around / and tell him what he doesn't see." With Amichai, who was a close reader of Celan, negation assumes a fabulous, wry intimacy in which the ideal of breaking language apart is itself negated for the sake of the simplicity of what is. With Amichai, *sod* is *peshat*.

In Jacob Taubes's meditations on the respective political authorities of Moses and Paul, Martin Kavka (chapter 16) finds a contribution to a politics of negative theology. This suggestive phrase refers not to the negation of secular power in the name of a *deus absconditus*, for that would dialectically authorize a clerical absolutism in which negativity is exchanged for brute power, as Maimonides's political theology arguably does. Nor does it refer to the infinite deferral and therefore practical termination of secular power in the name of the one and only true Power that no eye has seen. Rather, excavating *The Political Theology of Paul* by recourse to earlier essays collected in *From Cult to Culture*, Kavka discerns an account of the demos as the ultimate mystical authority of any political structure and law. This affords Taubes, in Kavka's view, a mystical view of democracy that is antiliberal and at the same time antiauthoritarian. Taubes's "transtheistic" politics is a type of political theology Spinoza might have favored: *vox populi sive vox Dei*, a pantheistic politics of the people *as* the dissensual voices of God. In the final chapter, Kavka thereby ties up some lose threads in the chapters by Seeskin and Goodman. Negative theology does not need to abscond to the inscrutability of a political will that transcends popular wisdom. On the contrary, it finds political expression in the dissensus of the people constituted through the epistemic limitations each brings to the other.

Jacques Derrida's work has long been related to the apophatic, though the emphasis has been largely on Christian, Eastern, or Kabbalistic modes of negation. My contribution, chapter 10, aims to show how Derrida's conception of his own problematic Jewishness, an apophatic inwardness that was neither avowed nor abandoned, reverberates throughout his thought by enlarging and reiterating the problem of the perplexed, as Maimonides conceived it. I argue that Derrida's de-negation of identity is a correlate an experience of God that he shares with Maimonides. If it is true that for Derrida "every other is wholly other," while for Maimonides there is only one wholly other, it is also the case that the emancipatory effects of theological negation are entangled with an obscure experience of the heritage of Judaism. This entanglement makes it impossible to avoid the radical openness of the truth of theology, for this amounts to an orientation toward a true oneness that cannot be confined to this or that discursive field. Perhaps this goes some way to explaining why negative theology appears across the spectrum of Jewish modernity.

Notes

1. This list is neither complete nor uncontroversial. Figures such as Kafka and even more so Newman denied that their work was expressive of a particularly Jewish self-understanding. Hence the need to emphasize that it is *insofar as* and *to the extent that* critics and connoisseurs are able to show that a conception of Judaism is nonetheless operative in their work that such a conception is of Judaism as negative theology. Scholem's regard of Kafka is illustrative of this, as is the contested reception history of Kafka's Jewishness more generally, and so too is Steven S. Schwartzchild's attempt to theorize a Jewish conception of art in his "Aesthetics," in *Contemporary Jewish Religious Thought*, ed. Arthur A. Cohen and Paul Mendes-Flohr (Philadelphia: Jewish Publication Society, 1987), 1–6. Menachem Lorberbaum similarly, albeit briefly, links Rothko's abrogation of representation and figuration to Jewish negative theology in *Dazzled by Beauty: Theology as Poetics in Hispanic Jewish Culture* [in Hebrew] (Jerusalem: Ben-Zvi Institute, 2011), 120. For a relevant, historically critical

discussion on the negativity of Jewish art, see Kalman P. Bland, *The Artless Jew: Medieval and Modern Affirmations and Denials of the Visual* (Princeton, NJ: Princeton University Press, 2001), esp. 51–58.

2. Jacques Derrida, *On the Name*, ed. Thomas Dutoit, trans. David Wood (Stanford, CA: Stanford University Press, 1995), esp. 51–53.

3. For a succinct outline of the *Arabic Plotinus* and its impact on medieval Jewish thought, see Joel L. Kramer, "The Islamic Context of Medieval Jewish Philosophy," in *The Cambridge Companion to Medieval Jewish Philosophy*, ed. Daniel H. Frank and Oliver Leaman (Cambridge: Cambridge University Press, 2003), 38–68; and for more detail on Neoplatonism in Maimonides, the most celebrated medieval Jewish exponent of negative theology, see Alfred Ivry, "Neoplatonic Currents in Maimonides' Thought," in *Perspectives on Maimonides*, ed. Joel L. Kraemer (Oxford: Littman Library, 1991), 115–140.

4. In particular, see the essays in this volume by Agata Bielik-Robson (chapter 12), Idit Dobbs-Weinstein (chapter 9), Sarah Pessin (chapter 8), and Shira Wolosky (chapter 7). For an argument distinguishing Maimonidean from Neoplatonic negation, see Josef Stern, *The Matter and Form of Maimonides' Guide* (Cambridge, MA: Harvard University Press, 2013), e.g., 45, 121, 189, 205, 246–247.

5. The distinction is already explicitly invoked by Maimonides, who compares liturgical praise that speaks about God to gossip, see Moses Maimonides, *The Guide of the Perplexed*, trans. Shlomo Pines (Chicago: The University of Chicago Press, 1974), 1:59, 141–142

6. For example, Yeshayahu Leibowitz, "Of Prayer," in *Judaism, Human Values, and the Jewish State*, ed. Eliezer Goldman, trans. Yoram Navon, Zvi Jacobson, Gershon Levi, and Raphael Levy, rev. ed. (Cambridge, MA: Harvard University Press, 1995), 30–36.

7. In this respect, conventional atheism is subject to a similar criticism to the one Kant directed at the ontological argument for the existence of God, namely, that the argument treats God's existence as a superior predicate to God's nonexistence. For Kant, God's existing (like all existing) would be a matter of the exemplification of a concept rather than the attribution of a property or the possession of a predicate. Since in his view such an exemplification is impossible, God can be only an object of faith not knowledge. But for this reason there can also be no epistemologically warranted denial of God.

8. Maurice Blanchot, *The Writing of the Disaster*, trans. Ann Smock (Lincoln: University of Nebraska Press, 1986), 90.

9. Nonconceptual atheisms emerged in particular in France, in the climate of post-Nietzschean and post-Heideggerian antiessentialism and antifoundationalism. For thinkers such as Althusser, Bataille, Blanchot, Foucault, and Derrida, secular humanism was deeply mistaken in naturalizing the individual, the site of introspection and consciousness, as the ground of all meaning, prompting them to contest this humanistic credo in a similar fashion (and often through direct inspiration) to the contestation of positive conceptions of God as the ground of all meaning. Whereas conceptual atheism exchanges a determined concept of God for an alternative foundation to knowledge and meaning, antihumanist atheism denies that those alternatives succeed in grounding meaning. Hence: "Between the man of faith and the man of science, there is little difference: both guard against destructive chance and reconstitute the requirements of order; both appeal to a constant which they pray to

or theorize about; both are . . . conservers of eternity, always in quest of something stable, and pronouncing the word 'ontological' with confident fervor (Blanchot, *Writing of the Disaster*, 90). For a discussion of nonconceptual atheism in modern French thought, see Stefanos Geroulanos, *An Atheism That Is Not Humanist Emerges in French Thought* (Stanford, CA: Stanford University Press, 2010); on Blanchot in particular, including his relation to apophatic theology, see Kevin Hart, *The Dark Gaze: Maurice Blanchot and the Sacred* (Chicago: The University of Chicago Press, 2004).

10. Thomas A. Carlson calls this resemblance the "apophatic analogy" according to which nonconceptual atheism can neither be distinguished from, nor identified with, negative theology; see his works *Indiscretion: Finitude and the Naming of God* (Chicago: The University of Chicago Press, 1999); and *The Indiscrete Image: Infinitude and Creation of the Human* (Chicago: University of Chicago Press, 2008).

11. Nicholas Wolterstorff, "How Philosophical Theology Became Possible," in Oliver D. Crisp and Michael C. Rea, eds., *Analytic Theology: New Essays in the Philosophy of Theology* (Oxford: Oxford University Press, 2011), 156–168, at 168. Wolterstorff argues that the demise of classical foundationalism facilitated the emergence of analytic theology by creating a space of epistemological pluralism that legitimizes diverse metaphysics. He thinks that continental philosophers remain stuck in Kant's dilemma of justifying knowledge on the basis of a comprehensive critique of reason and therefore refrain from entering into a pluralistic epistemological and metaphysical terrain. This is not an unreasonable portrayal though it omits acknowledging how profoundly influenced the modern continental tradition has been by negative theology. There is something approaching a division of labor. If "analytic philosophical theology has been almost entirely kataphatic rather than apophatic" (168), continental philosophical theology has been almost entirely apophatic rather than kataphatic. Jewish philosophical theology has until recently been practiced in a more continental and (therefore?) more apophatic vein, as this volume makes clear. Whether this is entirely the result of historical reasons to do with the status of Jews and Judaism within European philosophy, or whether there are theological-philosophical reasons for it, remains to be seen. Sam Lebens's essay (chapter 4) stands out as a timely attempt to redraw these lines.

12. Moses Maimonides, *The Guide of the Perplexed,* trans. Shlomo Pines (Chicago: The University of Chicago Press, 1974), 1:59, 138; Joseph Gikatilla, *Gates of Light / Sha'Are Orah*, trans. Avi Weinstein (San Francisco: Harpercollins, 1994), Fifth Gate.

13. For a lucid account of the "skeptical" and the "mystical" reading of Maimonides, see Moshe Halbertal, *Maimonides: Life and Thought* (Princeton, NJ: Princeton University Press, 2015), esp. 301–310.

14. Particularly useful studies include Raoul Mortley, *From Word to Silence*, 2 vols. (Bonn: Peter Hanstein, 1986); Deidre Carabine, *The Unknown God: Negative Theology in the Platonic Tradition: Plato to Eriugena* (Louvain, Belgium: Peeters Press/W. D. Eerdmans, 1995); and Andrew Louth, *The Origins of the Christian Mystical Tradition: From Plato to Denys*, 2nd ed. (Oxford: Oxford University Press, 2007).

15. Louth, *Origins of the Christian Mystical Tradition*, 18, see also pp. 17–34 for an account of Philo's *via negativa* in relation to his psychology. For a handy sample of texts by

Philo in which negative theology features, or seems to feature, prominently, see William Franke, *On What Cannot Be Said: Apophatic Discourses in Philosophy, Religion, Literature, and the Arts: Volume 1: Classic Formulations* (Notre Dame, IN: University of Notre Dame Press, 2007), 114–122. Plato's nephew and the first successor of the Academy, Speusippus, is the best candidate for the real "father of negative theology." His work, preserved only in fragments, is the first to elevate the One above the Good, Being, and Intellect, from whence the entire Neoplatonic tradition will unfold.

16. Mortley, *From Word to Silence*, 1:39–46, 155–156.

17. Carabine, *The Unknown God*, 220.

18. This is brought out nicely by Diana Lobel, *A Sufi-Jewish Dialogue: Philosophy and Mysticism in Bahya Ibn Paquda's "Duties of the Heart"* (Philadelphia: University of Pennsylvania Press, 2006), 35–41.

19. Mortley's point, *From Word to Silence*, 2:15, applies to medieval Jewish thought as much as to its Christian and Islamic counterparts:

> The attack on anthropomorphism is clearly a negative thrust against the limits of available concepts, but it does not seek to go beyond them, or to annul them. It modifies them, so as to present them in slightly altered form. God is not human, but super-human, in that he is what a human would be if he were beyond himself to some extent. In this sense, one could consider the anti-anthropomorphic language of Judeo-Christian orthodoxy to be elementary negative theology, but only in the most superficial sense. The *via negativa* eliminates all personal and human imagery from the description of the ontological essence, but not only this, it goes further in order to eliminate every familiar characteristic, so that not only the image of the personal is annulled, but also the entire language of the external world. All existential, positional, temporal, qualitative, and moral concepts are eliminated. Language itself is eliminated, and thought is redefined.

20. See note 3 above. See also Elliot R. Wolfson, "*Via Negativa* in Maimonides and Its Impact on Thirteenth-Century Kabbalah," *Maimonidean Studies* 5 (2008): 393–442 and the informative volume *Neoplatonism and Jewish Thought*, ed. Lenn E. Goodman (Albany: State University of New York Press, 1992). Needless to say, the adoption of Neoplatonic tropes and methods was a common feature of medieval monotheisms; see *Neoplatonism and Christian Thought*, ed. Dominic J. O'Meara (Albany: State University of New York Press, 1981) and *Neoplatonism and Islamic Thought*, ed. Parviz Morewedge (Albany: State University of New York Press, 1992).

21. This point is lucidly drawn out with respect to Hegel's conception of the negativity immanent to the reflexive becoming-whole of Mind by William Franke, *A Philosophy of the Unsayable* (Notre Dame, IN: University of Notre Dame Press, 2014), chap. 2. Among Jews, the identification of divine oneness as the whole of being is usually associated with the Kabbalistic tradition of the divine Infinite (ʾyn sôf); on this see Valabregue's chapter, the first in this volume. Later, and in a very different way, the Lurianic concept of *tsimtsum* will do the work of negating the divine Infinite in order to separate the divine One from the divine

All. This concept was familiar to European philosophers through the translation of Zoharic and Lurianic texts made by Christian Herr von Rosenroth, *Kabbala Denudata*, 2 vols. (Sulzbach, 1677, and Frankfurt am Main, 1684) and thereby played a not inconsiderable role in the development of German Idealism; on this see Paul W. Franks, "Rabbinic Idealism and Kabbalistic Realism: Jewish Dimensions of Idealism and Idealist Dimensions of Judaism," in Nicholas Boyle, Liz Disley, and Nicholas Adams, eds., *The Impact of Idealism: The Legacy of Post-Kantian German Thought* (Cambridge: Cambridge University Press, 2013), chap. 9.

22. Here I am indebted to Shira Woloski's contribution to this volume.

23. On Maimonides as a critical-skeptical negative theologian, see Kenneth Seeskin's essay (chapter 2) in this volume and his *Searching for a Distant God: The Legacy of Maimonides* (New York: Oxford University Press, 2000). See also Shlomo Pines, "The Limitations of Human Knowledge According to Al-Farabi, ibn Bajja, and Maimonides," reprinted in his *Studies in the History of Jewish Thought*, eds. Warren Zev Harvey and Moshe Idel (Jerusalem: The Magnes Press, 1997), 404–431; and Stern's systematic treatment of this topic in *The Matter and Form of Maimonides' Guide*. Stern associates negative theology with Neoplatonic intuitive illuminations and therefore denies that this is what Maimonides's skepticism involves.

24. This distinction is informed by John P. Kenney, "The Critical Value of Negative Theology," *Harvard Theological Review* 86, no. 4 (1993): 439–453.

25. For example, Jean-Luc Marion, *In Excess: Studies of Saturated Phenomena*, trans. Robyn Horner and Vincent Berraud (New York: Fordham University Press, 2004), 134, 157. John D. Caputo nicely draws out the way Marion's project of attending to saturated phenomena, and above all to the "doubly saturated" phenomena of Revelation, articulates a phenomenological *via eminentiae* in his review of Marion's book on Augustine; see *Notre Dame Philosophical Reviews*, January 18, 2013, http://ndpr.nd.edu/news/36791-in-the-self-s-place-the-approach-of-st-augustine/.

26. Note how versions of this dispute reiterate in the course of modern philosophical theology. Kierkegaard's criticism of Hegel ultimately concerns the extent to which God correlates with the ultimate scope of Mind, both in principle and concretely in history. The Dane's stylized struggle with Hegel resembles established articulations of negative theology in its attempt to wriggle out of a principled correlation of (divine) Geist with (human) Mind. It is no accident that Jewish thinkers have consistently held fast to Kierkegaard in this dispute. A related, subsequent iteration of the quarrel motivated Karl Barth's vehement rejection of the Thomistic doctrine of an analogy between God and Being as an "invention of the Antichrist"; for a recent discussion of the important debate between Barth and Erich Przywara, who influentially and brilliantly expounded a Thomistic account of the *analogia entis*, see Thomas Joseph White, ed., *The Analogy of Being: Invention of the Antichrist or Wisdom of God?* (Grand Rapids, MI: Wm. B. Eerdmans Publishing, 2010). In rejecting the *analogia entis*, Barth steers toward the pure Logos of Revelation, thereby shoring up the negativity that threatens to overwhelm in the absence of all analogy. But Barth's criticism of the analogy of God and Being played an important role in the emergence twentieth-century Jewish negative theology, which often adopted this hostility to the *analogia entis* while remaining skeptical of the (Protestant) resort to *one* Incarnate Logos. Moreover, in both Jewish and Protestant versions, the rejection of the *analogia entis* sometimes results in

a confusion or conflation between negativity and Gnosticism (avowed by Barth and Scholem, disavowed by Rosenzweig and Levinas). For a discussion see Bielik-Robson in this volume and Benjamin Lazier, *God Interrupted: Heresy and the European Imagination between the World Wars* (Princeton, NJ: Princeton University Press, 2009), part 3.

27. Derrida spoke in this vein at length, speaking of "the becoming-theological of all discourse," by which he pointed to the way *positive* discourse aims to close the gap between the appearing of an object and its being, or its meaning and reference. The impossibility of closing this gap with certainty, for which he argued at length, caused his views to be associated with the tradition of negative theology, insofar as that tradition denies that one can close the gap between God (as referent) and the name of "God" (as sense).

28. Admittedly, this modern development is already anticipated by the emergence of ancient skepticism and the decline in confidence in the logos in the ancient world. Mortley finds it already in Plato's *Parmenides* 165b in which it is conceded that apprehension of the one must be "broken up into tiny sections"; Raoul Mortley, "What Is Negative Theology? The Western Origins" (1981) at http://works.bepress.com/raoul_mortley/37/. Ancient skepticism would already be a generalized response to the problematic relation between logos and being. Even so, in medieval thought the difficulty of relating logos to being is a specifically theological problem, not a general epistemological problem.

29. See, for example, Leora Batnizky, "The Image of Judaism: German-Jewish Intellectuals and the Ban on Images," *Jewish Studies Quarterly* 11 (2004): 259–281; and Bland, *Artless Jew*, chap. 1.

30. This is the starting point of Kenneth Seeskin's extensive work on negative theology, on which see chapter 2 of this volume and also his works *Jewish Philosophy in a Secular Age* (Albany: State University of New York Press, 1989), chap. 2; and *Searching for a Distant God: The Legacy of Maimonides* (New York: Oxford University Press, 2000). Maimonides's account of mental representation as idolatry is also lucidly discussed by Moshe Halbertal, *Maimonides: Life and Thought* (Princeton, NJ: Princeton University Press, 2015), 284–285; Moshe Halbertal and Avishai Margalit, *Idolatry* (Cambridge, MA: Harvard University Press, 1994), chap. 2; and Stern, *Matter and Form of Maimonides' Guide*, chap. 6. For valuable criticism of the view that mental representation is idolatrous representation, see Leora Batnizky, *Idolatry and Representation* (Princeton, NJ: Princeton University Press, 2000).

31. Immanuel Kant, *Critique of the Power of Judgement*, trans. Paul Guyer and Eric Matthews (Cambridge: Cambridge University Press, 2001), 156.

32. Moses Mendelssohn, "On the Sublime and the Naïve in the Fine Sciences," *Moses Mendelssohn: Philosophical Writings*, trans. and ed. D. Dahlstroom (Cambridge: Cambridge University Press, 1997), 202; cited in Gideon Freudenthal, *No Religion without Idolatry: Mendelssohn's Jewish Enlightenment* (Notre Dame, IN: University of Notre Dame Press, 2012), 207.

33. G. W. F. Hegel, *The Phenomenology of Mind*, trans. J. B. Baillie (New York: Harper, 1967), 366.

34. Emmanuel Levinas, *Difficult Freedom: Essays on Judaism,* trans. Seán Hand (Baltimore, MD: Johns Hopkins University Press, 1990), 238.

35. As Horkheimer and Adorno put it, "The disenchanted world of Judaism . . . places all hope in the prohibition on invoking falsity as God, the finite as infinite, the lie as truth.

The pledge of salvation lies in the rejection of any faith which claims to depict it, knowledge in the denunciation of illusion"; Max Horkheimer and Theodor W. Adorno, *The Dialectic of Enlightenment: Philosophical Fragments*, ed. Gunzelin Schmid Noerr, trans. Edmund Jephcott (Stanford, CA: Stanford University Press, 2002), 17.

36. On Rosenzweig's negative theology, see William Franke, "Franz Rosenzweig and the Emergence of a Postsecular Philosophy of the Unsayable," *International Journal for Philosophy of Religion* 58, no. 3 (2005): 161–180; and Elliot R. Wolfson, *Giving Beyond the Gift: Apophasis and Overcoming Theomania* (New York: Fordham University Press, 2014), chap. 2.

37. For an insightful discussion, see Sarah Hammerschlag, "Troping the Jew: Jean-François Lyotard's *Heidegger and 'the jews,'*" *Jewish Studies Quarterly* 12 (2005), 371–398; and *The Figural Jew: Politics and Identity in Postwar French Thought* (Chicago: The University of Chicago Press, 2010), 166–200.

38. William Franke also emphasizes the prevalence of Jewish writers the in emergence of modern negative theology; see especially the introduction to William Franke, *Volume 2: Modern and Contemporary Transformations* of *On What Cannot Be Said*. Steven Schwarzchild provides an illustrative case of an informed and lucid apology for this position, while Gillian Rose is the most compelling, if sometimes inscrutable, critic of the "diremption" of the "broken middle" where modern Jewish thought has been placed.

39. Agata Bielik-Robson, *Jewish Cryptotheologies of Late Modernity: Philosophical Marranos* (London: Routledge, 2014), which includes compelling reflections on Jewish negativity in modern thought.

40. Harold Bloom, *Ruin the Sacred Truths: Poetry and Belief from the Bible to the Present* (Cambridge, MA.: Harvard University Press, 1987), 150–152.

41. For a wonderful collection that explores this topic from a predominantly Christian perspective, see Chris Boesel and Catherine Keller, eds., *Apophatic Bodies: Negative Theology, Incarnation and Relationality* (New York: Fordham University Press, 2010).

42. For example, see Benjamin D. Sommer, *The Bodies of God and the World of Ancient Israel* (Cambridge: Cambridge University Press, 2009), who explicitly links biblical incarnationalism to Kabbalistic conceptions of God's incarnate negativity.

43. This applies to Levinas's abundant use of such tropes, and also to Horkheimer and Adorno's account of Jewish negation which, in the continuation of the passage cited in note 33, they explicitly dub "not abstract."

44. Martin Kavka, *Jewish Messianism and the History of Philosophy* (Cambridge: Cambridge University Press, 2004), chap. 3; as Kavka emphasizes, negativity for Cohen is ontological, not epistemological: we enjoy positive knowledge of God through the moral teleology in which we participate, by *imitatio dei*, even though such knowledge refers to an infinite, unrealizable end.

45. Gershom Scholem, "Reflections on Jewish Theology [1974]," *On Jews and Judaism in Crisis: Selected Essays* (Philadelphia: Paul Dry Books, 2012), 283. In *Jewish Cryptotheologies of Late Modernity*, Bielik-Robson rightly emphasizes that an interpretation of the Lurianic doctrine of *tsimtsum* plays an important role in metamorphosizing Jewish negativity into modernity by *incorporating negativity into creation*.

For a critical discussion of Scholem's overemphasis on the negativity of the Kabbalah, see Moshe Idel, *Old Worlds, New Mirrors: On Jewish Mysticism and Twentieth Century Thought* (Philadelphia: University of Pennsylvania Press, 2009), 119–132. Idel's critique, however, adopts an overly historicist approach to Scholem's deployment of Jewish negativity, focusing on its inventive nature without considering how it self consciously disrupts the historicism he takes for granted.

46. We also discover a great irony of intellectual history here insofar as the German Idealist tradition appropriated a certain conception of Lurianic negativity (see note 21).

47. Cf. Franke's comments on Celan's poem "einmal" in *A Philosophy of the Unsayable*, 86–88. There is an uncanny resemblance here to Reb Nachman's famous sixty-fourth teaching in *Likutey Moharan*. My proposal to call this "negative panentheism" is, I think, commensurate with Franke's account of "the hollow in Pan's pipe" by which he characterizes the anti-Hegelianism of postsecular negative theology throughout his impressive work. This suggests, as one would entirely expect, that such a notion is by no means "essentially Jewish," even if, as I have argued, it can be distinguished from intuitionist, unitive, disclosive, and other-worldly forms of negative theology and one to which Jewish thinkers and writers have been especially drawn.

48. Moses de Leon, *Sefer Shekel ha-Kodesh*, ed. Charles Mopsik (Los Angeles: Cherub Press, 1996), 19–20.

49. The secular negative theological correlate of this negative Jewish anthropology is the equally famous aphorism: "There are only two things. Truth and lies. Truth is indivisible, hence it cannot recognize itself; anyone who wants to recognize it has to be a lie."

ONE

The Limits of Negative Theology in Medieval Kabbalah and Jewish Philosophy

SANDRA VALABREGUE

"Nothing!" would be the ineluctable answer to the question: "what can be said of God?" For whatever God is—it is beyond the scope of human knowledge. Indeed, such a statement is very common not only in medieval Jewish philosophy but in medieval Kabbalah as well. However beyond that shared consensus, hide different conceptions of negative theology; this and more, alternative conceptions present at times a real challenge to the very definition of negative theology. To better understand what kind of negation is at stake in a given theological system, one needs to understand what kind of limits, as well as what is off-limits, the work of negative theology comes to set. What is the meaning of that "nothing" will indeed broadly depend on the role given to the delimitation of knowledge.

This essay offers a general overview of the different role played by negative theology in medieval Jewish philosophy and Kabbalah, in light of their different degree of commitment to negative theology. It is my intention to downplay the hegemonic tendency of negative theology and propose instead new ways to think about the interaction between negative and positive theologies. To my view, negative theology as a system that considers negation as the only possible approach is, as a matter of fact, marginal not only in Kabbalah but in Jewish philosophy as well. The main problem we encounter when attempting to assess the role of negative theology comes from its own paradoxical thinking and its hegemonic nature which, at face value, seems to leave no place for an alternative. It is nevertheless very rare to see negative theology eradicate all positive theology, for most of the time, it opens up or gives place to alternative theology. Whereas the role of what I propose to call "comprehensive negative theology" is better known, that of restrictive negative theology has not yet been properly assessed. However, even in the case of Maimonides, the main advocate of comprehensive negative theology, the extent of his negative theology is still an open question and scholarship offers a wide range of interpretations.

The role of negative theology in medieval Kabbalah is even the more problematic for, contrary to the comprehensive Maimonidean theology, it develops a restrictive use of negative theology. In Jewish philosophy and even the more so in Jewish mysticism, the rational/theological inquiry is usually challenged by the performative and contemplative relation to God opening up to nonspeculative approaches. In Jewish mysticism, Gershom Scholem's understanding of the Kabbalistic theological structure is articulated on an ontological distinction between revealed God and concealed God.[1] The problem raised by such a distinction is that it presupposes a theological system articulated on negative theology before we even get a chance to study the role of negative theology in a given system. Moshe Idel has pointed out the importance of thinking about theological conceptions in their diversity. This is not merely a call for pluralism, but also a revision of what is understood as the abstract and ineffable God.[2] In the same vein but in a different perspective, in his pioneering article, Elliot Wolfson has also greatly unsettled our understanding of Kabbalah by challenging its negative theology in light of its positive assertions.[3]

In what follows I wish to push further that inquiry into the role of negative theology in medieval thought and describe in large strokes the limits themselves of negative theology. To that purpose I will address the question by inverting the formula of Elliot Wolfson and discussing positive theologies in light of negative assertions. This change of perspective will help us to understand aspects of negative theology and its relation to positive theology in a more fundamental way beyond their apparent contradictions. To that task it is crucial to distinguish between theological systems dedicated to negative theology and theological system where negative theology has a place but not necessarily a dominant one. To better understand the role of negative theology, I therefore propose to distinguish restrictive uses of negative theology from comprehensive negative theology. Restrictive because it cohabits with alternative positive conceptions that are not coming from within the work of negation. After a general overview of negative theology in philosophy and in Jewish philosophy, I will present the place of negative theology in medieval Kabbalah. The nature of the corpora discussed dictates that Jewish philosophy will be presented chronologically, whereas the Kabbalistic material will be organized thematically. While philosophical texts and authors present an organized corpus, this is not the case with Kabbalistic literature which is a much more fragmented and eclectic corpus.

In Jewish traditions, expression of negative theology goes back to Philo of Alexandria in the first century. Philo discusses the conception of God's unknowability on the basis of Exodus 33:20 and its twofold Glory conception.[4] However, the remote status of God does not disqualify every relation, since for Philo nonknowledge is the acknowledgment of human nothingness and as such presents a gateway to an encounter with God: "for then is the time for the creature to encounter the creator when it has recognized its own nothingness."[5] This mixture of total inaccessibility and the possibility of access nevertheless through negation is the very mark of the comprehensive approach of negative theology.

At face value, however, Philo's negative theology became the legacy of the Christian church and the extent of his influence on Jewish thought has not yet been properly evaluated. Following a renewed interest in Neoplatonic and Aristotelian philosophies, the unknowability of God will become a motto among the medieval philosophical traditions both Muslim and Jewish. The Middle Ages, with the renewal of philosophy in Islam and consecutively in Judaism, sees the question of the divine attributes at the center of the debate. In the Islamic tradition, Al Kindi,[6] Al Farabi, Avicenna, Al-Gazali, and Averroes will all exacerbate the unknowability of God. The exaltation of the ignorance has also been at the heart of medieval texts such as in the *Theology of Aristotle* and those of Muslims thinkers.[7]

In the spirit of their time, Jewish philosophers adhere as well to the idea of unknowability. Following the philosophy of Kalam, David ibn Merwan al-Mukammas, Saadia Gaon, and Joseph ibn Zaddik reject the semantic validity of divine attributes; nevertheless, they would accept predication only if it truly reflects God's essence.[8] A common use of negation aims to establish what He is not. For Al-Mukammas, for example, when we affirm that God is alive, we are in fact denying that He is dead.[9] However, this approach should be seen as a partial negative theological approach, for Al-Mukammas nevertheless follows the view of the Mu'tazilites, whom accept terms that are equivalent to God's essence. This view stands in contrast to the more comprehensive and exclusive negative theology of the *Book of Causes*, in which nothing not even an attribute of essence can be predicated: "This is because description only comes to be by means of discourse, and discourse by means of intelligence, and intelligence by means of reasoning, and reasoning by means of imagination, and imagination by means of sense. However; the First Cause is above all things, since it is their cause; as a result then, it comes to be that it does not itself fall under sense or imagination or reasoning or intelligence or discourse; consequently, it is not describable."[10]

For Saadya Gaon, rational knowledge and prophecy are equivalent, prophecy being superior only in virtue of its divine origin. Even though the epistemological dimension of the limit of knowledge is an important aspect of Saadya's philosophy, the central point is still the divine unity in conformity with the philosophy of Kalam. In the controversy of his time between those who believe in attributes and those denying them, Saadya opt for a position that put forth the inner divine unity. Promoting the simplicity of God's unity is meant to resolve the problem of attributes by refraining to resort to predication. Even though God cannot be known, the specific aspects of the divine unity are reflected in a formulation that offers some solution to important semantic problems. For example, the notion of divine simplicity excludes any differentiation in God and consequently gives an account of God's essence but not by means of real attributes, modes, or attributes of essence. How can something partial be said about God without implying multiplicity in the Divine? For the problem of human-limited semantics lies in its equivalent partial approach to God. Simple, undifferentiated unity is the best testimony of His wholeness, since by denying multiplicity and attribution it affirms indivisible unity.[11]

Accordingly to his Neoplatonic heritage, Bachya ibn Paquda will also profess the unknowability of God. In the *Duties of the Heart*, the existence, unity, and eternity of God as essential attributes are opposed to attributes of action, distinguishing therefore attributes of God before and after the creation: "For He is exceedingly close to you in His activities, but infinitely remote in any representation of His essence or comparison with it. As already stated, we will never find Him in this way."[12] Through acknowledgment of God in the world, that is, of His actions, one can nevertheless experience God. Negative assertions have therefore a limited action, even if they are part of a process of purification of the soul and reason, worshiping God can only come from another way. Apparently, God's revelation in His actions is a sufficient source of knowledge where the creature meets His creator, knows Him intimately and worships Him: "With the knowledge of God that is in their hearts; they serve Him as if they were with the holy angels in the highest heavens."[13]

Shlomo ibn Gabirol, another central Neoplatonic philosopher, argues that "direct knowledge of the primary Existent is impossible why . . . because it is above and beyond all things and is illimitable."[14] Such a view can be tracked back to Isaac Israeli and his disciple Dunash ibn Tamim.[15] For Gabirol, God is pure essence, and we only perceive his essence through a composite of form and matter such as it is reflected in God's actions. Along with a notion of God's essence as being above of everything, Gabirol promotes a view that will influence Kabbalah notably through its *nachleben* with Moshe ibn Ezra's *Arugat ha-Bosem*. In *Fons Vitae*, the Master declares that "because the knowledge of any knower requires him to encompass what is known the illimitable cannot be encompassed by knowledge."[16]

Even though apophatic approaches can be traced back very early in the Middle Ages, only with Maimonides can one find a comprehensive system of negative theology. According to his view, predication on God's essence is strictly impossible, and the only knowledge possible is that of His actions. Maimonides's negative theology rejects the ontological approach of his predecessors who while adhering to negative theology would have nevertheless allowed some kind of positive predication. Following the inner logic of negative theology, negative assertions are more valuable than any positive assertions; therefore, the more we predicate of something the more we know: "in a similar way, you come nearer to the apprehension of Him, may He be exalted, with every increase in the negations regarding Him."[17] By negating what is not true, one comes closer to the truth while emptying predication of any content, for what is beyond physics cannot be known with certainty. In this perspective, the greatest achievement of philosophy is in the understanding of God as principle of causality—by contemplating on the world and on the manner in which natural causality reflects God's perfection. At crucial points of his metaphysical doctrine, Maimonides opts for ambiguous if not contradicted positions. The place of negative theology in Maimonides's philosophy is no exception and has been the subject of numerous discussions.[18] On the one end of the spectrum, Maimonides's negative theology leads to the so-called skeptic approach. Shlomo Pines offers to read Maimonides in light of Al Farabi with whom he agrees that the union with the active intellect is impossible for there is no resemblance between man and God even on this level.[19] Following that lead, the result of the critic of theology is a comprehensive negative theology—not only is knowledge above the physical world impossible but, in contrast with other negative theologies that give place through negation to a mystical path, it is completely restrictive to personal fulfillment in that world. The skeptical approach lately received a new expression in a book by Micah Goodman, interpreting Maimonides in a modern relativistic perspective.[20]

On the other end of the spectrum, as represented by two main schools of interpretation, we find the possibility nevertheless of some experience of what is beyond negation.[21] Recently, Menachem Lorberbaum has offered to read Maimonides's philosophy not as a critique of theology but rather as a critical theology, which cumulates in a state of illumination.[22] Following this reading, Maimonides's critique of language should be understood as a way to empty language from any content in order to make place for the experience of what is beyond the limits of language. This understanding of the role of negative theology in Maimonides's philosophy is to be counted alongside the skeptical one, both presenting a comprehensive negative theology. Major differences are nevertheless to be noted, for whereas the "skeptic" offers a limitative and exclusive position, the other one is extensive since it seeks to experience what is above language. This reading is made possible by considering the poetic dimension of language. Following a number of conditions, the human intellect has access to divine knowledge, even if the price is silence. It is not surprising, therefore, that the Sufi tradition has been precisely the path taken by Maimonides's son and grandson. An interesting example of this path of negative theology can be found in the words of the famous Andalusian Sufi and philosopher Ibn al-'Arabi who promotes silence as an alternative to ignorance: "There are some of us who profess ignorance as part of their knowledge maintaining that: 'to realize that one cannot know (God) is to know.' There are others from among us, however, who know, but who do not say such things, their knowledge instilling in them silence rather than [professions] of ignorance. This is the highest knowledge of God, possessed only by the Seal of Saints."[23] Of special interest here is the critique of the profession of ignorance as ultimate knowledge. The text introduces an important difference between ignorance as the highest degree of knowledge and the highest degree of knowledge that can only be acknowledged through silence. The comparison between the two gives us a good insight on different negative theological schools and eventually on the crucial difference between the two main streams of comprehensive negative theology: those of the "skeptic" and the "mystic." According to the skeptical approach, the rational inquiry stops at the acknowledgment of its ignorance—since ignorance is the only insight possible, it is the highest level of knowledge. The mystical approach passes the limits of knowledge toward an apophatic experience, where the limits of knowledge are apprehended within a silent acknowledgment. The silence in this case is not ignorance; it is all together an acknowledgment of the limits and a state of indescribable knowledge.

Whereas the "poetic" reading of Maimonides's philosophy and the Sufi approach open to the apophatic experience, the third way to interpret Maimonides's theory of knowledge should be understood as a restrictive negative theology. If one is to understand in Maimonides's philosophy the union with the active intellect as possible, then the negative theology plays only a role of limitation. Even though this way opens to noetic experience beyond regular knowledge, it does not belong to the comprehensive negative theology because it is not the result of the apophatic process. Following this school, if the conception of union is possible, this is only because it presumes the resemblance between God and Man. In fact, the possibility of union in its Averroistic tone has been the prevalent interpretation of Maimonides, shared by his translator and interpreter Shmuel ibn Tibbon, and medieval Kabbalah as well.[24] It is important to mention yet another aspect of Maimonides's philosophy that allows some positive theology and demands therefore to reassess the role played by negative theology in his metaphysic. This is his conception of the Tetragrammaton—the only name that resists Maimonides's critique of divine predication. According to him, among all the names given to God, this is the only one that should be understood as a proper name, as His personal name.[25] As such, just as the name of someone does not predicate anything about him but is simply attached to him, the Name of God is the only name that contains, even undisclosed, something of God's essence, and therefore is a positive representative of God.

The motto of the negative theology, nothing can be said about God, being shared by all philosophical systems discussed herein is not sufficient to distinguish between one system of negative theology and another. The variety of negative theological approaches in Maimonides's philosophy comes only to enhance the importance in understanding the role of negative theology in a given system. Interestingly enough, the three different readings of Maimonidean negative theology covers the principal tendencies.[26] The first two are the principal voices of comprehensive negative theology: the skeptical one and the poetic/mystical one. The third regards negative theology as a theological moment surpassed by the union with the active intellect, which is made possible only because it supposes reciprocity between God and man. Among these, the last one is the most prevalent one from a historical point of view since it has been the line of interpretation of Maimonides's negative theology in the Middle Ages while the other two represent essentially modern readings.

It appears that in Jewish medieval philosophy, the prevalent view is a restricted negative theology, for as we have seen, alongside the negative theological conception stands different aspects of positive theology that are considered legitimate. Consequently, in most of the cases, negative theology is not the last word in terms of metaphysics but a necessary metaphysical practice, which comes to set the condition of possibility of a positive theology. A good example of this particularly sensitive aspect regarding the interface between negative theology and positive theology can be found in Hasdai Crescas's critique of Maimonides. In his view, to stipulate that God's essence is not graspable is common knowledge and not a philosophical achievement.[27] Such a statement aims to relativize the role given by Maimonides to negative theology, for it does not teach us anything that we did not already know. For Crescas, positive attributes are possible. More so, taking on Maimonides's conception of the Tetragrammaton, real names are possible but he also rehabilitates attributes of relation, for in certain cases, the relation of reciprocity between God and others is not incompatible with His perfection. For Crescas, the necessity of essential attributes of God is ineluctable even though it only gives access to partial knowledge of God.[28]

In the following, I will try to assess to what extent medieval theosophical Kabbalah relies on negative theology. The different scholarly positions are a good starting point to understand the complexity at stake. Our basic comprehension is still indebted to Gershom Scholem's distinction between *deus absconditus* and *deus revelatus*—inferring an ontic dichotomy between *eyn-sof* and the *sefirot*. At the heart of this distinction is indeed our understanding of the notion of *eyn-sof*. This is the term that the theosophical Kabbalah over the generations has chosen to represent God in the mystery of His essence. It is also a term that has been mostly understood by scholars as the main voice of Kabbalah's negative theology. However, such a distinction between an ineffable God and a revealed one has been seriously shattered during the past decades, to the extent that it has become obsolete to our understanding of theosophical Kabbalah.[29] Moshe Idel, for example, has contrasted the apophatic notion of *eyn-sof* with anthropomorphic notion of *eyn-sof*.[30] Elliot Wolfson's research has also deeply contributed to rethinking our ways to address theological categories by questioning the relation between apophatic and cataphatic.[31] What is left of negative theology's reliability once we consider the Kabbalistic inclinations toward positive theology? What is there to be said of contradictory conceptions such as ineffable infinite and all-encompassing infinite? Since the mid-1990s, Wolfson has intensively researched the paradoxical hermeneutics that lay at the bottom of such contradictions as *coincidentia oppositorum*.[32] For, only such a paradigm gives a sense of the mix of positive and negative assertions, and its paradoxical articulation. According to such a view, the tension between positive and negative assertions finds an answer precisely in the art of contradiction so peculiar to negative theology. However, alongside this understanding of negative theology that is equivalent to what I offered to call comprehensive negative theology, more temperate voices of negative theology can be heard.

The different poles of negative theology in medieval theosophical Kabbalah evolved alternatively or consecutively around a number of statements expressing God's inconceivability. Among the principal anchors to negative theology we count the conceal (*ne'elam*), the neant (*'ayn*), the One, and the *eyn-sof*. The first two are more peculiar to Kabbalah and the mystical tradition, whereas the simple and transcendental unity as such as the infinite (*eyn-sof*) are also central to philosophical systems. The differences in the philosophic and Kabbalistic approaches, as we will see, lie in their respective positive theologies, and more particularly in their alternative conceptions of unity and infinity. However, as I shall argue, the divine unity and infinity, contrary to what can be expected, contribute only to restricted negative theological views, whereas a full-range negative theology is more likely to develop within the conception centered around the *ne'elam* and the *'ayn*.

Ha-*ne'elam* (concealed) or *ha-nistar* (hidden) refers in theosophical texts to God in his essence. Such a view goes back to the conception of the double *kavod*, where *nistar* designates the upper part.[33] Nachmanides was a major medievalist scholar and *ha-ne'elam* plays a major role in his Kabbalatic work, in which it becomes the principal appellation for God essence.[34] His reluctance to name at all the unnamable together with his specific view on *torah ha-sod* and the absence of occurrence of the term *eyn-sof* in his writings, conjecture to a comprehensive negative theological position. This point is crucial to understand the differences between Kabbalistic negative assertions. For, choosing the *ne'elam* over the One and Infinite not only posits *ne'elam* as the most adequate and apparently only designation, but also views the One and the infinite as irrelevant, because they seem to say too much already. In more than one aspect, this position represents one of the most extreme negative theological positions among the Kabbalistic schools mostly because of its uncompromising position. However, Nachmanides's conception was not to become the dominant one among theosophical Kabbalah where reference to infinite and God's unity are numerous.[35]

Alongside the conception of pure ineffability conveyed within the conception of *ne'elam*, *nistar* and *'ayn* (neant) represent another major voice in Kabbalah advocating for complex hermeneutics of negative theology. Even though the *nistar* conception cannot properly be called skeptical it recalls nevertheless the skeptical views of negative theology, mainly because of its absolute submission to the ontological difference and its total noetic abstention. By contrast *'ayn* conceptions offer a full-range negative theology hermeneutic, that is, a work of negation that enables paradoxical ontology.

This can be sensed within the coexistence of contradictory stance where *'ayn* designates altogether the total absence of (graspable) essence and ultimate divine presence. As argued by Daniel Matt, the *'ayn* is not empty, on the contrary it is the ultimate being because of its inaccessibility.[36] The very metaphysical status of *'ayn* as expressing the summons of negative theology is nicely exemplified in a passage of Moshe de Leon's that offers a radical interpretation of Ecclesiastes 3:19. Whereas there is no (=*'ayn*) difference between men and animals, in that very nondifference (=*'ayn*) lies all the difference.[37] The "no (*'ayn*) difference" is therefore the acknowledgment of the superiority of the *'ayn* precisely in this paradoxical statement that gives to *'ayn* "substance."

It is a common philosophic view to discuss divine unity as a unity that is not in number but precedes every other unity/number.[38] In the same vein, Joseph Gikatilla distinguishes between the absolute One equal to itself and the mundane singular unities: "Nowhere, is the One truly (one) be found, except only in God."[39] Indivisibility is another aspect of the divine unity in philosophy as such as in Kabbalah. Such a conception finds its expression already at an early stage of theosophical Kabbalah in the notion of equal unity (*aḥdout shavah*).[40] In another formulation, that goes back to Maimonides, God's equanimity is describe as an unity that is equal on all sides.[41] We read, for example, in Jacob ben Sheshet's book: "The wisdom comes forth from Neant (*'ayn*); that is, from a subtle essence that the thought cannot grasp for the word Neant (*'ayn*) designates an essence equal on all sides that cannot be thought of or suggested since it is so subtle and pure that it is impossible to think about it or to polemicize on its signification" [my translation].[42] This conception of equanimity endorses at first glance the total transcendent divine unity; however, and this is what makes this Kabbalalistic version interesting, it ultimately gives ways to an alternative conception—that of a dynamic divine unity. Indeed, along with that common consensus on simple divine unity, Kabbalah endorses a very different notion of unity—a conception of a divine unification.[43] Equal unity (*aḥdout shavah*) needs to be understood in theolosophical Kabbalah in light, principally, of its power of unification, as it results from many texts, the same is true for the notion of unity that is equal from all sides. We read therefore in the *iyyun* literature: "No creature can truly comprehend the essence of His existence and His nature, since He is in a state of balanced unity, for in His completeness the higher and lower beings are united. He is the foundation of everything that is hidden and revealed. . . . He comprises all sides, hidden and revealed. He begins above and ends below. . . . He is One being unified in the balanced unity."[44] The coexistence in theosophical Kabbalah of two contradictory models of unity—simple unity versus unified unity—has been a subject of theological tension, the discussion of which goes beyond the scope of this chapter.[45] It suffices nevertheless to say that if, on the one hand, this tension is answered apologetically, then, on the other hand, it is also understood as the sign of Kabbalah's superiority over philosophy. For if they share the knowledge of the simple unity, philosophers, claim Kabbalists, have nevertheless no knowledge of the complex inner articulation of its parts.[46]

Infinity is also to be counted among the principal notions in philosophy and Kabbalah to express God's essence and ineffability. Its remoteness and inaccessibility makes *eyn-sof* a great candidate for the negative theology. Following a saying found in different sources, *eyn-sof* is the most appropriate name to designate the unnamable. His highly esoteric status is meant to explain why there is no reference to *eyn-sof* in Jewish traditional books.[47] Nevertheless, this conception of *eyn-sof* is not very dominant among the theosophical literature. Whereas in philosophy infinity is subordinate to the divine unity, in Kabbalah infinity will find a different ground for its development and will soon become the principal denomination for God's essence. Such a conceptual autonomy explains also the theological liberty taken with the theosophical notion of *eyn-sof* and the alternative positive conceptions that it offers to the more notorious view of apophatic infinity.[48] Not only, as has been stipulated, is *eyn-sof* sometimes described in anthropomorphic terms, but also, as regards the *sefirotic* system, the remoteness of *eyn-sof* needs to be seriously reassessed. Furthermore, the ontic separation between *eyn-sof* and the *sefirot* meets several contradictions and is in fact not found easily. The principal reason is that *eyn-sof* and the *sefirot* belong to the same ontological realm. This is what resorts from the historical development of the theosophical notion of *eyn-sof*, which cannot be separated from the notion of *sefirot* itself, for they form, at the beginning of the theosophical Kabbalah, one entangled notion.[49] Therefore, it would be a mistake to see *eyn-sof* as a pure transcendental notion remote from everything. Instead of a pure transcendence, *eyn-sof*, because of its intimate relation with the *sefirot*, needs to be understood as the vertical prolongation of the *sefirotic* world and an extension of the mundane world.

It is not surprising therefore to see the first *sefirah keter* in direct prolongation of *eyn-sof*, for in some Kabbalistic tradition, *keter* is not only coexistent with, but also identical to *eyn-sof*.[50] Moreover, the inaccessible status of God extends sometimes not only to *keter*, but also to at least the three first *sefirot*.[51] At the very early stage of the theosophical Kabbalah, "that which thought cannot attain" was one of the very first appellations given to the first *sefirah*.[52] This formulation recalls another one, found in Shlomo ibn Gabirol's writing, that the intellection by way of encompassing cannot grasp what is infinite.[53] Between the first generation and the second generation of theosophical Kabbalists, as pointed out by Scholem, "that which thought cannot attain" is translated into "the annihilation of the thought" (*Afissat ha-Machshava*)[54] or ʿ*ayn* (Neant),[55] the latter becoming, from the second third of the thirteenth century, the major appellation for *keter*.[56]

Such a turn in the terminology points to a move from a mere descriptive epistemological statement to something more abstract and substantive. The reference to the cognitive process does not nevertheless disappear, the specific entanglement between the cognitive process and the emanative one is in fact very indicative of the theosophical lore. Such a move is crucial to assess correctly the role of negative theology in that theosophical system. Where the investigation stop is precisely where God's realm starts and it is not by accident that ʿ*ayn*, *machshavah*, *machshavah tehorah*, *hohmah*, and *binah* refer to stages of human cognition as well as to *sefirot*. To the limits of the thought and to its annihilation echoes the infinite of God's depth since "that which thought cannot attain" is also the thought that "extends to the infinite." For, the infinite that is beyond the limits of the thought is also the thought that extends to *eyn-sof*.[57] Truly the ambiguity between the two levels of thought, human and divine, is meant to blur precisely their differences. This and more, pointing to the limits of the cognitive process, place nonetheless the unlimited in the prolongation of the limited. Moreover, alternatives to the limitative cognitive process are offered. The suction, for example, is presented as superior to the process of cognition because of its direct access to *eyn-sof*.[58]

Scholars have constantly pointed to the contradictions that accompany negative theology's conceptions, focusing their research on negative theology's inner hermeneutics and on its fascinating paradoxical statements. Such an approach to negative theology surely shows the most striking mechanism of negative theology and teaches us about negative theology in its most accomplished form, but it tends to dismiss moderate forms of negative theology. The survey of different philosophical and Kabbalistic trends of negative theology offered in this chapter, though not exhaustive, intend to show that beside the classical form of negative theology other tendencies not only exist, but are in fact more commonly encountered. Moreover, the ability to distinguish between comprehensive and restricted approaches of negative theology reflect an important change of methodology. All in all, negative assertions agree that God cannot be known; there precisely lays the difficulty, in the ability to break that consensus and in the fact that such a statement is already an act of knowledge. For, it is a fact that beyond that apparently unbreakable consensus, the degree of unknowability differs from one system to the other. Furthermore, only a few systems will embrace fully the consequences of human intellectual limits. It is more likely, as we have seen in this chapter, to find negative theological assertions that nevertheless go along with positive ones. Therefore, only the study of the interaction between negative and positive theologies has permitted us to better assess the differences underlying the shared consensus. There is an important difference between the deconstruction of positive theology in the negative theological process and the positive theology generated by that very process; for negation can be fully weighted only in its interaction with positive theology, not only at its starting point, but also precisely at the end of the theological hermeneutic process.

For this reason, I have proposed to restrict what we generally understand as negative theology to negative theology in its full range, that is, comprehensive negative theology relying only on negation as a trigger for higher stages of knowledge. Besides this high form, we need to recognize limited uses of negative theology as presenting a different approach to negation. Although also beginning with a critique of knowledge, these nevertheless allow for positive theology when it seems to answer to the new noetic standard. For, if the first step of negative theology is to realize that human knowledge cannot properly apprehend God's essence, then the next step will determinate whether it is a comprehensive negative theology or a restricted negative theology. In this second step, the former avers that nothing can be said about God except by negation, whereas the latter opts for positive conceptions alongside those of negation. Indeed the beauty of the comprehensive negative theology is to be able to reach beyond the negation from within the negation. The impossible, to know the unknowable, is exactly in the power of negative theology (with the exception of the skeptical trend). For such secrets are meant to be disclosed, and the epistemological process of negation is meant to be replaced and overcome by alternative hermeneutics. Only the skeptical approach of negative theology abrogates from that spectacular turnaround. For unlike other classical negative theologies that articulate anew the void created by negation, skeptics understand the limits of knowledge as what cannot be overcome.

Another striking outcome of this survey is that among the different systems presented, only Maimonides seems to offer a whole system of negative theology. The question as to how his apophatic conception should be understood, whether as a comprehensive theological system and to what extent, is a matter of interpretation. Among the three interpretations presented, two represent main versions of comprehensive negative theology, the skeptical and the poetic/mystical version. The third type of interpretation, for whom the union with the active intellect is possible, should in my view be understood as a restricted negative theological system. For union with the active intellect is possible only because it relies on identification between the human and the divine intellect. Therefore, since the union with the active intellect is not the effect of negation, it should not be considered as such but rather as a positive theological model that stands alongside the work of negation. Moreover, this school of interpretation was dominant throughout the Middle Ages, which in my view tends to speak in favor of a restricted negative theology even for Maimonides.

In a sense, Nachmanides should be structurally compared with Maimonides. First, his system is also in a minority position and, second, because his comprehensive negative school resembles the skeptical version. Comprehensive because the concealment of God is absolute, and skeptical because he is very reluctant to use any appellations at all. For the other systems, philosophical ones prior to Maimonides and after him, as for the other theosophical schools beside Nachmanides's, the role of negation and thus the extent of negative theology should be understood mostly in a restricted sense. In these Kabbalistic systems, the use of negative theology is mostly an isolated moment that gives way rapidly to alternative approaches that are not produced through negation. Even the conception of 'ayn, which is apparently the only voice given to apophatic theology in Kabbalah, does not stand as the last moment of theology for Azriel of Gerona, Moshe de Leon, or even Shem Tov ibn Shem Tov.

My sense is that skeptical or apophatic systems, even if they represent the two most important paradigms, they do not reflect common use of negative theology in medieval systems of thought. Instead, one can see in medieval Kabbalah and even in medieval Jewish philosophy a variety of systems whereby the way of negation is integrated into alternative positive theologies. If one considers the most popular reading of Maimonides, his conception should also be understood as belonging to a restrictive conception of negative theology. All in all, the importance of negative theology in the Middle Ages should not be underestimated, though it should be understood within the boundaries of its limited applications, for positive theology seems to prevail most of the time. We can then conclude that recent interest in medieval negative theologies reflects a contemporary intellectual development that found a paradigm for modern and postmodern theologies.

Notes

1. Gershom Scholem, *Origins of the Kabbalah*, trans. A. Arkush (Princeton, NJ: Princeton University Press, 1987), 261–289, 431–443; *Major Trends in Jewish Mysticism* (New York: Schocken, 1995), 207–209, 214–217; *Kabbalah* (New York: Dorset Press, 1974), 87–105; and *On the Mystical Shape of the Godhead* (New York: Schocken, 1991), 38–42, 158–159. On the

importance of negative theology in Scholem's work, see Gershom Scholem, *"Zehn Unhistorishe Satze uber Kabbala," Geist und Werk: Aus der Werkstatt unserer Autoren: Zum 75. Geburstag von Dr Daniel Brody* (Zurich: Rhein-Verlag, 1958), 212–213; David Biale, "Gershom Scholem's Ten Unhistorical Aphorisms on Kabbalah," in *Gershom Scholem*, ed. Harold Bloom (New York: Chelsea House, 1987), 110–113; Harold Bloom, "Scholem: Unhistorical or Jewish Gnosticism," in *Gershom Scholem*, 207–210, 220; and Steven Wasserstrom, *Religion after Religion: Gershom Scholem, Mircea Eliade, and Henry Corbin at Eranos* (Princeton, NJ: Princeton University Press, 1999), 87–90.

2. Moshe Idel, "The Image of Man above the 'sefirot'" [in Hebrew], *Daat* 4 (1980): 41–56; see its extended version in English: "The Image of Man above the 'sefirot': R. David ben Yehuda he-Hasid's Theosophy of Ten Supernal 'Sahsahot' and Its Reverberations," *Kabbalah* 20 (2009): 181–212; and his "On the Theologization of Kabbalah in Modern Scholarship," in *Religious Apologetics Philosophical Argumentation*, ed. Yosseff Schwartz and Volkhard Kreech (Tubingen: Mohr Siebeck, 2004), 148–158. For a similar view opting for a multiplicity of conception on Christian negative theology, see Paul Rorem, "Negative Theologies and the Cross," *Lutheran Quarterly* 23 (2009): 214–331.

3. Elliot Wolfson, "Negative Theology and Positive Assertion in the Early Kabbalah," *Daat* 32–33 (1994): v–xxii.

4. Harry Wolfson, *Philo* 2 (Cambridge: Cambridge University Press, 1947), 119. Wolfson's reading of Philo as the origin of the conception of the ineffable God has been criticized: David Winston, *Two Treatises of Philo of Alexandria: A Commentary on De Gigantibus and Quod Deus sit Immutabilis* (Chico, CA: Scholars Press, 1983), 217ff.

5. Philo, *Who is the Heir of Divine Things*, VII 30.

6. For Al Kindi, the unknowability of God follows from its definition as simple unity, for such simplicity excludes every definition. The true One is not an intelligible object and is therefore unknown; *Al Kindi's Metaphysics*, ed. and trans. Alfred L. Ivry (Albany: State University of New York Press, 1974), 96–114.

7. Paul Fenton, "Le Thème de la Docte Ignorance dans la pensée musulmane et juive médiévale," in *La théologie négative*, ed. Marco Olivetti (Padova: CEDAM, 2002), 555–573.

8. Harry Wolfson, *Repercussions of the Kalam in Jewish Philosophy* (Cambridge, MA: Harvard University Press, 1979), 40–74.

9. His book is quoted in Yehuda Barzeloni, *Perush Sefer Yetsirah*, ed. S. J. Halberstam (Berlin, 1885), 80. The use of negative interpretations of affirmative predications of God goes back to Albinus: Harry Wolfson, "Albinus and Plotinus on Divine Attributes," *Harvard Theological Review* 45 (1952): 115–130.

10. *The Book of Causes*, ed. and trans. Dennis J. Brand (Milwaukee: Marquette University Press, 1984), verse 65.

11. Saadia Gaon, *The Book of Belief and Opinions*, trans. Samuel Rosenblatt (New Haven, CT: Yale University Press, 1976), II 4, 91, 92; II 7; Israel Efros, *Studies in Medieval Jewish Philosophy* (New York: Columbia University Press, 1974), 3–36.

12. Bachya ben Joshep Ibn Paquda, *Duties of the Hearts*, trans. M. Hyamson (Jerusalem: Feldheim, 1970), 1:113–115.

13. Ibid., 2:375.

14. *Fons Vitae*, I 5; Shlomo ibn Gabirol, *The Fountain of Life*, trans. Alfred B. Jacob (Stanwood, WA: Sabian Pub. Society, 1987), 7. For a reading of negative theology of Gabirol as apophatic, see Sarah Pessin, *Ibn Gabirol's Theology of Desire: Matter and Method in Jewish Medieval Neoplatonism* (New York: Cambridge University Press, 2013).

15. Alexander Altmann and Samuel M. Stern, trans., *Isaac Israeli* (Oxford: Oxford University Press, 1958), 151.

16. *The Fountain of Life*, 8; Paul Fenton, "Traces of Moseh ibn Ezra's 'Arugat ha-Bosem' in the Writings of the Early Qabbalists of the Spanish School," *Studies in Medieval Jewish History and Literature*, ed. Isadore Twersky and J. M. Harris, vol. 3 (Cambridge, MA: Harvard University Press, 2000), 62–63. A similar view is expressed by Johannes Scotus Eriguena: "If, then, no wise man asks of all essence in general what it is since it cannot be defined except in terms of the circumstances which circumscribe it, so to speak within limits . . . when he understands very well concerning it that it cannot be defined and is not any of the things that are and surpasses all things that can be defined?" *Periphyseon*, II 586b–587d. Emmanuel Falque, "Théologie négative et théophanie chez Jean Scot Erigéne," in *La théologie négative*, 539–554.

17. *The Guide for the Perplexed*, I 59, trad. Shlomo Pines) Chicago: The University of Chicago Press, 1963) 139.

18. Harry H. Wolfson, *Studies in the History of Philosophy and Religion*, vol. 2 (Cambridge, MA: Harvard University Press, 1977), 133; Wolfson, "Maimonides on the Negative Attributes," in *Louis Ginzberg: Jubilee Volume* (New York: American Academy for Jewish Research, 1945), 411–446; Joseph A. Buijs, *Negative Language and Knowledge about God: A Critical Analysis of Maimonides' Theory of Divine Attributes* (Ottawa: National Library of Canada, 1980); Eyal Bar-Eitan, "*Moreh Derekh* to God's Knowledge: Positive Aspects of the Guide of Perplexed Negative Theology" (MA thesis, Hebrew University of Jerusalem, 2001).

19. Shlomo Pines, "The Limitations of Human Knowledge According to Al-Farabi, ibn Bajja and Maimonides," in *Studies in Medieval Jewish History and Literature*, 82–109. Among Maimonides's prominent scholars, see also Josef Stern's agnostic reading, Josef Stern, *The Matter and Form of Maimonides' Guide* (Cambridge, MA: Harvard University Press, 2013); and his, "Maimonides on the Growth of Knowledge and Limitations of the Intellect," in *Maïmonide, philosophe et savant (1138–1204)*, eds. Tony Lévy and Roshdi Rashed (Leuven: Peeters, 2004), 143–191. For a similar view, which nevertheless accepts a model of refinement through the outpouring of the active intellect on the human intellect: Alexander Altmann, "Maimonides on the Intellect and the Scope of Metaphysics," *Von der Mittelalterlichen zur Modernen Aufklarung Studien zur Judischen Geistesgeschichte von Alexander Altmann* (Tubingen: Mohr, 1987), 79–84.

20. Micah Goodman, *The Guide of the Perplexes' Secrets* [in Hebrew] (Tel Aviv: Devir, 2010).

21. Elliot Wolfson, "Via Negativa in Maimonides and its Impact on Thirteenth Century Kabbalah," *Maimonidean Studies* 5 (2008): 393–442.

22. Menachen Lorberbaum, *Dazzled by Beauty: Theology as Poetics in Hispanic Jewish Culture* [in Hebrew] (Jerusalem: Yad Yizthak Ben-Zvi Institute, 2011), 51–121; and "Mystique mythique et mystique rationnelle," *Critique* 728–729 (2008): 109–117.

23. Ibn al-'Arabi, *Bezels of Wisdom*, trans. R. W. J. Austin (New York: Paulist Press, 1980), 65–66.

24. Adam Afterman, *Devequt, Mystical Intimacy in Medieval Thought* [in Hebrew] (Los Angeles: Cherub Press, 2011), 134–138, 154–158.

25. Menachem Lorberbaum, "Mystique mythique et mystique rationnelle." A similar position can be found in *Zohar hadash*, 112.

26. Moshe Halbertal, *Maimonides: Life and Thought* (Princeton, NJ: Princeton University Press, 2014).

27. *Or Adonay*, I, III 1, 3; Zeev Harvey, *Hasdai Crescas* [in Hebrew] (Jerusalem: Zalman Shazar Center, 2010).

28. Harry A. Wolfson, "Crescas on the Problem of Divine Attributes," in *Studies in the History of Philosophy and Religion* 2:247–337.

29. On this subject, see my book *Concealed and Revealed: "Eyn Sof" (Infinity) in Theosophic Kabbalah* [in Hebrew] (Los Angeles: Cherub Press, 2010).

30. See note 2.

31. Elliot R. Wolfson, *"Megilat 'Emet we-'Emunah*, Contemplative Visualization and Mystical Unknowing," *Kabbalah* (2000): 60–61; see also his important article, "Via Negativa in Maimonides."

32. For *coincidencia opositorum* between moral discernment and transcendental oneness (religious observance finds its fulfillment in transgression): Elliot R. Wolfson, *Venturing Beyond: Law and Morality in Kabbalistic Mysticism* (New York: Oxford University Press, 2006), 186–285; *A Dream Interpreted within a Dream: Oneiropoiesis and the Prism of Imagination* (New York : Zone Books, 2011); "Nihilating Nonground and the Temporal Sway of Becoming," *Angelaki: Journal of the Theoretical Humanities* 17, no. 3 (2012): 31–45.

33. On the *kavod* that the eyes cannot see: *Hekhalot Zurtarti*, ed. Rachel Elior (Jerusalem:Magnes, 1982), 25; Mark Verman, *The Books of Contemplation: Medieval Jewish Mystical Sources* (New York: State University of New York Press, 1992), 38n9.

34. Haviva Pedaya, *Nahmanides, Cyclical Time and Holy Text* [in Hebrew] (Tel Aviv: Am Oved, 2003), 392–411; Moshe Halbertal, *By Way of Truth; Nahmanides and the Creation of a Tradition* [in Hebrew] (Jerusalem: Shalom Hartman Institute, 2006).

35. On that topic, see *Concealed and Revealed*.

36. Daniel Matt, "Ayn the Concept of Nothingness in Jewish Mysticism," in *The Problem of Pure Consciousness: Mysticism and Philosophy*, ed. Robert K. C. Forman (Oxford: Oxford University Press, 1990), 67–108.

37. R. *Moshe de Leon's Sefer Sheqel ha-Qodesh*, ed. C. Mopsik (Los Angeles: Cherub Press, 1996), 20; Gershom Scholem, "Two Writings of Moshe de Leon" [in Hebrew] (Jerusalem, 1986), 374 (Scholem says this about *keter,* the second *sefirah*).

38. Valabregue, *Concealed and Revealed*, 99, 136.

39. Joseph Gikatilla, *Ginat Egoz* (Jerusalem: Yeshivat ha-Rayim ve-ha-Shalom, 1989), 118.

40. The expression *aḥdout shavah* is quite common in Kabbalah: Daniel Abrams, *The Writings of R. Asher ben David, His Complete Works and Studies in His Kabbalistic Thought* [in Hebrew] (Los Angeles: Cherub Press, 1996), 119; Verman, *Books of Contemplation*, 34, 38–39; Azriel of Gerona, *Sha'ar ha-Shoel*, in Meir Gabay, ed., *Derech Emunah* (Berlin, 1850), 3.

41. *Mishney Torah, hilkhot yesod torah* 2:10; *Moreh Nevukim* (trans. Alharizi) 1:51; Jonathan Dauber, "Competitive Approaches to Maimonides in Early Kabbalah," *The Cultures of*

Maimonideanism, ed. James T. Robinson (Leiden: Brill, 2009), 80. Latter too in Isaac ibn Latif we find similar expression of the limits of the thought, whereas His unity is said to be equally equal in all directions: see *Sha'arey Shamay*, chap. 2–4, ms. Vatican 335 (F375).

42. Jacob ben Sheshet, *Sefer meshiv devarim nekhoḥim,* ed. I. Tishby (Jerusalem: Academia ha-leumit le-madaim, 1968), 153.

43. On the differences between the philosophical and Kabbalistic notions of God's unity, see Charles Mopsik, "Unity de l'être et du monde," *Les Chemins de la Cabale: Vingt-cinq études sur la mystique juive* (Paris: Éditions de l'éclat, 2004), 71–104. For a reconsideration of that distinction, see Dauber, "Competitive Approaches to Maimonides in Early Kabbalah," 57–88.

44. Verman, *Books of Contemplation,* 69.

45. To only cite some principal texts dealing with that question: Abrams, *The Writings of R. Asher ben David,* 47–122; Moshe de Leon, *Shekel ha-Kodesh,* ed. Charles Mopsik (Los Angeles: Cherub Press, 1986), 99–103; Joseph Dan, "Sefer Sha'arey ha-Sod veha-Yerud veha-Emunah from Eliazar of Worms," *Tamirion* 1 (1982); Raphael Cohen, *The Book of Unity attributed to Rabbi Shem Tov Faro* [in Hebrew] (Jerusalem: Cohen, 1998), 1–13; *Sefer Ma'arekhet ha-Elohut,* chap. 2; *Sha'ar ha-Shoel.*

46. For example, see Azriel of Gerona, *The Commentary on the Agadot,* ed. I. Tishby [in Hebrew] (Jerusalem: Magnes, 1945), 101.

47. *Sefer Ma'arekhet ha-Elohout*, chap. 7, 80b; Nahora Gabay, "Sefer Sha'ar ha-Shamayim by Rabbi Yacov ben Sheshet Girondi" [in Hebrew] (MA thesis; Tel Aviv: Tel Aviv University, 1989), 105; Gershom Scholem, *Ha Kabbalah be-Gerona* [in Hebrew] (Jerusalem: Mifal ha-shirpul, 1964),142; Moshe Idel, "Magical and Neoplatonic Interpretations," in *Jewish Thought in the Sixteenth Century,* ed. by B. D. Cooperman (Cambridge, MA: Harvard University Press, 1983), 141.

48. Valabregue, *Concealed and Revealed,* chap. 2 and 4.

49. This particular aspect of *eyn-sof* has a historical ground, for the development of *eyn-sof* needs to be understood in the context of the *Sefer Yetsirah,* where *eyn-sof* and the *sefirot* are an undissociable notion, rather than stemming from philosophical sources. Sandra Valabregue, "The Concept of Infinity ('Eyn-sof') and the Rise of Theosophical Kabbalah," *Jewish Quarterly Review* 102, no. 3 (2012): 405–430.

50. Valabregue, *Concealed and Revealed,* 94–118.

51. Adolph Jellinek, *Beiträge zur Geschichte der Kabbala II* (Leipsig, 1852), 13; David S. Ariel, *"Shem Tob Ibn Shem Tob's Kabbalistic Critique of Jewish Philosophy in the "Commentary on the Sefirot": Study and Text,"* vol. 2 (PhD diss., Brandeis University, 1981), 24, 78.

52. Gershom Scholem, *The Kabbalah in Provence* [in Hebrew] (Jerusalem: Mifal ha-shirpul, 1963), appendix, 1.

53. See notes 19 and 21.

54. *The Book of Pomegranade, Moses De Leon's Sefer ha-Rimmonim,* ed. E. Wolfson (Atlanta: Scholars Press, 1988), 26; Moshe de Leon, *Shoshan Edut,* 334.

55. "The inner power is called *ayn* because neither thought nor reflection grasps it. Concerning this Job said wisdom comes into being out of *ayn*." Abrams, *The Writings of R. Asher ben David,* 105.

56. Gershom Scholem, *Studies in Kabbalah* [in Hebrew], vol. 1 (Tel Aviv: Am Oved, 1998), 32; Azriel of Gerona, *Perush ha-Agadot*, 116; Scholem, *Studies in Kabbalah*, 197; Ezra of Gerona, *Kitvey ha-Ramban*, ed. Chavel, vol. 2 (Jerusalem: Mosad ha-rav Kook, 1988) 483b, 102a; Zohar, II 114b; Joseph Gikatilla, *Sha'arey Ora* (Jerusalem: Mosad Bialik, 1965), 290.

57. Scholem, *Kabbalah in Provence*, appendix, 3.

58. For example, Isaac the blind speaks of a status of suction that replaces the cognitive approach. A similar idea can already be found in his father's writing, stressing out that even if God is hidden from the eyes, he is nevertheless present in every heart. Abraham ben David of Posquiere, *Sefer Baaleh ha-nefesh*, ed. Yosef Qafiḥ (Jerusalem: Mosad ha-Rav Kook, 1965), 127.

TWO

"No One Can See My Face and Live"

KENNETH SEESKIN

This chapter takes as its point of departure the passages in the Bible that describe God as a destructive force and warns people not to get too close to God. The most famous is Exodus 33:20, which is the title of this essay. Moses is alone with God on the mountain and says that if he has found any favor with God, he would like God to show him his glory (*kavod*).

Although God's answer is complex, and will be discussed at greater length as I proceed, part of that answer is that neither Moses nor anyone else can see God's face and live. It is not that they will be punished for trying to look, but that the face of God is simply too much for any mortal to take in. In a similar way, Exodus 19 warns the people not to try to look at God and the priests to consecrate themselves lest God break out against them and destroy them.

Why does the Bible say it is dangerous to get too close to a God that most religious traditions—including Judaism—portray as benevolent? Logically speaking, if God has the power to create heaven and earth, he also has the power to destroy them. As the Bible sees it, however, God's power is not just something we infer but something whose presence poses a serious threat to human welfare. We can begin to understand the nature of this threat by recognizing that in a monotheistic context, holiness involves boundaries: light and darkness, the sacred and the profane, the divine and the human. To try to cross or confuse them is to upset the foundation on which the world is based. Thus, when God banishes Adam and Eve from the Garden of Eden (Genesis 3:24), he remarks that "man has become like us" and places monsters (*cherubim*) at the gate and a flaming sword to guard the entrance.

To say that boundaries are important *in a monotheistic context* raises the deeper question of what that context is. At first blush, the answer seems obvious: in contrast to paganism, which professed belief in a plurality of gods, monotheism (mono + theism) is the belief that there is only one God. It is often said that this belief constitutes Judaism's greatest contribution to world culture. But it only takes a moment to see that this answer is too simple.

Suppose that a person living in a pagan culture such as ancient Greece believed that of the twelve gods and goddesses supposed to dwell on Mt. Olympus, eleven are bogus: the only true deity is Athena. Suppose too that this person believed that Athena is pretty much the way Homer described her and Greek art depicted her. Would we say that such a belief is "monotheistic" as Judaism, Christianity, and Islam understand the term? After all, Athena does have a claim to exclusivity. Or, to put the question another way: Is there a principled difference between monotheism properly so called and single deity paganism?

The answer is yes, and the difference is critical. The emergence of monotheism was important not only because it reduced the number of gods to one, but also because it asserted something important about the nature of God. Simply put, exclusivity is not enough. This means that in addition to being exclusive, a monotheistic God must be perfect or absolute, conditioned by nothing. Not only does this rule out a god who yields to natural forces such as wind, rain, or floods, from a philosophical perspective, it rules out a god who faces anything in the way of restriction or limitation. Let us say, therefore, that in addition to being exclusive, God is unique in the sense that nothing resembles God or can stand as a rival to God.

To take the next step, uniqueness implies that we cannot arrive at a proper conception of God by looking at created objects and imagining that God is bigger, stronger, or more exalted. If a monotheistic God resembles nothing else, then we cannot proceed as if the same categories that apply to normal objects of experience also apply to God.

At a simple level, this means that God has no height or weight, does not wear clothes or eat meals, and does not reside on the top of a mountain. At a more advanced level, it means that strictly speaking, even categories such as king, teacher, or judge have no application to God if understood in their normal sense. Kings die, teachers have limits, and judges make mistakes; so too power, wisdom, and goodness. The power to command an army into battle or to move mountains bears no resemblance to the power to create an entire universe out of nothing. And the wisdom one acquires by reading books bears no resemblance to that involved in contemplating all of reality in a single instant.

So God is not a bigger, stronger, better version of something found on earth. That much could have been said of Zeus or Athena. I submit that this is part of what Exodus 33 implies when it says that no one can see the face of God and live. Unlike Zeus or Athena, God is too awesome to contemplate. If so, we have no choice but to ask how we are to think about God. If the Bible tells us that we cannot see God's face and should be wary of trying to get too close to God, the challenge we face is how to convert these warnings into a systematic view of the relation between God and the human intellect.

I.

According to Maimonides, Exodus 33 is a parable whose purpose is to express the fact that God's essence is unknowable.[1] His argument rests on the claim that unlike everything else in the universe, God is not susceptible to definition. According to the Aristotelian logic prominent in the Middle Ages, definition proceeds by genus and specific difference. If God cannot be contained or conditioned by anything, then there is no wider category under which God can be subsumed and therefore no possibility of a cause prior to God as *living thing* is prior to *mammal*.

If no definition can be given of God, then "His essence cannot be grasped as it really is."[2] In addition to the logical reason, there is also an epistemological one. According to Maimonides, matter—even heavenly matter—is a strong veil that prevents us from apprehending things that are separate from matter as they truly are.[3] If even Moses could not grasp God's essence when alone with God on the mountaintop and free of the normal distractions, then by Maimonides's reasoning, it is impossible for us to grasp it as well.[4]

This insight forms the cornerstone of negative theology. While much of that theology relies on sophisticated arguments, Maimonides maintains that some of it—for example, that God does not resemble anything in the created order—is so central to Judaism that even the multitude, who have no training in philosophy, need to learn it.[5] As the prophet Isaiah (46:5) asks, "To whom will you liken me that I should be compared?" No matter what we pick, we run the risk of bringing God down to the level of a normal object of experience or of raising a normal object of experience up to the level of God.

To repeat, monotheism requires boundaries. There is God and everything else. To underscore the point that nothing in the created order resembles God, Maimonides insists that any term we use to describe God—even something as basic as "exists"—is completely equivocal as applied to God and as applied to us.[6]

When it comes to what meaning to ascribe to terms such as "knowledge," "power," "will," and "life" when applied to God, Maimonides's first response is to turn to negation. Grammatically, "God is powerful" resembles "John is tall" in that both ascribe a relational property to a subject. We saw, however, that God does not fall under a larger category or concept. To avoid this mistake, Maimonides proposes that "God is powerful" be analyzed as "God does not lack power or possess it in a way comparable to us." So while "God is powerful" is true, it does not classify God or say anything substantive about the kind of power that God has. Again God's power is not just more than ours but something of a completely different sort.

I say that negation is Maimonides's *first* response because eventually he argues that even negations seek to classify God and impose limitations. According to Maimonides, then, the most that negation can do is provide an approximation to the truth rather than a precise formulation of it. As he puts it, negations "conduct the mind toward the utmost reach that man may attain in the apprehension of Him."[7] This is another way of saying that while negation may have heuristic value in the sense that it gets us to see that God cannot be a normal subject of attribution, it too is subject to limitation.

In the end, Maimonides maintains that all semantic functions, whether attribution, description, or definition, fail when applied to God. Quoting Psalm 65 ("Silence is praise to Thee"), he concludes that the best we can do is recognize the limits of human discourse and say nothing. The only exception he recognizes is the Tetragrammaton (YHWH), the proper name of God whose exact pronunciation is unknown.[8]

In Jewish tradition, the Tetragrammaton was to be pronounced only by the priests in the Temple and the High Priest on the Day of Atonement. Since the destruction of the Temple, and the abolition of the priesthood, not only is it forbidden to pronounce it, no one can be sure how it should be pronounced. Taking all these limitations into account, one cannot help but think of Plotinus, who said centuries before Maimonides that there are contexts in which silence actually contains more truth than speech.[9]

It is clear that what Maimonides has done is to replace the physical destruction described in the book of Exodus with semantic or intellectual destruction. It is not that we will be blown away by a ball of fire if we try to comprehend the nature of God, but that our categories and intuitions will break down. Along these lines, he recounts the legend of the four rabbis who entered the garden (*pardes*) where esoteric subjects were revealed.[10] One went mad, one killed himself, and one became an apostate. Of the four, only Akiba went in and came out in peace.

The lesson Maimonides draws from this is that only Akiba recognized his limits and stayed within them. We can take this as further evidence of what will happen if one comes too close to God. The alternative is to keep our distance and maintain a studied silence. In a moment of eloquence, Maimonides writes: "Glory then to Him who is such that when the intellects contemplate His essence, their apprehension turns into incapacity; and when they contemplate the proceeding of His actions from His will, their knowledge turns into ignorance; and when the tongues aspire to magnify Him by means of attributive qualifications, all eloquence turns into weariness and incapacity!"[11] So understood, the effort to know God is not like that involved in discovering a new particle or developing a new process. In the latter cases, knowledge advances when concepts are revised and theories are extended. Maimonides's contention is that rather than conceptual revision, the effort to know God will culminate in the recognition of something to which no category or description will ever be adequate. Again from Isaiah (40:17), "All the nations are as nothing before him; they are counted by him as less than nothing." Substitute "concepts" for "nations" and you have the crux of what negative theology is about.

II.

In a modern context, the mention of conceptual destruction brings to mind the thought of Emmanuel Levinas.[12] Accordingly to Levinas, the biblical God "signifies the beyond being, transcendence," something that overflows every human capacity and thus "breaks up" thought.[13] Turning from the Bible to philosophy, Levinas finds the same sentiment expressed in Descartes's Third Meditation. Students of the history of philosophy will recall that Descartes tried to establish the existence of God by arguing that because my idea of God depicts something with an infinite amount of reality or perfection, as a finite being, I could not possibly be the cause of it. The only thing that could be the cause of this idea is something that contains as much reality as the idea depicts. The only thing that contains this much reality is an infinite being. Therefore an infinite being exists.

According to Levinas, the key to the argument is the recognition that our idea of the infinite must come from something other than ourselves because we do not have enough perfection to formulate such an idea on our own. So the idea of the infinite is exceptional in that the object of the idea or *ideatum* completely surpasses the idea itself.[14] As Levinas puts it, the intentionality of the idea "aims at what it cannot embrace."[15] This means that when I contemplate the degree of perfection represented by the idea, I will come to see that my thought is overwhelmed. Levinas concludes that the infinite affects thought by devastating it.[16] Like Maimonides, he has replaced the physical destruction associated with coming too close to God with conceptual destruction.

At this point, a few words of qualification are needed. First, Levinas introduces the idea of the infinite and its effect on thought not to speculate on the nature of a transcendent substance but to argue for the absolute alterity of the Other. But despite a difference in their respective projects, Levinas and Descartes share this much: they are both trying to deal with the consequences of holding an idea whose full meaning is too much for our minds to grasp.

In my view, this is the same problem that Moses encounters at Exodus 33 and that Maimonides wrestles with in the chapters on negative theology. As Levinas himself recognizes, his interpretation of Descartes departs from the letter of Cartesian philosophy, at least as expressed in the *Meditations*. One can see this by recalling that for Descartes, while there may be an infinity of things in God that I cannot understand, it is nonetheless true that I have a clear and distinct idea of God. If I did not, none of the proofs Descartes offers for the existence of God would work. It is therefore going beyond Descartes's intention to describe the effect that God has on thought as devastation.

In fact, Levinas would have been on firmer ground if he had looked beyond the *Meditations* and considered Descartes's correspondence. For example, in a letter to Mersenne, Descartes writes: "The mathematical truths which you call eternal have been laid down by God and depend on Him entirely no less than the rest of his creatures.... Indeed to say that these truths are independent of God is to talk of Him as if He were Jupiter or Saturn and to subject Him to the Styx and the Fates."[17] The typical scholastic position was that the eternal truths are inherent in the nature of things and do not result from a free choice of God.[18] Descartes's point is that such a view amounts to a return to paganism because it conditions God by subjecting him to a greater power. The alternative is to say that what we refer to as "eternal" truths are established by God and are dependent on him to the same degree as are birds and bees.

Let us be clear what this means. According to Descartes, God *made* the theorems of geometry true; and if he had wanted, he could just as easily have made them false. Not only is there no essential nature independent of God, there is nothing that inclines God to pick one set of mathematical laws over another. As he sees it, "supreme indifference in God is the supreme proof of his omnipotence."[19]

How can we understand a world in which the theorems of geometry are false? Descartes admits we cannot. In a letter to Mesland, he concedes: "As for the difficulty of conceiving how it was a matter of freedom and indifference for God to make it not true that the three angles of a triangle were equal to two right angles, or generally that contradictions cannot exist together, one can easily remove it by considering that the power of God cannot have any limits."[20] Rather than say God cannot make a triangle whose angles do not equal two right angles, it would be better to say *we cannot understand* how God can make a triangle whose angles do not equal two right angles.

Shortly before the passage just quoted, Descartes explains this by saying:

> But I do not think that we should ever say of anything that it cannot be brought about by God. For since everything involved in truth and goodness depends on His omnipotence, I would not dare say that God cannot make a mountain without a valley, or that one and two should not be three. I merely say that He has given me such a mind that I cannot conceive a mountain without a valley, or an aggregate of one and two which is not three, and that such things involve a contradiction in my conception.

If God's power has no limits, it is beyond our comprehension—once again an idea whose meaning is too much for our minds to grasp. In fact, as Descartes says to Mersenne, "the very fact that we judge it incomprehensible makes us esteem it more greatly."

Needless to say, this doctrine is controversial, and it is unclear how far Descartes meant to take it. Does it apply only to finite essences such as triangles or does it also apply to the basic laws of thought? The answer would seem to be that it applies to everything or else we would be back in the position of subjecting God to the Styx and the Fates. How, then, do we approach our understanding of God? Could God render his own omnipotence ineffective? Could he make it a good thing to deceive humans who use their rational faculties correctly? Having willed one thing, could God make it so that he had never willed it at all? Scholars disagree, in part because such questions take us beyond the bounds of rational sense.[21]

For my purposes, the important point is that once we introduce the idea of unlimited power, we open the gates to questions that strike at the heart of consistency and rationality, which was precisely the point Levinas urged on us: the infinite affects thought by devastating it—or at least raising the question of its devastation. Along these lines, both Maimonides and Aquinas compare the human attempt to know God with looking directly at the sun and conclude that the result would be blindness.[22]

Descartes is more extreme. To appreciate the full significance of conceptual devastation, we should recognize that for him the proofs purporting to establish the existence of God presuppose the very rationality that God's destructiveness threatens. So it is as if having shown through rational arguments that God exists, we come to see that his existence may render those very arguments invalid.

Obviously we are not obliged to accept the Cartesian position. Why, for example, should we assume that the laws of thought stand to a monotheistic God in the same way that the Styx and the Fates stand to a pagan one? One has to do with physical strength, the other with the limits of intelligibility. Here I should confess that I am far from sure that Descartes is right and more sympathetic with those who, like Leibniz and Spinoza, were convinced he is wrong.

Suppose someone were to ask me to prove that he is wrong. What argument could I give to decide the question of what God can or cannot do? Just as obviously, there is none. If I am far from sure that he is right, honesty forces me to say that I have no certainty that he is wrong. The upshot is that when it comes to God, normal intuitions about what is possible or impossible wear thin. To the objection that if true, Descartes's position would lead to incoherence, the appropriate answer is that indeed it would. Once we agree that the laws of thought are made rather than discovered, the prospect of incoherence stares us in the face.

As soon as we allow the possibility of incoherence in the door, we are faced with the prospect that God could be anything at all. Let in one idea whose meaning is too much for our minds to grasp and before you know it, every idea becomes suspect. As we saw in our discussion of Maimonides, all semantic functions fail when applied to God. This means we can characterize God as wise, free, or powerful only if we keep in mind that at some level, these and all similar claims will have to be given up in favor of a studied silence.

III.

How we are to cope with such a radical view? If thought has no purchase on God, what does? Here we face the danger that if thought is overwhelmed, people will turn to something else. The danger is heightened by asking how an infinite or absolute God could be satisfied with anything less than an infinite or absolute response from us. In short, does monotheism demand fanaticism?

One hardly has to mention that extreme behavior, whether in the form of asceticism, self-mutilation, child sacrifice, or the massacre of whole communities, has played a part in all monotheistic religions. While such behavior is revolting, we should not blind ourselves to the fact that it raises a legitimate question. Why should we suppose that a God who is too dangerous to approach and too incomprehensible to make sense of would be satisfied with the normal habits of human beings? As Kierkegaard argues in *Fear and Trembling*, if God can do anything, then surely God can make murder a holy act.

One does not have to look far in the Bible to see that extreme behavior—either on God's part or ours—often carries the day. In short order there is a flood that destroys almost all life on earth, the near sacrifice of Isaac by Abraham, a series of deadly plagues, the destruction of whole cities during the conquest of Palestine, and the promise of destruction bordering on cosmic upheaval unless Israel changes its ways. In the words of Gershom Scholem, "Jewish messianism is in its origin and by its nature . . . a theory of catastrophe."[23] In this context, "catastrophe" is a synonym for "devastation," which takes us back to the idea that to get close to God is to risk everything so that the safer course of action is to stand back.

It should come as no surprise that I am not recommending extreme or violent behavior. If God is as incomprehensible as I am suggesting, there is no reason to suppose that extreme behavior is any more pleasing to God than quiet or modest behavior is. If the Israelites heard thunder at Sinai, Elijah experienced God in the silence of a cave. Once consistency and rationality are shown to be suspect, all bets are off.

From a Cartesian perspective, the appropriate response would be to adopt a form of epistemological humility. Rather than say the interior angles of a triangle equal 180 degrees, I should say that while I cannot conceive of how they could equal anything but 180 degrees, this is a claim about how my mind understands things rather than a claim about what God can or cannot do. Rather than say that God cannot be a deceiver, I should say that I cannot imagine how a just and perfect God could deceive anyone, but like everything else, my imagination imposes no restrictions on God. And rather than say that God cannot will himself out of existence or undo the past, I should say that contemplating such things leads to absurdity, not that they are inherently impossible.

Although Maimonides does not countenance logical absurdity in God, he does go out of his way to stress the importance of humility in the face of God. In his discussion of character traits in the *Mishneh Torah*, for example, Maimonides points out that while it is normally advisable for a person's behavior to follow the middle way between extremes, there are some exceptions—the most obvious being humility.[24] In fact, it is not enough merely to be humble, a person must hold himself low and have no pretensions. In support of this, he cites Numbers 12:3, which says that Moses was not just humble but *very* humble. With respect to our attitude toward God, he points out that Moses hid his face and was afraid to look on God at the burning bush (Exodus 3:6), while the nobles of Israel were overhasty at Exodus 24:11 and achieved an imperfect apprehension as a result.[25]

Beyond Moses, there is the case of Job. Unlike Moses at Exodus 33, Job himself is never in physical danger. But when God begins to speak to him, he soon learns that the universe contains mysteries and monsters too great for him to understand. In keeping with Psalm 65, he too comes to the conclusion that there is nothing to say. In light of everything that has been said, it is not too great a stretch to say that the humility achieved by figures such as Moses and Job involves a recognition of the limits of human knowledge, the vanity of much human striving, and the qualified nature of any human achievement. To put it another way, the ultimate theological virtue is a feeling of awe and wonderment in the presence of something vastly greater than what we can understand.

IV.

If this were all that the Bible had to say about the human effort to know God, it would be difficult to see how it could constitute the foundation of a religion. We would have skepticism and humility but no clear sense of what God wanted from us and nothing approaching a doctrine of *imitatio dei*. Fortunately this is not all we are told. Although God will not let Moses see his face, as a consolation he tells Moses that he will cause all of his goodness to pass in front of him. To be specific, he says that he will put Moses in the cleft of a rock and cover him with his hand for protection. After God has passed by, he will remove his hand so that Moses can see his backside. The passage ends with God repeating that Moses cannot see God's face.

What are we to make of this? According to Maimonides, the goodness that God allows Moses to see is identical to that mentioned at Genesis 1.31: "And God saw everything that he had made, and, behold, it was very good." I take this to mean that everything God made has a reason to be and exists in harmony with everything else. Maimonides concludes that while Moses could not know God directly through intuition of his essence, he was able to know God indirectly by focusing his attention on the *ways and works* of God, in other words, what God has made or done. This implies that we can praise the world God has created without knowing the true nature or identity of God. It would be as if a scientist in a laboratory could measure the radiation emanating from a black box without knowing anything about what is inside.

For a medieval thinker such as Maimonides, this means that nature is a well-designed system in which each species is given the means necessary to protect itself and obtain food—hence the oft-repeated claim that nature does nothing frivolous or in vain. To take Maimonides's own example, nature is structured so that the embryos of living things are protected from destruction. As a result, God is called merciful. Because a father who shows pity or compassion to his child is also called merciful, we have the beginnings of a theory of *imitatio dei*.

According to Maimonides, there is nothing wrong with this theory as long as we recognize that the father is not imitating God himself but God's ways or works, the consequences of effects that flow from God rather than God himself. He elaborates, "The meaning here is not that He possesses moral qualities, but that He performs actions resembling the actions that in us proceed from moral qualities—I mean from aptitudes of the soul; the meaning is not that He . . . possesses aptitudes of the soul."[26] Even this formulation of the theory is misleading if we take *actions* to mean that God makes day-to-day decisions about the governance of the world. Instead, what we are supposed to see is that divine activity creates and sustains an order in which one can detect gracious or merciful features in the overall design.

Owing to human linguistic practice, when gracious or merciful features proceed *from* God, the predicates "gracious" or "merciful" are applied *to* God. This is what allows people to compose prayers and hymns that offer praise to God. In the *Guide of the Perplexed*, as in the *Mishneh Torah*, Maimonides strives for greater rigor by avoiding the claim that God *is* merciful or gracious and saying instead that God is *called* merciful or gracious. The difference is significant because to say that God *is* merciful would imply that God has a merciful disposition or has developed the habit of acting mercifully over a period of time.

This way of speaking is clearly anthropomorphic and runs counter to the whole thrust of negative theology. Because God has no material component, Maimonides insists that it is impossible for God to have dispositions or affections.[27] By limiting ourselves to what God is called, we make no claim about God himself and direct our attention to how *we* characterize divine activity given the limited perspective that we enjoy.

There is no question that the sacred literature of monotheistic religions encourages us to view God as a judge who listens to pleas of mercy and grants clemency. Maimonides's point is that however useful this language may be in getting people to fear God and repent, strictly speaking, it cannot be true. In fact, the denial of habits and dispositions in God leads Maimonides to conclude that if a person really wants to imitate God, she should act in a completely dispassionate way. To continue with the previously quoted passage from the *Guide*, "It behooves the governor of a city, if he is a prophet, to acquire similarity to these attributes, so that these actions may proceed from him according to a determined measure and according to the deserts of the people who are affected by them and not merely because of his following a passion." If a judge is going to grant mercy, the reason should not be that she has developed merciful feelings toward the criminal but that, independent of any feeling, the criminal deserves merciful treatment.

By the end of the *Guide*, Maimonides goes further. Human perfection consists in apprehension of God *to the degree that it is possible* and knowledge of God's providence as it extends over creatures and is manifested in the acts of creation and governance.[28] After achieving this apprehension, he continues, such a person will always have in view loving-kindness, righteousness, and sound judgment.

Again we must give up the idea that God governs the universe in the way that a mayor governs a city. But it does make sense to say that having seen the world that God created and sustains, a world that avoids excesses and deficiencies, Moses was inspired to propose a body of law that emphasizes orderly behavior, purity of purpose, and control of the emotions. Put otherwise, if God acts for a purpose and does nothing frivolous or in vain, it makes sense to say that we should act in a similar way. Note once again that by adhering to the laws of the Torah, we are not imitating God as much as the features of God's governance of the world.

In this way, we can be asked to imitate God, but if we do, our imitation is never simple or direct. As Genesis 33 makes clear, what we are imitating is God's backside, not his face. If Maimonides is right, the person who succeeds in such imitation will have no desire to act in a selfish, arrogant, or unforgiving manner. He will insist on fairness above all else and see to it that the various parts of his domain live together in harmony. The result will be that just as God is called merciful or gracious, he will be called the same thing. We should keep in mind, however, that between God as he is in himself and the consequences or affects that flow from God, there is no similarity. One is simple, the other complex; one necessary, the other contingent; one the creator, the other the creation. It is only the latter that we can understand and to which we can assimilate our behavior.

Though Maimonides often speaks of getting close to God, we also must keep in mind that "closeness" in this context involves a measure of irony: we are close to God to the degree that we recognize the unbridgeable nature of the gap that separates us. Accordingly, "a man sometimes has to labor for many years in order to understand some science and to gain true knowledge of its premises so that he should have certainty with regard to this science, whereas the only conclusion from this science in its entirety consists in our negating with reference to God some notion of which it has been learnt by demonstration that it cannot possibly be ascribed to God."[29]

This is the highest level of contemplation we can achieve. Though the knowledge it gives us is negative, Maimonides is adamant that it still counts as knowledge. Once it is achieved, we can proceed from God to God's governance of the created order, but in so doing, we always run the risk of speaking in anthropomorphic terms and spreading confusion. In the end, the correct way to understand our situation is that we are enjoined to cultivate mercy and graciousness not because God has cultivated them but because God has blessed us with a world in which signs of mercy and graciousness are clearly visible.

With the qualification provided by Exodus 33 ("You can see my backside"), we are in a position to say that while the epistemological humility that follows from not being able to see God's face is still needed, provided we are careful in how we formulate our position, there is more to say. The prayers and hymns that constitute the foundation of religious practice are perfectly legitimate.

Danger lurks only if we think one can read the prayers and hymns in a literal fashion and come to know God as a result. But this should not surprise us. There is a danger in reading *any* book in a literal fashion and ignoring the conceptual problems to which literal interpretation inevitably leads. Suppose, for example, that a person were to pick up a science book and interpret terms such as *atom, black hole, light ray, quantum jump,* or *cell wall* literally. It would not be long before our understanding these things led to paradox.

The qualification expressed in Exodus 33 also allows us to reject the idea that extreme or violent behavior is pleasing to God. Although violent acts in nature occur, Maimonides argues that by surveying the whole of nature, we will be led to loving-kindness, righteousness, and sound judgment. This is all a way of saying that while we can never lose sight of epistemological humility, there is more to religion than hiding one's face in the presence of God. While Moses hid his face at the burning bush and stood behind the rock when God's goodness passed by in Exodus 33, he also led a people out of slavery and mandated a set of laws dealing with everything from festivals to fast days, from marriage to mourning, from war to peace. Important as they were, his moments of humility were limited to times when he was alone with God and could focus his attention on God alone.

V.

For all its textual support and rational cogency, negative theology is not for everyone. It would be foolish to attend a wedding or funeral and point out that everything is as nothing before God. To make the same point in another way, if silence is the highest praise we can give to God, no one can remain silent forever or stand before God indefinitely. Like Moses on the mountaintop or the escaped prisoner from Plato's cave, we all have to return to the everyday world and work to make it a better place. From a religious perspective, God is both the foundation of that world and something whose incomprehensible nature threatens to devastate it. The challenge we face as human beings is the ability to keep both perspectives firmly in view.

Notes

I have shortened and simplified some of the issues in this essay in order to make them suitable for general audiences in Kenneth Seeskin, *Thinking about the Torah: A Philosopher Reads the Bible* (Lincoln: University of Nebraska Press, 2017).

1. Maimonides, *Guide of the Perplexed*, 1.52. All citations to the *Guide of the Perplexed*, trans. Shlomo Pines (Chicago: The University of Chicago Press, 1963), vol. 1, 108–127.

2. *Guide*, 1.54, 123. For further discussion of this point and the historical precedents behind it, see Alexander Altmann, "Essence and Existence in Maimonides," *Studies in Religious Philosophy and Mysticism* (Ithaca, NY: Cornell University Press, 1969).

3. *Guide*, 3.9.

4. In a similar way, Aquinas (*Summa Theologica* 1.12.11) maintains that the mode of knowledge follows the mode of the nature of the knower. Because in this life, our soul has its being in corporeal matter, it knows naturally only what has a form in matter or what can be known by such a form.

5. *Guide*, 1.35, 80.

6. *Guide*, 1.56, 131.

7. *Guide*, 1.58, 135.

8. For Maimonides's analysis of the Tetragrammaton, see *Guide*, 1.61, 147–150.

9. Plotinus, *Enneads*, 5.5.6.

10. *Guide*, 1.32, 68–69. The reference is to *Chagigah*, 14b.

11. *Guide*, 1.59, 137.

12. As far as I know, the only person to draw a connection between Maimonides and Levinas on this point is Michael Fagenblat in *A Covenant of Creatures: Levinas's Philosophy of Judaism* (Stanford, CA: Stanford University Press, 2010), especially chap. 4.

13. Levinas, "God and Philosophy," *Basic Philosophical Writings*, ed. Adriaan Peperzak, Simon Critchley, and Robert Berlusconi (Bloomington: Indiana University Press, 1996), 130, 135–136.

14. In Cartesian parlance, the formal reality of the *ideatum*—God—is such that it cannot be contained by the objective reality of the idea.

15. Levinas, "Philosophy and the Idea of Infinity," *Collected Philosophical Papers*, trans. Alphonso Lingis (Pittsburgh: Duquesne University Press, 1998), 54.

16. Levinas, "God and Philosophy," *Collected Papers*, 138.

17. *Descartes: Philosophical Letters*, ed. Anthony Kenny (Oxford: Clarendon Press, 1970), 18–19.

18. See, for example, *Guide*, 3.15.

19. "Reply to Objections VI," *The Philosophical Works of Descartes*, vol. 2, ed. Elizabeth S. Haldane and G. T. R. Ross (Mineola, NY: Dover Publications, 1955), 248.

20. *Philosophical Letters*, 15.

21. For two classic discussions of this problem, see Harry Frankfurt, "Descartes on the Creation of the Eternal Truths," *Philosophical Review* 56 (1977): 36–57; and E. M. Curley, "Descartes on the Creation of the Eternal Truths," *Philosophical Review* 93 (1984): 569–597.

22. *Guide*, 1.59, 139; *Summa Theologica*, 1.12.1.

23. Gershom Scholem, *The Messianic Idea in Judaism* (New York: Schocken Books, 1971), 7.

24. *Mishneh* Torah 1. Character Traits, 2.3. For more on Maimonides's view of humility, see Raymond L. Weiss, *Maimonides Ethics* (Chicago; The University of Chicago Press, 1991), 38–46, 102–105, 107–115.

25. *Guide*, 1.5.

26. *Guide*, 1.54, 124.

27. *Guide*, 1.35.

28. *Guide*, 3.54, 638.

29. *Guide*, 1.59, 138.

THREE

What Is Positive in Negative Theology?

LENN E. GOODMAN

The arguments for negative theology are laid out clearly by Maimonides. He is also pretty clear about his motives. So we can see just where his arguments strike home: Like Plato, who coined the term "theology" and defined it as an effort to speak properly about the divine,[1] Maimonides aims to speak of God only in terms of perfection. Like the early *mutakallimūn*, whose debates with Christian theologians are caught in the amber of Muʿtazilite theology, Maimonides is chary of predications that might suggest plurality, change, or any other compromise with imperfection.

Early Muslim theologians swiftly learned to sidestep a Christian dialectical ploy: to agree that God has wisdom risks a trinitarian response: God's wisdom is what we mean by the Logos. Philo had pioneered the thought that God's word or wisdom is His way of manifesting Himself. But Origen and the Gospel of John attached the idea to the person of Jesus. Philo's question, How could God be both immanent and transcendent, as the Torah expects, became: How could Christ mediate between God and the world and serve as intercessor as well, by offering himself as the lamb of atonement? Muʿtazilites soon learned the cautious formulation: "God is wise, but not by way of wisdom."

Maimonides echoes that response in his denial of divine attributes: God is not rightly assigned predicates from the repertoire we use to describe finite things. God has no proper predicates because He has no attributes. There are no essential traits constitutive in His being. Nor do any accidental traits pertain, typified by the shifting qualities that cling to matter like aprons on a ragdoll. Even the most general terms cannot successfully class God with other beings: He "exists but not by way of existence and is one but not by partaking of unity."[2] Maimonides will not quite say that God is beyond being, but he reaps the same result by saying that God, as a necessary being, exists in a wholly different way from anything else. Attributes, at any rate, are all too readily hypostatized: "if God had multiple attributes there would have to be multiple eternal beings. There simply is no monotheism without belief in one simplex Being, uncompounded and utterly undifferentiated, one from every standpoint and perspective—indivisible causally and conceptually, subjectively and objectively."[3]

It is not just a Christian gambit that Maimonides dodges here. The ancient Neoplatonists had unfolded their pantheon from the absolute unity of the One by relying on the recursiveness of divine thought. Their writings, in Arabic translation, had a profound impact on such philosophers as al-Fārābī and Avicenna, who made Neoplatonism the high road of philosophy in Arabic. Emanation, for them, *unending and unbegun*, was the key to rational theology for anyone who took seriously the constructive work of reason. Against that backdrop we can readily see how Maimonides's denial of attributes sought to free the Godhead of any hint of a hypostasis, be it trinitarian or Neoplatonic. But there was a positive side to negative theology as well in Maimonides's commitment to scriptural ideas of creation and transcendence. Creation, as Avicenna had seen clearly, entails the contingency of all beings but God. Yet timeless emanation, as Avicenna's Muslim critic al-Ghazālī saw with equal clarity, did not adequately preserve that contingency. A timeless procession from the Highest—yielding an eternal world if it yielded anything at all—did not avoid reducing God's creative act to something automatic, making the world a mere corollary, as it were, of God's eternal truth. Eternalist emanation might claim the high ground of reason. But its intellectualism risked making all events logical entailments, shutting out empiricism regarding nature and voluntarism regarding God. Its ultimate outcome, if not atheism, as Ghazālī charged, was a block universe—a sudden return to Parmenidean unity, allowing no divine expression whatever.

Like the Neoplatonists, whom he and Ghazālī call by the name they had adopted from the Greek, the Philosophers (*al-falāsifa*), Maimonides too would appeal to the recursiveness of thought—not to uncoil divine hypostases like the tendrils of some insistent fern, but to preserve God's unity. Like Ghazālī and many another scriptural monotheist, he would reconfigure emanation, relying on volition to explain how God's unity could yield our colorful and multifarious world: God must be understood in terms of will as well as wisdom, not reduced to an internal necessity, lest emanation transform the world into a number line and make God a mere unit and not an active unity.

Like Ghazālī, Maimonides insisted that a timeless plan can yield temporal effects.[4] So divine volition was not inconsistent with divine changelessness. Still, before this essay ends, we will need to ask how Maimonides, despite rejecting divine attributes, could ascribe both will and wisdom to his God and how he could prevent God's will from being swallowed up in divine wisdom, as it seemed to be in the intellectualism of the Philosophers. Beyond that, we will need to see how Maimonides, and how we in our own way, can relate divine unity to nature's dynamic—and the open future. But our first question is how the Rambam preserved God's unity while describing God in mentalistic terms. He did so, I have suggested, by turning to the same recursiveness in thought that had allowed Neoplatonists to find a pantheon in the pregnant potentiality of the One:

> You know how celebrated the Philosophers' saying is that God is the Thought, the Thinker, and the Act of Thinking, that these three are one and not differentiated in Him. I cited this in my big work too.[5] It's a mainstay of our religion, as I explained there, that He is one absolutely: Nothing attaches to Him. Only He is eternal. That's why it says, *as God lives* (cf. Amos 8:14) and not "by God's life." God's life is nothing distinct from Him, as I made clear in rejecting divine attributes.[6]

It was Aristotle who had seen the perfection of divine activity in the perfect actuality of God's thought, where thought, thinker, and the act of thinking are one and the same.[7] Maimonides calls this view "a clearly demonstrated truth, as theistic philosophers have shown." He identifies with those philosophers in rising to its defense, calling it "our saying that God is Thought, Thinker, and the Act of Thinking" (I 68).

Maimonides's stringency about God's unity reflects the logic of Avicenna's argument for a necessary being, which pivots on a premise drawn from the Kalām and familiar to us in the Principle of Sufficient Reason: Whatever is and need not have been requires a cause. Any contingent being, then, ultimately presupposes some Necessary Being. For no infinite causal series can reach an actual effect. But no finite or temporal or otherwise determinate being escapes contingency since there is no contradiction in its having been other than it is, or nonexistent altogether. Any being we confront, then, and any empiric fact, points ultimately to a Necessary Being.[8] That is why Maimonides can say, echoing Ghazālī, that the realized monotheist sees God in all things, and why he can interpret the theophany of Moses as God's revelation through the panoply of nature:[9]

> All determinate things point beyond their proximate cause to an Ultimate—unless we are to surrender causality and the very idea of explanation. For our commitment to the causal principle makes no sense if the search for explanations is dropped before reaching ultimacy. Otherwise we're left with causal kiting, explanations that pass the buck from one to the next, covering one contingent check with another and leaving an unending, unsupported line of credit. Only a self-explanatory Being (as Maimonides and Spinoza both saw) can cap the series and resolve the threat of epistemic bankruptcy. And only a necessary, self-sufficient Being, can be self-explanatory.[10]

The Necessary Being that a world of contingent beings requires cannot be other than it is and cannot fail to be. So God is changeless—and indivisible objectively and subjectively: if God could be cut up at the joints conceptually, as Socrates liked to carve an argument, God's existence would not be necessary. For whatever depends on the coalescence of its parts is contingent. Those parts need not have been united as they are. Even a conceptual division would wreck the logic of monotheism. For if God were *notionally* composite, compounded of matter and form say, there would be no contradiction in those constituents' being unconjoined: the being they compose would lack the hallmark of self-sufficiency.

The same reasoning sustains God's impassivity. God's varied acts, Maimonides writes, "imply no variance in the Doer." Change is just a temporal way of slicing multiplicity. A God who can be otherwise is not a necessary being. Bolstering the radical monotheism of the Kalām, Maimonides says of God: "all His varied acts are done by His Identity alone, and nothing else."[11] Natural and human history unfold timeless patterns. Powers are delegated, the Rambam stipulates. God, as Ghazālī puts it, is the Cause of causes.[12] To Maimonides this means that God imparts the powers by which all things act as their natures dictate—rocks fall, medicines heal, food nourishes, and we humans use our measure of power to choose and chart our course. God does not alter with the changes. A necessary being does not shift from potency to act.

Kalām is familiarly described as dialectical theology, reflecting al-Fārābī's charge, not unjustified, that it is not apodictic reasoning. And the principle of sufficient reason is metaphysics, not logic. But it did not just spring from the fertile imaginations of the *mutakallimūn*. It was the distillate of their reading of scripture and the world: as scripture makes dramatically clear, the world need not have been as it is.[13] It need not have been at all. Its being requires an adequate cause. Its goodness requires beneficence in that cause. The relative goodness found in the world points to absolute goodness in its Creator.

That last, we can say, is the monotheistic leap—not a leap in the dark in an unknown direction, but an extrapolation from our limited experience of goodness to infinite goodness in its Source. How reason might manage that progression is suggested in the *Modim* passage of the *Amida* prayer, recited by observant Jews three times each day, acknowledging God "for our souls in Thy charge, for Thy miracles daily with us, for Thy constant marvels and favors, morning, noon, and night—Thou Good whose mercies are unfailing, Merciful Giver whose acts of grace never cease." The marvels and miracles here called continuous are seen not in disruptions of the natural order but in its constancy: God's transcendence is glimpsed in the steady flow of light through the latticework of natural providence.

It is God's goodness that leads Plato to expect theology to speak well of God. The same goodness underwrites the Principle of Sufficient Reason, answering the expectation that reality makes sense: contingency presupposes adequacy. Reason bolts at the thought that things just are. The same demand for understanding that gives birth to the sciences rejects the notion that things just are with nothing to make them as they are.

Maimonides's Necessary Being does not live in splendid isolation but is the cause of all that is contingent. Nor is the Ultimate stranded at the apex of value. For what God causes is the fullness and flourishing in nature: life and light, love and understanding. The poetic powers of prophetic voices break down before the sheer Perfection that is the divine: "every godly sage and master with such truths as these to share speaks poetically and in riddles, using multiple figures of all sorts, shifting from image to image, and even to a different domain . . . finding no one image adequate throughout to the idea addressed."[14]

As the ultimate reality and cause, God is also the ultimate value, aligning all lesser values in a single scale of perfection, ontic and axiological. For, as in Plato, all affirmative values go hand in hand in the metaphysics of monotheism. So, as scripture proposes, God is the source of every moral imperative and call to perfection, invitations as varied as the realities receptive to them. Just as Plato's highest good must also be the Most Real, so biblically what is most real, the divine I AM, is the pinnacle of goodness and Judge of all the world, as He was even when He judged the first object of creation, and found it good.

God's necessary being and primacy as the Source of all goodness and summation of all authentic value entail God's uniqueness. But uniqueness compounds the problems of ineffability: human language counts on general terms, most relating to sensory experience, if not to our internal feelings and thus to our embodiment. So we must concede the inadequacy of human language in any attempt to characterize God. How can we possibly portray what is beyond anything familiar? This is the problem addressed in the opening chapters of Maimonides's *Guide to the Perplexed*. Hasty readers often imagine that these chapters aim to "refute" anthropomorphism. But to understand any philosophical discussion we need to discriminate what it assumes from what it argues. Maimonides offers no argument against anthropomorphism until his "lexicon" of biblical anthropomorphisms is complete. And when the promised argument is finally unlimbered, it is far broader and more radical than a vague dismissal of anthropomorphic language.

Historically, a wide-ranging tribute to transcendence had long been all but canonical in the Aramaic renderings of scripture ascribed to Onkelos and Jonathan ben Uzziel. Maimonides appreciates the exclusion of corporealism and anthropomorphism that these classic translations enshrine.[15] Indeed, he expects readers to follow their guidance if they are unable to mount the scaffolding of philosophical argumentation for themselves.[16] But he also understands that a targum, unlike the essay form he chooses for the *Guide*, cannot really stop and step aside to explain itself. The format does not leave room to voice a thesis, let alone an argument.[17] Maimonides's thesis, when he does set it out, articulates an idea of transcendence far more radical than any mere rejection of anthropomorphic language. That might have been accomplished by some innocent qualifier such as the midrashic *k've-yakhol*, "as it were." But Maimonides will call the ascription of any real attributes to God further astray—"more hateful" to God in the sense he assigns to *that* biblical anthropomorphism—than polytheism.[18] So much for the notion that he hides his philosophical light under a politic bushel!

In a thoughtful article, Hannah Kasher seeks to navigate the strait between Maimonides's denial of divine attributes and his calling God the supreme, self-thinking mind.[19] She marks the apparent disparity as one of the "contradictions" Shlomo Pines cited in the well-known introduction to his translation of the *Guide*. Pines found it "very implausible" that Maimonides could be so "muddle-headed" as to miss so glaring a contradiction.[20] But if the discontinuity was intentional on the lines Leo Strauss laid out to guide one through the *Guide*, signaling Maimonides's dissatisfaction with his own overt position and pointing to an esoteric view, the question remains just which view is embraced and which is the camouflage, the cover story Maimonides "intended to appease his readers."

Pines, as Kasher reports, "reluctant to suggest that Maimonides actually was concealing his real opinion," at different times, considered both Straussian possibilities: Was his God the self-thinking Mind of Aristotle, shrouded in negative attributes "to veil the excessive proximity" of Aristotle's God to nature?[21] If so, "the Neoplatonic version is nothing but a mask, necessary to further the popular conception of a separate, supreme God." Or was Maimonides, "basically a Neoplatonist"?[22] Plainly Maimonides had inclinations in both directions. Indeed the philosophical tradition he knew best was a synthesis of Platonic and Aristotelian ideas, as was Neoplatonism itself. Yet the God of negative theology, Kasher writes, stands "at the greatest possible distance" from humanity, separated by "an impassable barrier" from a worshiper's prayers. The "self-cognizing subject" of *Metaphysics*, Lambda, seems hardly more alluring: "neither the intellectual god of the Aristotelians nor the cold, impersonal godhead of the Neoplatonists reflects the popular creed of a caring, personal God; neither doctrine could possibly be a suitable theology for the masses."[23]

Maimonides, however, hardly expects mass appeal to drive and steer theology. Even children, he urges, should be taught that God is not a person. And he finds the higher reaches of theology ill-suited to popular consumption and dangerous for beginners. God knew that societies need practical norms that depend ultimately on religious beliefs. So He did use accessible notions in Scripture alongside numerous suggestions of their inadequacy, all swathed in riddling symbols and poetic indirection, lest the richer fare of prophetic inspiration prove harmful to unprepared appetites.[24]

Eliezer Schweid proposed a way of easing the "contradiction" Pines found so troubling.[25] Kasher follows up on Schweid's reflections with her own thoughts about how to ease the "tension," as she prefers to call it. Her final proposal, drawing on Rudolf Otto, Yeshayahu Leibowitz, and the general phenomenology of religious experience, is that the tension "between the idea of God as an absolutely distinct entity, on the one hand, and a superlative supreme being on the other," is in a way unavoidable, even if it does prove resolvable "by careful analysis of the relevant texts."[26] But the outcome of that analysis, she argues, must favor negative theology, since "Maimonides' description of God as an intellect relies on negative attributes."[27] Still, as Kasher recognizes, calling God a mind is not wholly inconsistent with Maimonides's thoughts about transcendence.

In one way at least man too transcends familiar limitations: human thought, insofar as it becomes conceptual, does escape the limits of our physicality. It is by reference to the rational intellect that human beings are said to be created in God's image.[28] The human mind, we can say, does have a boundlessness to it, not just in the presumed timelessness of conceptual thinking or its professed independence of the body, which modern thinkers rightly find problematic, but also in its power to universalize, as we do in the sciences, and in our capacity to intend objects beyond the physical, such as numbers, Euclidean figures, or ordinary facts—a power Maimonides typifies by inviting us to think, say, of a piece of wood and hold that idea in mind, divorced from the object's matter. When we think of something in this way, he argues, the mind is what it thinks. It is the subject and object and act of thinking, just as God is.

Now, "living people," Kasher hastens to concede, "are never an actualized intellect." Never *fully*, at any rate. But it is not quite true for the Rambam that human minds are never actualized as minds. "Before a man has a concept of a thing, he is a potential knower. Once he knows a thing . . . his reason is functioning as such, and he is an actual knower."[29] Human experience *is* temporal. Still, it is not quite fair to translate as Pines does, "We pass from potentiality to actuality, however, only from time to time"—as though knowing and discovery were rare or chance events. The key distinction, in Maimonides's more balanced language, is that God "is not now aware, now unaware."

We humans do move from potentiality to act—and only at certain times. Still, as Kasher notes, Maimonides includes 'mind' and 'knowing' among the terms with wholly different senses when applied to human beings and to God.[30] God's timelessness plays no small role in that distinction. But, despite the immeasurable distance between finitude and the Infinite, Maimonides does mark an opening here, not humanizing God but allowing access to the human seeker, in the affinity between our awareness and God's eternal knowledge. Temporality compromises the unity of human thought. But, "In us too thought, thinker, and the object of thinking are one and the same—when our mind is actually thinking."[31] The human mind at such a moment is, like God's, "no different from the idea it knows!" Maimonides insists on the analogy and uses the phenomenology of reason to explain to anyone "unversed in the literature on the mind" or "unfamiliar with its nature and character" how God can be Thought, Thinker, and the Act of Thinking:

> The intellect in act is no different from what is known by it . . . the act of any mind is what that mind is. . . . Don't take it into your head that the thinking mind is something that exists on its own, without awareness, and that consciousness is something else inside it. The mind itself, its very reality, is awareness. When you posit an intellect in action, that mind is the awareness of the idea known to it. This will be very clear to anyone who tries to represent this process in his mind.[32]

In God, the unity of Thought, Thinker, and the Act of Thinking is absolute. But even in a human mind, once a concept is grasped, the three are one. "So you'll never find a mind that's one thing and an idea that's something else, unless the two are taken to be potential."[33] Granted divine awareness is unchanging and eternal. Human consciousness still mirrors the reflexivity of God's thought, not distinct, for Maimonides, from God's life and being.[34] The reflexivity that secures God's unity, then, helps us fathom (insofar as mortals may) how God, is indivisible yet active and alive.

In the first *Alcibiades*, Socrates makes the pupil of one eye the perfect mirror of another person. Pressing the analogy, Plato has Socrates say, "If a soul is to know herself, she must surely look at a soul" and ask, "Can we find any part of the soul more divine than that which is the seat of knowledge and thought. . . . This part of her resembles God, and whoever looks at this and comes to know all that is divine will gain thereby the best knowledge of himself."[35] For medieval authors that thought became a touchstone: if God is the mirror of the self, the self might be the mirror in which we catch a glimpse of God. There is a rich medieval tradition, as Alexander Altmann showed, treating self-knowledge as our surest route to God.[36] It is with that affinity in mind, the affinity of human reason to divinity, that Maimonides read the affirmation in Genesis that man and woman were created in God's image.[37] It is hard to find a clearer appropriation of that idea than Maimonides's treatment of the reflexivity of conceptual thought in man and God.

Maimonides is fond of the image of the asymptote and cites Apollonius's *Conic Sections* (II Theorem 13) for the proof that one line may approach another, growing ever closer, without ever reaching it, even if extended to infinity.[38] He uses the case to illustrate the gap between conceptual thinking and imagination. But it stands equally well for the range of variation he finds in human thoughts about God—and the progress he invites in that regard.[39] For it is knowledge of God that Maimonides sees as the ultimate human goal[40] and indeed the warrant of all the suffering to which our embodiment makes us vulnerable.[41] The distance between man and God remains infinite as ever. But it is misleading to paint Maimonides's God as unapproachable—even though the best milestones on that approach are inscribed with negations.

It is not the process, the dialectic of discovery, let alone the agony of search and loss, debate, halting dialectic, and misunderstanding that realizes our affinity and puts us in touch with God. It is the moment of realization that Maimonides construes as the consummation of the human quest. Such moments of epiphany, as he acknowledges in calling them lightning flashes, may be rare and may never be repeated.[42] The problem, in a way, is an Aristotelian one: if the good life is one in which we realize and exercise our human capabilities for the use of reason, one must acknowledge that human contemplation (pace the medieval aspirants for timeless intuition) is inevitably temporal, whereas God's life and thought are pure actuality, never a process of actualization. Alongside that issue, Maimonides sees a cognate problem: we know God most fully not by contemplating His unity but by exploring the world He created. The hedge blocking our vision of Eternity now seems to grow still higher and thicker.

But if these problems are Aristotelian, so is the solution: just as Aristotle's celestial intelligences express their love of God's pure actuality in the choric dance of the heavenly bodies, so must human minds pursue their likeness to God in temporal, not timeless ways. Even the Active Intellect, Maimonides remarks, may, through no fault of its own, lose its focus on God's Perfection.[43] We humans will emulate God's Self-knowing in our own distinctly human, temporal ways. That will mean not just meditation but study of nature, where we find the marks of God's wisdom and grace. Our contemplation *is* discursive, distinctively human in its intellectual mode, just as it is dialectical and interactive in its practical mode, where we emulate God's generosity through acts of kindness to our fellow creatures, as Moses saw when God revealed to him—*through* the panoply of nature—the mercy and grace by which nature is governed.[44]

Biblical poetics, Maimonides argues, are the key to scripture.[45] He assumes a reader ready and worthy[46] to search for that key. But he also assumes, before arguing the case, that biblical anthropomorphisms cannot be taken at face value (*'alā ẓāhirihā*). A major aim of the *Guide* is to determine how they *should* be taken. What, then, is Maimonides's object in the opening dozens of chapters of the *Guide*? Applying Saadiah's method, borrowed from the Arabic lexicographers and ultimately from the Greeks, he assumes that scriptural descriptors applied to God must have some poetic sense. For, taken literally, they speak unworthily of God. Surveying the canon, he proposes a higher sense for the anthropomorphic, anthropopathic, or corporeal terms. But the higher senses he proposes direct us consistently away from physicality and toward the intellectual.

There are two outcomes of the lexicography, then, one explicit, the other implicit. Explicitly, the *Guide* lets the Torah deconstruct its anthropomorphisms, assigning to God what would humanly be deemed perfections but winnowing away the inevitable connotations of limitation that any term reflecting human experience must bear.[47] The implicit outcome is to elicit from the Torah an ontological/axiological hierarchy rising from matter toward the Absolute, guided by the recognition that with each advance toward the intellectual reality and goodness increase, pari passu, for the two—reality and goodness—are, in fact, the same. The best term Maimonides finds for this union of being with goodness, is 'perfection,' the same term he uses to mark the pathway of human intellectual and moral growth.

The hierarchy of perfection is imaged for Maimonides in the ladder of Jacob's dream. God stands unshakably at the summit, much as Plato's Good surmounts the Line.[48] Like Plato, Maimonides interprets the rungs of this hierarchy cognitively, matching the phases of awareness to the ontic status of their objects. But the dynamic of Jacob's ladder matches still more closely to the Ladder of Love in the *Symposium*. For this ladder too is aspirational. Reality and perfection, once glimpsed, evoke love, and love provokes action and pursuit of ever higher knowledge, a climb toward the Summit and the love that God invites and biblically commands (Deuteronomy 6:5). For, biblically, the aspiration that Plato calls eros is both a blessing and a command (much as Plato's eros is the child of Poros and Penia, Means and Want).

For Maimonides, fusing the spiritual with the intellectual, our regnant aspiration must be to clamber up the ladder of perfection, in pursuit of the goodness, beauty, joy, and reality that merge in God's Perfection. A life spent in pursuit of that goal in a way already reaches it.[49] For we are not merely what we know but also what we hanker after. It is because the knowing mind is in touch with things eternal that Maimonides can promise that no harm befalls those who connect with God.[50] There is an economy here, of course. The claim is not the simpleton's expectation that no pain or suffering will befall the innocent. We know all too well that it can, and so did Maimonides. But real harm is loss of one's intellectual link with God. Physical goods and ills are real enough in their way. But theirs is not the coin in which true value, or true being is to be weighed.[51]

Like Plato, Maimonides expects the enlightened to come down to earth as well as rise. They are called to share what they have learned, giving guidance, moral and spiritual, to those who remain below,[52] much as the wise in Plato are called to share their wisdom with those still captive in the darkness of the cave, if prudence and their hearers' limitations permit—and much as bodhisattvas return with help and guidance for the still unenlightened, since they, as the name bodhisattva implies, have reached an awareness of a higher reality.

It is tempting to read negative theology of any sort as a thinly disguised disavowal. Too many readers to be cited here read Maimonides in this way. I offer just one extreme case, since it comes from a friend. Roger Scruton speaks of Alain Badiou's convoluted "nonsemes" as constructing a kind of theology in "the apophatic tradition of thinkers such as Dionysus the Areopagite, Al-Ghazzali, and Moses Maimonides." In Badiou's case, the unnamed god proves to be "Revolution."[53] But none of the religious thinkers Scruton names was simply framing "tantalizing linguistic constructions that suggest meanings too deep for words." Nor was it their goal, with all the difficulties of the quest, to "hide their god in the realm of the indescribable." As Herbert Davidson writes, "Because the ultimate esoteric interpretation of the *Guide for the Perplexed*, which makes Maimonides a covert atheist, is so outlandish . . . it has failed to register in academic circles. It has survived, however, in a more straightforward and somewhat less radical version. Here Maimonides is represented as having concluded that not only knowledge of God's essence is impossible but all knowledge of God, including knowledge of His existence, is impossible. No longer a full-fledged atheist . . . he now becomes an agnostic."[54]

Some readers are sure that no one as smart as Maimonides could possibly believe all that he professes: he can't be a creationist, his talk of providence and revelation must be a ruse, its thick mantle of reasoning discreetly covering an unseemly disaffection that would be evident if its clay footings were laid bare. But that is an odd conclusion to draw when Maimonides goes so far to defend creation and freely allows that we might readily allegorize the Genesis account, as he allegorizes biblical anthropomorphisms wholesale, were there sound and cogent arguments against the world's origination. Odd too to expect the Great Eagle to fear rabbinic displeasure when he lambastes the superstitions of complacent rabbis and ridicules vulgar images of an angel, say, that can enter a woman's womb to form her fetus and yet loom up as "a body of flaming fire one third the size of the entire world."[55] If Maimonides were a cautious man, why does he outspokenly denounce so familiar and seemingly orthodox a notion as that of divine attributes and call the affirmation of attributes no belief at all but doubletalk, no more coherent logically than talk of the Trinity—and more offensive than idolatry to any true conception of God?[56]

Part of what gives color to the notion that Maimonides's negative theology is a blind is his supposed assertion that even relations are not predicable of God. That idea does seem to isolate God. At least it would if Maimonides had said that. The evidence that he did not, prima facie: that view would run the *Guide* into a mass of contradictions, not in chapters remote from one another but in sentences that stand side by side. What can we make of the Rambam's saying that there is no relation between God and his creatures (as Pines translates the passage)?[57] Is this one of the contradictions Maimonides cites in his introduction, arising perhaps from inattention or culling from disparate sources? Are numerous scholia needed before the incompatibility of "no relations" with divine creation heaves into view? Has Maimonides suddenly changed his mind in mid sentence? Is he speaking figuratively or oversimplifying pedagogically? Or is he trying to conceal something, leaving visible only the contradiction, to alert close readers to his insincerity?

Let me offer an alternative. Maimonides readily accepts the idea that God is scripturally compared with lesser beings, albeit equivocally.[58] What other language do prophets have? Is it not inevitable, as the rabbis put it, that the Torah speak in a human tongue? There is an exigency, the Rambam argues, pressing prophets to use ordinary words. But they do so in ways that point us toward perfection even as their language signals its own inadequacy.

The rule of charity is a good strategy in reading any text: do not make it your first assumption that an author is thoughtless or has lost his drift. If Maimonides really said that God has no relation to His creatures, he would be contradicting himself within a single phrase. But the English word 'relation' covers so broad a range that it is impossible to say of *anything* that it has no relation to other things. Even *that* would count as a relation. What Maimonides intends, however, is made very clear by the arguments and instances he offers. Here is how Phil Lieberman and I have rendered the passage about relations in our draft translation of the *Guide*:

> A thing might be described by linking it to something else—a time, perhaps, or a place, or another individual—as when you call Zayd So-and-so's father, So-and-so's partner, the man who lives in such-and-such a place, or who lived at such-and-such a time. This sort of predicate does not entail plurality or change in the subject. The Zayd intended may be 'Amr's partner, Bakr's father, Khālid's client, Zayd's friend, resident at so-and-so, born in such-and-such year. Relations of this kind are not the thing itself and are not attached to it like qualities.[59]

At first glance it might seem acceptable to describe God in this way. But closer, more exacting scrutiny shows it is impossible. Plainly God is not linked to time or space.[60] For time is an accident of motion, viewed as earlier or later and made quantitative, as the texts devoted to the subject make clear. Motion pertains to bodies, and God is no body. So He is not connected to time—nor, by the same token, to space.[61]

The topic we need to examine and investigate is whether He and any of the substances of His creation have some real link in terms of which He might be described.[62] That He is not the correlative of any of His creatures is clear at a glance: correlatives, distinctively, are interdependent. But He exists necessarily, and all else is contingent, as I will show (II 1). So they are not counterparts.[63]

It might seem sound to posit some kinship[64] between Him and other things. But it is not. No comparison is conceivable between mind and color, although they exist in the same way on our account.[65] So what conceivably can be compared with One who has nothing in common with anything else? For even existence, we hold, is said of Him and of all else in wholly different senses. So there is no real kinship of any sort between Him and any of His creations.[66] Things can be compared only if they are of the same, necessarily proximate, species. If they belong only to the same genus, there is no basis for comparison. That's why we don't say, this red is redder than that green, or less so, or as red—even though they fall under the same genus, of color. If they're of different genera, even the common run of opinion would not jump to the conclusion that there's any basis of comparison at all, even if they can be brought under some higher grouping. There's no comparing, say, a hundred cubits with the hotness of peppers. The latter is a quality; the former, a quantity. And there's no comparing knowledge with sweetness, or clemency with bitterness, although they all count as qualities.

How, then, can He be compared to any of His creatures, given the immense, unparalleled gulf between His reality and theirs? Any kinship with them would attach an accident of likeness to Him, not proper to Him but still an accident in the broad sense.[67] So even comparisons afford no way of describing Him as He really is, although they are the preferred ways of characterizing the divine tolerably, since they imply no multiplicity in the Eternal and no change in Him as the things change that are linked with Him.

The key word here is *nisba*, kinship, link, connection, or comparison. It is overbroad to translate this term as 'relation.' Maimonides's argument demarcates the scope of his apophasis: God and creation are not correlatives. The clear target here is the doctrine of the eternalist Philosophers who argued that creation must be eternal lest God seem to change His mind and spring into action after eons of activity. That is the first point sharply pressed in the eighteen arguments for the world's eternity that Proclus forwarded in his polemic against creation, arguments well known in Arabic and rebutted by Ghazālī.

Second, Maimonides rejects any spatial or temporal link of God to His creation, lest that draw God into the natural realm and render Him, as Saadiah warned, just another natural phenomenon to be explained.

Third, Maimonides rejects quantitative comparisons: God does not have a size. He is not a body only larger and more splendid than the rest. The story of R. Hanina's telling his disciple that his efforts at creative liturgy were like praising a mortal king who had millions in gold for having silver, prompts Maimonides to call the differences between God and His creatures differences of kind, not of degree.[68] Now *that is* a pedagogical simplification: there is no intention here to imply that God belongs to a kind. If being is the broadest category, God differs from His creatures even in His mode of being, since His existence is not contingent, as we have seen. So God is not comparable to creatures, not describable univocally in the same terms.

We can say that there is no ratio or proportion between the Infinite and the finite. But there is no likeness either. Ratio and comparison or proportion are just senses of *nisba* arising from its historic senses of link and kinship. The word *can* mean 'relation.' But, semantically, context rules, and connotations hold the reins. The abstract term 'relation' is ruled out here by Maimonides's insistence on the asymmetry of God's relation to His creation: there is a relation between creature and Creator. But (pace Proclus) the reality of the Creator does not *entail* that of His creations. Nor does it determine all there is to know about those creatures, as Neoplatonists tended to assume.

Many Neoplatonists recapped their efforts to make God and the world correlatives by treating cause and effect in general as correlatives. In the Arabic texts, they rely on the verbal connection between the terms *sabab* (cause) and *musabbab*, its passive participle—suggesting that neither cause nor effect can conceivably exist without the other. Long before Hume, Ghazālī put paid to that ploy, and we can see Maimonides stoutly guarding naturalism and the sciences without succumbing to the Neoplatonic treatment of all necessities as logical necessities. He insists on distinctive *natural* necessities, embedded in the system God ordained at the creation. He thus adroitly preserves God's will and grace from collapsing into necessary implications of God's wisdom. Creation, for him, is not just the realization of whatever inevitably must be. Accordingly, Maimonides preserves empiricism in science and the open future in nature, future contingency in all beings and freedom in human choices. For creation, as he sees it, brings a delegation of powers and does not depend on the flickering light of the occasionalist cinema.

We know that Maimonides does not reject all relations between God and His creatures, not just because creating is a relation but also because he speaks freely of God's purposes. He sees God's glory in things existing for their own sakes, not just ours. He insists that the Torah's laws are not pointless but have a purpose—not God's improvement but ours. He assumes (and offers evidence) that the Torah comes from God and should be read as a guide to life in every age. And he sees its core imperative in its call to emulate God's holiness. All this assumes a relationship: we must know of God's perfection and not float in a sea of unknowing. And we do know something of what perfection means and in which direction God's perfection must lie.

For Maimonides, pursuit of God's perfection means pursuit of our own perfection as human beings, morally and intellectually: Morally, as the rabbis taught, we emulate God's ways by finding and showing one another a human counterpart of grace, through charity and justice. Spiritually, we pursue perfection by recognizing that the inner affinity with God that the Torah poetically calls our creation in God's image is intellectual—and by seeking intellectual perfection in knowing God.[69]

God's relations with the world go further: Revelation, Maimonides holds, makes sense. The Torah's laws afford a healthful regimen attuned to human nature and within our power to accept and fulfill.[70] The Torah's worldly truths and practical counsels enshrine deeper insights[71] that demand (and elicit) scientific learning, philosophic acuity, and poetic sensibility. Nature, he argues, reflects not only the Creator's will (which may look like chance to us) but grace and wisdom.[72] God knows His creatures, Maimonides affirms, not as we might know particulars but as the smith must know tailoring if he is to fashion a needle. And we know God by His work. Thus the passage that prompts the awkward talk of "actional attributes" sometimes heard among Maimonides scholars. Here is what the Rambam wrote about that:

> The fifth type of positive predicate characterizes a thing by what it does.[73] I don't mean a subject's craft or profession, "carpenter" or "smith," say. Those terms belong to the category of quality, as I've noted. I mean what a subject produces—as you might say, It is Zayd who framed this door, built that wall, or wove this robe. Descriptions of this type stand apart from the subject itself. So they may be applied to God, once it's understood that these varied acts imply no variance or multiplicity in the Subject, as will be shown. For all His varied acts are done by His Identity alone, nothing else, as I've explained.[74]

What is rejected here is Paley's line of argument that risks reducing God to a glorified watchmaker. The Torah's effort, so respected by Maimonides, to keep God's face offstage as it sets the scene of its human drama, would be undermined if such reverse engineering were countenanced. God's work, as the Rambam understands it, is what Moses saw when God (in response to Moses's plea for a vision to guide him in governing Israel) vouchsafed a vision of "His back"—more literally, *what follows after Him*, that is, His wake, His ways in governing nature.

God's work, for Maimonides, is what is known by those who reach the highest phase of monotheism, who see God in all things, in the language Maimonides echoes from Ghazālī. Immersion in the natural sciences opens a window on such understanding. But the science here is not reductionistic: its findings confirm the

Torah's themes of love and wisdom, echoing Galen's Stoic vision of divine caring (*pronoia*) and design manifest in nature's order and stability.

If common nouns inevitably signify by grouping things in classes, it would seem the only kind of Godtalk Maimonides would welcome would be expressions like I AM THAT I AM and its shorthand equivalent, the Tetragrammaton, or related expressions such as Shaddai. But only the wise, the Rambam reasons, will probe such compact expressions of the ontic and axiological ultimacy of the absolute—let alone plumb the depths of the argument they make for God's reality. Most fare better with a cosmological argument. But, in either case (as Kant observed), the argument hinges on the idea of a necessary being. And, in either case, the Perfection that is that being will orient an ontology/axiology that invites the intellectual love of God and His moral emulation.

The hierarchy Maimonides sees is Neoplatonic. It privileges intellect and subordinates matter, relegating physicality, ultimately to mere relativity—otherness, receptivity, the ground of privation and debility, if also the field for the expression of God's creativity and grace. To many of us the scheme may prove unwelcome, for its intellectualism, its scapegoating of matter, its openings to mind-body dualism—even though the palpable deficiencies of today's rather brash variants on materialism and reductionism may prompt inquirers to take it more seriously than some of our predecessors have done.

If we are to make use of negative theology today, I suspect we will need a new ontology, still preserving Maimonides's Platonic and Mosaic insights as to the unity of being and value, lest the fruitful perplexity that goads inquiry decline into mere confusion and the projection onto matter of properties that matter without form cannot possibly live up to. My own inclination here is toward Spinoza, the most penetrating philosopher to have trodden this ground until now, bringing matter in from the cold and situating God, still transcendent in the infinite variety of His infinite expressions, in intimate, even loving contact with humanity and the world.

The great flaw in the Rambam's scheme, if we must name one, is rooted in its intellectualism, not because the life of the mind is cold and uninviting. To allow oneself to be trapped by that cliché is to betray an innocence of the life of the mind and the intellectual love of God that moves and energizes it. Maimonides's problem, rather, is twofold: part lies in his turning away from matter, and part in his neglect of the infinite ways beyond and beside those of intellect in which Perfection may express itself. As for matter, Maimonides is hardly the worst offender. He does not make matter evil or call the body a sepulcher or crypt. He rejects the extremes of asceticism and blames Saadiah for accepting the notion that evils outweigh goods in this world. Like Saadiah, he affirms life. And although he scorns the Epicurean equation of goods with pleasures and ills with pains, he knows that sufferings are ills, and he counts pleasures as critical, if instrumental in the pursuit of perfection through realization of our intellectual affinity with God.

But he also blames the Philosophers for failing fully to exploit their own recognition that matter is otherness, the concomitant of finitude and thus, at once, a fruit of God's creative act and the seat of all deficiency and vulnerability. Matter, for Maimonides, is the base required if form is to be instantiated, allowing divine wisdom to find expression in a world. Allegorically, matter well disciplined, is the good woman of Proverbs 31. Left undisciplined by form, it is the married harlot of Proverbs 7, unsteady and unstable, ever changing forms and negating order. Both matter and form are expressions of God's creative grace. But matter shows us what we can only construe as God's will. Form displays what we more readily grasp as God's wisdom.[75]

In God's unity, will and wisdom are one, neither subordinate to the other. Their seeming divergence in nature results from human incapacity to follow the interplay of what we make out now as chance, now as order. We cannot *deduce* the rule by which God's wisdom finds expression. At best we learn inductively how things work. We grasp a bit of how the cosmos makes sense, but only a posteriori. So we come upon the surest grounds for reading nature as created rather than eternal in the recognition that not every determination need have been made as it was. In the last analysis, none of these determinations was a categorical necessity. Will and wisdom, in the end, remain just another pair of anthropomorphisms we apply when we investigate nature with a view to making out God's handwriting. The two are analytical tools, each reflecting our human limitations in discerning the true nature of things.

To overcome the intellectualist bias that Maimonides betrays, we must hold fast to his recognition of both matter and form as expressions of God's grace, united at the Source. Neither is evil. Beyond that, we must recapture the Aristotelian insight into the intimate and dynamic union of matter and form. In our world neither exists without the other. Souls are not disembodied, and bodies are never without energy and system.[76] Spinoza is the philosopher who comes closest to a faithful reintegration of the two as expressions of God in the human person and in the cosmos. When we can track the interplay of chance and necessity in matter and chart the varied levels at which chance at one order of magnitude becomes order at another, we will have a closer reading of that handwriting, which sometimes, with our present tools, looks illegible to us.

My colleague Idit Dobbs-Weinstein sees a sort of antifeminism in the Rambam's treatment of matter and form.[77] In a way, I think, that judgment needs to be reversed: Maimonides does not so much blame the married harlot for being like matter. His point, rather, is to set matter in the role of the married harlot, for what he views metaphorically as its inconstancy—the changeability that makes it the root of instability and vulnerability. But one cannot deny that Maimonides reflects the Aristotelian association of women with passivity and men with activity. Platonism, moreover, sets matter for him in the role of the Receptacle, the ultimate otherness. So the polarity of matter as potential and form as actuality does orient his ontological/axiological hierarchy. To overcome that prejudice, whether in its misogynistic outcroppings or at its metaphysical base, we need a new ontology and axiology.

Augustine can ruefully second guess even his own God, by arguing, in his commentary on Genesis, "If it was company and good conversation that Adam needed, it would have been much better to have two men together as friends, not a man and a woman."[78] A woman was needed only because she could bear the man's children! But that is not the Torah's view. There Eve is Adam's counterpart, his helpmeet (*'ezer ke-negdo*)—and, as Genesis itself stresses, just as much as Adam, created in God's image, and thus, in Maimonides's terms, an intellectual being. Augustine in his remark was still in rebellion against his own sexuality. But the guilt and ambivalence he projects on his embodiment reflects his personal history. It does not deserve to be made the orienting principle of being and value. Nor is it, biblically. The Torah does not flinch, as Manicheans did, on Abraham's saying to his servant, in having him take an oath, *place your hand beneath my thigh* (Genesis 24:2). Augustine himself came to see through the misplaced highmindedness of his former sectarian guides who rejected the Torah for its embrace of the flesh in lines like these.[79] But he still struggles with the polarity of flesh and spirit. In a way, so does Maimonides. And although the conflict is generalized and sublimated to the plane of cosmology and beyond, its roots are doubtless social and psychological, not physiological and still less genuinely ontological.

If we are to overcome the ambivalence, we must heed the Torah's wisdom on the subject and Maimonides's own wise advice: matter, well disciplined is our base; the human body is a gift no less than the soul, to be cherished and preserved to the best abilities of the scientific arts of health and medicine, no more to be scorned than to be mortified or abused—but neither to be worshiped or served as if it were a god. Biblically, human flesh, like human blood, is sacred, precisely because the body bears God's image, as the vehicle through which human consciousness and conscience, moral agency and creativity, emerge. That is why we may not mutilate our bodies or even leave the corpse of an executed criminal hanging vindictively or as a warning. Love itself is sacred, as the wording of our marriage promise clearly and publicly declares, not properly a source of shame or guilt but of joy and contentment.

With holiness, as the rabbinic saying goes, we do not downgrade. To say that love, or sexuality is holy is not to reduce holiness to love or sexuality. It is not the case that every yearning of the flesh is to be sanctified or that the embrace of our physicality will warrant the fascination of narcissism or render sacred all that can be done in the name of eros—any more than recognition of the beauty of a gemstone or a mountain stream renders it worthy of worship. Balance and integration are what we need, as the Torah seeks to show in the ethos its practices set forth.

Our second corrective to Maimonides's scheme will again be Spinozistic. For to construe God sheerly and solely in terms of intellect and make intellect the very dimensionality of perfection, does, in a way, seem all too anthropomorphic. Has Maimonides, with all his sophistication, fallen into the projective trap Xenophanes warned of at the dawn of rational theology in the West, making God in one's own image, much as Aristotle would do in taking God to be pure mind. Plotinus, a founding figure of negative theology, reminds his readers, lest they be tempted to follow Aristotle here, that Mind cannot be the highest God since Mind is not the best of things. God is One, Infinite, and Good. Not merely Mind.

Kasher cottons onto the problem when she suggests, within the human sphere, that there are many ways in which perfection might be gauged[80] (just as there are many different kinds of intelligence, some overlapping, some distinct). Spinoza's solution is to say that God, being Infinite, expresses Himself in infinite ways. Only two, thought and extension, are known to us since we have nothing in common with the rest. But God, Spinoza tells us, stands forth in infinite ways, each of which expresses His perfection. None is self-sufficient, as God is. All, in a curious way, are one. The very diversity in which they fan out gives them unity. That thought allows us one more reason to say, with Maimonides, that when we speak of God as one what we mean is nothing like what we must mean when we speak of the number one in more familiar contexts.

Notes

1. Plato, *Republic*, II 379a.

2. *Guide to the Perplexed*, I 65. The term "partaking" echoes Plato's model of particulars participating in oneness. References to Maimonides's *Guide to the Perplexed* are to the new translation and commentary by L. E. Goodman and Philip Lieberman, forthcoming from Stanford University Press. All passages quoted here are from that translation of Maimonides's Arabic; references are by part and chapter; where page references are given they are by volume and page in the Arabic edition of S. Munk: *Le Guide des Égarés*, Arabic text, edited with French translation by S. Munk (Paris, 1856–66; reprinted, Osnabrück: Zeller, 1964), 3 volumes.

3. *Guide*, I 51; Munk, 58a.

4. See Ghazālī, first discussion and first objection in *Tahāfut al-Falāsifa*, ed. M. Bouyges (2nd ed., ed. Majid Fakhry; Beirut: Catholic University Press, 1962), 49–53 = ed. and trans. M. Marmura (Provo, Utah: Brigham Young University Press, 1997), 15–17. As Van Den

Bergh points out, Ghazālī's argument follows Philoponus's sixteenth in *De Aeternitate Mundi*, ed. Rabe, 567–568 = p. 70 in Philoponus, *Against Proclus On the Eternity of the World*, trans. James Wilberding (Ithaca, NY: Cornell University Press, 2006); cf. Augustine, *City of God*, 12.15. See Van Den Bergh's translation of Averroes, *Tahāfut al-Tahāfut*, translated by Van Den Bergh as *The Incoherence of the Incoherence* (London: Luzac, 1954) 2.3, note 3 to p. 1.3. A key example to illustrate al-Ghazālī's case: A man (in Islamic law) might tell his wife: "If I see that fellow here again, you're divorced." The divorce might then take effect without change on the husband's part.

5. Maimonides, *Mishneh Torah, Hilkhot Yesodei ha-Torah*, I.

6. *Guide*, I 68; Munk, 86ab. Hosea (at 4:15) cautions the people not to swear, *by the* Lord's *life*. Rashi, taking a hint from Jeremiah 12:16, understands the admonition as a rebuke to Israel's faithlessness: When they were serious, he writes, commenting on the Hosea verse, they swore by Baal. But Maimonides takes Hosea's warning as a caution against hypostatizing God's life. He has no difficulty with the psalmist's exclamation, *the* Lord *lives!* (18:46).

7. Aristotle, *De Anima*, III 4. The tripartite identity is found in Ghazālī's *Tahāfut* just after the example of the deferred divorce.

8. Goodman, *Avicenna* (Ithaca, NY: Cornell University Press, 2006).

9. *Guide*, I 54.

10. Goodman, *God of Abraham* (New York: Oxford University Press, 1996), 71–78.

11. *Guide*, I 52; Munk, 1.61b.

12. See Goodman, "al-Ghazālī and Hume on Causality," *Ishraq: Islamic Philosophy Yearbook* 4 (Moscow: Vostochnaya Literatura, 2013), 448–472; another version in Ali Paya, ed., *The Misty Land of Ideas and the Light of Dialogue* (London: ICAS Press, 2013), 49–80.

13. See Goodman, *Judaism: A Contemporary Philosophical Investigation* (London: Routledge, 2015), chap. 1, "Biblical Logic."

14. *Guide*, Maimonides's Introduction; Munk, 4b.

15. *Guide*, I 27, 28.

16. *Guide*, I 27, 36.

17. See *Guide*, I 28. Maimonides's search for a consistent rule in Onkelos's renderings finds unevenness at I 48 and 66. Onkelos, he writes (at Exodus 24:9–10) "excludes anthropomorphism," but "does not enlighten us" as to what the elders of Israel actually apprehended "or what this symbolism means."

18. *Guide*, I 36.

19. Hannah Kasher, "Self-Cognizing Intellect and Negative Attributes in Maimonides' Theology," *Harvard Theological Review* 87 (1994): 461–472; quoted here, p. 472.

20. Pines, in his translator's introduction to *The Guide of the Perplexed* (Chicago: The University of Chicago Press, 1963), xcviii.

21. Shlomo Pines, *A History of Jewish Philosophy from Maimonides to Spinoza* (Jerusalem: Hebrew University Students, 1963/64), 31; Hebrew text quoted in translation by Kasher, 462.

22. Kasher, "Self-Cognizing Intellect," 462–463.

23. Ibid.

24. *Guide*, I 33–36.

25. Eliezer Schweid, *Maimonides and the Scope of his Influence* (Jerusalem: Akademon, 1968), 127.

26. Kasher, "Self-Cognizing Intellect," 472.

27. Ibid., 472.

28. *Guide*, I 1.

29. *Guide*, I 68.

30. Kasher, "Self-Cognizing Intellect," 465.

31. *Guide*, I 68; Munk, 1.88a.

32. *Guide*, I 68; Munk, 1.87a.

33. *Guide*, I 68; Munk, 1.87b.

34. *Guide*, I 68.

35. *Alcibiades 1*, 132b–133c. The theme has a kind of universality. Mencius, the great Confucian philosopher (ca. 385–312) is reported to have said, "One who knows his own nature will know Heaven. Possession of one's own heart and the nurturing of one's own nature are the means by which one serves Heaven." After D. C. Lau, trans., *Mencius* (Hong Kong: The Chinese University Press, 2003), 287.

36. Alexander Altmann, "The Delphic Maxim in Medieval Islam and Judaism," in *Studies in Religious Philosophy and Mysticism* (Ithaca, NY: Cornell University Press, 1975), 1–40.

37. Genesis 1:26–27 and *Guide*, I 1.

38. *Guide*, I 73; Munk, 115a.

39. *Guide*, I 59.

40. Maimonides, "Eight Chapters," 5, edited by J. Kafih as Hakdamah le-Masekhet Avot in *Mishnah 'im Perush Mosheh ben Maimon* (Jerusalem: Mossad ha-Rav Kuk, 1961).

41. *Guide*, III 16–17, 23.

42. *Guide*, Maimonides's Introduction; Munk, 4a.

43. *Guide*, I 68; Munk, 1.88a.

44. *Guide*, I 21, 38, 54, 58; reading Exodus 33:23.

45. *Guide*, Maimonides's Introduction; Munk, 1.6a.

46. *Guide*, Maimonides's Introduction; Munk, 2a, l. 12: *ahlan*.

47. *Guide*, I 47.

48. *Guide*, I 15. For ladder motif, see Altmann, "The Ladder of Ascension," in *Studies*, 72.

49. Cf. Mishnah Avot 2.21: "You need not complete the task, but you are not free to desist." And compare Rāzī's claim that even the least intellectual apprehension cleanses the mind and thereby frees the soul; and Maimonides's belief, in *Perek Helek*, that all Israelites have a portion in immortality—by virtue of the beliefs and practices that put them in touch, even if only implicitly, with the divine idea.

50. *Guide*, I 23–24, III 17–18. The Arabic term for this connection is *ittiṣāl*; in Hebrew, *devekut*.

51. *Guide*, III 12; cf. I 30.

52. *Guide*, I 15.

53. Roger Scruton, reviewing Alain Badiou's *The Adventure of French Philosophy* in *TLS*, August 31, 2012, 8–9.

54. Herbert Davidson, *Moses Maimonides: The Man and His Works* (Oxford: Oxford University Press, 2005), 401. Maimonides writes that existence means something quite different in God's case from what it does in that of finite beings—as it must if God's existence is necessary and eternal rather than temporal and contingent. But He carefully avoids the Plotinian dictum that God is above being. Even if read as a paradox or a koan, that statement would only be misleading. It would not help alleviate the perplexity the *Guide* sought to address but would only deepen it.

55. *Guide*, II 6.

56. *Guide*, I 50.

57. *Guide*, I 52; trans. Pines, 117–118.

58. *Guide*, I 11; cf. Plotinus, *Enneads*, V 3, 12, 13–14, V 4.7, etc.

59. In excluding predications with regard to God, Maimonides surveys the categories of Aristotle. Nearing the end of the list, he considers relations. But, as Munk notes in his French translation of the *Guide* (1.200n1), Maimonides does not use the Arabic *iḍḍāfa* here, the usual term for Aristotle's category of relation. See Aristotle, *Categories*, 7, and the early Arabic translation, edited by Khalil Georr in *Les Catégories d'Aristote dans leurs Versions Syro-Arabes* (Beirut: Institut Français de Damas, 1948), 332–338. (The *Categories* was translated into Arabic early on and was well known, for example, by al-Kindī, the first major philosopher to write in Arabic.) Maimonides reserves the term *iḍḍāfa* for correlatives, where the existence of one term entails that of the other (if there is a half, there must be a double). Here he chooses the word *nisba*, classically, a link of kinship or, more abstractly, a ratio or proportion. As Munk's note makes clear, what Maimonides categorically rejects is any kinship or proportion between God and His creatures. He does not deny any relation. For God is the Creator. What exercises him most, clearly, is the eternalists' contention that God and world imply each other, allowing one to infer not only from the world to God as its Author, but also (as Proclus did) from the givenness of (an essentially) creative God to the necessary and eternal existence of the world. One consequence of Maimonides's strong stance against any such symmetry is his expectation that inference from the world to God will be inductive, an outcome consistent with his empiricism regarding human knowledge. See *Guide*, III 19, 21.

60. Ibn Tibbon translates *nisba* as *yaḥas*, thus underwriting Pines's translation of it as "relation." Buxtorf (1629), also working from the Arabic and comparing Ibn Tibbon's Hebrew, seems more sensitive: "*Nulla etenim est comparatio vel proportio inter Deum et Tempus vel Locum*" See Johannes Buxtorf, fil., translation of the *Guide* as *Doctor Perplexorum* (Basel: Genath, 1629; reprinted, Westmead, England: Gregg, 1969) 80.

61. "*Quocirca inter Ipsum et inter Tempus nulla est comparatio. Sic nulla quoque proportio est inter Ipsum et inter Locum*" (Buxtorf). If one renders *nisba* as "relation," Maimonides would mean that there is no spatial relation between God and nature.

62. "*Res tamen consideratione digna hoc loco est; An nulla planè sit proportio inter Deum Benedictum et Creaturas eius, à qua Deus denominari possit?*" (Buxtorf, 80–81).

63. Here, Buxtorf gives *relatio* for *iḍḍāfa*, as the usage of the *Categories* would lead one to expect.

64. The term is *nisba* again. Buxtorf uses *relatio* but then follows Maimonides in ruling out any *comparatio*.

65. Both exist contingently, "on our account," as opposed to that of the eternalists, which tends to render the mind at least a necessary being.

66. Maimonides may conceivably take aim here at ideas of incarnation.

67. If God were comparable to His creatures in any way, there would have to be some feature in terms of which He is like them. In the broad sense that would be an accident marring God's simplicity.

68. *Guide,* I 59.

69. Maimonides's biblical humanism responds to this point. For all humanity were created in God's image, as the Torah stresses when it generalizes the trope in the prohibition of murder: Genesis 9:6.

70. His gloss of Psalms 19:8.

71. Thus Maimonides's treatment of the image of scripture's wisdom as a golden apple chased with silver. *Guide,* Maimonides's Introduction; Munk, 1.6b–7a, glossing Proverbs 25:11.

72. *Guide,* I 64: "insensate beings, like those that are inanimate, also exalt Him, as it were, since their natures bespeak the wisdom and power of Him who gave them being."

73. Maimonides has already ruled out passivity or affectedness as well as the sorts of relations that most concern him. Of Aristotle's ten categories, that leaves only action, although some types of acts, those that are transitive, do involve one kind of relation. The relation of creature to Creator, which Maimonides has repeatedly assumed, is notably not reversible as he understands it: God, as a creator does not depend for His existence on the existence of what He creates. Proclus's argument that God would not be a Creator if the world did not exist, as Maimonides would see it, rests on a verbal trick: God remains a necessary being; the world, its existence being deniable without self-contradiction, remains contingent.

74. See *Guide,* I 46; see also I 53.

75. See Goodman, "Matter and Form as Attributes of God in Maimonides' Philosophy," in *A Straight Path: Studies in Honor of Arthur Hyman* (Washington, DC: Catholic University of America Press, 1987), 86–97.

76. See Goodman and D. G. Caramenico, *Coming to Mind: The Soul and Its Body* (Chicago: The University of Chicago Press, 2013).

77. See Idit Dobbs-Weinstein, *Maimonides and St Thomas on the Limits of Reason* (Albany: State University of New York Press, 1995).

78. Augustine, *De Gen. ad litteram,* 9.5.9.

79. See *Ep. Secundini ad Aug.* and Augustine's response in *Contra Secundinem,* 23.

80. Kasher, "Self-Cognizing Intellect," 466.

FOUR

Negative Theology as Illuminating and/or Therapeutic Falsehood

SAM LEBENS

Continental philosophers are much more likely to approve of apophaticism than analytic philosophers are. Apophaticism is keenly aware of the limits of reason. Apophaticism often characterizes logic and language as inherently human affairs. These traits fit naturally with a number of continental philosophical trends; trends that question the omnipotence and species-neutrality of logic.[1] This chapter, however, seeks to defend Jewish apophaticism to philosophers in the *analytic* tradition. A much harder sell!

Plato and Socrates thought of *ethics* as the most foundational branch of philosophy. Aristotle shifted the foundation of philosophy to *metaphysics* and *ontology*. Descartes tried to place that weight on *epistemology*. But, according to David Smith,[2] it was Russell, in the founding moments of the analytic tradition, who sought to establish *logic* as the foundational branch of philosophy. Consequently, analytic philosophers tend toward a doctrine of the sovereignty of logic, and they become uncomfortable when we start to talk about the limits of reason.[3] And thus, perhaps, there is an inherent pull within analytic theology away from apophaticism.

The task of analytic metaphysics is, broadly construed, to give a description of the way the world is, or to engage in conceptual analysis of our most fundamental notions. To be told that God is not the sort of thing that you can describe, nor the sort of concept that allows for analysis, is then, at least at first glance, to be told that analytic philosophical theology is a nonstarter. To date, there has been very little Jewish philosophy conducted in the analytical style. But, we can see from the much more established Christian tradition of analytic philosophy that apophaticism is unlikely to fare well. Christian philosophers in the analytic tradition have tended to reject apophaticism vehemently, or to ignore it altogether.[4] There *have* been Christian analytic philosophers who have taken apophaticism more seriously—one of whom, Jonathan Jacobs, we will turn to later—but they form a distinct minority.

In his discussion of the problem of evil, Peter van Inwagen,[5] for example, wants to limit our attention to a Deity with "just those properties ascribed to God in common by Jews, Christians, and Muslims—the properties that adherents of these religions would all agree belong to God." He has in mind properties such as omnipotence, omniscience, and omni-benevolence. But, he makes a telling qualification:

> By 'Jews, Christians, and Muslims', I mean 'Jews, Christians, and Muslims who lived before the twentieth century.' If you are puzzled by this qualification, I invite you to examine two quotations from the writings of a theologian of considerable reputation:
>
> > To regard God as some kind of describable or knowable object over against us would be at once a degradation of God and a serious category error.
> >
> > It is a mistake, therefore, to regard qualities attributed to God (e.g., aseity, holiness, omnipotence, omniscience, providence, love, self-revelation) as though they were features of a particular being.

The theologian in question happens to be Gordon Kaufman who certainly held many radical views, but, looking at these two quotations, and nothing else, we seem to be presented with nothing more than a run-of-the-mill apophaticism. And yet, van Inwagen says that "These words mean almost nothing. Insofar as they mean anything, they mean 'There is no God.'" So, apophaticism is just atheism by another name.

Furthermore, van Inwagen heavily implies that apophatic talk did not exist among Jews, Christians, and Muslims before the twentieth century. He subsequently decides to "push the date back to 1800, just to be on the safe side," since Richard Swinburne had pointed out to him that there were some pretty crazy theologians in the nineteenth century too! And thus, on van Inwagen's revised view, there was no apophaticism before then. So, Saadya Gaon, Maimonides, Pseudo-Dionysius, and Ibn Sina (any of whom could have penned the two quotes in question) simply did not exist. And thus, van Inwagen ignores a massive slice of theological history.

Instead of ignoring apophaticism, Alvin Plantinga vehemently bats it away.[6] He dedicates the first two chapters of his *Warranted Christian Belief* to a rebuttal of apophaticism. He voices three main concerns. First, it struggles to be coherent since, as soon as you start talking about a thing that cannot be described, you seem to have violated your own constraint and described it as a thing that cannot be described. Second, if you escape this absurdity and say that some concepts *can* apply to God and that others cannot, then you will most likely end up with an ad hoc and unmotivated form of apophaticism (why apply some predicates and not others, and how do we draw the distinction between which *can* apply and which *cannot?*). Finally, apophatic theologians, especially contemporary ones such as Kauffman, tend reductively to reinterpret all religious language. The central Christian claim that Jesus died on the cross for our sins, for example, may end up meaning something like, *it is generally a good thing to sacrifice for the greater good of society*. Plantinga is unimpressed: "This [revisionism] is not a matter of pouring new wine into old wineskins: what we have here is nothing like the rich, powerful, fragrant wine of the great Christian truths; what we have is something wholly drab, trivial, and insipid. It is not even a matter of throwing out the baby with the bathwater; it is, instead, throwing out the baby and keeping the tepid bathwater, at best a bland, unappetizing potion that is neither hot nor cold and at worst a nauseating brew, fit for neither man nor beast."[7] The challenge is to find a variety of apophaticism that is coherent, and then to ensure that it is well motivated and not offensively revisionist. The challenge is to find a formulation of the view that does not offend against the scruples of analytic philosophy. If this cannot be done, it looks as if analytic *Jewish* philosophy will have to ignore or reject the apophaticism of Saadya Gaon, Maimonides, the Zohar (which is apophatic about the *Ein Sof*—i.e., God in his transcendence), and the Hassidism (who tend to adopt the apophaticism of the Zohar)—just as certain analytic Christian philosophers tend to ignore or to reject the apophaticism of the Cappadocian Fathers, John Chrysostom, and John of Damascus.

Saadya Gaon and Maimonides

Saadya Gaon was perhaps the first systematically apophatic theologian in the Jewish tradition. Having established to his satisfaction that God exists and created everything else that exists, he writes: "There does not, therefore, remain a substance or accident or attribute that was not defined or determined or put together by Him or about which it is not certain that this Creator was its maker. Hence it is out of the question and impossible to declare Him to be anything that he has Himself created."[8]

Gabriel Citron (in an unpublished paper) unpacks this argument into the following steps:

1. Whatever is to count as the Creator of everything must have created all substances and properties.
2. If *a* created *b*, then *b* is ontologically dependent upon *a*.
3. By premises 1 and 2, all substances and all properties are ontologically dependent upon the Creator.
4. For something to be a substance, or have a property, is for it to be ontologically dependent upon that substance or that property.

5. If a≠b, and a is ontologically dependent upon b, then b cannot be ontologically dependent upon a.
6. By premises 3, 4, and 5, whatever is to count as the Creator of everything, cannot be a substance, nor have any properties.

Citron observes a flaw in this argument. Premise 4 seems to suffer from two problems. First, to be a substance is not to be ontologically dependent upon that substance so much as to be *identical* to that substance. Saadya seems to confuse the issue. Second, things are not ontologically dependent upon their accidental properties. Rather, one is only ontologically dependent upon one's *essential* properties.

I would raise a further issue. The argument fudges an important distinction. We have only established that b is *historically* dependent upon a; not that b is *still* dependent upon a.[9] By failing to index the ontological dependences to a time, we smuggle in claim 5, which is only true if the dependence of a on b is indexed to the same time as the dependence of b on a. God could have created properties that continue to exist without his intervention. Those properties would be independent of him from that point onward. God can then come to instantiate them. But, his *essential* properties, he presumably always had. So, once again, the argument would be stronger if we focus on essential properties to the exclusion of accidental ones.

Revising in light of these complaints, the argument becomes:

1. Whatever is to count as the Creator of everything must have created all properties.
2. If a created b, then b is historically ontologically dependent upon a.
3. By premises 1 and 2, all properties are historically ontologically dependent upon the Creator.
4. To have a property essentially is to be constantly ontologically dependent upon that property.
5. If a≠b, and if a is constantly ontologically dependent upon b (as God would be upon any property that he held essentially), then b cannot be historically ontologically dependent upon a (as all properties are upon God [cf. 3]).
6. By premises 3, 4, and 5, whatever is to count as the Creator of everything cannot have any properties essentially.

This seems like a valid argument. Is it sound? Admittedly, the first premise might spoil the party. It is not obvious that properties stand in need of creation.

Did God create the number two, and the color red, or did he rather create all actual pairs of *objects* and all red *things*? Furthermore, if the property of *being-a-creation* (or the property of *being-a-creative-act*) needs to be created before it can be instantiated, then we seem to be in some logically muddy waters (how could any creation occur before such properties exist?). But, if you *do* accept the first premise, it seems as if you have now got pretty good grounds for denying that God has any essential properties.

Van Inwagen might say that this conclusion amounts to atheism. If existence is a property, then it is something that all objects essentially instantiate. And thus, saying that God has no essential properties seems like a long-winded way of saying that God does not exist. You might try to get out of this by saying that existence is not a property. But, as Citron points out, Saadya explicitly accepts that something with no properties does not exist and is "deprived of all reality."[10] I am not suggesting we should feel compelled to accept Saadya Gaon's apophatic conclusion. But, at least we have a grasp over the sort of argument that led him there.

Despite its atheistic appearance, Saadya Gaon only presents this argument once he has convinced himself that God exists and created all that is.[11] And thus we find, in Saadya Gaon's *Book of Beliefs and Doctrines*, a strange and self-defeating argumentative structure. First, Saadya argues for the existence of a God who created everything that is. At stage two, he argues that if there were such a God, he could have no essential properties, including existence.

A similar question arises for Maimonides. Maimonides formulates a number of arguments for God's existence (e.g., *Guide for the Perplexed*, II 1). As a result, God is posited as the first-cause. But this, apparently, entails that God cannot be composite. If God were composed of parts *a* and *b*, you could reasonably ask what causes *a* and *b* to come together in this way; to search, *per impossible*, for a cause that is *prior* to God (e.g. *Guide*, II, introduction premise 21).[12] And thus, God is said to be simple. To make a predication of God, even if you predicate an essential property, is, apparently, to make a distinction between him and his properties; it is to violate his simplicity (e.g. *Guide*, I 51). Furthermore, his being the first-cause implies that he cannot fall under any genus or species. If God fell under a genus, that genus would be conceptually prior to God, which the cosmological argument rules out (e.g. *Guide*, I 52). We obviously have a problem. Maimonides's argument for God's existence describes God as falling under the genus "cause." And thus, Maimonides's argument for God's existence violates the linguistic constraints that it is supposed to introduce.[13]

The problematic structure we found in Saadya Gaon's thought is thus echoed in the thought of Maimonides. In the face of such incoherence, the nascent movement of analytic Jewish philosophy looks as if it may be compelled to ignore or reject these key claims made by the founding fathers of the Jewish philosophical tradition.

Religious Experience

It is important to note that the problem of this essay is not merely generated by a desire to be faithful to an intellectual tradition. The problem arises long before you have opened a book of medieval theology. Across different religious traditions, people immersed in a religious way of life often claim to experience God. Furthermore, there are two ways in which God seems to be experienced. There are people who claim to experience God as falling under quite straightforward concepts. For instance, people experience God as a source of love, and people experience God as a source of council or calling. These sorts of experience are said to entail the following sorts of predications: "God loves me" and "God has called upon me to do x." We will call these experiences cataphatic-experiences, and the simple subject-predicate claims that they are said to entail, we will call cataphatic-claims.[14] Scripture and tradition also make a great many cataphatic-claims.

But, there are also people who claim to experience God in what seem like paradoxical ways. They claim to experience God as a God who defies description. Sometimes these experiences occur in the midst of mystical rapture, but sometimes they are much less dramatic—somebody claims to experience an "indescribable presence" accompanying them in their everyday lives. These experiences, just like Saadya's and Maimonides's arguments, are said to entail the following, paradoxical, sort of predication: "God defies all description." Let us call these sorts of experience, apophatic-experiences, and the claims that they are supposed to entail, apophatic-claims.[15]

Our religious traditions contain both cataphatic-claims and apophatic-claims. Moreover, the religious life is punctuated by both cataphatic-experiences and apophatic-experiences. Indeed, many people reportedly have both types of experiences within a single life, even within a single extended experience! And so we have two problems, before we have even turned to the philosophical tradition: (1) apophatic-claims seem to contradict cataphatic-claims and yet people often feel compelled to make both sorts of claims (how can God be beyond description if we claim that he is good and that he is the creator?), and (2) the apophatic-claims seem to be internally incoherent (how can God be beyond description if he satisfies the description "beyond description"?).

The remainder of this chapter looks to find ways out of this quagmire, both to salvage a major feature of the Jewish intellectual tradition, and, more fundamentally, to make sense of our religious life.

Route 1: Apophaticism as True Contradiction

The first route out of the quagmire would claim that we have a real paradox on our hands. That is to say that we have a contradiction (or, more accurately, two contradictions: the contradiction between our cataphatic-claims and our apophatic-claims, as well as the internal contradiction *within* our apophatic-claims)[16] and that the contradiction is such that we feel equally compelled to assert both sides of it. This could be because we have equally vivid cataphatic-experiences and apophatic-experiences. Or, it could be because we feel equally committed, say, to Maimonides's cosmological argument as we do to his argument that apophaticism follows from it. The first route urges us simply to accept apophaticism as a true paradox; a true contradiction.

Most philosophers, especially in the analytic tradition, take for granted the law of noncontradiction. To be a contradiction is to be false, or nonsense. But there are some noteworthy philosophers who dissent, most notably, in the analytic tradition, Graham Priest.

Priest argues that the axioms of naïve set theory provide the best motivated account of what a set is. A set is just a collection of things that share a property: the set of red things, the set of bicycles, the set of sets, etc. Naïve set theory allows us to construct any set we like, and thus it allows us to talk about *the set of all sets that are not members of themselves*. Unfortunately, it turns out that that set is a member of itself if and only if it is *not* a member of itself. This paradox, known as Russell's paradox, forced set theorists to develop new conceptions of what it is to be a set. According to nonnaïve theories, sets cannot have themselves as members; sets are stratified into a logical hierarchy and can only draw members from logical levels below them. This helps them to escape the paradox.

Priest argues at length[17] that the alternatives to naïve set theory are often inadequate by their own standards: they often fail to solve the underlying problem, giving rise to new versions of the paradox; they fail to account for all of the mathematical data, "they produce novel and spurious problems; they bristle with *ad hoc* protuberances; they partake in a degenerating research programme; and so on."[18] By contrast, Russell's paradox aside, we have good reason to accept the axioms of naïve set theory. Priest's suggestion is that we drop Aristotle's law of noncontradiction. Given that we have really good reason to accept the axioms of naïve set theory, and given that there are no good alternatives, it looks like we should accept the theory, and therefore accept that this particular contradiction is true. The Russell set is both a member of itself and not a member of itself.

In response, you might argue that it is impossible to believe a contradiction. Priest disagrees: "Many, in fact most, of us believe contradictions. The person who has consistent beliefs is rare."

You might refine your objection. You might suggest that dialetheism, the view that there can be true contradictions, requires us not merely to have inconsistent beliefs but to have *consciously* inconsistent beliefs, and that this is impossible. Priest responds: "Again, this is just plain false. The moment one realises that one's beliefs are inconsistent, one does not *ipso facto* cease to believe the inconsistent things: rather, it becomes a problem, and often a very difficult one, of how to revise one's beliefs to produce consistency. This, of course, takes time."[19]

And thus, you *do* sometimes find yourself consciously believing in a contradiction, albeit, with the hope of finding some way out. The next objection might charge that even if it is possible consciously to believe a contradiction, it can never be rational to do so. In fact, one watermark of rationality might be the disposition never consciously to believe a contradiction and to seek a repair whenever an inconsistency is found. In a nutshell, Priest rejects this conception of rationality. For a belief to be rational, it is sufficient to have good reasons for holding it. Priest has given us what he takes to be good reasons for adopting the axioms of naïve set theory and for rejecting its alternatives. This means that he has good reason to believe in the contradiction that the Russell set is both a member of itself and not a member of itself. Having good reason for this belief is, for Priest, what makes it rational.

If you still need convincing that it can be rational consciously to believe in a contradiction, Priest[20] invites you to consider the *paradox of the preface*. A conscientious and reputable scholar writes a book that contains a fairly significant number of claims. She believes everything that she has written, with good reason. But, "she is aware that no factual book [with this number of claims] has ever been written which did not contain some falsehoods. The inductive evidence for this is overwhelming." So, she is forced into believing the conjunction of all of her theses, as well as the belief that at least one of them is false. Her belief state is inconsistent, and yet she is "paradigmatically rational." It might strike you that there is something wrong about Priest's presentation of this example, but it certainly is not easy to locate the flaw. We will come back to this example later.

Given a fuller account of what it takes to have good reasons for a belief, route 1 would argue that the apophatic theist has good reasons to accept her apophatic-claims, and, if she also makes cataphatic-claims, that she has good reason to accept them too. And thus, she has good reason to accept the contradiction internal to apophaticism, and, if she also makes cataphatic-claims, she has good reason to accept the contradictions that arise between her apophatic-claims and cataphatic-claims. Maimonides and Saadya can claim that they are equally convinced by their arguments for the existence of a God as they are by their arguments for his ineffability; that they have equally good reasons to accept both arguments. If the conjunction of these beliefs are contradictory, then so be it. We must have a true contradiction on our hands! To be clear: I am not suggesting that Maimonides or

Saadya would have endorsed this route. They were wedded to the law of noncontradiction. I am merely suggesting that this route would offer them a way of making sense of their position.

Even if dialethism is true, it will not be the case that all contradictions are true. In fact, we may very rarely have equally good reasons to assert both sides of a contradiction. But, if you think that human logic and language is ever predisposed to degenerate into contradictions and paradoxes, then it would be a good bet to wager that it will happen when talking about God.[21] And this form of apophaticism should not really be too much of a threat to analytic theology. We can still *describe* God. Some descriptions will be completely false. He is not evil, for example. And, some descriptions will be true as well as false. For example, he is wise as well as indescribable.[22]

One way of phrasing the central problem of this chapter is that apophaticism is host to a prima facie absurdity in its claim that we can describe God as indescribable. Route 1 out of the problem would suggest that the prima facie appearance of absurdity is illusory and based upon an ill-motivated allegiance to the law of noncontradiction; a law that sometimes admits of exception. However, and despite Graham Priest's preeminence as an analytic philosopher of logic, his eccentric conclusions have never found favor with more than a handful of his peers. He provides us with some resources, I think, to draw a possible route forward for the analytic Jewish philosopher who does not want to jettison her own apophatic traditions. But, the notion that some propositions can be both true *and* false cuts so deeply against our intuitions that almost any other route would, I believe, be preferable to what I have called route 1.[23]

Route 2: Apophaticism as a Truth about Fundamental Truths

The next route seeks to distinguish between different levels of truth. In one of the few "analytic" defenses of apophaticism, this route has recently been defended by Jonathan Jacobs.[24] He bases his defense of apophaticism on a distinction between fundamental and nonfundamental truths. This distinction, he illustrates using the following diagram:

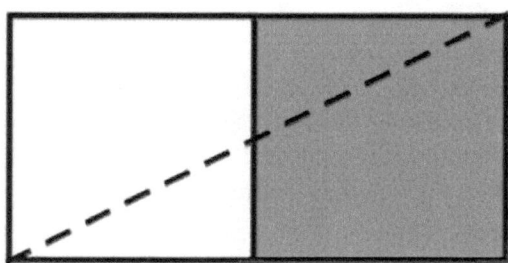

Here are some true sentences about that rectangle:

1. Half of the rectangle is black, and half is white.
2. The area of the rectangle that is black is equal to the area of the rectangle that is white.

But, we could imagine a different linguistic community, with a different conceptual scheme, who carve reality up in different ways. Instead of thinking of the significant color division here in terms of two divided halves, top to bottom, "they conceptualize it as divided color-wise in half by a dotted line from the lower left corner to the upper right corner. . . . They have a concept for the color of the top left triangle, 'whack', and a concept for the color of the lower right triangle, 'blite.' "[25] And thus, using their concepts, the following two sentences are true:

3. Half of the rectangle is whack, and half is blite.
4. The area of the rectangle that is whack is equal to the area of the rectangle that is blite.

Even though we cannot deny the truth of claims 3 and 4, the color concepts they employ seem "gerrymandered. They don't, as Plato put it, carve nature at the joints."[26] Following Ted Sider (2012) and Kit Fine (2009),[27] Jacobs wants to argue that sentences 1 and 2 express *fundamental truths* (or, at least, relatively fundamental truths) whereas sentences 3 and 4 express *nonfundamental truths*. This is not to belittle sentences 3 and 4. By saying that a sentence/proposition is nonfundamental: "You are not saying that it is unimportant. You are not saying that it is mind-dependent. You are not saying that it is metaphorical. It might be literally, objectively, mind-independently, importantly true. You are, however, saying that it does not carve nature perfectly at its joints, that it is in some way gerrymandered, ontologically imperspicuous."[28]

Jacobs is committed to the following three assertions:

1. Apophaticism makes no claim concerning truths about God's relationship to the world.
2. Apophaticism only makes a claim concerning propositions about God's intrinsic properties.
3. For any proposition, P, about God's intrinsic properties, apophaticism will claim that P is not fundamentally true, and that P is not fundamentally false.

That God is wise, for example, is neither a fundamental truth, nor a fundamental falsehood. But, it can still be (literally, objectively, mind-independently, and importantly) *true* as a nonfundamental truth. Unlike route 1, route 2 does not give up the claim of classical logic that every proposition is either true or false (and never both). The proposition that God is wise, for example, must either be true or false (and not both), even if it is neither *fundamentally* true nor *fundamentally* false. What the apophatic tradition tells us, apparently, is that, while the claims of Judaism (or, in Jacobs's case, Christianity) may be true, those which concern God's intrinsic properties cannot be *fundamentally* true, because there are no fundamental truths about how God is intrinsically.

Jacobs wants to escape the prima facie absurdity of apophaticism by claiming that our intuitions against ineffability are only true at the level of nonfundamental truths. At first glance, this does not seem to go far enough. On Jacobs's account, we still end up claiming that God is fundamentally ineffable, which is, in turn, to say something about what he fundamentally is, which is to contradict oneself. As I understand him, he tries to escape this problem by saying that it is not *fundamentally* true that he is fundamentally ineffable. It is only nonfundamentally true that he is fundamentally ineffable. This move successfully saves Jacobs's view from absurdity.[29]

Looking to Saadya and Maimonides, route 2 says the following: the arguments for God's existence (as creator of everything, or as first-cause) are true, but not fundamentally true. Furthermore, those nonfundamental truths reveal a further nonfundamental truth about what God is fundamentally: that "For any proposition, P, about God's intrinsic properties, P is not fundamentally true, and P is not fundamentally false." The nonfundamental truth of God's being nonfundamentally the first-cause, for example, entails that it is not fundamentally true that God is fundamentally the first-cause and that it is not fundamentally true that he *is not* fundamentally the first-cause. There is no internal contradiction within apophaticism. Apophaticism is not the claim that God is indescribable, for that would be self-defeating. The claim of apophaticism actually contains a tacit switch between levels of truth. As Jacobs puts it, "God is non-fundamentally effable [hence our cataphatic-claims], and fundamentally ineffable [hence our apophatic-claims]."[30]

Jacobs's defense of apophaticism is elegant and coherent, but still leaves some grounds for concern. We want to say that our nonfundamental truths are grounded in fundamental ones. For example, if sentences 3 and 4, about the rectangle, are true, they will only be true because of some *fundamental* facts about the rectangle. It is the fundamental reality of the white-black color-distribution that makes those *nonfundamental* claims true. But, if there are no fundamental truths about

God, what is it about the world, as it fundamentally is, that makes our cataphatic-claims nonfundamentally true?

Jacobs is aware of this question. His preferred response seems to be this: a nonfundamental truth does not have to be grounded in a fundamental truth, but merely in an *object*. God, rather than fundamental truths *about* God, but *God Himself*, is what grounds the nonfundamental truths of our cataphatic-claims. And thus Jacobs concludes that it is "perfectly consistent" with his formulation of apophaticism "to claim that the orthodox Christian doctrines are grounded in *God*."[31] But, even if I accept that an object, rather than a proposition or a fact, might be the grounds for something's nonfundamental truth, it is far from clear that, according to Jacobs, *God* can be the fundamental grounding for any truth. Why? Because, according to Jacobs, the claim that God exists is not fundamentally true. Admittedly, for Jacobs, the claim that God exists is not fundamentally false either.[32] But, it is remarkably hard to see how an object whose existence is not a fundamental matter can be the fundamental grounds to nonfundamental truths about that object!

To put my concern another way: there is something odd about grounding a large number of nonfundamental truths upon a very thin fundamental basis. If nothing can be said about God, fundamentally, then how does that God ground the (nonfundamental) truth of the claims of Orthodox Christianity rather than the claims of Orthodox Islam? I think the only option open to Jacobs is to accept that cataphatic-claims about God, if ever true, are *mysterious*. They are true but they have no grounding. The difficulty now becomes, why should we believe them? How can we verify them? What privileges the cataphatic-claims of one religion over the cataphatic-claims of another religion? I do not see how any of these questions can be straightforwardly answered if we think cataphatic-truths to be basically groundless. Many in the apophatic tradition seem happy to accept that some things are mysterious. That may even be an essential feature of apophaticism. But, making all cataphatic-truths about God's intrinsic properties groundless might be going too far.

Route 3: Apophaticism as Illuminating or Therapeutic Falsehood

The third route takes its lead from Wittgenstein's *Tractatus Logico-Philosophicus*.[33] At a first glance, the *Tractatus* seems to be after an account of what the world must be like, and what language must *do*, in order for language to be able to represent the world. But, Wittgenstein's arguments lead him to conclude that language must be incapable of representing how it relates to the world. Unfortunately, this conclusion uproots the entirety of the foregoing book! The *Tractatus*, up until its conclusion, is all about the relationship between language and the world, which the conclusion tells us cannot be spoken about. Once again, we have a conclusion that uproots its premises, just as we had with Saadya and Maimonides.

Wittgenstein tries to remove the sting with the following words:

> 6.54: My propositions serve as elucidations in the following way: anyone who understands me eventually recognizes them as nonsensical, when he has used them—as steps—to climb up beyond them. (He must, so to speak, throw away the ladder after he has climbed up it.)
>
> He must transcend these propositions, and then he will see the world aright.

The *Tractatus* is generally read in one of two ways. The most fashionable reading calls itself the "therapeutic" or "resolute" reading. Crudely put, the therapeutic reading understands the *Tractatus* as an attempt to cure us of the irrational desire to do metaphysics. Building upon the efforts of Frege and Russell, Wittgenstein had made what he hoped to be the best attempt one could expect to make at describing the fundamentals of reality and its relationship to language. Watching the best possible attempt at such metaphysics descending into nonsense is supposed to teach us that the job simply cannot be done. The *Tractatus* is a course of *therapy* to cure us of the desire to do metaphysics.

In contrast to the therapeutic reading, the traditional reading claims that the *Tractatus* really was an attempt to do some serious metaphysics. Wittgenstein hoped that, despite his book's failure to *say* anything about the nature of language and its relationship to the world, it was somehow able to *show* us things—deep metaphysical findings—that simply could not be *said*. On the therapeutic reading, the quote that I highlighted is read as the admission that the whole book was nothing more than the ruse of an antimetaphysical therapist. The traditional reading reads the same quote as follows: *despite* being nonsensical and failing to say anything about the topics it hoped to cover, the *Tractatus*'s nonsense was elucidatory—it was able to *show* us things that could not be *said*.

The traditional reading can be divided into two camps. The first camp finds the book slightly ridiculous. To echo Ramsey's famous response, you cannot say what cannot be said, and you cannot whistle it either. In his introduction to the *Tractatus*, Russell shares his suspicion that some mistake *must* have been made, because, after all, "Mr. Wittgenstein manages to say a good deal about what cannot be said, thus suggesting to the sceptical reader that possibility that there may be some loophole through a hierarchy of languages, or by some other exit." And thus Russell and Ramsey, though appreciative of much of the book, think that there must be some mistake made at some point, since what cannot be said cannot be said, nor shown, and this book is actually a *good* book that manages to say some important things. The second camp, within the traditional reading, thinks that Wittgenstein's attempt to *show* what cannot be *said* was a commendable philosophical move. The most notable members of this second camp are likewise stalwarts of the analytic tradition: Elizabeth Anscombe and Peter Geach.[34]

I do not want to arbitrate between the therapeutic and traditional readings of the *Tractatus*. But I think that each reading can inspire a distinctive form of apophaticism. To start with, I merely seek to ask the following question: if you happen to adopt the traditional reading, why on earth would you side with Anscombe and Geach over Ramsey and Russell? Why not view with suspicion the attempt to *show* the unsayable? Roger White makes perhaps the best contemporary case for the supportive camp within the traditional reading.[35] In order to explicate the thesis that there are some things that cannot be said, but which *can* be shown, White makes three claims, which he attributes to Wittgenstein.[36]

1. Preconditions for representation cannot be stated: One of the main objectives of the *Tractatus* is to sketch what the world must be like in order to make representation possible. Suppose that we conclude our inquiry with the finding that, for representation of a world to be possible, p, q, and r must all be true of that world. As White points out, "*Saying* this would lead straight to a contradiction, since we can now form the following description: 'a world in which at least one of p, q, and r is false,' which *ex hypothesi* would be a description of an indescribable world."[37] The wrong conclusion to draw here, it seems to me (and White and Wittgenstein), is that there are no preconditions for representation. Indeed, every possible world has a property in common—the property of being representable. It is just that *Wittgenstein* thinks that we cannot *say* this. Introducing the concept of *being representable* into our vocabulary would be toxic, allowing us, upon its negation, to describe the indescribable. Logical space itself *shows* you what the preconditions to representation are, but they cannot be stated.
2. Unrestricted generalizations cannot be made: Language is compositional, built out of elementary building blocks. The possible combinations of those building blocks determine the possible elementary propositions (just like the English dictionary determines the realm of possible English sentences). The limits of what can be said are determined by those propositions and by truth-functions of those propositions. Imagine that p, q, and r are

the complete set of elementary propositions. What can be said is merely what can be said by them and by their truth-functions. It follows that we cannot make a completely unrestricted generalization. That p, q, and r are *all* of the elementary propositions is, itself, not a truth-function of p, q, and r, and thus it cannot be said. Rather, if we run out of elementary propositions, we would have been *shown* that, say, p, q, and r were all of the elementary propositions, but this fact would not be something that could be said.

3. The logical type of an *entity* cannot be expressed: Predicates play a different role, in language, to names. Russell and Frege were led to believe that this deep grammatical distinction was being forced upon them by some deep ontological distinction. On their view, the logical type of the symbol was correlated to the logical type of the entity that that symbol represented. Predicates symbolize one type of thing: say, abstract properties. Names, on the other hand, might represent another type of thing: objects. And thus, we have good motivation to divide our ontology into different types of things. But, if these different types of entities are distinguished by the different grammatical type of their names, then you cannot put the name for one type of entity into the same place as a name for another type of entity. But, if that is the case, then you are not going to be able to draw the distinction to begin with. You will not be able to say something like, *"everything* is either an object or a property." If you could say such a thing, then the term "everything" seems to be functioning as a placeholder, or a name, for both types of things, but, ex hypothesi, no word can name both types of things, and no space in a sentence can be reserved equally for *both* types of things. Wittgenstein's solution is to say that *x being an object* is something that is shown to us by the grammar of language, but cannot meaningfully be said. Instead, it can be *shown* to us by the way that its name is forced to behave in the grammar of our language.

On all of these issues, Wittgenstein may be wrong (and probably is). It is not obvious that the property of being representable gets us into the mess that Wittgenstein thought it did. To admit that there is a class of unrepresentable things is not to represent any of the members of that class, at least not *de re*. The class may be empty. Likewise, the notion that unrestricted quantification is impossible is open for debate.[38] I am not looking to defend Wittgenstein's reasoning here, so much as to defend his distinction between *saying* and *showing*. The reasons I have canvassed were (among) the reasons that led Wittgenstein to that distinction. If we assume—just for the sake of argument—that Wittgenstein's arguments were right, we are led to this *distinction*, and then, even once we discharge our assumption, perhaps concluding that Wittgenstein was wrong about the nature of quantification, for example, we will still have discovered a distinction that may or may not have uses elsewhere.[39]

There may be an immediate temptation to compare Wittgenstein's notion of *showing the unsayable* with the mystical tradition in philosophy and theology that claims there to be a realm of deep truths that cannot be put into words. The temptation would be to save Saadya Gaon and Maimonides by taking a *Tractarian* turn. Indeed, Wittgenstein himself seems to have been drawn somewhat to comparing his views with mystical tradition (6.522). But Roger White,[40] despite his support for Wittgenstein's general project in the *Tractatus*, thinks that Wittgenstein was ill advised to draw any such comparison, and finds the *Tractatus*'s remarks about ethics and religion to be "deeply unsatisfactory."

White pushes a key difference between the apophatic tradition and the *Tractatus*:

> The earlier mystical traditions were typically concerned with a form of esoteric knowledge of that which transcended normal experience and understanding. Wittgenstein, however, when he talks of "what is shown" is talking about something that is shown by our ordinary everyday use of language, and that is therefore at least tacitly known and understood by all of us—by everyone who has mastered their mother tongue. Consequently many of the difficulties surrounding the supposition that mystical theologians were genuinely engaged in an act of communication when they wrote about the ineffable do not beset the project of the *Tractatus*.[41]

White holds that the *Tractatus* can only communicate its insights to those who already have a tacit knowledge of those insights—making explicit what was only ever known implicitly—but I will say exactly the same thing regarding the arguments of Maimonides and Saadya; no more and no less. Maimonides and Saadya are addressing a religious audience. As we have said, in the religious life, cataphatic-experiences and apophatic-experiences are relatively common place, especially apophatic-experiences, which can be very undramatic (an inchoate sense that something somehow indescribable is accompanying you through the journey of your life).[42]

Simply to utter an apophatic-claim, even though it will be internally contradictory, and thus, nonsensical, has the power to communicate to the religious believer something that she might, as of yet, only know tacitly. She has apophatic-experiences of an undramatic variety. Her religious experiences cause her to know something that cannot be said. When someone tries to describe to her a God who cannot be described, and she sees how the attempt collapses into nonsense, some of those unsayable things that she tacitly knows are *shown* to her, and her knowledge is made explicit. This, I call the apophaticism of *showing*. It is analogous to the way in which utterances of "*x* is an object" are supposed to collapse in on themselves, and how, in so doing, they are supposed to *show* speakers of English something that they only knew tacitly until then; some ineffable fact that is shown to them by the grammar of language.

Perhaps the apophatic-claims, though literally false, are here functioning as a *metaphor*, in the way that Elizabeth Camp[43] pictures metaphors sometimes to function, as almost ostending toward properties that have no literal name (yet) in the language. We *point* to ineffable Divine properties using apophatic metaphors. But, perhaps in the case of apophaticism, it is the very way in which the utterance somehow *collapses in on itself* that helps to point to the ineffable properties it targets. This is apophaticism as an illuminating falsehood. It *shows* you something that cannot be *said*.

Interpreting Maimonides in this *Tractarian* light can help him out of a very particular puzzle. Gersonides could not understand why, according to Maimonides, it is good to say that God is not ignorant, but, it is bad to say that God is not wise. If Maimonides was really serious about his apophaticism, Gersonides contended, he should have accepted that both negative claims were true: God is neither wise nor ignorant.[44] Well, not necessarily. Perhaps both are false, but perhaps only one is illuminating.

To arbitrate that discussion, we would need a test for a sentence's illuminating powers. If, for example, the goal is to make certain items of knowledge salient, there is good reason to think that only some theological falsehoods are going to be powerful; just as only certain metaphors about a lover have the power to illuminate what it is you want to say—describing her in terms of a snowflake might just strike you as more appropriate than describing her in terms of a bottle of Coca-Cola. What we really need, but are still sorely lacking, is a theory to explain what makes certain illuminating falsehoods *apt*. That is a task that lies beyond the scope of this chapter; but it is not solely a theological problem, and there is reason to think that such a theory would provide Maimonides with an answer to Gersonides.

Just as there are two mainstream readings of the *Tractatus*, perhaps we can fashion two Tractarian varieties of apophaticism. The apophaticism of *showing* corresponds to the traditional reading of *showing* in the *Tractatus*. But, there is also a therapeutic reading of the *Tractatus*. According to the therapeutic reading, the *Tractatus* was not trying to illuminate some unsayable something; it was trying to cure you of the desire to engage in ultimate metaphysics. Well, perhaps we could develop a *therapeutic* form of apophaticism.

One of the things that Maimonides and Saadya might be trying to convey to their audience is that they should not be overly confident in their systematic theology. To have a systematic theology is not just to believe, or even to know, certain things about God. Rather, one has to assimilate those things that you believe/know into some sort of *system*. The system will tell you which theological claims are most significant, and how the different claims interact with one another, and with nontheological theories. Accordingly, let us imagine that you make certain cataphatic-claims: God is wise, God is good, God is loving, etc. But, you know, because of your apophatic-experiences, that there *are*, in addition to these facts, facts about God that you cannot reasonably *hope* to describe. You may have had some sort of direct epistemic access to some of these facts, in a religious experience, but you certainly know that you cannot do them justice in words. This should make the task of systematizing what you know, daunting, to say the least.

If you are reading a novel about a character, you may be led to believe that the character is a wicked individual motivated by evil in all that he does. But, then, in a final twist, perhaps in the very last paragraph of the book, you learn something about that character that changes your interpretation of everything that came before. Upon finding out this final fact about the character, you reappraise everything that you thought you knew about him. And thus, even the beliefs that do not *change* might still receive a new *significance* once you know all that there is to know. Knowing that some or much of God's nature is unknowable to us, should make us very humble. Even the things that we *do* know might be less or more significant than we currently think them to be. And thus, we can already see how apophatic-experience might warrant a course of therapy aimed at encouraging, at least, a certain degree of *humility* in arriving at a systematic theology.

Maimonides and Saadya both lead their readers into a contradiction. They start with certain cataphatic-claims that are supposed to seem really well motivated. They argue, with all of their logical and rhetorical might, for the conclusion that God created all that there is, or that God is the first-cause. They then argue that these conclusions entail, in turn, that you cannot say anything at all about God. Of course, they know that there is a contradiction here. Could they have missed that? But what affect should that have? Perhaps they are conducting a certain sort of therapy.

We could probably find the false premises in the arguments that supposedly give rise to apophaticism, both in the work of Maimonides and Saadya. But, *they* probably thought that their arguments were good. Their hope was that you *would not* be able to find a false premise. I would suggest that the reasonable thing to do, in such a situation, is to continue believing every premise, apart from the ones that are *internally* contradictory (like the explicitly apophatic-claims), but to lower your credence in all of them. One of them must be wrong, but you do not know which!

When I say that God cannot be described, I say something that cannot be true, on pain of contradiction. If he cannot be described, then I should not be able to describe him as being indescribable. But, if this falsehood follows from lots of things that I believe, and have equally good reason to believe, then, if I cannot isolate the false premise that is guilty for generating my contradictory conclusion, then perhaps it should cause me to lower my credence in each of the things that collectively entails the falsehood. If our best shot at systematic theology gives rise to palpably false conclusions, we should be humble in our theological aspirations.

So, the second type of Tractatus-inspired apophaticism, I call the apophaticism of argumentation. The idea is that once you have seen an argument move from your firmly held cataphatic-beliefs to a nonsensical apophatic-conclusion, you will be shown how little you know of God, and how you should turn down the credence you have in all of your cataphatic-beliefs. This in turn should point you toward your own apophatic-experiences, and to the conclusion that there is much about God that you *cannot* know (at least not propositionally—you might experience some of these facts, but you cannot describe them); and thus you *cannot* know how those unknown or unpresentable facts would make you reappraise what you currently believe.

Belief is not a zero-sum game. It comes in degrees. (Degrees of credence range from 0 to 1. A sufficiently high degree of credence—say 0.51 is necessary [and perhaps sufficient] for belief.) In the paradox of the preface, the author believes all of her conclusions to a high enough degree to be characterized as believing in all of them, indeed, to a high enough degree to feel comfortable *publishing* each one. And yet her credence for the *conjunction* of all of the propositions will have to be lower than her credence for any given conjunct. When she finds out that a book of this length almost always contains at least one error, she should probably revise her credences—since she knows (or has good reason to believe) that there is an error somewhere. What should she do?

Since she does not know where the error is, but believes that there probably is one, she should lower her credence in each claim of the book, but not necessarily to such a degree that she cannot still be said to *believe* in each conjunct. By lowering the degree of credence in each conjunct, she lowers her credence in the whole conjunction even further. Furthermore, she does not *know* that her book contains an error. She only believes that it is likely that it does. So she has a certain credence, above 0.5 but below 1, that the book contains an error. Well, if the belief in the very long conjunction of the book's theses, a credence that need not be *all* that high, added to the belief that there is an error, does not exceed 1—which seems plausible to me—I do not see how there is anything paradoxical going on at all.

By comparison, if you have a long series of propositions about God that you believe, and then you realize that an absurdly apophatic-claim follows from them, but you cannot figure out which of the propositions is having this toxic effect, I think that this should function to lower your credence in each of the propositions that collectively gave rise to the absurdity, without rescinding your *belief* in any of them. Am I saying that you should engineer a situation in which your belief in the conjunction of the premises that gave rise to the apophaticism should be so low that that when you add it to your near certainty that apophaticism, taken literally, is false, you do not exceed a credence of 1? No. Because here, to believe in the truth of apophaticism in conjunction with your cataphatic beliefs is not to subscribe to a *logical* contradiction (but to something like a *performative* contradiction—the contradiction between apophaticism and cataphaticism does not emerge merely in consideration of logical form, or syntax [see note 16]). So you are not in exactly the same situation as the paradox of the preface—which is supposed to force a *logical* contradiction upon the author. But I do think, that at the very least, the fact that your theological premises have given rise to an *absurdity* should be a cause of humility. Revise your credences down!

The apophaticism of *showing* recognizes that apophatic claims are false, but thinks of them as *illuminating*. The apophaticism of *argumentation* recognizes that apophatic claims must be false, but sees their emergence from theological arguments as a useful form of *therapy*. Even though the two schools of *Tractatus*-interpretation cannot both be historically accurate, there is no reason to think that the two forms of apophaticism that they inspire cannot rub shoulders more easily. Apophatic claims can be both illuminating *and* therapeutic. I will not make the audacious claim that I have really understood how Maimonides and Saadya justified to themselves the overtly paradoxical argumentative structures of their work. I merely claim that these *Tractatus*-inspired forms of apophaticism give us the resources to salvage something from their work, as the Jewish tradition is dragged into the analytic age.

The problem we hoped to solve was the prima facie absurdity of apophatic-claims (as well as their conflict with cataphatic-claims). Route 1 suggests that the appearance of absurdity is illusory—sometimes contradictions can be true. Route 2 also suggests that the appearance of absurdity is illusory because apophaticism is saved from contradiction when we appeal to two distinct levels or types of truth. Route 3, on the other hand, admits that apophatic-claims taken at face value really are absurd. Apophatic-claims are false. They cannot be true. Contradictions can never be true. Nor are they seeking to make a distinction between the fundamental and the nonfundamental. Rather, apophatic claims are falsehoods (or nonsense) with the power (somehow or other) to *show* you things and to cure you of certain intellectual maladies.

Route 3 champions either, or both, of my *Tractatus*-inspired apophaticisms. The apophaticism of *showing* regards apophatic-claims as *illuminating* falsehoods, and the apophaticism of *argumentation* regards them as *therapeutic* falsehoods. My argument against Plantinga is that he takes apophatic-claims at face value. I agree with him that there is a prima facie absurdity in doing so, but perhaps these claims are not supposed to be taken at face value. They are not assertions of fact so much as illuminations of what cannot be discursively described as well as epistemic correctives to arrogant theology. We should engage in analytic philosophy, but we should do so with extreme humility.

Apophaticism is part of everyday religious experience. Apophaticism is a large part of the Jewish, Christian, and Muslim tradition. Analytic philosophers of religion need not ignore apophaticism, and we need not reject it. I have offered three routes toward its adoption. All three routes give rise to coherent theologies, though I would argue that the first is too exotic, and comes at too high a cost, and that the second is home to even more *mystery* than theology generally demands. You can have your apophaticism as a true contradiction, or as a nonfundamental claim about fundamental truths. I, on the other hand, would offer it as an illuminating and/or therapeutic falsehood.

Notes

Thanks to Mike Rea and Dan Howard Snyder, both of whom graciously read an earlier draft of this chapter. Their comments were immensely helpful. This chapter owes a great deal to conversations with, and the work of, my dear friend, Gabriel Citron. I thank Carl Moser and all my other colleagues at the Centers for Philosophy of Religion at Notre Dame and Rutgers. Thanks also to Michael Fagenblat who helped me to shape this chapter into its current form.

1. By "species-neutrality of logic," I mean the view that logic is not merely a human construct but should rightly regiment all rational thought irrespective of what species we may belong to.

2. David Woodruff Smith, "Phenomenology," *The Stanford Encyclopedia of Philosophy*, ed. Edward N. Zalta, Winter 2013 edition, http://plato.stanford.edu/archives/win2013/entries/phenomenology/.

3. One cannot really summarize the distinction between continental and analytic philosophy in two paragraphs. I certainly do not intend to belittle either tradition. I merely intend to illustrate that apophaticism is a more natural fit for continental philosophers than for analytic ones.

4. Michael Scott, "Religious Language," *Philosophy Compass* 5, no. 6 (2010): 505–515, documents how recent work in analytic philosophy of religion has adopted the same set of responses to expressivism about religious language, for the same sorts of reasons.

5. Peter van Inwagen, *The Problem of Evil* (Oxford: Oxford University Press, 2006), 19.

6. Alvin Plantinga, *Warranted Christian Belief* (Oxford: Oxford University Press, 2000).

7. Ibid., 42.

8. This translation is Gabriel Citron's (unpublished), making a small emendation from Samuel Rosenblatt's translation of *Saadia Gaon: The Book of Beliefs and Opinions* (New Haven, CT: Yale University Press, 1989), 111. Gabriel Citron, "On the possibility of a non-atheistic apophaticism: a case study from Sa'adia Ga'on," pdf, September 16, 2012.

9. For more on the distinction between historic and continuous ontological dependence, see Amie Thomasson, *Fiction and Metaphysics* (Cambridge: Cambridge University Press 1999), chap. 2.

10. *Saadia Gaon: The Book of Beliefs and Opinions*, 89.

11. Ibid., 38–86. A point that is emphasized by Citron.

12. As Mike Rea pointed out to me, it does not follow from the fact that you can reasonably ask a question that the question has to have a good answer. One could say that *nothing* caused God's parts to come together, they have always been and must necessarily be together in just that way. But, here I am merely trying to lay out the sorts of considerations that lead *Maimonides* to apophatic conclusions; there may well be faulty premises along the way, indeed, I think that there must be, but that is not my immediate concern here.

13. There are more and less radical readings of Maimonidean apophaticism—for a particularly radical account, see Josef Stern, "Maimonides on Language and the Science of Language," *Boston Studies in the Philosophy of Science* vol. 211, (2000), 173–225.

14. William James, *Varieties of Religious Experience* (London: Longmans, Green and Co., 1902), and William Alston, *Perceiving God* (Ithaca, NY: Cornell University Press, 1991), provide examples of people claiming to have had cataphatic-experiences and making cataphatic-claims in their wake.

15. In his unpublished paper, Citron gathers some examples of people claiming to have had apophatic-experiences, and people making apophatic-claims, seemingly on the back of their own religious experiences. For example, *Angelo of Foligno: Complete Works*, trans. Paul Lachance (Mahwah, NJ: Paulist Press, 1993), 191–192, talks of her personal religious experiences that left her claiming to know "with the utmost certainty that the more one feels God, the less is one able to say anything about him" because of "his infinite goodness being so far beyond anything you could possibly say or think." Citron also points to the Hassidic master, the *Kedushat Levi* (Y. Levi, *Kedushat Levi* [Warsaw: Yitzchak Gellerman, 1875/1876]), who seems to think that the more you *experience* God, rather than think about him, the more you come to realize that none of your predicates can apply to him, such that you end up calling him, paradoxically, the "great nothing" given that there is *no thing* such that that *thing* can be predicated of God! Clearly, the *Kedushat Levi* is talking about apophatic-experiences.

16. Some of the contradictions will not be logical contradictions but *performative contradictions*, like the sort that would arise if a person said, "I believe that there are no beliefs." You can assert that "God is wise," call that proposition p, and you can assert the proposition that "p is inexpressible," call that proposition q, and you can assert the conjunction of p and q without ever falling into a logical contradiction—a contradiction that can be read directly off of the syntax of the claims and allow you to derive both that p and that not-p. Some of the contradictions here *are* logical ("God is describable and God is indescribable") and some

of them are *performative*, rather than logical ("God is wise and one cannot say that God is wise"). Route 1 should thus be taken to advocate the claim that some *performative* contradictions are true, as well as the claim that some logical contradictions are true. Thanks to Mike Rea for discussing these issues with me.

17. Graham Priest, *In Contradiction: A Study of the Transconsistent* (Oxford: Oxford University Press, 2006), esp. chap. 2.

18. Ibid., 101.

19. Ibid., 96.

20. Ibid., 100.

21. For an argument of analytical philosophy that concludes that there may very well be something akin to true contradictions about God, see Sam Lebens, "Hassidic Idealism: Kurt Vonnegut and the Creator of the Universe," in Tyron Goldschmidt and Kenneth L. Pearce, eds., *Idealism: New Essays in Metaphysics* (Oxford: Oxford University Press, forthcoming).

22. Substantive philosophical theology can still continue, albeit with an unsightly paraconsistent logic.

23. In his unpublished paper, Gabriel Citron argues for a variation of route 1. He makes his case, mining the works of the later Wittgenstein, instead of the work of Graham Priest.

24. Jonathan Jacobs, "The Ineffable, Inconceivable, and Incomprehensible God: Fundamentality and Apophatic Theology," in Jonathan Kvanvig, ed., *Oxford Studies in Philosophy of Religion*, vol. 6 (Oxford: Oxford University Press, 2015), 158–176.

25. Ibid., 161.

26. Ibid., 162.

27. Ted Sider, *Writing the Book of the World* (Oxford: Oxford University Press, 2012); Kit Fine, "The question of ontology," in D. Chalmers, D. Manley, & R. Wasserman (Eds.), *Metametaphysics: New Essays on the Foundation of Ontology* (Oxford: Oxford University Press, 2009), 157–177.

28. Ibid., 170.

29. Mike Rea (in correspondence, March 11, 2014) has suggested that there may be a contradiction lurking in the background of Jacob's view. Though Jacobs accepts classical logic and therefore the principle of bivalence, it seems that he is committed to the denial of bivalence at the level of fundamental truths. Jacobs thinks that it is not fundamentally true that God is wise, and that it is not fundamentally true that God is not wise. Fundamental-bivalence would be the view that, for any p, p is fundamentally true or not-p is fundamentally true. Jacob's views about God violate fundamental-bivalence, which may allow us to derive contradictions. In Sam Lebens, "Why So Negative about Negative Theology: The Search for a Planting-proof Apophaticism," *International Journal for Philosophy of Religion* 76, no. 3 (2014): 259–275, I included an attempt to derive such a contradiction, in a footnote, which was, lamentably, based upon a rudimentary error. But I think it fair to fear the denial of fundamental-bivalence for similar reasons (though not identical) to the reasons that might make us fear the denial of bivalence itself.

30. Jacobs, "The Ineffable, Inconceivable, and Incomprehensible God," 166.

31. Ibid., 174.

32. Ibid., 169.

33. Ludwig Wittgenstein, *Tractatus Logico-Philosophicus*, translated by David Pears and Brian McGuiness, with an introduction by Bertrand Russell (London: Routledge Classics, 2001).

34. Elizabeth Anscombe, *An Introduction to Wittgenstein's Tractatus* (Hutchinson, KS: Hutchinson, 1971); Peter T. Geach, "Saying and Showing in Frege and Wittgenstein," in J. Hintikka, ed., *Essays on Wittgenstein in Honour of G. H. von Wright* (Amsterdam: North Holland, 1977), 54–70.

35. Roger White, "Throwing the Baby Out with the Ladder: On 'Therapeutic' Readings of Wittgenstein's *Tractatus*," in Rupert Read and Matthew A. Lavery, eds., *Beyond the Tractatus Wars: The New Wittgenstein Debate* (London: Routledge, 2010).

36. Ibid., 24–30. He actually makes six claims, but I only report three, to illustrate the general thrust of his reading of the *Tractatus*.

37. Ibid., 24.

38. Cf., for example, A. Rayo and G. Uzquiano, *Absolute Generality* (Oxford: Oxford University Press, 2006).

39. For another route to the distinction between saying and showing, see Lebens, "Why So Negative about Negative Theology."

40. White, "Throwing the Baby Out with the Ladder," note 22.

41. Ibid., 31.

42. The claim that something is accompanying you through the journey of your life is not apophatic, it is only made apophatic by the qualification that that something is indescribable . . . , of course, it is not *truly* indescribable: if you can say of it that it is accompanying you then you are describing it, but that is just to point out that apophatic statements are self-defeating.

43. Elizabeth Camp, "Metaphor and That Certain je ne sais quoi," *Philosophical Studies* 129 (2006): 1–25.

44. See Feldman's synopsis of Levi Gersonides, *The Wars of the Lord*, trans. Seymour Feldman (Philadelphia: The Jewish Publication Society, 1987), 79, and Gersonides's own argument there on pp. 111–112.

FIVE

"My Aid Will Come from Nothingness": The Practice of Negative Theology in *Maggid Devarav Le-Ya'akov*

JAMES JACOBSON-MAISELS

One of the hallmarks of modernity, along with its vision of progress, its optimism, mechanism, scientism, and other qualities, is the deep anxiety and uncertainty it produces, the way in which it uproots, overturns, and dissolves premodern values and structures, whether familial, communal, economic, religious, national, or political, often leaving the modern actor feeling untethered and uncentered, expressed most extremely, perhaps, in nihilism and nihility, the abandonment of all structure, meaning, and value. Among the many responses to the anxiety of modernity, we find a liberal progressive optimism that sees this dissolution as the movement from the irrational to the rational, a reaffirmation of tradition, in religious fundamentalism or forms of romanticism and nationalism, which opposes such dissolution through the imagined return to traditional structures, a totalitarianism that replaces destabilized values and social forms with new modern totalizing structures, an exuberant Nietzscheanism that embraces this dissolution as the path to a transvaluation of values, an existentialist assertion of meaning in the face of a cold universe lacking inherent meaning, and perhaps even a quietist withdrawal that treats all structures and forms, dissolution and generation, with indifference.

In this chapter I would like to explore another response, one I believe was presented by the early Hasidic masters, the embrace of Nothingness as the fundamental underlying nature of existence and divinity and the radical opening and release into that Nothingness, always in dialogue with Being, as a way of living in the midst of emptiness with grace, clarity, and trust. In contrast to Rivka Schatz-Uffenheimer's seminal work, which argued that Hasidic engagement with nothingness was a form of quietism, and to Gershom Scholem's claims that the Hasidic interest in nothingness and the stripping of corporeality was world-denying, I want to argue that divine nothingness in early Hasidism is creative, unifying, and world-affirming. Negative theology as a practice in early Hasidism is activist, productive of human connection, and, despite its at times fearful quality, ultimately a path to freedom from anxiety, disconnection, and instability. That is, the turn to a psychological and experiential mystical Nothingness in early Hasidism, negative theology as a practice and dispositional attitude rather than an intellectual theory, can be seen as another response to modernity that radically embraces dissolution in the context of a largely traditional religious framework. My claim is not that the Hasidic masters speak of the turn to nothingness in precisely this way, but that when we properly understand the nature and meaning of nothingness in their theology, it provides a fascinating example of an alternate mode of relating to the instability of existence, an instability heightened and radicalized in the modern world.

This use of the notion of nothingness, the Hasidic term *ayin*, that we will be discussing here begins with R. Dov Baer the Maggid of Mezherich and profoundly influences the Hasidic masters who follow him. Dov Baer is arguably the founder of Hasidism as an actual religious movement, and his notion of nothingness is the basis for every subsequent Hasidic discussion and sets the very tone and nature of subsequent Hasidic discourse more broadly.[1] Our exploration will therefore center on his work and his claims about the nature of nothingness.[2]

While the term *ayin* literally means nothingness, we will see that its semantic range and the roles it plays are extremely wide indeed. These meanings and functions will emerge organically as we explore the concept in its fullness. Yet each of these roles will connect to its core meaning as a place of emptiness, openness, nonbeing, or perhaps nonparticularity. Its unifying nature, potential for change, and holder of possibilities are all connected to its nonparticularity, its emptiness of any particular essential quality, its lack of being or essence, its lack of separateness, in that sense.

Exploring the concept of *ayin* will of necessity touch on many other aspects of the Maggid's philosophy that cannot be fully explored, but most particularly it will delve into *ayin*'s dialectical partner *yesh*, being or suchness.[3] We will have to consider how nothingness, or the annihilation of reality and the self, relates to being, corporeality, and selfhood. Despite initial appearances, it will be argued that the concept of *ayin* represents not a rejection of *yesh* but its integration into a larger dynamic whole. In this way, we will explore the function and role of *ayin* within a dialectic process in which *ayin* is a moment in that process and a component of a dynamic unity rather than an ultimate goal or end.[4]

Let us begin with an early teaching of the Maggid's from *Maggid Devarav Le-Ya'akov* that will provide the frame for our discussion:

> "[Abraham looked up and saw] a ram after [it had been caught by its horns in a thicket]" (Gen. 22:13). It is brought in the Zohar (I 120b)

that this is the ram which was created at twilight [before the first Shabbat of creation] and it was one year old. The meaning of "twilight" (literally: between the suns) is something which mediates between day and night. For in everything there are four elements: fire, water, wind, and earth. And they are things in opposition, water extinguishes fire, fire scatters earth. So there needs to be one other thing which joins them together and this is the quality of *ayin*. For when the element of water comes to annihilate the element of fire, it is annihilated from reality and reaches the quality of *ayin*. And with love and fear[5] it is also thus. For a corporeal thing which loves something does not fear that thing at the time of the act and when it fears something it does not love it. However with God there is love and fear as one, for He joins them together. And the power of the actor is in that which is acted upon. And *ayin* is called wisdom on the basis of "Where (*mei'ayin*) can wisdom be found?" (Job 28:12). And Wisdom is beginning, "The beginning (*reishit*) of wisdom is fear of the Lord" (Ps. 111:10). And when it is called beginning (*reishit*), then it is has a number. For the meaning of one is unity, but first (*rishon*) is the beginning of numbering. And it can be assumed that there is a level higher than wisdom. And day is called "radiance" for a person sees the radiance of God. And night is called "darkness" when a person, God forbid, does not see His radiance. And that which joins them together is *ayin*. And this is twilight, the thing which joins day and night. And this was the matter in the binding of Isaac, that Isaac[6] was offered up to include him in the quality of love. "And God (*Elohim*[7]) tried Abraham" (Gen. 22:1), [which means] Gevurah (might, judgement) rose up[8] from the power of love, and certainly it was necessary to raise her through the quality of *ayin*. "And [the ram] was a year (*shana*) old" (Zohar I 120b). The meaning of "a year" (*shana*) is change (*shinui*). That is to say, through this it is possible to change, for it is written "[God] founded the earth with wisdom" (Prov. 3:19). He, may He be blessed, dwells in wisdom, and wisdom is a lesser level than Him, may He be blessed. And it [wisdom], with Him, was only the beginning of thought.[9]

This teaching provides an overview of many of the central themes associated with *ayin*. *Ayin* here is that which unites opposites, it is wisdom, the liminal space between states, the level below God Himself, and the capacity for change and transformation. We will begin where the teaching ends, with this capacity for change and transformation.

Ayin and Transformation

Playing on the word "year" in the Zoharic quote "And [the ram] was a year (*shana*) old," the Maggid tells us that: "The meaning of 'a year' (*shana*) is change (*shinui*). That is to say, through this it is possible to change, for it is written '[God] founded the earth with wisdom' (Prov. 3:19)." *Ayin* therefore is the capacity that makes change possible and this is so precisely because *ayin*, synonymous with wisdom for the Maggid, is the very instrument of creation and the foundation of the world. That is, by returning to its original formless state in *ayin*, out of which all creation or *yesh* emerged, one thing can become another. As the Maggid explains:

> And it is known that everything in the world, when it is brought to its root, it is able to be transformed from what it was previously. For example, when one wants to transform a wheat kernel in order to make from it some wheat, one brings it to its root, which is the vegetative power in the earth. Therefore it will not grow in any place other than earth. And also it will not grow there until rain falls and moistens it and it loses its form and it comes to the aspect of *ayin*, which is the *hylic* matter, which is the aspect of wisdom as is known. And it is the root of all as it is written "You made everything with wisdom" (Ps. 104:24). Then the vegetative power is able to enter it and some wheat sprouts.[10]

Ayin is then both the origin of everything in the world and its capacity to become something else and these two facets of *ayin* are intimately related. In our original teaching, this capacity of transformation is clearly connected to *ayin*'s ability to unite opposites such as fire and water and to bridge the gap between alternate states such as day and night. *Ayin*'s capacity to do this comes directly from its nothingness or formlessness as indicated in the previous quotation. That is the significance of the Maggid's equation of *ayin* with *hylic* matter, that which, in his words, "strips off form and dons it."[11] *Ayin*, as *hylic* matter, as the formless groundlessness out of which the world emerges, is completely unconstrained, indeterminate, and indefinable. It can therefore become anything and so makes transformation possible. As the Maggid explains in a recurrent metaphor: "Nothing can change from one kind to another [without *ayin*]. Like an egg which becomes a chick which needs first to completely annul itself from the kind of egg, that is, from the first kind, then afterwards it is able to be a different kind. And so everything must be thus. [Each thing] must come to the level of *ayin* and afterwards it is possible to be something else."[12] Each thing in the world has its particular form and identity which, for the Maggid, locks it into a particular existence. Only by annulling that form and freeing itself from the constraints and definitions of that kind or identity can anything be transformed into something else. *Ayin* can do this precisely because it is *ayin*, nothingness, and therefore free from the particular definite nature of *yesh*.

The embrace of nothingness is, then, not nihilistic but rather generative. The destabilization and dissolution of structure is that which enables a productive transformation rather than leaving one untethered. In the literal dissolution of prior form, the rotting of the seed, there is a liberation, yet the embrace of that liberation and dissolution is not ultimately anarchistic but organic, allowing growth and birth (seed and egg) to take place from that which has lost its form. Dissolution is embraced as the path to creation.

This capacity for transformation is not only a metaphysical principle but a personal one as well. Initially, new thought and creativity require *ayin*, "One [should] turn away from that [prior] object [of thought] totally to the place called nothingness (*efes*), and then a new topic comes to mind. Thus transformation comes about only by passing through nothingness."[13] It is *ayin* that allows the creative leap from one thought to the next, and the greater the leap, the Maggid tells us, the more *ayin* is required.[14] The same is true of personal transformation. The quotation concerning the manner in which a seed is transformed into wheat through *ayin* continues: "And so too with a person. When he brings himself to his root, that is the aspect of *ayin*, which reduces himself, like the wisdom which reduces him [or: itself], then he attains the transformation of qualities such as love and awe and other such qualities, all of which are only for the sake of God."[15] Spiritual growth for the Maggid occurs through the attainment and deepening of qualities such as love and awe. But that growth is only possible, the transformation of the self is only possible, when the person brings himself to *ayin*. That is, just as with any other object in the world, each human self is beset by constraints, definitions, particularity, and separateness. In particular, as we will see, these constraints are centered around the attachment to the ego as expressed in pride, selfishness, and corporeal desire. The erasure of self, which is the return to *ayin*, is then the capacity of the spiritual practitioner, through abandoning the self, to let go of the identity, self-definitions, isolation, and self-concern of the ego that hinder that transformation and so enable a new self to be born. No longer clinging to himself, a new self emerges. Instability and the questioning of identity is then embraced as the key step to a new form of being.

If *ayin* is the means of both personal and metaphysical transformation, then it is inseparable from *yesh*.[16] *Ayin* as transformation is what makes creation and growth, the coming to be of a new *yesh*, possible. *Ayin* is not the end or final goal of the spiritual process, but a stage in the spiritual dynamic that allows the growth of the practitioner and the attainment and cultivation of spiritual qualities. This is not to say that realizing *ayin* is not *a* goal; it is, and we will see what it aims to attain. But *ayin* as the agent of change cannot be the final goal, for from each return to *ayin*, according to these texts, a new *yesh* emerges. Rather, *ayin* is part of a dynamic union with *yesh* and it is this world and meaning affirming dynamic union that is the goal of the practitioner. Such a view challenges Schatz-Uffenheimer's contentions concerning quietism that seem to rest on the position that self-annihilation as passivity and quietism is the goal of the spiritual life.[17] Rather, here we see a notion of annihilation that culminates in activism and an opening to nothingness and dissolution for the purposes of birthing a new world and a new self.

Ayin and Metaphysical Unity

In our original teaching, *ayin* as change is where the teaching ended, not began. Let us now return to the beginning of the teaching to understand *ayin*'s capacity for unification. We are told, "The meaning of 'twilight' (literally: between the suns) is something which mediates between day and night. For in everything there are four elements: fire, water, wind, and earth. And they are things in opposition, water extinguishes fire, fire scatters earth. So there needs to be one other thing which joins them together and this is the quality of *ayin*."[18] *Ayin*, due to its formless undefined nature, has the capacity to bring opposing forces together whether temporal, physical, emotional, or psychological. It is the place where paradox is possible, where the coincidence of opposites takes place. Itself boundless, it creates the space in which two opposites can coexist through the shared recognition of their essentially *ayin* nature. As the Maggid explains:

> It is known that all coming into being in the world is done through wisdom, as it is written "You have made them all with wisdom" (Ps. 104:24). And our eyes see that wisdom binds together and mediates peace even between to opposed things like the elements. For if not for the wisdom that is between them, fire and water would not be able to coexist. And despite this fact we see that they are combined together. And all this is because wisdom is between them. And each one sees the *ayin* which is in wisdom and therefore he does not overcome his fellow for he sees that the *ayin* is his life-force.[19]

The elements recognize their shared boundlessness and root in *ayin* and therefore are able to coexist.[20] *Ayin* is what enables reality to exist and be sustained. Dissolution then leads not to modern alienation, separation, and fear but, when understood and worked with correctly, to connection, unification, the very sustaining of life, and, in the most literal sense, coexistence.

Ayin is therefore the condition of *yesh* and what brings it into existence. Any material existent, all of which are made of these four opposing elements, would be impossible without *ayin* which animates it, gives it life, and allows the elements out of which it is composed to subsist together. Indeed, the Maggid teaches that "In all coming into being there are three things . . . the quality of love . . . the quality of contraction . . . and for all the opposing forces there needs to be something which joins them together . . . [and this happens] through *ayin*. And these three things are called the power of the actor."[21] Creation or coming into being, which is the emergence of the material world and *yesh*, require *ayin*. Therefore, while *ayin* is that quality by which material reality is annihilated and returned to God, this is only one movement in the overall process, for it is also that quality by which material reality reemerges from God.

Ayin's ability to reconcile opposites extends beyond the physical realm to that of emotional and divine or sefirotic qualities as well. As we saw in our original teaching:

> So there needs to be one other thing which joins them together and this is the quality of *ayin*. For when the element of water comes to annihilate the element of fire, it is annihilated from reality and reaches the quality of *ayin*. And with love and fear[22] it is also thus. For a corporeal thing which loves something does not fear that thing at the time of the act and when it fears something it does not love it. However with God there is love and fear as one, for He joins them together. And the power of the actor is in that which is acted upon.[23]

One of the goals of the sefirotic system is the unification of the opposing forces of love and fear. Similarly one of the goals of the practitioner is to be able to be filled with both love and fear of God simultaneously. *Ayin* allows this unification in the same way that it unifies the opposed elements discussed.

Similarly, the human capacity to reach this state of the union of opposites comes precisely because humans emerge out of the divine nothingness and therefore "the power of the actor is in that which is acted upon."[24] That is, human rootedness in *ayin*, as "that which is acted upon," is what allows the practitioner to reach back to *ayin* and unify love and fear. It is precisely this reaching back to *ayin* that makes material existence, human life, and spiritual development possible. It is when one reaches the state of *ayin* that one can attain the more developed stage of holding love and fear together. As the Maggid taught, "And so too with a person when he brings himself to his root, that is the aspect of *ayin*, which reduces himself, like the wisdom which reduces him [or: itself], then he attains the transformation of qualities such as love and fear and other such qualities, all of which are only for the sake of God."[25] *Ayin* therefore cannot be understood as a passive denial of reality but rather must be understood as a particular way of relating to and helping create reality. Returning to *ayin* allows a more spiritually developed existence *within* the material world. Here again the metaphysical reality makes possible and provides an explanation for the spiritual path which is being taught; the personal and metaphysical are intertwined. Here it is not that "the center cannot hold," alienation is not the result of nothingness, but that the center is precisely held, stability and connection are found, in entering that formlessness that is the very substrata of existence.

Ayin and Existential Unity

We must therefore explore more deeply this personal or existential aspect of unity that is intertwined with the metaphysical. Just as with *ayin* as transformation, *ayin* as unity is given a strongly personal interpretation alongside the metaphysical one. In our original teaching we see this not only in the discussion of love and fear but also in the epistemological and spiritual claim that *ayin* is the ability to hold together God's presence and absence. The Maggid tells us that "day is called 'radiance' for a person sees the radiance of God. And night is called darkness when a person, God forbid, does not see His radiance. And that which joins them together is *ayin*. And this is twilight, the thing which joins day and night."[26] The experience of God's presence and absence is a common aspect of the religious life. *Ayin*, as twilight, allows the practitioner to hold both those experiences together without eliminating either one.[27] Just as *ayin* allows the metaphysical coexistence of opposing physical forces, so too opposing psychological forces are able to exist together in one who has reached the level of *ayin*. Indeed this dual consciousness is crucial to the Maggid's program. *Ayin* is not merely the affirmation of God's overwhelming presence. Rather, the practitioner must be able to affirm the constant presence of God while at the same time experiencing God's absence in order to allow for independent human action and in order to fulfill creation's role of giving pleasure to God. That is, rather than atheistic (God is dead) or fundamentalist (God lives) responses to the uncertainties of modernity, with its experience of divine presence and absence, the Maggid teaches that *ayin* allows the Hasid to hold both moments in one broader unity.

Before we continue to discuss the personal implications of *ayin*, we need to be clear about precisely what it means for a human to reach the state of *ayin*, and what the personal qualities are that make such a state possible. Fundamentally one reaches *ayin* through humility, which is also lowliness, selflessness, fear, and shame, and through a nonattachment to the material world that culminates in equanimity.

The Maggid continually stresses that the way to achieve *ayin* is through humility and fear, humility when considering one's own status as a lowly human and fear and awe before the majesty of God.[28] Indeed, fear/awe comes to be treated as almost a synonym for *ayin* in the Maggid's texts.[29] This dual quality of fear/awe and humility can be seen in the Maggid's description of the realized practitioner's path where he tells us: "and then he considers himself *ayin* upon seeing and grasping the exaltedness of the blessed God. And [he considers himself *ayin*] afterwards because of [his] great humility in that he doesn't consider himself anything and he diminishes himself."[30] We should stress the fact that "he doesn't consider himself *anything*." These types of phrases are repeated often in the Maggid and demonstrate that the humility he is describing is not developing a lowly assessment of one's self, but abandoning all attempts to hold onto the self at all. One is to consider oneself completely nothing and therefore without an identity, self-worth, desires, life plans, and pride. It is letting go of these *yesh* impediments that allows the unity and transformation which is *ayin*. In this way, humility and fear/awe are intimately linked to the second major attainment of personal *ayin*, that of nonattachment.

As the Maggid puts it, "*ayin* desires nothing."[31] At the level of *ayin*, the unity of the world is seen and the self and so selfishness are relinquished. There is therefore no desire. One simply accepts what the world brings and so attains contentment. As the Maggid says of Jacob, "he was satisfied with what he had because he was at the level of wisdom which is the level of *ayin*, and *ayin* does not desire anything."[32] This lack of desire and the contentment it brings means the temptation to sin is removed. As the Maggid explains, "It is because of the corporeality of things that the transgressions of food, drink, and sexuality come. But when a person transforms himself to *ayin*, then he separates [himself] from transgressions and returns in complete repentance."[33] At the level of *ayin* one is no longer pulled and enslaved by corporeal desire, but rather has separated oneself from it.

This does not mean such activities cease, but rather that they are engaged in in an entirely different noncraving spirit. One who has achieved *ayin* has achieved equanimity, an indifference to the vagaries of life and an absence of self-concern.[34] As the Maggid teaches, "A person must consider himself nothing. . . . They must abandon themselves and forget their suffering in order to come to the World of Thought where everything is equivalent. This is not the case when he is cleaving to [the] corporeality of this world."[35] To become nothing is to reach the world of thought, the place beyond time, where everything is equivalent and so equanimity reigns. One does not distinguish between "life and death, sea and dry land,"[36] but rather treats everything as equal. One can then still eat, drink, and engage in sexuality, indeed, to continue to do so is part of Hasidic spiritual practice, but it is done from a place of equanimity where the lack of these things does not cause pain and suffering and where one's craving for them does not cause improper behavior. It is these qualities, of humility and awe on the one hand, and nonattachment and equanimity on the other, that form the foundation for *ayin*'s unitary significance in the personal realm.[37]

Perhaps the first important effect of the attainment of *ayin* is the peace and wholeness this brings to the practitioner. We have already seen how *ayin* brings peace between the four elements and so between the conflicting elements that make up the human self. Similarly, one who achieves equanimity is no longer troubled by the sorrows of life. The attainment of *ayin*, which is the letting go of the self, seen in both nonattachment and humility, creates a person who lacks the kind of self that could be damaged, threatened, or hurt. No longer clinging to a conception of self and so no longer identifying any of his qualities, beliefs, self-conceptions, aspirations, and fears with himself, the ḥasid who has attained *ayin* is beyond suffering. As the Maggid explains:

> "Her gates have sunk into the ground" (Lam. 2:9). The interpretation is that brokenness (*shevirah*) is not applicable to something at the level of *ayin*, for brokenness is applicable to something which is a quality or a vessel. It is the case then if a person transforms[38] himself into *ayin* because of his cleaving to the blessed Creator, like a minister [who] even though he is the greatest minister in the realm . . . when he is before the king, he and all his qualities are annulled due to his fear and shame before the king. This is [the meaning of] "sunk into the ground." That is to say he transforms himself to *ayin*, to *ayin* in his eyes. "Gates," that is to say qualities. And when he has no qualities, then no brokenness is applicable to him.[39]

A person who gives up their qualities, who no longer holds onto a particular view of themselves, who no longer prides themselves on particular virtues, attainments, or relationships, who no longer prides themselves on anything, cannot be broken, the Maggid tells us. To be "sunk into the ground" is to attain humility, it is for the ḥasid to lower himself to such an extent that he gives up on a sense of self and becomes "*ayin* in his eyes."

Brokenness is then applicable only to that which is defined, that which is solid, "qualities and vessels" for the Maggid. How can a vacuum, nothingness, be broken? So too when a person makes themselves *ayin*, there is no definite quality or picture of the self that is being held on to and no desire for one thing instead of another that could cause brokenness. Failure to achieve a goal, loss of a precious object, or being personally attacked do not bring suffering when the practitioner no longer identifies with and clings to that goal, object, or aspect of himself. The dissolutions of modernity, in such a state, are not threatening, for there is no self to be threatened. An empty wholeness is achieved precisely by abandoning the quest for completion. Brokenness (*shevirah*) here stands in for suffering, fear, and pain in general. It is the cosmic cataclysm of the breaking (*shevirah*) of the vessels in Lurianic Kabbalah that is the source of the suffering and brokenness of the world, and the Maggid returns to this Lurianic myth many times. The attainment of *ayin*, the annihilation of the self, is therefore the attainment of a state beyond suffering, a state beyond the illusion of separation, and particularly beyond the illusion of a separate, independent, and self-interested self that is the root of that suffering. To become *ayin* in this sense is then to attain equanimity and free oneself from distress.

The openness and emptiness that is the achievement of *ayin* brings peace not just within the self, but between selves as well. *Ayin*, as we have seen, unifies disparate objects. It brings together opposites whether physical, metaphysical, emotional, epistemological, or psychological. It is similarly able to unite individuals. In a discussion concerning the desireless contented state and the spiritual connection achieved by those who attain *ayin*, the Maggid teaches, "For connection comes because of this, that is to say, wisdom. Because a person cannot connect with his fellow unless he reduces himself and sees himself as *ayin* in relation to his fellow. Through this he can connect to his fellow."[40] Giving up the self, the practitioner of the Maggid's path of nothingness can truly connect with the other, without any self to interfere. No longer concerned with his own qualities, aspirations, pride, and concerns, and no longer having those qualities acts as barriers and separation he can connect fully to the other. He can focus fully on the other, unhindered by the anxiety of the self, devoting himself completely to this connection. Nothingness brings not alienation but genuine connection.

This attainment of nothingness is also, as we have seen, a realization of the underlying unity out of which all existence emerges and which continues to bind all existence together. Indeed, in the same teaching, the Maggid continues "and lo when the zaddik arouses himself in fear, then he arouses fear and repentance in the heart of all Israel, for all Israel are guarantors (*arevim*) for each other, that is to say mixed up together (*me'uravim*)"[41] All Jews, and presumably all existence, given *ayin*'s nature as the fundamental metaphysical substrata, are connected. They are "mixed up together." This is particularly true, or particularly actualized, when fear, that is *ayin*, is aroused and brought to consciousness in the zaddik. This consciousness exposes the underlying unity of nothingness that is the root of all being. The consciousness of *ayin* therefore allows true connection between persons, both because it allows each person to let go of their self and be wholly present for the other and because this consciousness exposes the underlying interconnectedness and unity that denies the apparent separation between selves. Once again it is the metaphysical teachings of nothingness and wisdom as the ground of being that make possible this spiritual attainment and in that sense make a tightly coherent whole.

Ayin, therefore, rather than signaling a retreat from reality, corporality, community, and the material nature of human contact, enables human contact and communion of the deepest kind. *Ayin*, rather than producing a quietist retreat from the world and society, makes true engagement with another human being, true activism, possible. This is not to say that the attainment of *ayin* may not require some retreat. Indeed denial and the turning away from the world of a sort, at the very least the turning away from desire, are necessary to attain *ayin*. Yet this does not mean that *ayin* results in or ends in such a retreat. Rather, what we see here is that *ayin* results in a more profound engagement with one's fellows.

That engagement is not limited to the realm of personal relations. Rather, achieving *ayin* allows the practitioner to act in the lower and upper worlds as an effective agent of healing. The zaddikim who attain the level of *ayin* annul the sins of Israel and so bring the divine flow of love to the world—"transforming iniquity (*pesha*) to divine flow (*shepha*)."[42] They also achieve for Israel the special level of divine splendor (*Tiferet*), create an especially intimate relationship between God and Israel, and ultimately cause God to dwell among Israel.[43] That is, it is precisely their self-annihilation that makes them theurgically powerful and allows them to bring the divine to earth. *Ayin* is activist. Yet this healing accomplished through the annihilation that is *ayin*, must be done in the right way.

> All this is [only] if a person diminishes himself as was mentioned above. But if he considers himself something (*mah*) and thinks himself to be something (*mah*), and he lacks the quality of humility, if so, then "as water reflects face to face" (Prov. 27:19) also the Holy One Blessed be He, as it were, does not contract his Shekhinah and because of the great radiance of the light he is annulled. Even when he is a *zaddik* he is like a candle before a torch and his light is cancelled, and his actions are not effective at all.[44]

It is making oneself *ayin* that allows one to be theurgically effective and precisely the assertion of ego that causes one's attempts, even if one is a zaddik, to fail. It is precisely annihilation that makes possible a genuinely effective activism and healing of the world.[45] *Ayin* is then once again not an impetus for withdrawal or quietism, but rather the ability to bring the divine flow and God Herself, into the world. Indeed, it is striking that in this teaching the attainment of *ayin* does not result in the ascent of the *zaddik* but rather in the descent of the divine into the world, reaffirming the contention that *ayin* is part of a process of world.

Moreover this activist theurgic aspect of *ayin* deepens our understanding of the kind of humility and no-self the attainment of *ayin* achieves. What is achieved cannot be a paralyzing lack of self-worth. Rather it is a letting go of self that goes hand in hand with an awareness of tremendous theurgic power. It is through the abandonment of self that self-efficacy and self-confidence are achieved for it is in reference to those who have achieved the level of *ayin* that "God thinks what they think."[46] That is, God's presence and entry into the world is directly dependent on the consciousness of the ẓaddikim who have attained *ayin*. Self-annihilation then does not lead to a self that sees itself as incapable of action, but to a self filled with the knowledge and confidence of its healing capacity. The difference is that awareness of efficacy is no longer properly "self"-efficacy as it arises from a consciousness of the unity of existence. It is rather an awareness of the power and confidence that flows through this aspect of that unity. In this way, unlike the self-pride that is abandoned, it is a confidence and efficacy that does not properly *belong* to the self, though the self is its locus, and so is not a source of identification or attachment.

The ultimate expression of *ayin*'s unifying role however is found in the practitioner's mystical union with the divine. As the Maggid taught:

> "Make yourself two trumpets (*ḥatzotzrot*)" (Num. 10:2), the interpretation of which is, two half forms (*ḥetzi tzurot*), in the manner of "on the throne, a likeness in the appearance of a man above upon it" (Ezek 1:26), as man (ADaM) is but D and M (blood), and the speech dwells upon him. And when he unites with God, who is the Alpha of the world, he becomes ADaM. And the Holy One blessed be He performs various contractions through various worlds in order that there be unification with man, who is not able to bear His radiance. And man must separate himself from any corporeal things, to such an extent that he will ascend through all the worlds and be in union with God, until [his] existence will be annihilated, and then he will be called ADaM.[47]

In this mystical union, the practitioner does not only unify with the divine, but in fact becomes fully human. Together the practitioner and God, each two half forms, "when they cleave together, become a complete form."[48] One gets the sense that even God is not complete without this mystical union.

Indeed in general the achievement of *ayin* and annihilation of the self ought to be understood as divine union for the practitioner makes himself *ayin*, one of the highest levels of the divine array. As the Maggid describes the practitioner's experience of annihilation, "such great fear falls upon him until he is annihilated from reality before the King and enters the gate of *ayin*."[49] The *ḥasid*'s self is no more; he has become merged with the divine reality of *ayin*. Yet even this union is not purely an ascension and withdrawal from the world. The teaching concerning the two half forms continues by describing the theurgic efficacy of one who has reached such a state explaining that "if love is aroused in the ẓaddik, love is aroused in all the worlds, and so too with all the qualities."[50] Even union as ascension to the upper realms is part of a process of bringing the divine flow into the world.

Yet divine descent and dwelling upon the practitioner is an even more common description of the experience of union and it is *ayin* in particular that makes that possible. In one teaching the Maggid explains that it is precisely by making himself *ayin*, and acknowledging that in fact everything is the divine, that the practitioner makes it possible for God to dwell in him for, "the essential thing is to understand and grasp very well that there is nothing in him but the divinity which enlivens him and without this he is truly nothing (*efes*). Then preparation has been done so that [the divinity] can rest upon him."[51] When the ḥasid voids the self and acknowledges that he is nothing but God, it is the realization of the already present reality within him that allows God's dwelling upon him to be manifest.

Elsewhere, the Maggid describes *ayin*'s role as reciprocal. That is, "when he considers himself *ayin* and greatly diminishes himself it is the case that the Holy One blessed be He contracts his Shekhinah and rests upon him."[52] In response to the practitioner's extreme humility, the infinite divine imitates that quality as well and contracts itself into a form that can dwell in the world and humanity. Alternately, it is the infinite, unbounded, and indefinable nature of *ayin* that allows it to be a dwelling place for the infinite divine for, "when he [the practitioner] considers himself *yesh* and makes requests [from God] concerning his needs, then the Holy One blessed be He is unable to be clothed in him, for He, may he be blessed, is infinite (*ein sof*), and [so] no vessel can bear him. [But] this is not the case when he considers himself *ayin*, as was mentioned above."[53] The infinite cannot be contained by a finite vessel. The practitioner must therefore make himself infinite, *ayin*, in order to be able to contain the divine. This descent of God into the world is intimately connected with corporeality. In fact, the Maggid teaches:

> "A woman is [created] for naught but beauty." (Bavli Ta'anit 31a) That is, the Holy One created this physical world and created man within it in His image, so that he might reside within it. . . . when he [the practitioner] brings into his thoughts all the worlds, there descends upon them trembling and fear because of their fear of God, and they see a great shining light, and all this is revealed because of man, who is the lowest thing in the world, and he becomes very proud. And this is, "A woman is [created for naught but beauty]"—that is, the body is called woman, and because of the body there is born great beauty.[54]

Ayin, as that which allows the descent of the divine into the world, is, in its negation of corporeality, in fact an affirmation of corporeality. It is precisely the body that gives rise to "great beauty." It is *ayin*, as we saw earlier, that allows the divine to enter the world, and this, for the Maggid, was in fact the entire purpose of creation in the first place. *Ayin* does not negate creation but rather completes it, by allowing the divine to dwell within it. *Ayin* once again makes possible *yesh*. The infinite is brought into the finite, and to that extent the unity of *ayin* and *yesh* is achieved.

Yet the dynamic process that is *yesh* and *ayin* does not end there. Rather, the descent of the Shekhinah into the world once again enables an ascent to the divine realms. The Maggid teaches:

> When I want to ascend I must also ascend through wisdom . . . and upon arriving at the quality of fear he considers himself *ayin*. And *ayin* is wisdom and with wisdom he is purified. And this is "who covers the heavens" (Ps. 147:8), the intellect (*sekhel*), "with clouds," with corporeality [which is undone through *ayin* mentioned above]. "Provides rain for the earth" (Ps. 147:8), [means] just as the rain moistens the earth to cause produce to grow, so too the Shekhinah, as it were, comes to the lower levels in order that they will ascend. "For one who eats that which is not his is ashamed to look at it" (Yerushalmi Orla 1c), and the lower levels are ashamed to ascend. But the Shekhinah comes within the lower levels like rain which comes to the earth and causes produce to grow.[55]

Ascent here happens through *ayin*, which we know also causes the dwelling of God upon the practitioner. The problem however is that the lower levels, humanity and the corporeal world, feel themselves too lowly to ascend to the divine heights. They are "ashamed to look at" that which is not theirs. That is, they feel themselves distinct from and infinitely below the divine and so cannot bring themselves to ascend. The divine response is to enter the practitioner, who has voided himself through *ayin* and abject humility. The practitioner is inhabited by and unified with the Shekhinah. The "food" is now "theirs" and shame is no longer necessary. That is, by inhabiting the practitioner, it is now the divine which reascends to *itself*, the lower levels no longer seeing themselves as distinct from the upper.

We see then in this very teaching the unfolding process of *yesh* and *ayin*. The practitioner is initially trapped, "covered," in the "clouds" of *yesh*, corporeality. He frees himself by entering *ayin* and abandoning material desire. This causes the Shekhinah to dwell upon him and enter the corporeal world. This in turn allows the ascent of that world, now unified with the Shekhinah, to the upper levels of divinity. That ascent in turn, as we saw, allows a new entrance of the infinite divine into the finite world and the process continues. As we saw from the first in our discussion of transformation, *ayin* is a crucial moment, even a sustained consciousness, in a spiritual practice that is very much concerned with engagement with the world. The *ḥasid* becomes active and efficacious precisely by giving up his self and allowing God to act through him. Through voiding himself he is filled with divinity, by opening to dissolution he achieves wholeness. This is indeed a quietistic surrender to the divine, but it is one that results in activism and engagement with the world.

The Dynamic of Unity and Separation

If the material world and activism, *yesh*, is not rejected and *ayin* is part of a dialectic process, how is the practitioner meant to hold the two poles of *yesh* and *ayin* together? They are held together by participating in the back and forth, the egress and regress of *yesh* and *ayin*. While God created the world *yesh* from *ayin*, it is the task of the ẓaddikim to reverse that process and "to make from *yesh*, *ayin*."[56] Indeed, the Maggid tells us that "the purpose of the creation of humanity was in order to raise up the worlds to their root, that is, to return them to *ayin* as they were previously through Torah, prayer, good deeds, and cleaving to God, may He be blessed."[57]

Yet we have seen that this does not actually entail a rejection of the world as we might think. Rather, it is a step that allows both a regeneration of the discrete world, for instance in the form of the teachings of the ẓaddikim, and a reengagement with the material world with the consciousness of *ayin*, such as the interpersonal and social acts of healing, the religious acts in the world, and the theurgic acts all performed by the those who have attained *ayin*. This reengagement and regeneration however now emerge from a completely different place. The teachings of the ẓaddkim who attain the level of *ayin* are true transmissions of divine knowledge.[58] The person who connects with his fellow, having attained *ayin*, does so in the deepest and most profound way. The ẓaddik who raises the sparks through eating and provides joy to God through his enjoyment of the food does it from a state of total nonattachment and equanimity.[59] The world of separation is reentered, but to a certain extent it is no longer believed as fully, a consciousness of *ayin* is maintained. Moreover, the regress itself is predicated on the egress and, as this process brings pleasure to God, presumably calls forth another egress to follow. Both creation and its annihilation happen through *ayin*, and together they fulfill God's purpose in the world. The practitioner therefore participates in both these poles, though in a transformed way.

The Maggid often describes the practitioner's engagement with this dialectic process as "touching and not touching."[60] If the *ḥasid* loses himself in *ayin* he will be lost from the world. If he loses himself in *yesh*, he has strayed from the path and will be negatively annulled. Rather he must maintain a back and forth between these two poles, touching and not touching that experience of unity that is *ayin*. For instance, when a *ḥasid* achieves *ayin* and causes the Shekhinah to rest upon him, this dwelling must be born in the manner of "touching and not touching" (Tosefta Hagiga 20:6, Yerushalmi Hagiga 77:a–b). That is, it is necessary for the person not to grasp this [intellectually], for if he will grasp it he will be truly annihilated from reality."[61] The Shekhinah may dwell upon the realized practitioner, but this can only be experienced, not understood. To reach the level of understanding would entail the practitioner's complete removal from reality, defeating the purpose of God's dwelling *within* reality within the practitioner. The ḥasid's task of "touching and not touching," is modeled on the divine, "For the Creator, may He be blessed, is infinite. Who can bear the light of the infinite (*ein sof*)? And therefore He is always at every moment 'touching and not touching' (Zohar I:16b). When He is touching it cannot be born and therefore He immediately is not touching."[62] In both cases, total presence is unworkable. Rather, the ḥasid, in imitation of God, must participate in a back and forth process that allows the maintenance of *yesh* while incorporating *ayin*.[63]

Ultimately, to hold this union of *yesh* and *ayin* dynamically is to transcend them and touch that level of divinity that is beyond even *ayin*. This the Maggid makes clear in the original text with which we started:

> And Wisdom is beginning (*reishit*). "The beginning (*reishit*) of wisdom is fear of the Lord" (Ps. 111:10). And when it is called beginning (*reishit*), then it is has a number. For the meaning of one is unity, but first (*rishon*) is the beginning (*hatkhalat*) of numbering. And it can be assumed that there is a level higher than wisdom. . . . He, may He be blessed, dwells in wisdom, and wisdom is a lesser level than Him, may He be blessed. And it [wisdom], with Him, was only the beginning of thought.[64]

Wisdom, *ayin*, is not the highest level of divinity. It cannot be, for it is still in opposition to *yesh*. Rather, there is a level beyond *ayin*, beyond even the particularity of nothingness that is not being, beyond even the particularity of first, which is not second, that unites *yesh* and *ayin*. Indeed, this is why the Maggid associates *ayin* with wisdom, the second highest *sefirah*, rather than with Keter, the highest *sefirah* as was often previously done.[65] He aims to stress that *ayin* is not the highest level. The highest level is rather beyond even the distinction between *yesh* and *ayin* and unifies them. Such a level may not be directly accessible to humans in this world, but participating in the dynamic process of *yesh* and *ayin* allows the practitioner to establish a kind of dynamic unity that gestures toward their true unity on high.

This still means that particular moments may be devoted to one pole or another, and especially to cultivating *ayin*. For instance, we are told that "in Torah and prayer they cleave themselves to *ayin*."[66] Indeed prayer in particular was singled out as a means to achieve *ayin* and this became the primary goal of prayer in the Maggid's school.[67] Moreover, *ayin* is stressed in the Maggid's writings to a greater extent than the components of *yesh*, though his continual return to the purpose of creation and the importance of separation for God's pleasure is a major and consistent theme.

Yet it is no surprise that *ayin* is stressed. *Yesh*, after all, that is, ego, separation, desire, selfishness, and pride, comes all too easily. It is *ayin* that must be stressed, taught, and cultivated, and which then allows a new and more positive engagement with *yesh*. One the one hand, theurgically, it allows the zaddik, upon reaching *ayin*, to bring down the divine flow of love and sustenance into the world. On the other hand, it allows an engagement with the world that carries with it the consciousness of *ayin*. As the Maggid explains, "In truth, the wise man makes no separation even in the lower world because he sees that all the stature and life-force of the lower world is from the upper [world], and if not for the upper world, the lower world would be absolute nothingness (*efes*). If so, he cleaves to the upper world, and just as there all is a simple unity, surely [it is so] here as well."[68]

It is this consciousness of *ayin in* the world that allows the practitioner to act in the world with nonattachment, humility, and equanimity and thereby achieve the peace and union both internally and in human relations that is the promise of *ayin*. Indeed, the previous teaching concludes "and this is [the meaning of] '[The Lord said to Aaron, "Go to meet Moses in the wilderness." He went and met him at the mountain of God,] and he kissed him' (Ex. 4:21). He cleaved to him soul to soul. That is, the two of them became a simple unity."[69] It is through this consciousness of *ayin* that Moses and Aaron, both as individuals and as symbolic representatives of Love and Fear, can truly meet and become one. The goal of the practice of *ayin* is not to abandon corporeality or to cease to act, but to act and engage with corporeality through the consciousness of *ayin*, to in a certain sense allow the divine to engage with the world and act through you. For, for the one who has reached the state of *ayin*, "whatever he does, God is doing it."[70]

The role of *ayin* then is that of a crucial component in a dynamic unity. The zaddik who realizes *ayin* continues on to bring that realization into the world of *yesh*, which is in turn returned to *ayin* as the cycle continues; reaching *ayin* transforms the practitioner's relationship to the material world to one of nonattachment, which precisely enables a wise relationship to the world and effective activism; achieving *ayin* brings the divine into the world, through *ayin* divine presence and absence are held together in a greater whole; *ayin* makes possible the dissolution of the practitioner for the purpose of generation, birth, and growth; the loss of the self makes possible genuine connection and fully opening to fear/*ayin* allows the only the sole authentic security and peace of nonattachment; and ultimately *ayin* is transcended by that which holds together both *ayin* and *yesh*.

In this way our investigation has, in a way, confirmed Scholem's position that early Hasidism "was centered upon the 'casting off of corporeality'"[71] but ultimately in the service of Buber's position that Hasidism was concerned with the "bringing down of God into the soul of man."[72] The ḥasid distances himself from materiality not to reject it, but to recognize its underlying union with the spiritual and to reenter it with a consciousness of that unity. Similarly, Hasidic quietism, pace Schatz-Uffenheimer, is not a Hasidic goal, but a step in a dynamic process that ultimately results in a deep nonattached activism.

The Maggid's account of negative theology as a practice provides a novel, creative response to the challenges of modernity, one that embraces uncertainty, dissolution, and instability. Through this embrace, these features of modernity result not in anxiety, disconnection, and nihilism but rather in transformation, growth, wholeness, security, meaning, and connection. It is a path that maps a way to live in and embrace the instability of existence (heightened by modernity) with grace and courage, it is negative theology as a transformative welcoming of the anxiety of modernity and its transformation into the equanimity and wisdom of "my aid will come from nothingness." It should again be noted that the Maggid is the central and foundational figure of the Hasidic movement, and thus it is not surprising that his view of the practice of negative theology is reiterated and developed by major subsequent figures from direct disciples such as Levi Yitzhak of Berdichev to twentieth-century masters such as the Kalonymus Kalmish Shapira of Piaseczne. In this way, the practice of negative theology became a mainstay of modern Jewish religious experience. It seems that this is another, crucial reason why Hasidism has become such a profound resource for modern Jews, for those living traditional Hasidic lives and yet still exposed to the crises of negativity in the modern age, for those reclaiming Jewish thought from amid alienation, and for leading exponents of Jewish religiosity who have embraced the divine exigency of discovering aid in nothingness.[73]

Notes

1. See Ada Rapoport-Albert, "Hasidism after 1772: Structural Continuity and Change," in *Hasidism Reappraised* (repr., London: A. Littman Library of Jewish Civilization, 1996), 76–140.

2. In our investigation of *ayin* we will attempt to construct a coherent picture of the Maggid's use of this concept. However that unity may not be logical or conceptual. That is, the Maggid is not an analytic philosopher but rather a religious thinker attempting to present a model of a religious consciousness and way of life. The coherence we will seek to understand is how *ayin* functions as part of that religious consciousness and way of life. *Ayin*, as we will see, will combine metaphysical, psychological, epistemological, and practical components into one whole. Our aim will be to see how that whole operates as a picture and model of the practitioner's relationship with God, others, and herself.

3. Rachel Elior is well aware of this fact in "The Paradigms of *Yesh* and *Ayin* in Hasidic Thought," in *Hasidism Reappraised*, ed. Ada Rapoport-Albert (London: Valentine Mitchell & Co. Ltd., 1996), 168–179, and I think it is the failure to consider the role of *yesh* that leads

Rivka Schatz-Uffenheimer to a slightly skewed portrayal of the Hasidic relation to *ayin* in *Hasidism as Mysticism: Quietistic Elements in Eighteenth Century Hasidic Thought,* trans. Jonathan Chipman (Princeton, NJ: Princeton University Press, 1993).

4. See Elior, "The Paradigms," 170; and Daniel Matt, "*Ayin*: The Concept of Nothingness in Jewish Mysticism," in *Essential Papers on Kabbalah,* ed. Lawrence Fine (New York: New York University Press, 1995), 87, 92. As he eloquently puts it, "*Ayin* is not the goal itself; it is the moment of transformation from being through nonbeing to new being."

5. Or awe.

6. Who represents the quality of fear.

7. The name of God associated with *Din* (strict judgment) or *Gevurah* (might).

8. Playing on the similarity between the word "tried" (*nasa*) in the verse and a similar verb meaning to raise up (*nasa*).

9. Dov Baer, "The Maggid of Mezhirech," in *Maggid Devarav Le-Ya'akov: Critical Edition with Commentary* by Rivka Schatz-Uffenheimer (Jerusalem: Magnes Press, 1990), teaching 6, 19–20. I will refer to this teaching throughout as our "original" teaching. All translations are mine unless otherwise noted.

10. *Maggid Devarav,* teaching 78, 134.

11. Ibid., teaching 60, 91.

12. Ibid., teaching 30, 49.

13. Ibid., teaching 131, 224. Translation in Matt, "*Ayin*," 87.

14. Ibid., teaching 131, 224.

15. Ibid., teaching 78, 134.

16. We should also note that here metaphysics, spirituality, and psychology are merged. The nature of the world reflects the nature of the divine which itself is mirrored in the structure of the human self. It is not that the Maggid psychologizes the cosmological claims of earlier Kabbalah, and gives *ayin* a more explicitly psychological and personal meaning, but that he sees the psychological, metaphysical, and spiritual as reflections of one underlying truth. The Maggid spends a considerable amount of time discussing the metaphysical implications of *ayin*, which are clearly significant for him. But these implications are always by extension implications for the human self as well. Metaphysics has an important role, but its role is to create the conceptual framework that enables the attainment of a particular spiritual consciousness.

17. See Schatz-Uffenheimer, *Hasidism as Mysticism,* 67–79.

18. *Maggid Devarav,* teaching 6, 19.

19. Ibid., teaching 60, 91.

20. It is particularly interesting that the Maggid speaks about creating "peace" between opposing forces, indicating already the human significance of this metaphysical discussion. It is through *ayin* that human differences will be similarly reconciled.

21. *Maggid Devarav,* teaching 80, 138–139.

22. Or awe.

23. *Maggid Devarav,* teaching 6, 19–20.

24. Ibid.

25. *Maggid Devarav,* teaching 78, 134.

26. *Maggid Devarav*, teaching 6, 20.

27. There are echoes here of R. Azriel of Gerona's discussion of faith as that which holds together *ayin*, the unknowable absent God, and *yesh*, the knowable experienced divine. See "The Path of Faith and the Path of Heresy" in Gershom Scholem, "New Fragments from the Writings of R. Azriel of Gerona" [in Hebrew], in *Studies in Memory of Asher Gulak and Samuel Klein* [in Hebrew], ed. Simhah Assaf and Gershom Scholem (Jerusalem: Hebrew University Magnes Press, 1942), 207.

28. See Schatz-Uffenheimer, *Hasidism as Mysticism*, 75–78.

29. It is fascinating to note that the fearful nature of dissolution, destabilization, and nothingness, the fear to which fundamentalist, traditionalist, and totalitarian responses to modernity react to, is here embraced as a crucial aspect of *ayin* and one which, related to properly and transformed to awe, creates the very transformation that *ayin* is capable of.

30. *Maggid Devarav*, teaching 191, 299.

31. Ibid., teaching 60, 94. See also ibid., teaching 132, 230.

32. Ibid., teaching 132, 230.

33. Ibid., teaching 56, 85.

34. See Schatz-Uffenheimer, *Hasidism as Mysticism*, 77–78.

35. *Maggid Devarav*, teaching 110, 186.

36. Ibid.

37. This nonattachment can be misunderstood as world-denying, but the Maggid is explicit about the value of importance of world engagement, in such activities as eating and drinking. See, for instance, *Or Ha-Emet*, 45b (Brooklyn, 1960, photo ed. of Hussiatin 1899). Taken from and translated by Schatz-Uffenheimer, *Hasidism as Mysticism*, 177. See also Tsippi Kauffman's extensive discussion of the Maggid's relationship to worship corporeality throughout her *In All Your Ways Know Him: The Concept of God and Worship in Corporeality at the Beginnings of Hasidism* (Ramat Gan, Israel: Bar Ilan University Press, 2009). What is transformed here is the relationship to those activities and how they are performed, not a rejection of them themselves.

38. Literally grasps to *ayin*.

39. *Maggid Devarav*, teaching 51, 74.

40. Ibid., teaching 132, 230.

41. Ibid., teaching 132, 231. This echoes a similar *derash* made by Moshe Cordovero in *Tomer Devorah*, chap. 1, fourth Midah.

42. *Maggid Devarav*, teaching 191, 296–297.

43. Ibid.

44. Ibid., teaching 191, 297.

45. Moreover, as we will see more extensively later, annulment is not always portrayed positively. Self-annihilation, becoming *ayin*, is indeed a spiritual achievement. But when a ḥasid hangs on to a sense of self, he is also annulled, but now in a negative almost violent way that robs him of his ability to connect to the divine and act effectively in the world.

46. *Maggid Devarav*, teaching 1, 11.

47. Ibid., teaching 24, 38–39. Translation based upon Moshe Idel, "Unio Mystica in Jewish Mysticism," *Kabbalah: New Perspectives* (London: Yale University Press, 1988), 65.

48. *Maggid Devarav*, teaching 24, 39.

49. Ibid., teaching 60, 94.

50. Ibid., teaching 24, 39.

51. Ibid., teaching 120, 197.

52. Ibid., teaching 191, 298.

53. Ibid., teaching 110, 186.

54. *Or Ha-Emet*, 45b. Taken from and translated by Schatz-Uffenheimer, *Hasidism as Mysticism*, 177.

55. *Maggid Devarav*, teaching 22, 36–37.

56. Ibid., teaching 9, 24.

57. Ibid., teaching 66, 109.

58. See *Or ha-Me'ir*, 95c, New York, 1954; translation in Schatz-Uffenheimer, *Hasidism as Mysticism*, 203.

59. It is important to note that nonattachment and equanimity do not imply a lack of enjoyment. The zaddik who has no desire for the food must still enjoy it to give God pleasure. Rather, the zaddik is no longer attached to that enjoyment and is untroubled if the food is taken away.

60. See *Maggid Devarav*, teaching 191, 296, and the sources cited in the following notes.

61. *Maggid Devarav*, teaching 120, 198.

62. Ibid., teaching 170, 267.

63. Here again neither presence nor absence, theism nor atheism are affirmed, but rather a kind of holding together of negative and positive theology, of disbelief and belief, in an experiential movement that touches them both.

64. *Maggid Devarav*, teaching 6, 19–20.

65. See, for instance, Gershom Scholem, *Origins of the Kabbalah*, ed. R. J. Zwi Werblowsky, trans. Allan Arkush (Philadelphia: Jewish Publication Society, 1987), 437–438, 452.

66. *Maggid Devarav*, teaching 73, 126–127.

67. See Schatz-Uffenheimer, *Hasidism as Mysticism*, 168–188.

68. *Maggid Devarav*, teaching 62, 101–102.

69. Ibid., teaching 62, 103.

70. Ibid., teaching 1, 12 (translation modified from Matt, *"Ayin,"* 90).

71. Schatz-Uffenheimer, *Hasidism as Mysticism*, 28. See pp. 24–33 for her discussion of Buber and Scholem. See their original disagreement in Scholem, "Martin Buber's Interpretation of Hasidism," *The Messianic Idea in Judaism* (New York: Schocken Books), 238–245; Schatz-Uffenheimer, *"Devekut*, or Communion with God," in *Hasidism Reappraised*, ed. Ada Rapoport-Albert (London: Valentine Mitchell & Co. Ltd., 1996), 225. Martin Buber, "Interpreting Hasidism," *Commentary* 33 (1963), 221–224; and *Hasidism and Modern Man* (Amherst, NY: Prometheus Books, 1988), 29–35.

72. Schatz-Uffenheimer, *Hasidism as Mysticism*, 28.

73. A partial list of important modern Jewish thinkers profoundly influenced by Hasidism would include A. J. Heschel, Louis Jacobs, Arthur Green, Adin Steinsaltz, Zalman Schachter-Shalomo, and Abraham Isaac Kook.

SIX

Secrecy, Apophasis, and Atheistic Faith in the Teachings of Rav Kook

ELLIOT R. WOLFSON

> Rien ne pèse tant qu'un secret.
> —Jean de La Fontaine

> ומה נכבד סוד זה וזה שער השמים ואין פותח
> —יצחק אבן לטיף

> איש בלי סוד כאוצר בלי מפתח
> —אברהם אבן חסדאי

In this chapter, I will focus on apophaticism and esotericism in the writings of Abraham Isaac Kook (1865–1935). Needless to say, many studies have been written on the mystical underpinnings of Kook's religious Zionism as well as the Kabbalistic sources that may have influenced his thinking, which Gershom Scholem tellingly described as a "veritable *theologia mystica* of Judaism."[1] What is lacking is a sustained analysis of the role of the rhetoric of secrecy in his teaching and especially how it relates to the aporetic claim that we cannot know the divine essence, an approach well attested in the history of Jewish philosophy and mysticism. This study is an attempt to fill that gap by assessing the relationship between the apophatic and the esoteric in Kook's religious philosophy. As I shall argue, a critical aspect of his hermeneutic of secrecy, which is now far more transparent since the uncensored diaries have come to light, is the atheistic relativization of theistic belief. If one follows the *via negativa* to its logical conclusion, we come to the paradox of needing to believe categorically in the relative truth of what we know to be untrue. Belief, on this score, would not only encompass unbelief but, paradoxically, would be most fully instantiated as unbelief. In a previous publication, I cited the succinct expression of this paradox by Henri Atlan: the "personal God" of monotheistic theology is the "ultimate idol," since "the only discourse about God that is not idolatrous is necessarily an atheistic discourse. Alternatively, whatever the discourse, the only God who is not an idol is a God who is not a God."[2] This dimension of Kook's thought has been noted, but its precise relation to his notion of secrecy and apophasis has not been adequately explored.³

Kabbalah and the Secret of Secrecy

To set the tone of this inquiry, let me cite the observation of Eliezer Schweid that Kook's "teaching is in no way intended to decipher that which remains in the realm of 'secret' and mystery." The author qualifies his categorical judgment by noting that while Kook "certainly embraces those supernal sources which contain within them an infinite truth remaining beyond all human knowledge and comprehension," he "only engages in speculation in order to reveal and understand in depth those things which he holds as truth which have already appeared within the ken of the scientific and philosophic-speculative reflections of contemporary man." Schweid concludes that Kook was not engaged in "revealing secrets" nor was he "concerned with the difficulty characteristic of most Kabbalists and mystics concerning the question—what and how much of what is known to them may they reveal?—even though he is aware of the problem."⁴

A different perspective was offered by Yehuda Mirsky's description of Kook as a "good Lithuanian Kabbalist," insofar as "he practiced his esotericism with regards to the study of Kabbalah."⁵ But what is implied by this practice of esotericism? Ostensibly, what is intended is that Kook deliberately concealed secrets or withheld elaborating them in writing. But if so, what was his motivation? Even if we were to accept that there is a peculiar Lithuanian penchant for reticence in the diffusion of esoteric matters, the question that begs to be answered is what purpose, intellectual or practical, is served by a hypothetically intentional desire to safeguard the secrets? If we assume this to be Kook's modus operandi, what is behind his frequent deployment of the traditional expression "mysteries of Torah" (*razei torah*)? Should this be viewed merely as a rhetorical device divested of substantive meaning, or is there a specific connotation the unearthing of which might shed light on Kook's utilization of esoteric language?

On the face it, it would seem that Kook transformed the esoteric into the mystical, divesting the notion of the secret of its secrecy. One of the strongest advocates for such a position is Benjamin Ish-Shalom, who argued that, for Kook, the term *mysteries of Torah* "refers not only to the *sefirot* of kabbalistic teaching but to those same speculations and thoughts common to the mind of every individual, and it makes no difference whether they are expressed in kabbalistic language or otherwise."⁶ In support of his contention, Ish-Shalom cites a passage where Kook mentions the "mystical thinking" (*hegyon ha-razi*) that constitutes the quality of "independence" (*ḥofesh*) exclusive to the Jewish soul (*neshamah ha-yisra'elit*). When that sense of autonomy ascends to its peak, then the "unique soul" (*neshamah yeḥidah*), possessed only by the Jewish people, is nourished from the "dew of life" that issues from the Shekhinah, referred to as the Assembly of Israel (*kenesset yisra'el*).[7] Through the agency of this "pure holiness," the mysteries of Torah are formed within the souls of individual Jews, whether they are expressed in the language and style customarily used by masters of the mysteries (*ba'alei ha-razim*) or in another literary form. The tradition transmitted to Moses on Sinai (*qabbalah le-moshe mi-sinai*), according to the time-honored locution, is identified symbolically as the Assembly of Israel, whence the efflux of the holy spirit overflows, illumines, and inspires the production of novel secrets.[8] According to Ish-Shalom's interpretation, Kook broadened the import of the term "kabbalah," for it connotes not "only a tradition of knowledge handed down from Adam to Moshe to our own day, as the kabbalists held, but also the original creation of the individual Jew. We find here an awareness and legitimization of innovation itself."[9]

Leaving aside the complex interplay of conservative and innovative tendencies attested in older Kabbalistic sources, the main point raised by Ish-Shalom is well taken.[10] In contradistinction to the formula of esotericism adopted by Kabbalists, in no small measure due to the influence of Maimonides, Kook seems not only to have been dedicated to the proliferation of mystical teachings, perhaps due to his messianic utopianism and the campaign to combat secularization, but also to encourage the fabrication of new ideas that would expand the parameters of the Kabbalah.[11] Indeed, as he put it in one passage, since the mysteries of Torah (*sitrei torah*) derive from the "supernal source," the "hidden strength of the inwardness of the soul [*ḥevyon ha-oz shel penimiyyut ha-neshamah*], which is the portion of the divine from above [*ḥeleq eloha mi-ma'al*]," they can enter into all hearts, even the hearts of those "who have not reached the measure of the expansive mindfulness [*de'ah reḥavah*] for the attainment of the wide and deep knowledge [*mada raḥav we-amoq*]."[12] According to another passage, the disclosure of the mysteries of Torah (*gilluy razei torah*) brings about the revelation of the light of the mysteries of the supernal by means of which the "idle matters" (*devarim beṭelim*) are elevated and transformed through the light of the messiah into holiness. In sharp contrast to the Maimonidean hermeneutic, the inclination toward the supernal mysteries (*razei elyon*) is not consequent to the acquisition of scientific or rational understanding; on the contrary, it is precisely the humility of people wanting this training that brings blessing to the world, and through "their pure will" they have the capacity to reveal the "great light of the knowledge of the holy ones" (*or gadol shel da'at qedoshim*), that is, the gnosis of the angels, which is superior to the discursive or scientific wisdom of human beings (*ḥokhmat ha-adam*).[13]

Passages such as these attest to the fact that the breach with the traditional code of esotericism was a crucial facet of Kook's orientation. But is there something of the secret that persists in Kook's worldview even as he overtly and repeatedly affirms that the disclosure of the mysteries is the means to promulgate the consciousness of the unity of the divine in all things? Is there a way of reading Kook such that the dilemma of communicating the secret is still a matter of concern for him or has any vestige of a real esotericism disappeared in his mystical vision? The ensuing analysis will grapple with this question and attempt to offer a more nuanced understanding of the role of secrecy and apophasis in Kook's mystical teaching.

Disseminating the Secret and Israel's Spiritual Vocation

In reassessing Kook's statements about secrets and the nature of esotericism, let me begin by mentioning an illuminating and self-revealing comment in which he writes about God planting in him the "constant desire for all that is concealed [*nistar*], for all that is exalted and lofty," and instilling in him—in spite of his "innumerable weaknesses and failings"—a "daring spirit" and an "inner purity" so that he could "illumine the world," by creating a "literature replete with the light of the mysteries of Torah," albeit presented in a fashion that is "popular" and "accessible."[14] Kook acknowledges both his craving for the esoteric and his ability to render it exoterically so that it may become available to all Jews. Indeed, we can detect a conspicuous passion for the secret. Consider the following candid self-disclosure:

> My soul yearns for the mysterious secrets [*nafshi sho'efet le-sitrei peli'ot*], for the hidden strength of the supernal mysteries [*le-ḥevyon oz razim elyonim*], and it does not find comfort in the abundance of knowledge, since they turn to trite matters. My feelings and the path of my thoughts lead me constantly to the supernal dimension, to the exalted and to the elevated, to contemplate the sublimity of the holy, in the breadths of the pneumatic emanation [*be-merḥavei ha-aṣilut ha-nishmatiyyim*]. It is no accident that the essence of the nature of my soul is that I experience pleasure and contentment by being engaged in the divine secrets [*ha-nistarot ha-elohiyyot*] abundantly and freely.[15]

This extract is proof enough that Kook's embrace of the esoteric entailed the confluence of the theosophic and the ecstatic. The secrets for which the soul yearns are the supernal mysteries, which comprise the sphere of the holy and which are identified further as the pneumatic emanations. To be engaged in the divine secrets, therefore, means to be engaged in contemplation of the *sefirotic* potencies. With regard to this engagement, Kook feels no constraint or tension; on the contrary, it is the source of his pleasure (*oneg*) and contentment (*naḥat ruaḥ*).

The transmission of this mystical knowledge, unencumbered by technical jargon, is clearly the overarching impulse motivating Kook in his prolific literary creativity.[16] I would add that this impulse is reflective of the predilection for popularization and propagation of esotericism attested more broadly in the twentieth century. In one passage, Kook went so far as to argue that publicizing the mysteries was necessary for the survival of Judaism in his time, and that the deterioration of the status of the Jews should be viewed as the descent (*yeridah*) that precedes and is, in some sense, identical to the ascent (*aliyyah*).[17] Anyone familiar with his writings, however, knows that Kook routinely retained the rhetoric of esotericism. In one passage, for instance, he remarks that the superlative esoteric knowledge (*ha-yediʿot ha-sodiyyot ha-yoter elyonot*) is not meant to be broadcast extensively in the world (*lehitpashet be-olam be-hitpashshetut kamutit*) lest the masses become conversant with this knowledge. At best, the multitude should be restricted to the "outer expression" (*signon ha-ḥiṣon*) of the secrets so that they know nothing of their "inner content" (*tokhen ha-penimi*). Insofar as the widespread circulation of occult wisdom could prove to be more detrimental than beneficial, the secrets infiltrate only into those who have the "supernal property" (*segullah elyonah*) of the "lofty contemplation" (*histakkelut gevohah*), the elite individuals (*yeḥidim*), who in their "spiritual stature" (*govham ha-ruḥani*) elevate the world from its depraved state just by their existence and not on account of any palpable influence. Even though the inner secrets (*razim ha-penimiyyim*) cannot be revealed, their illumination is refracted through whatever is manifest in the world and thus everything mundane is sanctified. The "universal propensity" (*megammah ha-kelalit*) of Israel's influence in the world—a comportment that is unrivaled among the nations—can be expressed in this manner: in virtue of having received the Torah, they possess knowledge of the mysteries but also the wisdom not to distribute it indiscriminately. The onus for the Jewish people, accordingly, is to elevate the world by embodying the "inner property" (*segullah penimit*) in the treasure of humanity—a disposition that corresponds to the higher level of prophecy ascribed to Moses, seeing the glory through a translucent speculum (*aspaqlarya ha-meʾirah*).[18] The preeminence of mystical wisdom (*ḥokhmat ha-razim*), the true and original wisdom of the Jews (*ḥokhmat yisraʾel*), is that it stimulates the overflow of the holy spirit that elevates all corporeality to spirituality, and all of the sensible and imaginary forms are hoisted to the "summit of emanation" (*merom aṣilut*) and the "supernal enlightenment" (*haskalah ha-elyonah*).[19]

In the final analysis, the imaginative faculty allows one to sense the "reality of the divine light" in the soul and in the world. Subsequent to that feeling (*hargashah*), there is the "pious comprehension" (*hassagah ha-torit*) through which one is illumined in the "great light," the holy spirit that begins "to appear in the world in majesty and splendor, to lift up the nations, and to sustain the spirit of the contrite."[20] Kook identifies this as the ethos of the Jewish people (*mussar ha-yisraʾeli*), which he further labels as an "individualistic ethic" (*mussar indiwwiduʾali*) as opposed to one that is familial (*mispaḥti*), nationalistic (*leʾumi*), or related to humanity in general (*enoshi kelali*). Kook is quick to point out, however, that Jewish particularity is expressive of the universal, or in his precise language, it is all-encompassing (*ha-kol kalul bo*), but there can be little doubt that Judaism is accorded a privileged status; the ethnic pride and strength derive from its divine status, which is linked to the fact that the Torah, the emanative force of creation (*hamshakhah shel yeṣirah*), is the inimitable inheritance of Israel.²¹ Indeed, in one of his earliest compositions, Kook admonished against teaching words of Torah to the nations of the world for their "imperfect souls" (*nefashot bilti mushlamot*) may not be capable of assimilating the trace of holiness contained therein, even though, by his own admission, that trace is a boon for the physical and spiritual welfare of both Jews and non-Jews.²² The shared task of the other nations is to cultivate the "universal culture" by perfecting human nature, but the incomparable part played by Israel is to spread the pure knowledge of God's unity. Even though the procurement of this knowledge is the common telos of the human species without qualification, it is an undertaking borne by the Jews alone.²³ Hence, the Jewish people, as Kook unabashedly affirms, are the "center of the world" (*merkaz ha-olam*) and the "center of humanity" (*merkaz ha-enoshiyyut*) on account of the institution of prophecy, which is indicative of the "eternal praise" of Israel. In spite of the prevailing doubt and skepticism characteristic of modernity, Kook is committed to the traditional epistemology that "there is one truth that stands forever, and this truth is engraved on the forehead of the celestial beast that walks upon the earth in the form of the nation whose name is Israel. The whole world knows that we are the 'choicest vine, entirely the true seed' (Jeremiah 2:21)."²⁴ The unity of the spiritual-ethical and the material-practical realms is expressed in the world by means of the people of Israel and uniquely in the land of Israel.²⁵ Only Israel can receive the faith of the true God (*emunat elohei emet*), whereas the other nations are collectively branded as the "human filth" (*zuhama ha-enoshit*), embodying "an alien and foreign culture" (*tarbut zarah we-nokhrit*) that is innately antagonistic to the spiritual temperament of the Jews.²⁶ The difference between the Jewish soul and the soul of the gentiles is greater than the difference between a human soul and an animal soul, since in the case of the latter, the difference is quantitative (*kamuti*) and in the case of the former, it is substantial (*aṣmi*) and qualitative (*eikhuti*).²⁷

One might be inclined to attenuate this ethnocentrism by appealing to the universalism presumed to be implied in the particularism—the exclusivity of the chosen people is the means to achieve a greater inclusivity that is the utopian ideal expressed in the prophetic idiom of the ingathering of all nations to worship the God of Israel, who is the one true God.²⁸ However, one cannot deny the problematic repercussions of maintaining that the source of the general culture is Israel,²⁹ that only with respect to the Jews is there no conflict between the national spirit and the universal spirit,³⁰ that all the religions of the world are sustained by the light that emanates from the Torah,[31] and that the rectification of the world (*tiqqun ha-olam*) can come about only through this ethnos.[32] I recognize that Kook maintained an isomorphic homology between God and Israel such that just as the former is all-inclusive and thus any delineation of one aspect apart from the entirety is a form of idolatry or cutting of the shoots, so with respect to the spiritual demeanor of Judaism, it is erroneous to restrict it to specific qualities to the exclusion of additional possibilities.[33] The Jewish soul comprises all spiritual tendencies, whether revealed or concealed, in the manner that emulates the enclosure of everything in the absolute divinity (*ha-elohut ha-muḥletet*).[34] The exclusiveness associated with the Jews is thus inclusive of its own others. We read, for instance, that the community of Israel is called *ṣedeq*, "righteousness," because its foundation is to bring eternal justice (*ṣedeq ha-olamim*) to the entire human species.[35] Or again, "Israel toils perpetually for the liberation and redemption of the point of faith, which is the point of destiny for every human and every creature."[36]

Throughout his long career, Kook tirelessly argued that the nationalism of the Jewish people is tied to its universal mission on behalf of all humanity.[37] Nonetheless, one would be hard-pressed to rationalize or justify claims to exceptionality masked under the pretense of universality. Interpreting the rabbinic dictum— linked exegetically to Ezekiel 34:31—that Israel is called Adam and not the idolatrous nations of the world, Kook explains that the term *adam* in its truest sense (*shem adam ha-amitti*) applies to the perfection of the intellect (*shelemut ha-sekhel*), but since the intellect cannot be perfected except by the Torah, the term is attributed exclusively to the Jews.[38] I do not think it is necessary to elaborate on the moral deficiency of this view. To take one final striking example: after arguing that the division into disparate nationalities makes it impossible for one to receive the spiritual overflow except through the garment of the channel that is unique to one's ethnicity, Kook writes that the community of Israel is unique in this matter because with respect to Judaism it is not just the garbing of the channel (*hitlabbeshut ha-ṣinnor*) that is necessary for the spiritual life but also the essence of the content (*aṣmiyyut ha-tokhen*). In the end, the other nations will become adapted to the essence of Judaism (*mistaggelet el ha-aṣmiyyut ha-yahadutit*) and they will come to know and accept the name of the God of Israel.[39] The absorption of the other in the identity of the same cannot be viewed as a genuine acceptance of alterity.[40]

Silence and the Rhetoric of Esotericism

While Kook may have not systematically expounded many of the theosophic mysteries with which he was no doubt familiar, he is beholden to the predominant hermeneutic of secrecy espoused through the centuries by Kabbalists: the language appropriate to express the secret is the language of secrecy; that is, the secret can be revealed only as the secret that is concealed.[41] What is ultimately revealed, therefore, is the concealment.[42] In Kook's own words:

> Mysteries [*razim*] must be explicated and comprehended solely by means of mysteries and not by means of revealed matters [*devarim gilluyim*], and this is the natural method of the disclosure of truths, which is inestimably superior to the method of translation [*targum*], which is numerologically equivalent [to the word for] slumber [*tardemah*]. The concealed [*ne'lam*] is explained exclusively through the concealed; and [in the] myriad of branches of mystery, each illumines the other, and the mystery is brought to light.[43] . . . The gradations that are on a par reveal and illumine one another, mystery united with mystery, and the torch of light will be disclosed.[44]

The method of disclosing truths is contrasted with the method of translation. The latter, which requires rendering one language into another, supposedly is a form of enlightenment but in fact it is a form of slumber, an allegation anchored in the numerical equivalence of the words *targum* and *tardemah* (the consonants of both equal 649). By comparison, the method of disclosing truths is evocative of a far greater suspicion about the efficacy of language as a suitable means of communication. The mystery must be exposed as mystery, the concealed revealed through the revelation of the concealment of the concealed.

In another aphorism, Kook writes about the "language of mysteries" (*sefat ha-razim*) as the "supernal language" (*ha-safah ha-elyonah*) that "speaks the absolute truth" (*ha-emet ha-muḥlaṭah*) without any sense of recoil. And yet, even in this context, the apophatic sentiment is apparent. Mystical discourse is identified as a "pure language" (*safah berurah*) that necessitates protection lest it fall "from the place where the secret light [*or ha-sodi*] dwells in its nature, and the linguistic connection [*ha-qishshur ha-sefati*] is bound to it in the depth of truth [*be-omeq ha-emet*]," to the "lowly place of this world of action, where there is naught but the language of deceit [*leshon sheqer*], and lies become a kind of acceptable content and naturally pass for truth." Those who articulate the "supernal language from the source of truth" in the guise of the "falsehood that is misappropriated [*mitgannev*] in the garb of the truth [*bi-levush ha-emet*] of the deceit of human beings [*kezev benei adam*]" will end up "destroying the world."[45] To speak of the mysteries that originate in the source of truth in language apposite to the world of action, which is the domain of duplicity, implicates one in cloaking truth in deception.

The language in which esoteric wisdom should be expressed, the pure language, brings to mind Benjamin's *reine Sprache*, the unspoken and wordless language that comprises the symbolic potential for phonemic and graphemic communicability in general rather than any existing semantic morphemes tied to a specific cultural-semiological milieu.⁴⁶ Kook's *safah berurah* is likewise a language that is qualitatively different from the preponderant modes of aural and written exchange. Moreover, in a manner that is reminiscent of the Buddhist distinction between absolute truth (*paramārtha-satya*) and conventional truth (*saṃvṛti-satya*), the forms of representation that prevail in the intersubjective sphere are predicated on the arrayment of truth unveiled in the veil of untruth, whereas the pure language is bound to the depth of truth to the extent that it obviates the viability of expression through the ploy of dissimulation.⁴⁷ We may surmise that this implies that the supernal language of mysteries, when judged from the standpoint of the sentient world, is an apophatic gesticulation, a language beyond language, a semantic field where letter is interchangeable with light. The secrets of Kabbalah belong most properly in this realm of the untainted truth that can be expressed only through its inexpressibility.

The paradox of apophasis, the verbal act of unsaying, is addressed in a poignant way in the following passage in which Kook poetically describes the circular motion of the *via contemplativa*:

> We must greatly expand thought, in length, width, depth, height, extension and size. . . . And we traverse repetitively from the great to the small and from the small to the great, from particularity to universality and from universality to particularity. We fly from emanation, from ideality, to embodiment, to materiality, to practicality, and we return and ascend from practicality to emanation, to ideality, and we are engaged continually in motion. . . . We desire to pronounce the name, we yearn to elucidate the supernal light, we are filled with transcendent thirst, saturated with delight, to fill the mouth with the praise of the God of gods. From the abundance of the pure fear, from the strength of the holy reverence, we return to the silence.⁴⁸

The contemplative expansion of thought involves the mind going from one thing to its opposite, from the great to the small, from the immaterial to the material, from the ideal to the practical. The movement, which is cyclical and repetitive, is also expressed as the desire to vocalize the ineffable name and to explicate the supernal light. Even though one may be filled with the kataphatic desire to offer praises before God, in the end one returns apophatically to the silence (*demamah*). "From the perspective of the absolute and necessary essence of the divine reality, no praise [*shevaḥ*] or adoration [*tehillah*] is appropriate, for what is essential is not praiseworthy. But the contemplation of the substance of the greatness of truth and goodness consummately perfects everything, and then we understand that the prevention of praise [*meni'at ha-shevaḥ*] is above every blessing and veneration, for the dispersion of the volitional governance [*ha-hanhagah ha-reṣonit*] is constricted [*meṣumṣemet*] vis-à-vis the complete loftiness [*ha-elyoniyyut ha-gemurah*], and it is especially the contracted [*ha-memu'eṭet*] that imparts place for adoration and praise."⁴⁹ Concerning the unspeakable and undefinable, the eschewal of adulation is the highest adulation. Kook writes fervently about the distress and frustration he felt from not being able to depict his experience adequately in words: "I hunger for the truth. Not for the comprehension of truth, and thus I am riding upon the skies, and I am entirely engulfed within the truth. I am utterly pained from the anguish of expression, how will I express the great truth, which fills my whole heart? ... All that I will speak only covers my splendor and clouds my light. Great is my suffering and great is my pain."⁵⁰ From the innermost pangs of his existential angst, Kook was able to summon the words to express the fact that any expression of the inexpressible of necessity entails covering what has been uncovered. Every articulation of the ineffable—speaking what cannot be spoken—must be symbolic insofar as the symbol is an image of unlikeness. It stands to reason that the imagelessness specularized through an image must be in conflict with that image inasmuch as it is without image. What is hidden in the exposure of the hidden is the hiddenness that has been exposed. Discovery of truth perforce is an act of recovering, concealing the concealment.

Ontological Dimensions of the Secret

Kook proffered an ontological understanding of the secret that is prevalent in Kabbalistic literature. Secrecy is not merely an epistemological or hermeneutical category, as it is often assumed by scholars, but rather one that relates to the nature of being as it is apprehended by the mystic visionary;⁵¹ that is, the one who experiences the world through a "spiritual contemplation" (*histakkelut ruḥanit*), a way of "gazing at everything together" (*seqirat ha-kol be-yaḥad*), in contrast to one who experiences it through the "ordinary intellectual contemplation" (*histakkelut ha-sikhlit ha-peshuṭah*), which is preoccupied with allegedly discrete objects and properties.⁵² Something of the elitism of the esoteric posture persists to the extent that the knowledge of the secrets relates to a transformative vision that is limited to the few who are considered to be the foundation of the world. Hence, as he writes in another passage, the "light of the mysteries of God" (*or razei el*), which sustains the supernal souls of the righteous, is compared to the "spirit of the resurrection of the dead," and it is through this "supernal light that is sown in the righteous" that the messiah will appear "to raise the horn of the eternal people."⁵³ Other comments, however, offer a perspective that seemingly undercuts the elitism and democratizes the esoteric ideal. To mention one conspicuous illustration: Kook informs the reader that conjecture with respect to the mysteries of Torah (*hashra'at razei torah*) is based on a "supernal capability that has no end or limit," but what ultimately ensues from such contemplative activity is a "phenomenological disclosure" (*gilluy hofa'ah*) of the "light of the life of all lives," the infinite energy that sustains reality, which is potentially available to all people.[54] The dissemination of the secret, therefore, is no longer restricted to exclusive fraternities of the cognoscenti in the manner that Kabbalists insisted for centuries, even if their own innovative exposition of traditions—often elicited exegetically from scriptural and/or rabbinic texts—complicates the degree to which they themselves subscribed to a rigid conservatism. "The current culture," muses Kook, "according to how it is presently established in the world, is built entirely on heresy and hatred, for they are the negation of the essential life. It is only possible to overcome this disease by revealing all the treasures of good from their storages of faith and love, and this is the goal of disclosing the mysteries of Torah."[55]

Further support for this may be elicited from an aphorism wherein Kook distinguishes philosophy (*filosofyah*) and esotericism (*sodiyyut*) on the grounds that the former is an "aristocratic" mode of thinking that is incapable of comprehending the underlying oneness of all phenomena, whereas the latter "discerns the unity that is everything," and therefore it penetrates to the profundity of all thoughts, feelings, inclinations, and strivings throughout the entire chain of being that is the multiverse. Precisely because the infinite, the "cause of all causes" (*illat kol ha-illot*), is beyond comprehension, it can be spoken of as an "esoteric surplus" (*ha-yitaron ha-razi*) through which all the "thoughts" and "spiritual sparks" comprised within it are unified. The secret (*sod*), accordingly, is identified as the "soul of faith" (*nishmat ha-emunah*) and the "soul of Torah" (*nishmata de-orayyta*). "The open unity of the mystery [*ha-aḥdut ha-mefuleshet shel ha-raz*] comprises all the creations, all the conditions of thought and feeling, all types of poetry and oratory, all the inclinations of life, all the aspirations and all the hopes, all the ambitions and all the ideals, from the depth of their foundation to the summit of their elevation. The oil of life of the supernal height of the divine loftiness [*ha-govah ha-elyon shel ha-illuy ha-elohi*], which only the splendor of prophecy and the translucent speculum [*zohar ha-nevu'ah we-aspaqlarya ha-me'irah*], the splendor of the first Adam and the supernal lights, can reveal."[56] For Kook, the expansive spiritual condition is one in which the mysteries of the world (*razei olam*), the mysteries of Torah (*razei torah*), and the secret of God (*sod ha-shem*) lay claim to the individual.[57] In another aphorism, he goes so far as to say that it is a matter of "deceit" (*sheqer*) to demand of the soul to attain the "true divine conjunction" (*devequt elohit amittit*) without the "amplification of the study of the depths of the mysteries of Torah."[58] The directive to interpret the Torah according to the four levels of meaning (*lidrosh et ha-torah be-fardes*), which includes the literal (*peshaṭ*), allegorical (*remez*), homiletical (*derash*), and mystical (*sod*), is for the sake of widening the boundary and magnifying the light of vitality in the world.[59]

Here we see a convergence of the ontological and the hermeneutical connotations of the term *raz*: it is through study of the mysteries conveyed in the scriptural text that one can be conjoined with the mystery of the divine light. There is thus an

> inclination in the soul for the image of the encompassing oneness [*ha-aḥdut ha-kolelet*], which discerns only divinity, and it knows as well that every disclosure of the particular is not the matter of divinity, but rather the totality, and the source of the totality, and that which is way above this. However that which separates the disclosure of the particular from divinity is not the matter of truth per se; this is caused by the blindness of our eyes, for we discern only the particularity. . . . This reality of the return of the totality to divinity [*ḥazarat ha-kol el ha-elohut*] is the supernal perfection in being [*ha-sheleimut ha-elyonah be-hawayah*], and there is no capacity to comprehend its value."[60]

From this vantage point, it might be more appropriate to render the critical term *sod* as mystical rather than esoteric, since the secretive knowledge consists of discerning the interconnectivity of all things through the infinite potency (*ha-gevurah ha-ein sofit*) as opposed to the more accessible and pervasive discernment of allegedly self-subsistent substances, which are reified through contraction (*ṣimṣum*) of the unlimited and impenetrable light.[61]

At the heart of Kook's worldview is the intersection of the esoteric and the political.[62] Prima facie, it seems untenable for the esoteric to serve as the basis for a sociopolitical movement, insofar as the latter calls for divulging and transparency and the former for obfuscating and opacity. To speak candidly, one would not expect that the spreading of secrets could serve as the spiritual underpinning of an ideological movement such as Zionism. It is reasonable, therefore, for Kook to have shifted from an elitist and exclusionary esotericism to an ideal of mysticism that is more inclusive and embracive. Kook transformed the rhetoric of esotericism as his thought matured and the Zionist component became more central to his vision. For the most part, as we have seen, the matter of disclosing secrets is not a revealing of the concealed by concealing the revealed, but rather the promulgation of the theomonistic belief that reality partakes of the light of infinity that is present in all things by being absent from all things, the light that is both immanently transcendent and transcendently immanent, indeed the one because the other, since transcendence can be manifest only through the façade of immanence. Nature evolves, according to Kook, to the point that there is an ever-increasing appreciation of the underlying unity of the untold differentiated beings—an inchoate aggregate whose form is incessantly being shaped by the ever-changing multiplicity of beings—often designated in his writings by the metaphor of the elevation of all things to the one true source of life. In that respect, immersion in the depth of the mysteries and hidden secrets has the task of enhancing the sense of good in the world and thereby rendering existence in its entirety nobler.[63]

Apophasis and the Atheistic Overcoming of Theolatry

The ontological claim regarding the underlying divine unity of all things corresponds to an epistemological presumption that there is a proper way to see the world such that the fragmentariness of what exists is overcome; our typical modes of perception and cognition through which we negotiate and navigate the world of discrimination compel us to see particularity and difference, one thing distinguished from another, but the mystical sensibility is a mode of perceiving the interrelatedness of all things in the "supernal holiness" (*qodesh elyon*), which cannot be discerned through intellection (*sekhel*) or sensation (*regesh*) but only through faith (*emunah*), the "inner yearning in the depth of the supreme holiness" (*she'ivah penimit be-omeq ha-qodesh ha-meromem*).[64] Kook further associates this faith with the "deeper wisdom" (*ha-ḥokhmah ha-yoter amuqah*), also identified as the "fear of the Lord."[65] Interestingly, he notes that the source whence this fear is formed is in the "depth of the soul" on account of the "wondrous combination of two opposites [*ha-harkavah ha-nifla'ah shel shenei ha-hafakhim*] related to the divine comprehension [*ha-hassagah ha-elohit*], the privation of absolute knowledge of the essence of divinity [*he'der ha-yedi'ah ha-muḥletet be-mahut ha-elohut*] and the certain knowledge of its perfect existence [*wada'ut ha-yedi'ah bi-meṣi'utah ha-sheleimah*]."[66] Mystical gnosis ensues from the *coniunctio oppositorum* of the apophatic and the kataphatic: the lack of knowledge of the divine essence ensures the certitude of the divine existence—to know that God exists means, therefore, to know that we cannot know the nature of that which we presume to exist. In place of striving to apprehend the divine essence, the accomplishment of which is humanly impossible, it is best to direct one's attention to the ethical mandate that follows from the apperception of the nothingness that is the matrix of all that is real, the supernatural transcendence that is immanent in every dimension of nature.[67]

Alternatively expressed, when seen through the mystical prism, the certitude of divine existence implies that all things ascend to the "unified substance" (*tokhen ha-aḥduti*) that is the source "above every image of divisions" (*ṣiyyur shel havdolot*), including the division between existence and nonexistence, the godly and the ungodly.[68] This unity—the one beyond the mathematical binary of the one and the many—is characterized as the "equanimity of values" (*hishtawwut shel arakhim*).[69] The supposition that differences among what appear to be oppositional—physical and spiritual, imaginative and intellectual, darkness and light, good and evil, holy and impure—are rendered indifferent in light of the fact that the various parts of reality are in accord with each other, and thus the particulars illumine the whole, each from its singular perspective. Whereas the "rational viewpoint" (*ha-habaṭah ha-raṣyonalit*) tends to incorporate particularities in the "universal illumination" (*he'arah ha-kelalit*), secrecy (*raziyyut*) involves seizing the universal through penetration into the details of the particular. The peril of esotericism is that it can lead the mind to be submerged in the "smallness of the particulars," but in the end its success consists precisely of showing the capaciousness of the hidden in the minutiae of the manifest, the wonders of the celestial in the configuration of the terrestrial.[70] Kook hints at this process when he writes that if any "revealed part" (*ḥeleq galuy*) is not appropriately discerned, it stands as a "curtain" (*masakh*) that hides the "extolled light" (*ha-or ha-nisgav*) of the "hidden and concealed part" (*ha-ḥeleq ha-ḥavuy we-ha-nistar*), which can only be seen through a "luminous inner vision" (*ṣefiyyah penimit behirah*). Sometimes a miracle is possible and the light breaks through as a crack in the wall, but the "enduring order" (*seder tediri*) is "to go from the revealed [*ha-gilluy*] to the hidden [*ha-nistar*], from the particulars [*ha-peraṭim*] to the general [*ha-kelal*]."[71] One thus fathoms that in the "light of the supernal, divine unity" (*or ha-aḥdut ha-elyonah ha-elohit*), the opposites found below in the world of differentiation are united in an indivisible oneness.[72]

Apropos of the stipulation to traverse from entanglement with singularity to absorption in generality, it is of interest to consider Kook's appropriation and condemnation of the *via negativa* promulgated by Maimonides. The latter argued that comprehension of the negative attributes bestows upon a person a superior form of negative knowledge (*yedi'ah ha-shelilit*) that brings one in closer proximity to the unknowable and incommensurable God. Kook challenges this viewpoint by noting that the heart is generally gladdened by positivity and not negativity. He acquiesces to Maimonides, however, and grants that if a person rises to "this quality of unity with the light of truth" (*middah zo shel hitaḥadut im or ha-emet*), then even negative truth (*emet shelili*) brings one joy, for indeed at this level "everything negative changes into something positive" (*kol shelilah nehpekhet le-ḥiyyuv*) and every "privation" (*he'der*) is transmuted into an "absolute attribution" (*qinyan gamur*). Nevertheless, Kook significantly modifies the Maimonidean perspective and argues that to bolster the popular diffusion of the knowledge of God (*da'at elohim*) in the world, it is necessary to overturn the apophatic orientation by kataphatically increasing the "positive images" (*ṣiyyurim ḥiyyuvim*) of God. If the logic of apophasis dictates that all the demarcated attributes are negated in the inexhaustible perfection of the divine, it is equally true that this negation must be negated. The insufficiency of these attributes is linked to considering their specificity in isolation from the totality in which they are incorporated, that is, in treating them as autonomous or self-subsisting entities rather than as coexisting and interdependent networks.

Necessity implies that everything contained within the nondifferentiated unity of divine perfection is as an actual possible of the possible actual. What we must negate, therefore, is the overemphasis on the delimitation (*hagbalah*) and particularity (*peratiyyut*) of the attributes, for this fallacy of misplaced concreteness, to borrow the Whiteheadian phrase, is what brings one to a state of sadness. However, when one contemplates these attributes from the perspective of *Ein Sof*, the indifferent substratum of the world of difference—the substance (*yesh*) of the all-encompassing insubstantiality, the indiscriminate emptiness that is the discriminate thusness of all that exists—then the particulars are elevated without being obliterated, and the knowledge of the divine is intensified.[73] Utilizing technical Zoharic terms, Kook describes evil as the "world of separation" (*alma di-feruda*) in which every particular stands by itself, and good as the "world of unity" (*alma de-yihuda*) in which everything forms "one collective" (*hativah ahat*) held together by one "comprehensive bond" (*qishshur ha-kelali*).[74] Echoing a quietistic note well attested in both Kabbalistic and Hasidic sources, Kook writes that the "supernal happiness" is strengthened by means of the "complete annihilation" (*bittul gamur*) of the reality of one's self (*mahut asmo*). The desire to be assimilated into the "infinite perfection of the supernal splendor" (*shelemut ein sof shel no'am elyon*) requires a preliminary act of "extreme modesty" (*ha-anawah ha-gemurah*) and "deep humility" (*ha-shiflut ha-amuqqah*), a sentiment (*hargashah*) that Kook—problematically in my opinion—contends is unique to the Jewish people, "for they belittle themselves with respect to every greatness that is bestowed on them."[75]

Kook's perspective is based on the firsthand experience of the "world of unity" (*olam shel ahdut*), which is marked by harmony (*harmoniyah*) and coincidence (*hat'amah*) in which distinctions are no longer discernible;[76] the speculative roots for this notion, however, can be found in the characterization of *Ein Sof* or *Keter* in some of the earliest Kabbalistic texts as the indifferent oneness (*ahdut ha-shaweh*), the immeasurable unity wherein it is no longer viable to distinguish between the antinomies that orient us in the world spatially, temporally, morally, legally, religiously, sociologically, and psychologically. To be properly attuned to the apophatic nothingness of infinity—the *complexio oppositorum* in relation to which we cannot discriminate between the nonbeing of being and the being of nonbeing, the affirmation of negation and the negation of affirmation—is disorienting as the polarities by which we empirically calibrate our everyday lifeworld are fundamentally disrupted.

The logical consequence of this insight is drawn frequently by Kook.[77] Thus, for example, he describes the "great sea of the light of infinity" (*ha-yam ha-gadol shel or ein sof*) as the site where "everything is unified, everything is elevated, everything is exalted, and everything is sanctified." Insofar as the supernal source is beyond all disparities, we can formulate a response to the age-old philosophical problem of theodicy: good and evil cannot be differentiated and this provides the justification for the "spiritual afflictions" that befall the magnanimous soul and bring it to the "lofty felicity" (*osher ha-meromem*).⁷⁸ Afflictions are only apparent since there is no evil that is not a manifestation of the good. On the face of it, the righteous individual (*ṣaddiq*) is marred by relentless suffering, but this suffering is the path that leads to the most pristine bliss, the realization that in the meontological source of all beings—the self-negating negativity that yields the positivity of the manifold that constitutes the fabric of the cosmos—there is no way to extricate exultation from misfortune and hence pain itself is transposed into pleasure. The pragmatic need to constrict oneself to the particularities of the differentiated world that we inhabit is the catalyst that causes the mind of the expansive soul (*ha-neshamah ha-reḥavah*) to endure such torment, but the travails must be borne out of love because they eventually bring one to the greatest fortune (*osher ha-yoter gadol*).⁷⁹ "Who knows the depths of my pain," opines Kook, "and who can estimate it? I am confined by many borders, in different boundaries, and my spirit craves the elevated expanses. 'My soul thirsts for God' (Psalm 42:3). The light of emanation is the life of my spirit. . . . All that is delimited is mundane vis-à-vis the supernal holiness."⁸⁰

Kook utilized an older Kabbalistic motif, attested in Zoharic literature, but exploited in Lurianic, Sabbatian, and Ḥasidic sources: the descent of the virtuous to the depth of sinfulness. Volitional acts of transgression provide the mechanism by which the *ṣaddiq* liberates the sparks of light entrapped in darkness as part of the messianic duty of rectifying the world. In this respect, the hardships of the righteous augment light in the world and thereby facilitate redemption.⁸¹ More profoundly, just as within the boundlessness of infinity opposites are no longer ontically distinguishable, so each collapse is the means by which one psychically comprehends not only that there is no joy without grief but that grief is the most sublime exhibition of joy. The full magnitude of the *coincidentia oppositorum*, the true sign of spiritual wakefulness, implies knowing that the descent is not simply for the sake of the ascent but rather that the descent itself is the ascent.⁸²

The positive value accorded rebelliousness (*meridah*) and dissent (*kefirah*) is attested in the ideal of repentance (*teshuvah*), the highest rung on the ladder of human perfection and the crux of Israel's eschatological mission to rectify the world. Without self-doubt, no one would suffer the shame and remorse necessary to seek amends for past indiscretions. The rupture (*qilqul*) caused by heresy (*harisah*) fosters the degradation (*shiflut*) that provokes one to repent in order to bring redemption to the world.⁸³ Occasionally, Kook was bold enough to draw the hypernomian implications of this radical shift in consciousness: heresy is the means that leads one to a deeper faith, a faith that takes the form of doubt, a piety that entails casting away the yoke of the commandments. To be sure, time and again, he insisted that in the current situation the commitment on the part of Jews to the ritual laws and customs must be upheld. Nevertheless, he painted the messianic future, which can be experienced proleptically by the spiritual elite, as a time in which the laws will be abrogated, since in the state of nonduality associated with that future, there is no basis to differentiate between permissible and forbidden, pure and impure. As Kook openly avowed, it is difficult for the righteous man to be limited by the exoteric study and practice of Halakhah. Adherence to the law, therefore, is a mandatory concession demanded by the sociopolitical need for communal cohesion, but it increases the agony of the magnanimous soul, who desires, above all, to be bound to the limitless light that transcends the constriction of the nomian framework predicated on the structure of duality.[84]

In the enlightened state, even the distinction between faith (*emunah*) and heresy (*kefirah*) is subverted. This idea was articulated already in the thirteenth century by Azriel of Gerona;[85] it is audaciously expressed by Kook in the following aphorism:

> With regard to the supernal divine truth, there is no difference at all between the conceived belief and heresy. Neither of them offer the truth, but faith brings one close to truth and heresy to deceit, and, as a result, good and evil ensue from these opposites, "the righteous will walk on them, while sinners will stumble on them" (Hosea 14:10). The world in its entirety, with all its spiritual and material values, it is all in relation to our assessment, and in relation to our assessment truth is revealed in faith, which is the source of good, and deceit in heresy, which is the source of evil. However, in relation to the light of *Ein Sof*, everything is equal. Heresy, too, is the disclosure of the force of life, for the light of life of the supernal splendor is garbed within it, and, consequently, spiritual warriors gather very good sparks from it.[86]

From the relative perspective of human judgment, we distinguish faith and heresy, and the good and evil that derive therefrom, but from the absolute perspective of *Ein Sof*, the two are transmutable. Indeed, in the sea of infinite indifference, the renunciation of faith is converted into the profoundest proclamation of faith, and the debris of darkness amassed from the deconstructive gesture of heresy becomes the foundation upon which the edifice of divine light is reconstructed.[87] As Kook put it in another passage: "The faith of Israel is affixed in *Ein Sof*, which is above all content of faith, and hence the faith of Israel is considered in truth to be the ideal of faith, the faith of the future, which is inestimably higher that the content of faith in the present. . . . The blemish of heresy occurs in the faith itself, but in the ideal faith there is no blemish of heresy at all because it is above the concept of heresy just as it is above the concept of faith."[88]

The faith of the future, which exceeds the faith of the present, is rooted in the indeterminate infinite and hence it transcends every positive content of faith. The utopian faith—the faith beyond faith, the faithless faith—is glossed with the words *ehyeh asher ehyeh*, "I shall be as I shall be," the divine name revealed to Moses at the epiphany of the burning bush (Exodus 3:14), a name that defies the standard function of a name insofar as it does not denote anything definitive but only indexically alludes to the absolute necessity of being that is concomitantly the pure potentiality of becoming.[89] Just as this ideal faith is above all faith, so it is above all heresy. In Kook's words: "There is no place in the ideal for anything opposing the ideal of faith even though there is the matter of the opposite [*hippukh*] and the parallel [*haqblah*] vis-à-vis the body of faith." In the ideal of faith—the *fons vitae* (*meqor hayyim*), the fiftieth gate of understanding, which was not even transmitted to Moses—the shell of heresy (*qelippat ha-kefirah*) is completely subjugated because the force of the unholy, the demonic other god (*el aḥer*), is no longer antagonistic to the holy.[90]

In accord with Maimonides, Kook was sensitive to the fact that theistic depictions of God are inescapably idolatrous, since they promote an imagistic portrayal of that which is inherently imageless.[91] The metrics by which we measure the "essence of faith" (*iqqar ha-emunah*) is the immeasurable "greatness of the perfection of the infinite" (*gedullat shelemut ein sof*), and thus whatever we imagine in our hearts about God is a glimmer that is "completely obliterated" (*battel legamrei*) when viewed against what really exists. Every name we assign to the infinite, whether in Hebrew or any other language, is "but a small and dim spark from the hidden light to which the soul aspires when it utters the word 'God' [*elohim*]. Every definition of divinity brings about heresy [*kefirah*], every definition is spiritual idolatry [*eliliyyut ruḥanit*], even the attribution of the intellect and the will, and even divinity [*ha-elohut*] itself, for the name 'God' [*elohim*] is a definition." Without the knowledge that every verbal or visual image applied to God is an inadequate definition, all positive God-talk would engender heresy. To be disdainful of the kataphatic descriptions of the indescribable infinity, which Kook refers to as the "limbs of the king" or the "garments of the king," is also to be guilty of irreverence. Even though these descriptions are fallacious, they serve a utilitarian purpose if the practitioner keeps in mind a clear distinction between them and the "essence of faith." The theistic depictions are "explanations" (*hasbarot*) that help bring one to the "source of faith," the infinite light that is beyond all linguistic, conceptual, and imaginary representation. However, as Kook points out, these explanations can have the adverse effect of diminishing an individual's material and spirituality vitality; indeed, the "greatest impediment" (*ma'ṣor gadol*) of the human spirit to achieving maturity is that the "conception of God" (*maḥashavah ha-elohit*) is fixed in a "particular form," which is "known amongst people on account of juvenile habit and imagination."[92] The ascendancy of atheism in the time that precedes the messianic liberation (*iqveta di-meshiḥa*) can be seen in a constructive light: the repudiation of belief is necessary "to eliminate the dross that has clung to the faith because of a dearth of knowledge and worship." The function of atheism is to remove the "specific forms" (ha-ṣurot ha-meyuḥadot) from our conception of divinity, to uproot the refuse that separates the human from the true divine light, to cleanse the mind so that the more sublime knowledge of God (daʿat elohim ha-nisgavah) can erect its temple.[93]

What separates the faith of Israel and idolatry is that the former unconditionally prohibits such images and in their place posits an "elevated and lofty image" (ṣiyyur naʿaleh we-nisgav) of the divine, which is "above every sentient figure" (naʿaleh mi-kol temunah muḥashit).[94] Kook already noted in his commentary on the aggadic passages in Berakhot that the admixture of "pure monotheism" (emunat ha-yiḥud ha-ṭehorah) and the "murkiness of corporeality" (maḥashakei ha-hagshamah) is purified periodically when an aspect of the anthropomorphism falls away. What might appear as the toppling of faith turns out to be its refinement. Israel's worship of God through the commandments is signaled out as being directed to the spiritual form (ha-ṣurah ha-ruḥanit) that is free of any corporealization.[95] The decisive return of the human spirit to the sphere of "pure belief" (ha-emunah ha-barah) will take place when the "last subtle shell of corporeality" (qelippat ha-hagshamah ha-aḥaronah ha-daqqah) collapses. This last shell consists of the "attribution of existence in general to divinity [yaḥas ha-meṣiʾut bi-khelalut el ha-elohut], for in truth all that we define by existence is incalculably removed from divinity." The "shadows of this negation" resemble the heresy of atheism—denying the existence of God—but in reality the expunging of any proclivity to represent the divine unity anthropomorphically or anthropopathically is the "highest level of faith."[96]

Ironically, insofar as the true expression of monotheism induces one to divest God of all positive attributions, atheism is the only elocution about God that is not culpable of endorsing a false image. As Kook writes about the relation of idolatry and monotheism in an epistle to Samuel Alexandrov, dated 13 Kislev 5557 (November 30, 1906), "By our values he is like one who is not [hu ke-mi she-eino], no intelligible or metaphysical form is found in him, but we know that it is impossible for it to be otherwise, since everything is from him. We do not speak or contemplate the source of sources, but from the fact that we do not negate him, everything lives and exists forever."[97] Insofar as the God of Judaism is presumed to have no form, it is not invalid ideationally or experientially to consider that God as nonexistent. The aniconic ramification of the monotheistic creed is the undoing of theism.[98] Although the tendency toward atheism might appear to damage and to contradict the general principle of religious faith, in fact, it brings one closer to the "pure divine unity" (ha-aḥdut ha-elohit ha-ṣerufah), which is the "foundation of the source of Israel," to the degree that it cleanses the mind of the pernicious impact of the imagination.⁹⁹ The absolute lack of similarity between the divine and every other existent renders even the attribution of existence to God equivocal. This is the meaning of Maimonides's utilization of the language of Avicenna to name God the "necessary of existence" (*wājib al-wujūd*; *meḥuyav ha-meṣi'ut*), that is, the being whose existence is necessitated by its very essence, a taxonomy of being that cannot be ascribed to any other existent.¹⁰⁰ It follows that to proclaim that God exists is an ambivalent and misleading statement. Kook found confirmation of the Maimonidean view in the Kabbalistic insistence that one cannot declare of the *Ein Sof* that it exists.¹⁰¹ If the infinite, as I have argued elsewhere, is truly neither something nor nothing, then it is not merely a presence that presents itself as nonpresent, but it is a nonpresence that is outside the either/or calculus that informs the economy of the binary of presence and absence indispensable to the vernacular of negative theology; it is, in short, the chiasm that resists both the reification of nothing as something and of something as nothing. To speak of this nothingness as the absence of presence is as inadequate as it is to speak of it as the presence of absence; it is technically beyond both affirmation and negation.¹⁰² The final iconoclastic achievement, therefore, would call for destroying the idol of the very God personified as the deity that must be worshipped without being idolized.¹⁰³ The apophasis of apophasis implied herein would represent the last stage on the path of purging monotheism of its incipient theolatry, a process that Kook deemed to be the distinctive vocation of the Jewish nation, to lead all of humanity to the ultimate perfection, the discernment of the one God, which means the discernment that there is naught but one reality, the divine light that permeates the pleromatic abyss at being's core.¹⁰⁴ When one reaches this shore of enlightenment, one awakens to the faith of the future, the faith that is marked by the signpost *ehyeh asher ehyeh*, as we already noted, the name that refuses to be named, the name that denotes neither something that is nothing nor nothing that is something, the name that signifies the insignificant, the infinity that both is what it is not and is not what it is because it neither is what it is not nor is not what it is. Within this imaginal space, there is no more distinction between faith and unfaith, belief and disbelief, and hence atheism emerges as the most pertinent and enhanced enunciation of theism.

Notes

1. Gershom Scholem, *Major Trends in Jewish Mysticism* (New York: Schocken, 1954), 354n17. For an incomplete but representative sample of scholarship on the relationship of Kook to Jewish mystical sources, including bibliographic references to earlier scholarship, see Tamar Ross, "Rav Kook's Conception of Divinity" [in Hebrew], *Da'at* 8 (1982): 109–128 and *Da'at* 9 (1982): 39–70; Yehudah Leon Ashkenazi, "The Use of Kabbalistic Concepts in Rav Kook's Teaching," in *The World of Rav Kook: Presentations from an Avi Chai-Sponsored*

Conference Held in Jerusalem August 19–22, 1985 on the Occasion of the 50th Anniversary of Rav Kook's Death, ed. Benjamin Ish-Shalom and Shalom Rosenberg, trans. Shalom Carmy and Bernard Casper (Jerusalem: Avi Chai, 1991), 149–155; Joseph Ben-Shlomo, "Lurianic Kabbalah and Rabbi Abraham Isaac ha-Cohen Kook's Philosophical System" [in Hebrew], *Jerusalem Studies in Jewish Thought* 10 (1992): 449–457; Yosef Avivi, "History as a Divine Prescription" [in Hebrew], in *Rabbi Mordechai Breuer Festschrift*, ed. Moshe Bar-Asher (Jerusalem: Academon Press, 1992), 709–771; Avivi, "Introduction to the Kabbalah of R. Abraham Isaac ha-Kohen" [in Hebrew], *Or Ḥadash* 13 (2011): 16–32; Lawrence Fine, "Rav Abraham Isaac Kook and the Jewish Mystical Tradition," in *Rabbi Abraham Isaac Kook and Jewish Spirituality*, ed. Lawrence Kaplan and David Shatz (New York: New York University Press, 1995), 23–40; Mordecai Pachter, "The Kabbalistic Foundation of the Doctrine of Faith and Heresy in the Teaching of Rav Kook" [in Hebrew], *Da'at* 47 (2001): 69–100; Jonathan Garb, "Rabbi Kook and His Sources: From Kabbalistic Historiosophy to National Mysticism," in *Studies in Modern Religions, Religious Movements and the Bābī-Bahā'ī Faiths*, ed. Moshe Sharon (Leiden: Brill, 2004), 77–95; Yuval Kahan, "Divine Faith: The Metaphysical Orientation of Rav Kook—Metaphysics, Theology, Mysticism" [in Hebrew] (MA thesis, Hebrew University, 2004), 97–120; Jerome Gellman, "Repentance in the Kabbalah: The Sources of Rav Kook" [in Hebrew], in *Shefa Ṭal: Studies in Jewish Thought and Culture Presented to Bracha Sack*, ed. Zeev Gries, Howard Kreisel, and Boaz Huss (Beer Sheva, Israel: Ben-Gurion University, 2004), 261–266; Jonathan Meir, "Longing of Souls for the Shekhina: Relations Between Rabbi Kook, Zeitlin and Brenner" [in Hebrew], *Jerusalem Studies in Jewish Thought* 19 (2005): 771–818, esp. 775–777; Elchanan Shilo, "Rav Kook's Explication of Lurianic Kabbalah: The Appearance of New Souls and Rectification of the World" [in Hebrew], *Iyyunim bi-Tequmat Yisra'el* 18 (2008): 55–77. For a detailed analysis of mystical experience, prophecy, and the pattern of creation in Kook's teaching, see Semadar Cherlow, *The Tzaddiq Is the Foundation of the World: Rav Kook's Esoteric Mission and Mystical Experience* [in Hebrew] (Ramat-Gan, Israel: Bar-Ilan University Press, 2012), 219–328.

2. Henri Atlan, *The Sparks of Randomness*, vol. 2: *The Atheism of Scripture*, trans. Lenn J. Schramm (Stanford, CA: Stanford University Press, 2013), 346—347 cited in Elliot R. Wolfson, *Giving beyond the Gift: Apophasis and Overcoming Theomania* (New York: Fordham University Press, 2014), xvii.

3. Benjamin Ish-Shalom, *Rav Avraham Itzhak HaCohen Kook: Between Rationalism and Mysticism*, trans. Ora Wiskind-Elper (Albany: State University of New York Press, 1993), 87–88; Bezalel Naor, "Rav Kook and Emmanuel Levinas on the 'Non-Existence' of God," *Orot: A Multidisciplinary Journal of Judaism* 1 (1991): 1–11. See also Tamar Ross, "The Cognitive Value of Religious Truth Statements: Rabbi A. I. Kook and Postmodernism," in *Ḥazon Nahum: Studies in Jewish Law, Thought, and History Presented to R. Norman Lamm on the Occasion of His Seventieth Birthday*, ed. Yaakov Elman and Jeffrey S. Gurock (New York: Yeshiva University Press, 1997), 479–528.

4. Eliezer Schweid, "'Prophetic Mysticism' in Twentieth-Century Jewish Thought," *Modern Judaism* 14 (1994): 167–168.

5. Yehuda Mirsky, "An Intellectual and Spiritual Biography of Rabbi Avraham Yitzhaq Ha-Cohen Kook from 1865–1904" (PhD diss., Harvard University, 2007), 236n55.

6. Ish-Shalom, *Rav Avraham Itzhak HaCohen Kook*, 36. See also Yuval Cherlow, *The Torah of the Land of Israel in Light of the Teaching of Rabbi Abraham Isaac Kook* [in Hebrew] (Ḥaspin, Israel: Yeshivat ha-Golan, 1988), 81–84, 226–227. In part, Cherlow follows the view of Steinsaltz; see note 16.

7. With respect to the view that the pneumatic aspect of *yeḥidah* is unique to the Jews, I presume Kook was influenced by Ḥabad literature. See Elliot R. Wolfson, *Open Secret: Postmessianic Messianism and the Mystical Revision of Menaḥem Mendel Schneerson* (New York: Columbia University Press, 2009), 70, 183–184, 232, 275, 301n1. The affinity between Ḥabad and Kook has been noted by previous scholars. See Cherlow, *The Tzaddiq*, 182–184, and notes 33, 54, and 64.

8. Ish-Shalom cites the passage from Abraham Isaac Kook, *Orot ha-Qodesh*, ed. David Cohen (Jerusalem: Mosad ha-Rav Kook, 1963), 1:135, sec. 118, which parallels Abraham Isaac Kook, *Shemonah Qevaṣim*, 2nd ed. (Jerusalem, 2004), 4:43, 16. Compare *Shemonah Qevaṣim*, 8:11, 432: "The mysteries of Torah are not revealed through the mundane intellect [*ha-sekhel ha-ḥuloni*] but rather through the holy overflow of the holy spirit [*shif'at ha-qodesh shel ruaḥ ha-qodesh*]." Regarding the publication of the *Shemonah Qevaṣim*, which first appeared in 1999, see Avinoam Rosenak, "Who's Afraid of the Hidden Treatises of Rav Kook?" [in Hebrew], *Tarbiz* 69 (2000): 257–291, and the revised English version, "Hidden Diaries and New Discoveries: The Life and Thought of Rabbi A. I. Kook," *Shofar* 25 (2007): 111–147.

9. Ish-Shalom, *Rav Avraham Itzhak HaCohen Kook*, 36–37. See ibid., 195.

10. It must be pointed out, however, that Ish-Shalom challenges the view (proffered, for instance, by Adin Steinsaltz) that Kook was committed to the popularization of Kabbalah (see note 16). Ish-Shalom affirms what might appear to be contradictory viewpoints: on the one hand, Kook extended the purview of Kabbalah to include creative innovations, but, on the other hand, he demonstrated a conservative restraint in transmitting esoteric lore. In many of my publications, I have questioned the reigning distinction between the so-called conservative and innovative Kabbalists. For instance, see Elliot R. Wolfson, "The Anonymous Chapters of the Elderly Master of Secrets: New Evidence for the Early Activity of the Zoharic Circle," *Kabbalah: Journal for the Study of Jewish Mystical Texts* 19 (2009): 159–172.

11. On the influence of Maimonides on Kook, see Itamar Gruenwald, "The Concept of *Teshuvah* in the Teachings of Maimonides and Rav Kook," in *The World of Rav Kook*, 283–304; Lawrence Kaplan, "The Love of God in Maimonides and Rav Kook," *Judaism* 43 (1994): 227–239; Kaplan, "Rav Kook and the Jewish Philosophical Tradition," in *Rabbi Abraham Isaac Kook*, 39–77; Yehuda Mirsky, "Rav Kook and Maimonides: A New Look" [in Hebrew], in *Iggud: Selected Essays in Jewish Studies*, vol. 1, ed. Baruch Schwartz, Abraham Melamed, and Aharon Shemesh (Jerusalem: World Union of Jewish Studies, 2008), 397–405; Uriel Barak, "The Formative Influence of the Description of Prophecy in the Guide on the Perception of 'The Beginning of Redemption' by Rabbi A. I. Kook's Circle" [in Hebrew], *Da'at* 64–66 (2009): 361–415; James A. Diamond, "R. Abraham Isaac Kook and Maimonides: A Contemporary Mystic's Embrace of Medieval Rationalism," in *Encountering the Medieval in Modern Jewish Thought*, ed. James A. Diamond and Aaron W. Hughes (Leiden: Brill, 2012), 101–128, esp. 104–106; Diamond, "A Kabbalistic Reinvention of Maimonides' Legal Code:

R. Abraham Isaac Kook's Commentary on *Sefer Hamada*," *Jewish Studies Internet Journal* 11 (2012): 11–40. On Kook's messianism and secularization, see Jonathan Garb, *The Chosen Will Become Herds: Studies in Twentieth-Century Kabbalah*, trans. Yaffah Berkovits-Murciano (New Haven, CT: Yale University Press, 2009), 23–29. Many have weighed in on the messianic dimension of Kook's religious philosophy. For a recent discussion with reference to previous scholarly analyses, see Cherlow, *The Tzaddiq*, 331–371.

12. Abraham Isaac Kook, *Orot ha-Torah* (Jerusalem: Mosad ha-Rav Kook, 1985), 30.

13. *Shemonah Qevaṣim*, 2:188, 300.

14. Ibid., 3:259, 437. The passage appears as well in Abraham Isaac Kook, *Hadarav: Peraqim Ishiyyim*, ed. Ron Sarid (Mevaseret Tsiyon, Israel: Ra'ot, 1998), 95.

15. Kook, *Hadarav*, 96.

16. This is the position adopted by Adin Steinsaltz, "Problematics in Orot ha-Qodesh," *Ha-Re'ayah: Qoveṣ Ma'amarim*, ed. Isaac Raphael (Jerusalem: Mosad ha-Rav Kook, 1966), 103, cited by Ish-Shalom, *Rav Avraham Itzhak HaCohen Kook*, 193. Steinsaltz compares the method of Kook to that of Judah Loewe, the Maharal of Prague, who wrote Kabbalah in a way that was not overtly Kabbalistic. Ish-Shalom opposes Steinsaltz's explanation because it "is at odds with Rav Kook's own words and does not correspond with the basic assumptions underlying his teaching." Ish-Shalom (194) cites in support of his own view several passages from Kook's oeuvre where he upholds the more traditional sense of esotericism and the need not to expose the secrets to the masses or to translate those secrets in a way that is not faithful to their arcane nature. On the question of the term "popularization" to characterize Kook's writings, see Ish-Shalom, *Rav Avraham Itzhak HaCohen Kook*, 316n5.

17. *Shemonah Qevaṣim*, 2:182, 299.

18. Ibid., 1:253, 82–83.

19. Ibid., 8:226, 472.

20. Ibid., 2:192, 301.

21. Ibid., 1:860, 237. Compare ibid., 8:246, 474: "The overflow of the holy spirit is unique to Israel, and it is greatly elevated in its gradation, and it is sui generis in comparison to all the means of the overflow of the holy spirit merited by everyone else in the world in accord with their actions. The Jewish overflow issues from the inwardness of the Torah."

22. Abraham Isaac Kook, *Li-Nevukhei ha-Dor* (Jerusalem, 2009), 73–74. See note 31.

23. Ibid., 189–191.

24. *Shemonah Qevaṣim*, 7:202, 391–392. Compare Abraham Isaac Kook, *Eder ha-Yeqar* (Jerusalem: Mosad ha-Rav Kook, 1985), 38. On the attribution of prophecy uniquely to the Jews, and the further assumption that every Jew, as a consequence, is a perfect manifestation of the divine, see *Shemonah Qevaṣim*, 3:436, 459.

25. *Shemonah Qevaṣim*, 3:269, 439. Compare ibid., 3:365, 463: "The universal soul [*ha-neshamah ha-kelalit*] of the Assembly of Israel does not dwell in the individual person [*ba-ish ha-peraṭi*] except in the land of Israel. Immediately when a person [*adam*] comes to the land of Israel, his individual soul [*nishmato ha-peraṭit*] is extinguished [*mitbaṭṭelet*] because of the great light of the universal soul that enters into him." And ibid., 7:148, 370: "The holy wisdom shines only in the land of Israel. Whatever is envisaged outside the land is naught but the product of the understanding and its branches. . . . By means of the deep vision to see

the land of Israel, some of the illumination from the splendor of the wisdom of the land of Israel glows, and it illumines the branching out of the understanding, which takes shape also outside the land."

26. Ibid., 2:289, 328.

27. Ibid., 3:347, 459.

28. Kook, *Li-Nevukhei ha-Dor*, 195; *Shemonah Qevaṣim*, 7:28, 301.

29. Kook, *Li-Nevukhei ha-Dor*, 193. See ibid., 197, where Kook states emphatically that Christians and Muslims derive their principles from the Torah. For an extended discussion of universalism and particularism in light of Kook's pantheistic tendencies, see Kahan, "Divine Faith," 89–93.

30. *Shemonah Qevaṣim*, 7:111, 351.

31. Kook, *Li-Nevukhei ha-Dor*, 198. In that context, Kook accepts that the leaders of other religions can merit the holy spirit consequent to their actions. In support of this view, he cites the dictum transmitted in the name of R. Meir in Babylonian Talmud, Bava Qama, 38a, that "even a gentile who is engaged in Torah is like the high priest." Even so, a careful scrutiny of the whole passage indicates clearly that compared to Israel the non-Jews are accorded an inferior status.

32. *Shemonah Qevaṣim*, 6:257, 273. Compare ibid., 7:138, 365.

33. Kook's view resembles the opinion expressed by Shneur Zalman of Liadi, *Liqquṭei Amarim: Tanya* (Brooklyn, NY: Kehot, 2010), pt. 1, ch. 22, 28a: "the essence and the root of idolatry is that something is considered to be a thing in itself, separate from the holiness of God, but it is not denying God entirely." The heresy (*kefirah*) connected with denying God's "true unity" involves treating entities as ontologically distinct, since all things are nullified in their autonomy vis-à-vis the one true reality of the infinite. According to Shneur Zalman, this is the intent of the older rabbinic juxtaposition of idolatry and haughtiness. The passage in *Tanya* seems to be echoed in Kook, *Li-Nevukhei ha-Dor*, 72.

34. *Shemonah Qevaṣim*, 1:273, 87.

35. Abraham Isaac Kook, *Ein Ayah al Aggadot Ḥazal she-be-Ein Ya'aqov: Berakhot*, vol. 2 (Jerusalem: Makhon al shem ha-Rav Ṣevi Yehudah Quq, 2007), 53, sec. 18.

36. Abraham Isaac Kook, *Orot ha-Emunah*, ed. Moshe Gurvitz (Jerusalem, 1985), 97.

37. Kook, *Li-Nevukhei ha-Dor*, 33–34, and consider the utopian hope for universal brotherhood passionately expressed on p. 72. Kook affirms the necessity to maintain multiple national identities but at the same time argues for the need to cultivate mutual love and cooperation, which is based on the assumption that all people will arrive at the knowledge of the one God. Nevertheless, the chosen people exclusively propagate this mutual knowledge. For a study that reflects the typical way this thorny topic has been broached by Jewish studies scholars, see Yoel Ben-Nun, "Nationalism, Humanity, and *Kenesset Yisrael*," in *The World of Rav Kook*, 207–254.

38. Abraham Isaac Kook, *Midbar Shur* (Jerusalem: Makhon al shem ha-Rav Ṣevi Yehudah Quq, 1999), 264. For the rabbinic dictum, see Babylonian Talmud, Yevamot 61a, and see the comments in Elliot R. Wolfson, *Venturing Beyond: Law and Morality in Kabbalistic Mysticism* (Oxford: Oxford University Press, 2006), 42n107. On the privileging of the Jew as the bearer of human perfection, see Kook, *Midbar Shur*, 125–126, 240. Kook's interpretation is close to that of the Maharal. See Wolfson, *Venturing Beyond*, 116–120.

39. *Shemonah Qevaṣim*, 2:302, 332. The passage is mentioned and partially translated by Yehuda Mirsky, *Rav Kook: Mystic in a Time of Revolution* (New Haven, CT: Yale University Press, 2014), 108, but he does not pay attention to the implicit chauvinism in Kook's utopian vision. In fact, he turns the matter on its head by arguing that it was precisely Kook's "appreciation for the spiritual diversity of nations that required him to maintain a belief in Israel's distinctiveness." Proverbially speaking, the cart has been placed before the horse: it is Kook's belief in Israel's distinctiveness that required him to acknowledge the spiritual diversity of the nations, a diversity that is dissolved in the eschatological recognition of the truth of the God of Israel. Compare Abraham Isaac Kook, *Arpelei Ṭohar* (Jerusalem: Makhon al shem ha-Rav Ṣevi Yehudah Quq, 1983), 62–63. In that passage, Kook observes that by explaining the Torah of Moses, the messiah will reveal in the world the vision of how all the nations and ethnicities suck the sap of their spiritual lives from the one elemental source of Israel. At the same time, he concedes that the content of that spiritual nourishment will be received differently by each nation in accord with its distinctive climatology.

40. For a different approach, see Mirsky, *Rav Kook*, 25–26, 106–109. I concur that Kook sought to strike a balance between Jewish particularism and universal ethics, but I am less sanguine that he succeeded. Mirsky does note that, for Kook, Israel is the one nation in the truest sense and it is thus ontologically different from all the other nations. Nevertheless, he attenuates this ethnocentrism by focusing on passages that would buttress the ideal of an "epistemological humility" that creates a space for an ethics predicated on leveling out the stark difference between Israel and the other nations. In my judgment, this is an apologetic reading that resolves an irresolvable contradiction in Kook. Along similar lines, see Benjamin Ish-Shalom, "Tolerance and Its Theoretical Basis in the Teaching of Rav Kook," in *Rabbi Abraham Isaac Kook*, 178–204, and Yoel Bin-Nun, "Nationalism,'" 207–254.

41. On the unsystematic character of Kook's thought, see Marvin Fox, "Rav Kook: Neither Philosopher nor Kabbalist," in *Rabbi Abraham Isaac Kook*, 78–80. For a more elaborate analysis of the question of system in Kook, see Shalom Rosenberg, "Introduction to the Thought of Rav Kook," in *The World of Rav Kook*, 16–127.

42. I have discussed this hermeneutic in many studies. For one of the more concise and accessible presentations, see Elliot R. Wolfson, "Teaching Jewish Mysticism: Concealing the Concealment and Disclosure of Secrets," in *Teaching Mysticism*, ed. William B. Parsons (Oxford: Oxford University Press, 2011), 103–117.

43. Job 28:11.

44. *Shemonah Qevaṣim*, 6:81, 214.

45. Ibid., 5:237, 166.

46. Elliot R. Wolfson, *Language, Eros, Being: Kabbalistic Hermeneutics and Poetic Imagination* (New York: Fordham University Press, 2005), 11–12, and see references to other scholars cited on p. 407n86.

47. *Paramārtha-satya* is the truth of the universal emptiness, codependence, and impermanence of all things that lies beneath empirical phenomena and is beyond verbal expression and conceptual discrimination, whereas *saṃvṛti-satya* relates to the ways that we routinely experience, classify, and describe sentient reality as a patchwork of reified and permanent substances. Many have written on this well-known doctrine. For some representative

examples, see Guy Newland, *The Two Truths in the Mādhyamika Philosophy of the Ge-luk-ba Order of Tibetan Buddhism* (Ithaca, NY: Snow Lion Publications, 1992), and *Appearance and Reality: The Two Truths in the Four Buddhist Tenet Systems* (Ithaca, NY: Snow Lion Publications, 1999); Dan Lusthaus, "The Two Truths (*Saṃvṛti-satya* and *Paramārtha-satya*) in Early Yogācāra," *Journal of Buddhist Studies* 7 (2010): 101–152. Let me note, finally, that despite the affinity I have detected between Kook's epistemology and the Buddhist doctrine of two truths, he was critical of the pagan aspect of Buddhism, especially related to its promotion of the idea of finding tranquility in "nothingness and absolute negation." See the text cited in *When God Becomes History: Historical Essays of Rabbi Abraham Isaac Hakohen Kook*, trans. Bezalel Naor (Spring Valley, NY: Orot, 2003), 116–117, and compare Jerome Gellman, "Judaism and Buddhism: A Jewish Approach to a Godless Religion," in *Jewish Theology and World Religions*, ed. Alon Goshen-Gottstein and Eugene Korn (Oxford: Littman Library of Jewish Civilization, 2012), 299–316.

48. *Shemonah Qevaṣim*, 8:191, 458. For a different translation of this passage and analysis, see Ish-Shalom, *Rav Avraham Itzhak HaCohen Kook*, 210–211. See also Mirsky, *Rav Kook*, 102–103. On the dialectic of speech and silence applied to the whole of existence, see *Shemonah Qevaṣim*, 8:230, 473–474.

49. *Shemonah Qevaṣim*, 1:252, 82.

50. Ibid., 3:280, 442.

51. Ibid., 3:252, 435.

52. Ibid., 1:632, 173.

53. Ibid., 1:775, 213.

54. Ibid., 1:737, 203. I respectfully take issue with the assertion of Ish-Shalom, *Rav Avraham Itzhak HaCohen Kook*, 33, that Kook's approach is not "radically phenomenological," inasmuch as he "believed fully in the existence of absolute reality. But in his opinion, the exact image, the way of being of this reality is not at the moment given to scientific understanding and, unavoidably must be approached by means of conjecture and imagination." I would counter that even for Kook this so-called "absolute reality" is not phenomenally accessible except through a disclosure of the divine, *hofaʿah ha-elohit* (*Shemonah Qevaṣim*, 4:44, 16), which is at the same time concealment, since the light of infinity can be revealed only through its occlusion. In this matter, which most scholars have called "acosmism" but what I have called "apophatic embodiment," there is proximity between Kook and older Kabbalistic sources, and especially the cosmological orientation of Ḥabad. See note 7.

55. *Shemonah Qevaṣim*, 1:225, 75. Compare ibid., 7:99, 344–346.

56. Ibid., 5:175, 133–134.

57. Ibid., 3:317, 451.

58. Ibid., 1:391, 114.

59. Ibid., 1:861, 237.

60. Ibid., 1:393, 114–115.

61. Ibid., 5:234, 183. For a recent examination of the Kabbalistic motif of *ṣimṣum* in Kook's writings, see Lilach Bar-Bettelheim, "The Concept of Zimzum in the Kabbalah of the Early Twentieth Century" [in Hebrew] (PhD diss., Ben Gurion University, 2012), 22–96.

62. On the relationship of the mystical and the social in Kook, see Cherlow, *The Tzaddiq*, 139–192. The author's discussion of mysticism and ethics (145–149) suffers from an inability to interrogate the deontological implications of identifying Israel as the true human. See Wolfson, *Venturing Beyond*, 17–128. The perspective of Kook is discussed there briefly on pp. 121–124.

63. *Shemonah Qevaṣim*, 1:631, 173.

64. Ibid., 3:215, 426. Kook's description of faith as the suprarational or metacognitive state bears a strong resemblance to the apophaticism of Ḥabad, which is, in turn, based on much older Kabbalistic sources. See Wolfson, *Open Secret*, 68–70.

65. *Shemonah Qevaṣim*, 3:220, 427.

66. Ibid., 3:221, 427.

67. Ibid., 1:64, 17.

68. Kook, *Orot ha-Qodesh*, 1:60, sec. 45.

69. *Shemonah Qevaṣim*, 1:556, 153.

70. Ibid., 1:614, p. 168. Compare ibid., 3:232, 430, and the analysis in Kahan, "Divine Faith," 48–50.

71. *Shemonah Qevaṣim*, 2:179, 298. Compare Kook, *Arpelei Ṭohar*, 64.

72. *Shemonah Qevaṣim*, 7:11, 293.

73. Ibid., 1:363, 107.

74. Ibid., 2:97, 279.

75. Ibid., 1:312, 96. On the breaking of the will through humility, see also ibid., 1:191, 66–67. On the predisposition of the Jewish soul to be annihilated in the light of the supernal splendor, see Kook, *Midbar Shur*, 302.

76. *Shemonah Qevaṣim*, 3:214, 425.

77. The material here is a reworking of my discussion in Wolfson, *Venturing Beyond*, 284–285.

78. *Shemonah Qevaṣim*, 8:259, 481. Sounding a similar note, in another passage, ibid., 2:255, 316, Kook contrasts the "rational conjunction" (*ha-devequt ha-sikhlit*) with God, which is experienced as pure joy without any admixture of sadness or bitterness, and the imaginative faculty, which displays both elation and despair. However, the two are unified in one point, which is encoded in the name Shaddai—the first letter *shin* stands for the intellect (*sekhel*), the second letter *dalet* for the imagination (*dimyon*), and the third letter *yod* for the point (*nequddah*) that connects them. On the inconsistent views expressed by Kook with respect to the imagination vis-à-vis the intellect, see Kaplan, "Rav Kook," 74n74; Ish-Shalom, *Rav Avraham Itzhak HaCohen Kook*, 32–34, 48–53, 57–58.

79. *Shemonah Qevaṣim*, 3:53, 380.

80. Ibid., 3:222, 427.

81. For discussion of the suffering of the righteous from a different perspective, see Kook, *Orot ha-Qodesh*, 4:462–463. In that context, Kook writes of the "suffering of conjunction" (*ṣa'ar ha-devequt*), that is, the righteous man apprehends the light in the material things from which he seeks to be released. Alternatively, the righteous man feels pain when he considers that he has not totally overcome his physical desires even though he experiences no pleasure or rest in the world. The distress that the righteous man feels in his bodily

limbs is connected, in turn, to the suffering of the divine presence (ṣaʻar ha-shekhinah). On the suffering that the love of God causes the righteous, see ibid., 395–396, and *Shemonah Qevaṣim*, 1:123–124.

82. *Shemonah Qevaṣim*, 2:182, 299. On the coincidence of opposites as it pertains to ritual observance and its transcendence in Kook, see Kahan, "Divine Faith," 70–73.

83. *Shemonah Qevaṣim*, 1:321, 98–99. See Benjamin Ish-Shalom, "Religion, Repentance, and Personal Freedom," in *The World of Rav Kook*, 373–419. For a recent discussion on shame, suffering, and sinfulness in Kook's thought, analyzed particularly from a psychoanalytic viewpoint regarding the depressive anxiety that inflicts the righteous soul, see Jonathan Garb, "Shame as an Existential Emotion in Modern Kabbalah," *Jewish Social Studies* 21 (2015): 108–110.

84. *Shemonah Qevaṣim*, 1:410, 118. See also ibid., 1:639, 175. On the question of the implicit antinomian aspects of Kook's thought, see Avinoam Rosenak, "Who's Afraid of Rav Kook's Hidden Treatises?" [in Hebrew] *Tarbiz* 69 (2000): 264–266; Jonathan Garb, "Prophecy, Halakhah, and Antinomianism According to the *Shemonah Qevaṣim* of R. Abraham Isaac Kook," in *Shefa Ṭal*, 267–277.

85. Wolfson, *Venturing Beyond*, 212, and references to Scholem and Pachter cited in note 92, and see, more recently, Sandra Valabregue-Perry, *Concealed and Revealed: "Ein Sof" in Theosophic Kabbalah* [in Hebrew] (Los Angeles: Cherub Press, 2010), 78–83, and Lawrence Kaplan, "Faith, Rebellion, and Heresy in the Writings of Rabbi Azriel of Gerona," in *Faith: Jewish Perspectives*, ed. Avi Sagi and Dov Schwartz (Boston: Academic Studies Press, 2013), 278–302. On faith and heresy in Kook, see also Kahan, "Divine Faith," 27–28, 51–52, 79–80.

86. *Shemonah Qevaṣim*, 2:20, 284. I previously translated and discussed this passage in *Venturing Beyond*, 285. See also Naor, "Rav Kook," 4–5, and Pachter, "The Kabbalistic Foundation," 74–75.

87. *Shemonah Qevaṣim*, 1:107, 31.

88. Ibid., 1:317, 97.

89. The gloss appears in the parallel to this passage in Abraham Isaac Kook, *Orot* (Jerusalem: Mosad ha-Rav Kook, 1993), 128, but it is curiously missing in the version in the *Shemonah Qevaṣim*.

90. *Shemonah Qevaṣim*, 1:317, 98.

91. The indebtedness to Maimonides for purifying the monotheism of Judaism of false representations based on a corporeal conception of the deity advanced by the imagination is explicitly acknowledged in Abraham Isaac Kook, *Ein Ayah al Aggadot Ḥazal she-be-Ein Yaʻaqov: Berakhot*, vol. 1 (Jerusalem: Makhon al shem ha-Rav Ṣevi Yehudah Quq, 1995), 61, sec. 152. See also Abraham Isaac Kook, *Ma'amerei ha-Re'ayah* (Jerusalem, 1984), 106. This text and the one mentioned in note 93 are partially cited by Naor, "Rav Kook," 3–4. An alternative approach to the atheism in Kook and Levinas is offered by Michael Fagenblat, *A Covenant of Creatures: Levinas's Philosophy of Judaism* (Stanford, CA: Stanford University Press, 2010), 142. Fagenblat argues that for Kook, the atheistic critique does not result in a permanent suspension of theology but it is rather a temporary purging of faith in order to raise it to a superior level of mystical knowledge, whereas, for Levinas, the metaphysical atheism is not a temporary denial but a "perennial religious imperative aimed at avoiding

the idolatry of all concepts of God," which would include Kook's own appeal to the "true light of godliness." Levinas is thus compared to Yeshayahu Leibowitz, who radicalized Maimonidean negative theology in order to contest belief as such and not only false beliefs. My own reading of Kook narrows the gap somewhat, since I think he, too, advocated for a more permanent atheistic cleansing of theism, albeit one whose full realization is deferred to a messianic future. For discussion of the atheistic elements in Levinas, see Wolfson, *Giving beyond the Gift*, 139–140. On atheism in Kook's mystical thinking, see Kahan, "Divine Faith," 9–10.

92. Kook, *Orot*, 124–125. All translations of this essay are my own, but the reader can find a complete English translation in *Abraham Isaac Kook: The Lights of Penitence, the Moral Principles, Lights of Holiness, Essays, Letters, and Poems*, translation and introduction by Ben Zion Bokser, preface by Jacob Agus and Rivka Schatz (New York: Paulist Press, 1978), 261–269.

93. Kook, *Orot*, 126.

94. Kook, *Li-Nevukhei ha-Dor*, 194. Compare *Shemonah Qevaṣim*, 7:103, 347; 7:117, 354.

95. Kook, *Ein Ayah al Aggadot Ḥazal she-be-Ein Ya'aqov: Berakhot*, vol. 2, 54, sec. 18.

96. Kook, *Orot*, 126–127.

97. Abraham Isaac Kook, *Iggerot ha-Re'ayah*, vol. 1 (Jerusalem: Mosad ha-Rav Kook, 1985), #44, 48. The passage is cited by Rosenberg, "Introduction," 46–47.

98. Wolfson, *Giving beyond the Gift*, xvi–xxii, 73–74, 263n21, 266–267n38.

99. Kook, *Iggerot ha-Re'ayah*, vol. 1, #44, 50. Needless to say, there are many passages where Kook adopts a decidedly critical view of atheism. See Rosenberg, "Introduction," 98–107.

100. Kook, *Ma'amerei ha-Re'ayah*, 108. On this point, I take issue with the conclusion reached by Naor, "Rav Kook," 5: "To say that God is beyond belief and disbelief, which is another way of saying, beyond existence and non-existence, is a far cry from Maimonides' 'absolute existence.' Maimonides had preserved 'existence' as meaningful God-talk by 'upping the ante' from lower-case existence to upper-case Existence. Rav Kook has abdicated 'existence' altogether as a signifier for God." At this point, Naor adds a comment in brackets to the effect that the difference between uppercase Existence and the positing of a reality that is beyond existence and nonexistence may be "purely semantic" and hence the philosophical and Kabbalistic traditions "dovetail neatly." My own reading moves in this direction. See Wolfson, *Giving beyond the Gift*, 78, 171–174. Of course, I acknowledge that others have read the Kabbalistic view on *Ein Sof* as at odds with the philosophical position of Maimonides (see the material cited by Naor, "Rav Kook," 9–10n18), but what seems beyond contention is the fact that Kook interpreted Maimonides through this prism. The necessary of existence is the technical term that marks the being that is beyond being and nonbeing, the existence that is beyond existence and nonexistence, the presence that is neither present nor nonpresent.

101. As Naor, "Rav Kook," 4, notes, Zevi Yehudah Kook cited (*Orot*, 182) as a source for the passage in *Orot* (see note 93) a comment in the *Sod ha-Ṣimṣum* that was included in the *Liqquṭei ha-GRA* and published at the end of the *Be'ur ha-GRA le-Sifra di-Ṣeni'uta*, edited and with an introduction by Bezalel Naor (Jerusalem, 1998), 138, which emphasizes that it

is forbidden to designate *Ein Sof* as the "necessary of existence" (*ḥovat ha-meṣi'ut*) or to apply to it or to Keter the word *yesh*, which denotes the sense of being; indeed, one cannot contemplate *Ein Sof* at all or even to call it by that name. For earlier Kabbalistic texts that affirm a similar view, see reference in note 102.

102. Elliot R. Wolfson, "Nihilating Nonground and the Temporal Sway of Becoming," *Angelaki: Journal of the Theoretical Humanities* 17 (2012): 31–45, esp. 36–39. I have taken the liberty to repeat some of my own language.

103. See the discussion of prayer and pantheism in Kook's writings in Kahan, "Divine Faith," 54–62.

104. Kook, *Li-Nevukhei ha-Dor*, 73.

SEVEN

Two Types of Negative Theology; Or, What Does Negative Theology Negate?

SHIRA WOLOSKY

Negative theology, like most religious terms and structures, is highly syncretist. It emerges in intersecting, overlapping ways from discourse to discourse and tradition to tradition. Therefore to speak of "types" of negative theology is an unstable project. No lines are impermeable. Especially today, when negative theology has reentered contemporary theology, philosophy, and theory, this instability is potent. Indeed, it is integral to the postmodern project as it deconstructs the metaphysical histories of philosophy. Negative theology has reemerged as a core site of postmodern critique of metaphysics, which Nietzsche explosively launched. Its references to a "beyond Being" promise a break in ontology that both arises within traditions of philosophical theology and exceeds them. To a large extent, what is taking place is a recasting of the ontological tradition from counterontological standpoints. The beyond Being that surfaces in Platonist discourses comes to be seen as a nonontology embedded within the tradition itself, thus escaping or disrupting its own metaphysical claims. Contemporary theory has thereby come to intersect with ancient tradition. The arcane becomes urgent.

To say that Emmanuel Levinas is a major figure in this recasting of ontology is to speak somewhat in reverse. The reinterpretation of (negative) ontology often points back to him, as Levinasian readings of Western philosophy that discover within it a counterontology that the tradition itself, at least as traditionally read by someone like Etienne Gilson, denied and would be pressed to recognize. Comparisons between Levinas and Platonism, for example, often already assume a Levinasian approach to Plato and Plotinus, and in this sense can be circular. The syncretist impulse is today at high intensity. This is fair enough. But what threatens to be dulled is the edge of metaphysical critique itself, and what is at stake in it. Critique is reabsorbed inside the tradition in ways that undermine its very critical project. If there never was a proper ontology, what is all the criticism about?

Yet Levinas pursues a critique that cannot be reabsorbed into ontological tradition so readily. His break is severe. Even the instances where he uncovers openings within ontology itself, as he does notably with Plato and Descartes, already incur a Levinasian element. These instances should not obscure the critical difference Levinas launches against the tradition, even if in doing so he opens points of intersection between his own project and traditional ones via ruptures he discloses within familiar philosophies. Intersection does not equal convergence.

Such contiguous but nonmerging tendencies arise in different trends of negative theology, which despite overlapping elements, pursue distinct trajectories. With a risk of schematism, their differences can be sketched out. The first, traditional negative theology is ontological; the second, Levinasian negative theology, is ethical.[1] This is one fundamental meaning in his declaring ethics to be first philosophy. In general, Levinas marks a swerve in philosophical discourse from the ontological and epistemological to the ethical. Ontology and epistemology always also had ethical implications, but these were exactly that, secondary implications. Levinas's version of ethics as first philosophy initiates a profound shift, very much felt in Levinasian negative theology and fundamental to its difference from traditional forms. This difference is registered most distinctively in the place of language in each approach. For while both invoke notions of the ineffable—the beyond-language—this is a vital case where similar, overlapping terms do not signal identical meanings. Yet this linguistic problematic is inextricable from ontological critique, the terms in which most negative theological discourses are put, and therefore this will be the topic of this essay.

What do negative theologies negate? Negation is introduced in (non)reference to the beyond Being as it surpasses the Being and Becoming of traditional Platonist schema. In terms of logic, this is already paradoxical, negating what is designated, and is hence often described as a performative contradiction, thinking and speaking about what you cannot think and speak about. In the field of ontology, questions focus on the negative relation between the ultimate beyond and mere being as it enters the world of time and change and multiplicity. But as Levinas reveals, from an ethical point of view what is at issue is how this division ultimately negates the world itself, which, as multiple, is regarded as ontologically and above all axiologically inferior. Being in Plato and its radicalization into beyond Being in Neoplatonism identified ultimate reality as absolute unity and eternity. Ethical negative theology, however, works the opposite way. The world of experience—which is necessarily temporal and material, changing and multiple—is affirmed. As in all negative theology, negation refers to what is beyond, but here in ways that return attention to this multiple world, defining its proper limits as against what remains beyond it. These emerge as ethical terms. The beyond-being, in Levinas's terms, the infinite, marks those limits. This is at once admonitory and regulatory. As regulatory, negation enters relationships as separation and difference across connection and likeness, toward upholding and unfolding creative orders. As admonitory, negation warns against unlimited claims that would override boundaries and the orders they keep. Levinas's most radical and impelling insight is that unity, so long sought philosophically as well as politically elevated as ideal, is instead a force of violent erasure; whereas multiplicity, so long disdained as chaotic, incoherent, and violent, is a principle and practice of ethics.

In ethical negative theology, beings are both separated and linked to each other by a sense of transcendence, expressed as negation, that it is forbidden to claim or transgress. Ontological negative theology negates the world of multiplicity, which it hopes to transcend into a unity beyond all time and difference. Ethical negative theology affirms the world of multiplicity, in relation to a transcendence that positively marks its limits and sustains its multiplicity. In this model, Levinas opens a postmodernity that is not nostalgic for lost metaphysical references, seen in a despair of meaning and values in what Nietzsche diagnosed as nihilism, and which has emerged in problems of radical relativism. He points to an ethical postmodernism regulated by normative difference.

Transcendence of What?

Schematically, the ontological tradition of negative theology reproduces the schema of ontology itself. Needless to say, this begins with Plato. Plato is a continuous topic throughout Levinas, where he appears in a range of guises. There is more than one Plato in Levinas, but then again there is more than one Plato in Plato.[2] Most crucially, for Levinas, Plato ruptures his own ontology in the key passage in *Republic* book VI 509 that is taken to found negative theology, where the Good is described as "beyond Being." This is a breach in the core Platonic system, so vividly illustrated in the allegory of the cave that immediately follows in book VII: the divisions into Being and Becoming, Idea and shadow, truth and image. But the "Good beyond Being" opens a gap in this systemization, hierarchy, regimentation of Being, as a breach within the Western ontological tradition itself. Levinas likewise repeatedly cites Descartes's Third Meditation, as proposing an infinity that exceeds any finite thought, rupturing the cogito in a breakout of subjectivity and consciousness.

There has been much discussion of Levinas's "return to Platonism," a phrase he himself uses at the end of an abstract for the thesis that became *Totality and Infinity*.[3] This return mainly focuses through the beyond Being, as Levinas himself develops. But Levinas is deeply critical of major trends in Platonism as it evolved through the tradition, which he sees, as Nietzsche does, as totalistic and ultimately betraying the conditions of the world we experience. "The ideal of Socratic truth rests on the essential self-sufficiency of the same, its identification in ipseity, its egoism. Philosophy is an egology."⁴ Elsewhere Levinas writes: "The Eleatic notion of being dominates Plato's philosophy, where multiplicity was subordinated to the one. Plato's Republic [is] one where the world imitates Ideas, without time, with an ideal of fusion."⁵ In Plato himself, the tendency of Greek metaphysics to seek "the return to and the fusion with Unity" is offset by Plato's "Good as separate from the totality of essences," which catches sight "of a structure such that the totality could admit of a beyond."⁶ Platonist tradition, however, especially as developed by Plotinus, reabsorbs all into the One. "Return[ing] to Parmenides," it represents "the apparition of the essence from the One by emanation and by descent."⁷ Emanation posits a continuity from ontological level to level that can be retraced upward, ultimately resolving into a unity that both founds and also ultimately reclaims all differentiation from it. But this birth of the many from the one is, Levinas insists and protests, seen as a fall. In the structure of emanation, "multiplicity seemed to be united in a totality." Intellect, the first emanation, encompasses all the Forms in a unified way, as he writes elsewhere, containing the Platonic Ideas but as these are "grasped in their multiplicity as completed."⁸ But multiplicity then is mere inexplicable "appearance," "taken to be the ontological fallenness of beings mutually limiting one another in their proximity." This has been the thinking of philosophy "since Parmenides across Plotinus."⁹

It is Plotinus who took up the challenge of Plato's Good beyond Being much more than Plato did himself. But Plotinus identified this beyond Being with the One as a "unity and repose, untroubled by any relation of multiplicity," as Levinas puts it in his mini-history of ontology in "Philosophy and Transcendence."¹⁰ The "multiplicity of ideas" are "gathered together" in "synthesis . . . in which temporal dispersion passes for a privation of intelligibility."¹¹ Unity remains the governing principle and also value. Multiplicity, as it emerges through the many levels of increasing distance from the One, marks attenuated ontological status. "Intellection" at the highest is "not separated from the one absolutely by that multiplicity," thus it retains the highest value in "a nostalgia for the One, homesickness."¹² The structure as a whole points, as Augustine wrote in the *Confessions*, upward and inward, back toward unity and away from the multiplicity that, as Levinas writes in *Entre Nous*, "disperses the essence of being."¹³ Such dispersion is seen as deprivation, privation, degradation—"a state of deprivation compared to the unity of the One."¹⁴ Philosophy, Levinas reiterates throughout these discussions, has "preserved the Neoplatonic schema" of "return and union, the identity of the identical."¹⁵ This extends into philosophies of consciousness such as Descartes, and then into phenomenology as well, which, "despite all its variations, has preserved the Neoplatonic framework [which mark] the return of absolute thought to itself."¹⁶ Again, as Nietzsche more or less asserted, Levinas sums up: all Western philosophy is Platonism.¹⁷

There is an irony of transcendence here. The beyond-being of Plotinus in fact sacrifices rather than constructs transcendence. For in its continuities of return, it idealizes the breach, or rather closes the breach of transcendence—"renounce[es] the transcendence of the One, [through] participation in the model of the unity of the One."[18] Levinas opposes to this ironic transcendence, which in fact overcomes transcendence into identity and union—"Transcendence toward the one with which union is possible"—a separation that is genuine, stark, and foundationally unbridgeable.[19] This is a "separation so complete that the separated being maintains itself in existence all by itself, without participating in the Being from which it is separated"; a condition Levinas dares to call "atheism," although he adds that the self is "eventually capable of adhering to it by belief."[20] Even as an initial position, such separation is what "alone makes possible the relation denoted by this idea of infinity," as a nontotalistic otherness never incorporated into the self (or vice versa)—a "relation between the same and the other [that] does not undo the separation attested by transcendence."[21] Where classical ontology founds existence on continuous participation, Levinas's ethics insists on rupture, discontinuity, difference.

Transcendental Negation

Levinas's rejection of the unitive alters not only the fundamental structure of traditional ontology, but also the structure and direction of traditional negative theology. Ontological negative theology is, like ontological positive theology, fundamentally hierarchical, as Dionysius's move from *Ecclesiastical Hierarchies* and the *Divine Names* to the *Mystical Theology* suggests. Just as cataphatic, positive theology marks the ladder of being in a series of ontological steps in procession from the One into world, so apophatic negative theology follows this ladder of gradations through the paths of return.[22] The way up, as the saying goes, is the way down, where positive theology in fact is the way down, in imagery of emanation or procession; while negative theology is the way of ascent, up through degrees of being toward and into transcendence.

The terms of negativity thus re-mark the rungs of the ontological ladder. Each step of ascent involves forms of negation that abstract, deny, and strip away multiplicity and materiality, culminating in the paradox that the ultimate, as beyond being, is affirmed through negation.[23] The ontological status of this negation is profoundly ambiguous. Is it nonbeing, or is it a form of ultimate being, a *"superesse"* as Derrida argues?[24] In either case, what is the status of the world of multiplicity, as defined against the One? As Plotinus insists, it is above all unity that distinguishes and identifies this ultimate (non)being:[25] He declares: "It is in virtue of unity that beings are beings. What could exist at all except as one thing? Deprived of unity, a thing ceases to be what it is called: could not exist without an inherent unity; break them apart and their very being is altered in the measure of the breach of unity" (*Enneads* VI.9.1). For Plotinus, unity establishes being. Only in terms of unity can anything be said to be truly real. As Plato foundationally asked, what would something be if it were not one? It would then be other than itself, not itself. Different from itself it could not be known, could not be eternal, could not be Being.

It is in the name of such unity that the One is expressed as negative. It exists beyond specific categories of being, categories that are negated to mark its superiority and absolute status. Compared to the world, the One is then nothing. But this negation's ontological superiority entails an axiological demotion of the multiplicity it transcends, reversing the sense of nothingness that, in terms of value, transfers to the world. The One is ultimate value, and it is the world that, compared to it, as multiple and material, is temporal and is nothing. This gives rise to a kind of reverse negativity. The One is negated as beyond difference, but this ultimately negates difference itself, leaving the One as true being against what is other to it as multiple.[26] A. H. Armstrong speaks of a "negative theology of positive transcendence," in which the One is "beyond being only because its reality cannot be adequately expressed in terms of the realities we know." Although it transcends being, "it must be an ousia. As first cause it must be a substance . . . more real than any being, better than any good." But this ultimacy of the real executes a reverse negativity. In that the "state of perfection is called state of nothing in being a state of totality," it inversely reduces what is not totality to what is nothing relative to it.[27]

Nothing here, in regard to the One, signals ultimate being. Already in Plato, the Good beyond Being (never defined further by Plato himself) has aspects not of a "non-being but a hyper-being or second-order being."[28] Beyond our intelligence, surpassing even the being of Forms, the One is a kind of double negation as "non-non-existence," which, however, is not nothingness. Writes J.-M. Narbonne: "The 'existential' status of the first Neoplatonic principle, curiously placed above being" at times seems to be "nothing," and yet is a "surplus of being, an over-being *sur être*."[29]

Is the One being, or is it not? The answer is: the One ultimately is, but is as not compared to everything else. Yet this also means that everything else compared to it is as not. The One remains the summit of what Armstrong calls the two world system: a system in which the upper world consists in "all that is real," while the lower is that of "contingent multiplicities."[30] Its absolute superiority to multiplicity is designated as nothing, meaning is like nothing beneath it. But in this sense, it is not the One that is negative, but the world of multiplicity that is. What lacks true reality is the world of phenomena. It is the world of phenomena compared to the higher world that is in fact characterized by or as relative nothingness.

Levinas's is not a two world system. In turning from the unitive to the multiple and plural as the realm of ethical value, Levinas abandons the architecture that distinguishes between the pairs Being and Becoming, intelligible and sensible, real and apparent, both ontologically and axiologically. He abandons the hierarchy that measures value through distance from the One, investing instead in the relationality among multiplicities in the world, all distinct from each other and from the ultimate as Other.[31] There is, so to speak, no Parable of the Cave in Levinas. As Levinas remarks in *Beyond the Verse*, he prefers "the shadows in the Cave to the uncertain calls from outside it."[32] There is "no world behind the scenes," as he states at the outset of *Otherwise than Being*.[33] Levinas's ontological world is one in which all is equally real. Narbonne distinguishes Neoplatonism from Levinas's philosophy as an "inscription of the transcendent beyond within the sensible" in ways that are "plurivocal," which is to say "inscribed in the diverse links which are formed among men," making transcendence "not simply the business of another world, but dwells first of all down here."[34]

The separation of the world from the beyond does not make it, however, a self-sufficient, enclosed system of being. Its status as distinct from transcendence therefore does not introduce a radical dualism as has been claimed. Levinas knows the position of "separated being no longer participating" in a higher world can alarmingly resemble an isolation that makes the world into pure spectacle: "Phenomenon would degrade into appearance."[35] This is indeed how various commentators have understood him. At the most extreme, Levinas has been described as "gnostic" and "Manichean" in his stark "opposition of God to creatures."[36] Such suspicions derive partly in Levinas's early critique of being as an "il y a" that is neutral and oppressive, from which one desires to escape. Such negative judgment of being leads one commentator to ask whether the "fall" in Levinas is not into nonbeing, but rather precisely into being.[37] Another commentator sees the "abysmal and infinite interval of nothingness" as an "unbridgeable interval of separation" that threatens to empty the world of the Good, which "seems to infuse all levels of reality with its light in Plato"; although she also puts this into the perspective of a generally modern world that has "lost the natural link between being, goodness, and divinity" for a Heideggerian thrownness into neutrality.[38] Regarding the Levinasian rupture between being and the beyond, Narbonne similarly asks: Is this a new Manichean opposition between the order of being and of the Good not found in Platonism?[39]

But such dualism is a grave misreading of Levinas. To take "separation" of the world from what is beyond to mean equating it with evil, or as cut off from sources of order and meaning, is to misunderstand both the world and the beyond in Levinas. Far from being dualist, Levinas's is a thorough, indeed revolutionary rejection of dualism, as it continues to operate within Platonism and Western philosophy itself.

As Narbonne also writes, Levinas's is an "inscription of the transcendent beyond within the sensible."[40] On the one hand, the transcendent remains beyond.

On the other, it is inscribed in the world, paradoxically as rupture, incursion, breakage of the tendency to merge, to blur distinctions that then engulf difference.

At issue, in one sense, is the distinction between emanation and creation. Levinas restages these age-old debates, not in terms of logical proofs, but rather in their implications for the status of earthly life. Emanation and other forms of intermediary that are structurally allied to it seem to provide a bridge connecting the different levels of being/becoming to their ultimate source. Yet they do so only via a rigorous exclusion of materiality from ontological privilege. Plotinus, as many have argued, is not dualist in the Gnostic sense of repudiating the body as independent evil. Nor is he dualist in later Cartesian senses of two substances, extended and thinking. Both mind and body for him originate with the One in its procession or emanation downward. But one does so as continuity and inclusion, the other as exclusion and demotion. Plotinus, although warning that the separation of "soul from body is not to be understood spatially," insists on their very different ontological status and ethical value. "To hold our rank [calls for] an attitude of alienation from the body in the effort to lead up and attach to the overworld" (*Enneads* V.1.10). As one scholar remarks, "It would be pedantic to deny that Plotinus was in [some] sense dualist."[41] Argues another, "The ultimate emphasis in Platonic transcendence is on the disembodied soul." The status of the body in Neoplatonism is determined by its exclusion from the ability to transcend towards being and the good." At best the body serves as a "place of passage," at worst a distraction, driving the self "deeper into the confusion of becoming."[42]

The problem of the body is its materiality, which is to say its multiplicity and changeability. It is the very medium of time, in opposition to eternity, and of change, in opposition to immutability. Perhaps above all, in ways that entail temporality and mutability, it is the very medium of multiplicity, in opposition to unity. Materiality is difference itself, as against the One as ultimate and highest principle of unity. For Plotinus, as one critic sums up, multiplicity as "differentiation" is "estrangement," indeed an opening toward "evil" as distancing from the One, "establish[ing] the self-identity of the same" in separation, leading to "dependence on earthly things" and turning toward them for "completion."[43] These hierarchies and oppositions run through Plotinus's writings. The body is "evil" in comparison with unity as the "pure" (*Enneads* VI.1). Matter marks the ladder of ascent out of exteriority inward and ascending up the scale of being as the good: "The Good advances by the opposite of Matter and, therefore, by a cleansing and casting away to the utmost possible at each stage: and the greatest good must be there where all that is of Matter has disappeared" (*Enneads* VI.28). Levinas, however, rejects this rejection of the body: rejects the notion of "Platonic soul, liberated from concrete conditions of his bodily and historical existence, [to] reach Empyrean heights and contemplate the Ideas."[44] In place of a two world system, of higher being paradoxically called nothing, as against lower becoming that is truly nothing compared to what is ultimate, Levinasian philosophy might be called a *two reference system*: where this world has reference to a beyond, realized through relations within the world and relation to the transcendent, which also penetrates into this world's orders and shapes relations within it. The distinction between them is one of absolute to relative, not of unity to multiplicity, or mind/spirit to body. The relation is not ontological status but ethical answering across the gap, which also signals connection.

This model presumes creation as against emanation, where creationism posits, foundationally, separation between creator and creature, with its many consequences and implications. In Plotinus, "Nothing is completely severed from its prior . . . all making a self continuous whole" (*Enneads* V.2.2). But this, paradoxically, entails the exclusion of materiality from participation in being that is by definition unitary. Creationism does not posit participation: in fact, participation is excluded, a point Levinas repeatedly insists on. Levinas quotes the Talmudic saying: "God never came down from Sinai; Moses never ascended to heaven."[45] Here emerges a suspicion of mysticism that is persistent in Levinas. Mysticism represents for him the loss of all separation, the absorption of all difference into unity. It turns desire into a nostalgia for return that erases both other and self. This is how Levinas sees Plotinus, whose "return to the One [is] the culmination of an ecstasy vanishing into attained or rediscovered transcendence."[46] A. H. Armstrong defines mysticism as "belief in the possibility of an intimate and direct union of the human spirit with the fundamental principle of being, in union which constitutes at once a mode of existence and a mode of knowledge different from and superior to normal existence and knowledge." As he notes, it is in Plotinus that this mystical union as *ecstasis* first appears, famously as the concluding passages of the *Enneads*:[47] "The man is changed, no longer himself nor self belonging; he is merged with the Supreme, sunken into it, one with it . . . he is become the Unity, nothing within him or without inducing any diversity" (*Enneads* VI.9.10–11). Here is an abrogation of otherness that is definitional for Plotinus: "The One is always present because it contains no otherness, we are present only when we rid ourselves of otherness" (*Enneads* VI.911.22). This, in Levinas's view, marks a way of erasure of anything outside the self-same, an "entry into the kingdom of absoluteness [that] announces, in the words of Plotinus, that 'the soul will not go towards any other thing, but towards itself.'"[48] Plotinus writes, "we must ascend to the Principle within ourselves; from many, we must become one; only so do we attain to knowledge of that which is Principle and Unity" (*Enneads* VI.9.3).[49] In contrast, as Brian Schroeder writes, in Levinas there is no union. The "irreversible separation which is a lack, an evil in Plotinus," is maintained in Levinas as a good: the "separation that is overcome in Neoplatonism is maintained in Levinas."[50] In Levinas's two reference system of world and transcendence, the created world refers to its creator, but sustains the difference from transcendence that emanationism bridges—and the incursion of rupture into the world that sustains difference within it.

It is therefore misleading to claim that "both" Levinas and Plotinus "maintain that the other's alterity consists of non-being."[51] Far from demoting this world in an ontological dualism that finds its ultimate image in the debasement of matter and the privileging of unitary intelligibility, Levinasian creationism embraces this world and its materiality, temporality, multiplicity as axiologically real and the space of ethical action. This world claims the value that, as Nietzsche insisted, traditional ontologies denied to it. Time is not "failed eternity"; becoming is not a "privation of eternity."[52] Time constitutes not the fallen form of being, but its very event.[53] "Time must not be seen as image and approximation of an immobile eternity."[54] The world in time is "greater than the eternity of Platonic Ideas or Aristotelian forms."[55] Levinas breaks with Greek philosophy, reconceiving transcendence as not Parmenidean unity that culminates in Neoplatonism. Movement occurs within the visible, not as freeing the soul from the fetters of the material body as in Plotinus."[56] Michael Fagenblat, rightly insisting that "Levinas's argument is entirely opposed to Manichean or gnostic hatred of creation," comments, "creation isn't a synonym for being but a way of acknowledging the originary and unsurpassable implication of being and ethics."[57] "The work of time," writes Levinas, "is profound. It is not simply a renewal through creation . . . more than a renewal of our moods and qualities, time is essentially a new birth."[58]

In Western tradition, negative theology is mystical theology of ascent out of the world of difference toward unity, as Dionysius's own *Mystical Theology* makes clear. In Levinas's second type of ethical negative theology, transcendence is precisely what cannot be entered into, what remains beyond, ungraspable, untouchable. Applying to it negative terms marks this absolute separation and difference, as not identical to experience, as ever beyond. This absolute exclusion from identity is what defeats dualism of the ontological kind. There is no "interior man" as "soul . . . belonging to another order than sense" whose thought is at best, in Plotinian terms, "uncontaminated . . . separate and not mingled into body" (*Enneads* V.1.10). "Finitude" in Levinas does not consist in "a nostalgia for the infinite, a longing for return." True being does not appear in the human as an interiority, an "interior man" as Plotinus put it, but as separation and exterior relations. The "double-person" theory of the soul as inner person, distinct from the body that becomes a "counter-person," calls for a process of purification from the body to assimilate to the divine.[59] It is, that is, the soul's privileged participation in being which lowers and excludes the physical self from such participation. The notion of participation itself, and the unity it promises, is what creates a dualism in which the inner is included, the outer excluded. And it is this path of inclusion that promises assimilation to transcendence, rendering all that is outside it negative. As Levinas writes, "Return to the One means: renouncing the transcendence of the One, participating in the model of the unity of the one."[60] To participate in transcendence is to renounce it. As Derrida writes in "Violence and Metaphysics," Levinas's true target is "complicity between theoretical objectivity and mystical communion."[61] Levinas's whole commitment to transcendence resists and rejects religion as "thaumaturgic," where transcendence "is already (or still) participation, submergence in the being toward which it goes," a state he calls "violence."[62] Levinas sums up, "philosophy [is] union with the one or fusion with it, inscribing itself in an ecstatic itinerary."[63]

In his interview with Wyschogrod, Levinas speaks of a "God who . . . has sent you to the other human being."[64] Or, as he puts it (much) more formally in *Otherwise than Being*, "the non-presence of the infinite is not only a figure of negative theology. All the attributes which state what is beyond the essence become positive in responsibility."[65] The infinite is a "non-presence" as in negative theology. But there is a reversal. The "negative attributes" that cannot be ascribed to God become transferred into the world of life. And, in Levinas's core move, they become a question not of unity but of multiplicity, not of ontology but of "responsibility" among finite beings in the world. Ontology proceeds from ethics, not the other way around. As he pursues at the conclusion of *Totality and Infinity*, against the tradition in which "multiplicity is a fall of the One, a diminution in being which each of the multiple beings would have to surmount so as to return from the multiple to the One," his own transcendental ethics (as I will call it) posits "that the relation between the finite and the infinite does not consist in the finite being absorbed . . . but in remaining in his own being, maintaining himself there, acting here below."[66] Finitude is not a "less" to some intelligible reality that is "more" as in Plotinus. It is the human world where value is to be sought and sustained.

Judaic Nonmetaphysics

Levinas's negations thus do not negate the imminent world. As in other negative theologies, he continues to designate transcendence in ways that are paradoxical but that specify a relation to immanence that confirms and indeed insists on its separation, as a positive axiological principle: one that confirms the value of creation but also binds it through limits to sustaining just such difference and separation as ethical principles. In this he draws on Judaic traditions of negation that have strong syncretist ties to other negative theologies but also pursue particular paths that are distinctive. Levinas himself emphasizes his ties to rabbinic, Talmudic trends as against mystical ones. Maimonidean negative theology affords one powerful precedent. Maimonides's negative theology is itself a highly syncretist version of Judaic, Aristotelian, and Neoplatonic discourses. But the severity of its guard against any knowledge of God or direct incursion into the transcendent makes it distinctive, making impossible, as Aquinas protested, any analogies that could apply to both creator and creature in terms of similarity.[67] In language that Levinas echoes, Maimonides asserts, "There is no correlation between Him and any of His creatures . . . for the characteristic of two objects correlative to each other is the equality of their reciprocal relation" (*Guide* I.52). Just so, Levinas repeatedly challenges the analogical traditions of Western being, where the "unity of analogy united all the thinkable" and all "the abysses of transcendence, all the intervals are cut across by 'analogical unity.'"[68]

This block on ontological access and epistemological grasp curves the relationship to the divine toward ethical action in the world. Levinas's own representation of Maimonides underscores how the negative attributes "receive a positive meaning from the moral . . . the attributes are given not in the indicative, but in the imperative . . . to know God is to know what must be done."[69] Divine attributes invoke not ontological categories but ethical imperatives. "The transcendence of God," Levinas writes of Maimonides, "can signify only negatively," that "everything culminates in the formulation of the negative attributes," a possibility that is "maintained as the ethical behavior of goodwill, judgment, and fairness as 'for the other.'"[70] As Maimonides himself said, experience of the divine is best imaged as "good government"; man's similarity to God inheres in the effort to "make his acts similar to the acts of God."[71] It offers, as Michael Fagenblat argues, an "ethical negative theology" that institutes a "negation of the metaphysical view of human beings and God" in ways of immediate relevance to postmetaphysical thinking.[72]

Levinas pursues this negation into other discourses with resonances from Judaic mystical traditions as well. One Kabbalistic construct to which Levinas does appeal is that of the *En Sof*, the Nothing as "Without-End" or infinite, as negative Name for the ultimate divine.[73] It is "indifferent to the hierarchy of worlds and beings," experienced not in union but in "the perfection of the moral intention that animates religious life as it is lived from the world and its differences."[74] "Perfection" here is a verb, not a noun: not the perfection of being, but of becoming— improvement of the world of difference and multiplicity.

Negativity here differentiates between the absolute and the world, not as two realms but as two references that stand in a double relationality: the relation of difference and the relation of connection. The world absolutely differs from the absolute, which is foundationally other to it. Yet the world stands in relation to the absolute, as its origin, as inscription of order. Levinas writes, "The human impossibility of conceiving of the Infinite is also a new possibility of signifying."[75] This double relationality of difference and connection—what Levinas, citing long tradition, calls "God on our side and God on his own side," a "relation without correlate"—penetrates the world as well, sustaining its articulation of integral, distinctive beings by on the one hand retaining the divergence of one from the other, yet also the interconnection among the beings across this difference.[76] Difference thus is a way transcendence penetrates the world, safeguarding its multiplicities from engulfing and consuming each other. Transcendence penetrates immanence in this sense of rupture that protects the uniqueness of each being in respect of each other. "The thought of the *En Sof* in its height . . . is also its abyss," an abyss that shields against engulfment, with God associated with the worlds in their differences."[77] Association confirms the positivity of creation, its very existence as gift. But association is not union. The negativity of the absolute retains each being in separation. Levinas draws on a creation myth to express this double relationality of difference/separation, alongside order/connection, the "originary contraction of the divine, the idea of the Tzimsum . . . God first contracts himself from creation in order to make space, next to self, for something other than self." It is this that leaves "space for the truth of the association of the infinite and the worlds."[78]

The creator as *En Sof* itself picks up on the ancient notion of creation ex nihilo, radicalized in Kabbalah to mean the divine itself as nothingness, creating out of itself.[79] Levinasian usage echoes such tradition as he elaborates creation as the ultimate event instituting not only the ontological emergence of the world but its ethical constitution as founded on difference: the difference from the divine, and among the elements and inhabitants of the world itself. Levinas writes in *Totality and Infinity*:

> The idea of creation *ex nihilo* expresses a multiplicity not united into a totality; the creature is an existence which indeed does depend on an other, but not as a part that is separated from it. Creation *ex nihilo* breaks with system, posits a being outside of every system, that is, there where its freedom is possible. Creation leaves to the creature a trace of dependence.[80]

> The absolute gap of separation which transcendence implies could not be better expressed than by the term creation, in which the kinship of beings among themselves is affirmed, but at the same time their radical heterogeneity also, their reciprocal exteriority coming from nothingness.[81]

The transcendent beyond, as the principle of negativity, permits, indeed authorizes, separation, difference, multiplicity, and the relation of connection, which affirms order among the disparate, multiple, changing things and beings of the ontological, which is to say human world. Multiplicity, differentiation is ethically positive, not only as the condition of experience, but as a good to be sanctioned, and not absorbed by transcendence. As Levinas pursues at the conclusion of *Totality and Infinity*, "against the tradition in which multiplicity is a fall of the One, a diminution in being which each of the multiple beings would have to surmount so as to return from the multiple to the One," his own ethics posits "that the relation between the finite and the infinite does not consist in the finite being absorbed . . . but in remaining in his own being, maintaining himself there, acting here below."[82] What Levinas offers is a critique of traditional metaphysics that, however, sustains ethical normativity. A surprising number of postmodern writers remain in the double nihilism Nietzsche described. They recognize traditional metaphysics as itself nihilistic by emptying the world of values to remove them to a higher ontology contradictory to earthly experience. But they largely are caught within Nietzsche's secondary nihilism, a nostalgic one in which the loss of metaphysical meaning is taken to mean the loss of meaning altogether. Levinas, in his own critique of metaphysics, accords with Nietzsche's analysis of it as nihilistic, denying meaning to this world in an idealization of conditions that negate the ordinary world: immutability, atemporality, unity. But Levinas then turns his critique away from metaphysics toward ethics. His is a true transvaluation, restoring axiological priority to the mutable, multiple world. The loss of immutable Being does not entail a fall into nihilism, nor into relativism. Paradoxically, the rupture of incursion sustains as well as interrupting positive order in the world, in the sense of maintaining the distinct existence of each element and being through a transcendence that penetrates into experience. Such rupture is absent in Plotinian emanation, which extends in indefinite emanation, in which all being is continuous but which thereby degrades difference.

Ethics entails facing the other, which is to say respecting each other as different from the self across an unbridgeable gap, but as positive responsibility in which each other is sustained. The other in these Levinasian terms is both a negative transcendence that ever remains exterior, but also demands positive responsibility in the relationality of sustaining difference. Its ultimate image is God. Levinas in his essay "The Image of God" contrasts the *En Sof* as creative contraction against the Plotinian One of unity. "Monotheism," he writes, can be "asserted in its absolute vigour without it being from the ontological perspective, and without the resemblance between the One of Deuteronomy and the One of the Enneads."[83] Levinas, concerned to distinguish the *En Sof* from the "God of metaphysics" and "the onto-theological perspective" suggests that the divine as One is not unified totality but rather absolute uniqueness of which "there is no other."[84] Just so, each being is unique, distinct from all others, each in its own association and difference from all others, emerging in time and material multiplicity in ongoing creation— "life as it is lived from the world and its differences."[85]

In a 1980 interview with Edith Wyschogrod, Levinas sums up his project as setting out to "think plurality otherwise than it had been thought by the NeoPlatonists. For the NeoPlatonists, plurality was always a privation of actuality, of the soul." But "existence is more than two: it is multiple, plurality, as already was the case in *Totality and Infinity.*" Love itself requires two, not one. As he comments in his interview, "Love: how much better it is to be two than to be alone."[86]

Notes

1. Michael Fagenblat describes Levinas's as an "ethical negative theology" in *A Covenant of Creatures: Levinas's Philosophy of Judaism* (Stanford, CA: Stanford University Press, 2010).

2. Both Jean-Francois Mattei and David Banon in the collection *Noesis Revue de Philosophie no 3 1999 La Metaphysique d'Emmanuel Levinas*, ed. Dominique Janicaud refer to "two Platos" in Levinas, the ontological one and the one that points to the Good beyond Being; see Mattei, "Levinas et Platon: Sur l'au-dela de l'etre," 9–26, 16; Banon, "Levinas Penseur Juif ou Juif pense," 27–42, 30. Francisco Gonzalez, "Levinas Questioning Plato on Eros and Maieutics," in *Levinas and the Ancients*, ed. Brian Schroeder and Silvia Benso (Bloomington: Indiana University Press, 2008), 40–61, sees conflictual readings of Plato in Levinas and suggests these are just "a failure on Levinas's part to see in Plato a consistent position," 50. See also Michael Naas in the same volume, "Lending Assistance Always to Itself: Levinas' Infinite Conversation with Platonic Dialogue," 78–102.

3. This thesis statement is reprinted in Theodoor Peperzak, *Platonic Transformations* (Lanham, MD: Rowman and Littlefield, 1997), 126–127; cf. Sarah Allen, *The Philosophical Sense of Transcendence: Levinas and Plato on Loving Beyond Being* (Pittsburgh, PA: Duquesne University Press, 2009), 116, 259. Cf. Emmanuel Levinas, *Humanism of the Other* (Champaign: University of Illinois Press, 2003), 37–38, for Levinas's critique of a return to Platonism.

4. Emmanuel Levinas, *Totality and Infinity: An Essay on Exteriority*, trans. Alphonso Lingis (The Hague: M. Nijhoff, 1979), 44.

5. Emmanuel Levinas, *Time and the Other*, trans. Richard A. Cohen (Pittsburgh: Duquesne University Press, 1987), 92.

6. Levinas, *Totality and Infinity*, 102.

7. Ibid., 103.

8. Emmanuel Levinas, *Entre Nous* (New York: Columbia University Press, 1998), 137, asserts: "Modern philosophy since Descartes, despite all its variations, has preserved the Neoplatonic schema of return and union . . . the return of absolute thought to itself." John Izzi, "Proximity and Difference: Levinas and Plotinus," in *Levinas and the Ancients*, 196–209, confirms that the "Intellect," though a manifold of forms, "comprises totality" (198), but attempts to distinguish it from the One as an "event." Yet even as "event," the One remains an "event of unification," "the very movement of coming to presence of all that is" (198).

9. Levinas, *Totality and Infinity*, 104.

10. Emmanuel Levinas, *Alterity and Transcendence* (New York: Columbia University Press, 1999), 6.

11. Levinas, *Alterity and Transcendence*, 9. Cf. Plotinus, *Enneads*, "All are elements in one entity, and from their totality the Intellectual realm—that which we know as being—derives its constitution," VI.2.2. *The Internet Classic Archives*, trans. Steven Mackenna and B. S. Page, 1994–2009, http://classics.mit.edu/Plotinus/enneads.html. Hereafter cited as *Enneads*.

12. Levinas, *Alterity and Transcendence*, 7.

13. Levinas, *Entre Nous*, 133.

14. Ibid., 134.

15. Ibid., 137.

16. Ibid., 137.

17. Emmanuel Levinas, *In the Time of the Nations*, trans. Michael B. Smith (Bloomington: Indiana University Press, 1994), 14; he also states, "transcendence can no longer be conceived of . . . as another world hidden behind the appearance of this one" (179).

18. Levinas, *Entre Nous*, 136.

19. Levinas, *Alterity and Transcendence*, 8.

20. Levinas, *Totality and Infinity*, 58.

21. Ibid., 60.

22. A. H. Armstrong, "Negative Theology," *Plotinian and Christian Studies* (London: Variorum Reprints, 1979), 176–190, esp. 176–177.

23. Harry Austryn Wolfson, "Albinus and Plotinus on Divine Attributes," *Studies in the History of Philosophy and Religion* (Cambridge, MA: Harvard University Press, 1973), 1:115–130.

24. Jacques Derrida, "On Speaking Denials," *Languages of the Unsayable*, ed. Sanford Budick and Wolfgang Iser (New York: Columbia University Press, 1989).

25. A. H. Armstrong explains in *Introduction to Ancient Philosophy* (London: Methuen 1965), 181, in Greek thought the principle of unity equals the principle of existence.

26. Denis O'Brien, "Plotinus on Matter and Evil," *Cambridge Companion to Plotinus*, ed. Lloyd Gerson (New York: Cambridge University Press, 1996), 171–195: "all other forms with the exception of being itself are 'non-beings,' not because they do not participate in being, but because, although they participate in being they participate also in otherness in relation to being, and are therefore not identical to being" (172).

27. A. H. Armstrong, *The Architecture of the Intelligible Universe in the Philosophy of Plotinus* (Cambridge: Cambridge University Press, 1940), 29–31, 3, 109.

28. Deborah Achtenberg, "The Eternal and the New," in *Levinas and the Ancients*, 24–39, 37.

29. Jean-Marc Narbonne, *Levinas and the Greek Heritage* (Leuven: Peeters, 2006), 51–52, 62, 68.

30. Armstrong, *Architecture*, 43. Armstrong describes the two world system in "Gnosis and Greek Philosophy," in *Plotinian and Christian Studies*, 86–124: "The principle opposed to the good is indefinite multiplicity, essentially negative and vague, such as occurs in the lower material world of space-time separation. In this two world system, the lower world of the principle of indefinite multiplicity does not submit itself completely to form and order." It is still not seen as intrinsically evil as in Gnosticism, yet there is a "strong sense of alienation from it and a sense that the true self belongs to the world of unity" (96–98).

31. For a discussion of hierarchy in Plotinus, see Dominic J. O'Meara, "The Hierarchical Ordering of Reality," in *Cambridge Companion to Plotinus*, ed. Lloyd Gerson (New York: Cambridge University Press, 1996), 66–81: "we can consequently say that as temporal and spatial succession [in the material world] are subordinate to other kinds of priority as emerging at the lowest stages of the order of priority by nature, so the priority by order and difference characterizing intelligible being is subordinate . . . to what is absolutely prior by nature, the One" (77–78). And yet, the One is also always present throughout the hierarchy: "The One is always present to those who are able to touch it, but is not present to one who is unable" (*Enneads* VI.9.7.4–5).

32. Emmanuel Levinas, *Beyond the Verse: Talmudic Readings and Lectures*, trans. Gary D. Mole (Bloomington: Indiana University Press, 1994), 114.

33. Emmanuel Levinas, *Otherwise than Being, or, Beyond Essence*, trans. Alphonso Lingis (Dordrecht: Kluwer Academic, 1991), 5. This is a position reiterated throughout Levinas's work. Cf. Emmanuel Levinas, *God, Death, and Time,* trans. Bettina Bergo (Stanford, CA: Stanford University Press, 2000), 105; cf., 111: "a beyond freed from the mythologies of ulterior worlds," and *In the Time of the Nations*, 14: "transcendence can no longer be conceived of . . . as another world hidden behind the appearance of this one."

34. Narbonne emphasizes, as does Diane Pepich, *The Ethics of Emmanuel Levinas* (Stanford, CA: Stanford University Press, 2008), and other commentators, that Levinas's system is not two-worldly. As Narbonne puts it, Levinas's philosophy does not involve the "passage from an apparent world to a real one"; *Levinas and the Greek Heritage*, 64, 68–69.

35. Levinas, *Totality and Infinity*, 90.

36. Philip Blond, "Emmanuel Levinas: God and Phenomenology," in *Post-Secular Philosophy: Between Philosophy and Theology*, ed. Philip Blond (London: Routledge, 1998), 103–120, 116. Cf. Michael Haar, "The Obsession of the Other," *Philosophy and Social Criticism* 23, no. 6 (1997): 95–107, 98, who calls Levinas Manichean.

37. Mattei, *Noesis*, 17 (my translation).

38. Sarah Allen, *Philosophical Sense of Transcendence*, 196; cf. Francisco Gonzalez, "Levinas Questioning Plato on Eros and Maieutics," who argues that the notion of creation in Levinas entails a separation as "self-sufficiency" that cuts off from transcendence, as against a Plotinian participation as continuity (53).

39. Narbonne, *Levinas and the Greek Heritage*, 58–59.

40. Ibid., 68–69.

41. Stephen Clark, "Plotinus: Body and Soul," in *Cambridge Companion to Plotinus*, , 275–291, 276. Cf. Armstrong, *Architecture*: as A. H. Armstrong sums up, "in all Platonism a fluctuation on valuation of material world" (109) and "there is a contradiction in Plotinian treatment of matter; on the one hand it is a purely negative conception, but it is also positively evil" (86).

42. Allen, *Philosophical Sense of Transcendence*, 72.

43. Izzi, "Proximity and Difference," 199–200.

44. Levinas, *Humanism of the Other*, 20.

45. Emmanuel Levinas, *Difficult Freedom*, trans. Sean Hand (London: The Athlone Press, 1990), 18; cf. *In the Time of the Nations*, 114. Notably the quote from *Difficult Freedom*

continues "But God folded back the heavens like a cover, covered Sinai with it, and so found Himself on earth without having even left heaven."

46. Levinas, *Entre Nous*, 136.
47. Armstrong, "Negative Theology," 170.
48. Levinas, *Difficult Freedom*, 16.
49. Narbonne points out that access to the beyond of thought becomes ritual later rather than philosophical cognition, p. 60.
50. Brian Schroeder, "A Trace of the Eternal Return? Levinas and Neoplatonism," *Levinas and the Ancients*, 219–220.
51. Izzi, "Proximity and Difference," 198.
52. Levinas, *Alterity and Transcendence*, 13.
53. Levinas, *Time and the Other*, 92.
54. Levinas, *Difficult Freedom*, 292.
55. Levinas, *Beyond the Verse*, 179.
56. Schroeder, "A Trace of the Eternal Return?," 222.
57. Fagenblat, *A Covenant of Creatures*, 48, 214n51.
58. Levinas, *Time and the Other*, 81.
59. T. M. Robinson, "Mind-Body Dualism in Plato," in *Psyche and Soma*, ed. John Wright and Paul Potter (Oxford: Clarendon Press, 2000), 37–55, 42.
60. Levinas, *Entre Nous*, 134.
61. Jacques Derrida, *Writing and Difference* (Chicago: The University of Chicago Press, 1978), 87.
62. Levinas, *Totality and Infinity*, 48. Interestingly, in this passage Levinas cites Plato as countering such "ecstatic" religion, with philosophy itself refusing a "false spiritualism of the pure and simple and immediate union with the divine." Narbonne notes that in later Neoplatonism, access to the beyond of thought came to depend on theurgical rather than philosophical procedures; Narbonne, *Levinas and the Greek Heritage*, 60.
63. Levinas, *Alterity and Transcendence*, 8.
64. Edith Wyschogrod, *Crossover Queries* (New York: Fordham University Press, 2008), 286.
65. Levinas, *Otherwise than Being*, 12.
66. Levinas, *Totality and Infinity*, 292.
67. *Summa Theologiae* q.7, a.5, ad 2m, 199:2; *Christian Classics Ethereal Library*, July 13, 2005, http://www.ccel.org/ccel/aquinas/summa.toc.html. Etienne Gilson stresses the importance of Maimonides to Aquinas's formulation of the divine essence in "Maimonide et la philosophie de l'*Exode*," *Medieval Studies* 13 (1951).
68. Respectively, Levinas, *Otherwise than Being*, 94–95 (cf. *Alterity and Transcendence*, 64), and *In the Time of the Nations*, 157.
69. Levinas, *Difficult Freedom*, 17.
70. Levinas, *In the Time of the Nations*, 170–172.
71. Moses Maimonides, *Guide of the Perplexed*, I.54.
72. Fagenblat, *A Covenant of Creatures*, 119.

73. Here I disagree with Michael Fagenblat, who claims that "Levinas and Luria cannot be reconciled," 61. His interest is in the status of evil in the fabric of creation, which he rightly claims Levinas to reject. But the image of the *En Sof* and contraction is very central to Levinas.

74. Levinas, *Beyond the Verse*, 165. This is not to claim that there is no unitive mysticism in Judaic culture, a central point of controversy between Mosh Idel and Gershom Scholem. Levinas, however, heavily leans toward the nonunitive such as Scholem describes. Elliot Wolfson likewise makes this claim in *Venturing Beyond: Law and Morality in Kabbalistic Mysticism* (Oxford: Oxford University Press, 2006), 7–9. Jewish mysticism does not necessarily "dissolve the concrete separateness of persons, which alone guarantees the alterity of the other." Michael Purcell in *Levinas and Theology* (New York: Cambridge University Press, 2006) similarly affirms that "access to God is not gained by way of mystical encounter," and that for Levinas, "a theology which tends towards the mystical approaches the divine by way of neglect of the world," 61. But he wrongly states that "neither negative nor apophatic theology provides any ultimate solution either, [for its] attempts to safeguard divine transcendence and unknowability [is done] at the expense of ethical engagement." But Levinasian negative theology, like Maimonides's, refocuses exactly on actions in the world: that is, the force of negating a second higher ontological realm as beyond.

75. Levinas, *Beyond the Verse*, 165.

76. Ibid., 165.

77. Ibid., 166.

78. Ibid., 166.

79. For fuller discussion of negation in Scholem, see Shira Wolosky, "Gershon Scholem's Linguistic Theory," *Gershom Scholem*, ed. Joseph Dan, Peter Schafer, and J. C. B. Mohr (Tubingen: Paul Siebeck, 2006), 2:165–205.

80. Levinas, *Totality and Infinity*, 104.

81. Ibid., 293.

82. Ibid., 292.

83. Ibid., 164.

84. Ibid., 163, 164.

85. Ibid., 165.

86. Edith Wyschogrod, *Crossover Queries*, 284, 287. Levinas proposes a different model of love than the one proposed in the *Symposium* in which two halves unite, but we cannot explore this further here. Cf. Allen, who sees the "fusional and ascending reading of erotic love" as diverted in Levinas to "creating others and relating to others" in contradistinction to Plotinian mysticism. Levinas's is thus "a new way of approaching Desire and Transcendence not entirely beholden to Greek philosophy"; *Philosophical Sense of Transcendence*, 270–271.

EIGHT

Khoric Apophasis: Matter and Messianicity in Islamo-Judeo-Greek Neoplatonism

SARAH PESSIN

I aim in this chapter to recover a lost Islamo-Judeo-Greek Neoplatonic khoric apophasis that, in its own self-reflective interrogation of the very limits of negative theology, exceeds traditional senses of negative theology as metaphysics of (absence as) presence and shares an atheological and messianistic optics with Levinas and Derrida.[1] On the theme of things unspoken, excavating this overlooked apophasis provides us with two openings: First, by turning to an important atheological tradition in which matter signals messianicity, this study explicates a unique tradition of unspeaking; second, by looking at a mostly *overlooked* tradition, this particular study of atheological unspeaking reveals to us a voice that has not yet been fully allowed to (un)speak.

Dionysian Preamble

Owing in part perhaps to Derrida's own encounter with Ps. Dionysius (henceforth, Denys), one can hardly find a postmetaphysical theology or atheology that does not highlight Denys as a paradigm for contemporary apophasis or as a case in point of the kinship between medieval traditions of "negative theology" and deconstruction. In the former spirit, Marion lifts Denys's "hymnic" theology above what he sees as a flattened out apophatic project in Plotinus, highlighting what is best in Denys "in contrast to the Neo-platonists who would overcome Being only for the sake of coming unto the One and would pass beyond the One only in order to retrieve it."[2] Such a comparison is simply unfair; as we will see in this chapter, the subtlety of Plotinus—and with him a robust Islamo-Judeo-Greek tradition of Neoplatonism—far exceeds Marion's uncharitable gloss and arguably goes further than Denys's own hymnic approach in enacting what is most promising about apophasis.

Turning to the many attempts to wed Denys and deconstruction, we must note with equal caution that Denys's Christology ought to make any such effort difficult at best. At the very least, the overtly Christian elements of Denys's writings subject his apophasis to Derrida's own concerns not only with an anthropotheological God of Revelation in general, but with Christian particularism in particular.³ While arguably unable to ultimately "escape presence," the unique Islamo-Judeo-Greek tradition of apophasis addressed in this chapter does avoid these particular Dionysian setbacks.⁴ Indeed, it exceeds any anthropotheological "God of Revelation" theology while at the same time self-reflectively wrestling not merely with the limits of language, but with the very limits of apophasis itself.

At the very least, this suggests to me that the Islamo-Judeo-Greek tradition ought to be invited to the contemporary atheology table alongside Denys. At the very most, this suggests to me that this tradition ought to be seated at the head of that table. Contrary to Marion's sense that (non-Christian) Neoplatonism falls short, we will argue that it interrogates saying and unsaying in ways that make it an exemplary partner for the best contemporary messianistic atheologies.

Khoric Opening, 1: Derrida's Desert-in-the-Desert as Refusal of the God of Revelation

Derrida, in his essay "Khōra," explains:

> But what is said about *khōra* is that this name does not designate any of the known or recognized or, if you like, *received* types of existence, *received* by philosophical discourse, that is, by the *ontological logos* which lays down the law in the *Timaeus*: *khōra* is neither sensible nor intelligible. There is *khōra*; one can even ponder its *physis* and its *dynamis*, or at least ponder these in a preliminary way. But what *there is*, there, is not; and we will come back after to what this *there is* can give us to think, this *there is*, which, by the way, *gives* nothing in giving place or in giving to think, whereby it will be risky to see in it the equivalent of an *es gibt*, of the *es gibt* which remains without a doubt implicated in every negative theology, unless it is the *es gibt* which always summons negative theology in its Christian history.⁵

In what we may call the khoric apophasis of his own deconstructive optics, Derrida is struck by the Timaean *khōra* (henceforth, khora) as the "desert-in-the-desert,"⁶ a "taking place" and a "spacing from 'before' the world" and "from 'before' . . . any revelation"⁷ that is the "anachrony of being."⁸

Turning in particular to our reflections on Derrida's concerns with an anthropotheological God of Revelation, consider the emergence, in Derrida's comments to Kearney, of khora as the foil to languages of resurrection:

> I am not against resurrection. I would share your hope for resurrection, reconciliation and redemption. But I think that I have a responsibility as someone who thinks deconstructively to obey the

necessity—the necessity of the possibility—that there is *khôra* rather than a relationship with the anthropo-theological God of Revelation. At some point, you, Richard, translate your faith into something determinable and then you have to keep the "name" of the resurrection. My own understanding of faith is that there is faith whenever one gives up not only any certainty but also any determined hope. If one says that resurrection is the horizon of one's hope then—since one knows what one names when one says "resurrection"—faith is not pure faith. It is already knowledge. . . . That is why you have to be an atheist of this sort (someone who "rightly passes for an atheist") in order to be true to faith.[9]

It is khora—and not the anthropotheological God of Revelation—that (restlessly) sits at the heart of Derrida's own atheological religion-without-religion. Indeed, we may say that it is precisely this khoric hypervigilance to avoid theological (over)determination that Caputo seizes on in his own comparison of Derrida with Augustine. Reflecting on Derrida's Circumfessional moment of deconstruction as a move away from Augustine's Confessional moment of prayer, Caputo describes Derrida in terms of "a slightly atheistic quasi-Jewish Augustinian[ism]."[10] Engaging Derrida's relation (in his *Circumfessions*) to the Augustinian question "What do I love when I love my God?" and exposing Derrida's sense of the "pure messianism" of the open-ended and unforeseeable *à venir* ("to come") in contrast with "concrete messianisms," Caputo notes: "Derrida shares Augustine's restless heart—*inquietum est cor nostrum*, our hearts are restless until they rest in you, Augustine had said—but Derrida cannot bring his restlessness to rest in a settled way upon a singular object of love, like Augustine's God."[11] In line with his need to avoid an anthropotheological God of Revelation, Derrida emerges in Caputo as exceeding even Augustine's restlessness when it comes to setting his sights on the prize (theological or otherwise). This, we may say, is key to Derrida's khoric faith.

Turning to Greek, Islamic, and Jewish Neoplatonists, we find this same khoric refusal of a God of Revelation. In their talk either of God as "One beyond being" or as "creator who emanates," Neoplatonists underscore their refusal to speak an anthropotheological God (of Revelation or otherwise).

But there is, beyond that, a special strand of Neoplatonism that, manifesting the further subtleties of Derridean deconstruction, additionally refuses to speak refusal, opting instead to defer this refusal of God to a new topic entirely, namely a God-born "matter" at the heart of all existence (and even at the heart of the more standard Platonic and Aristotelian matters).[12] It is to this unique Islamo-Judeo-Greek tradition of *"khōra-of-khōra"* (henceforth, "khora-of-khora") that we now turn.

Khoric Opening, 2: Matter-Talk as Hylomythic Iteration

Mirroring a tradition of intelligible matter in Plotinus, Ibn Gabirol—as part of a Ps. Empedoclean Islamo-Jewish tradition—highlights a material core at the root of all beings, prior to form, and first-born signal of God's emanative (non) disclosure.[13] Arguably moving within a Plotinian dynamic, but adding his own flourish to the voicing of that dynamic, Ibn Gabirol rehearses the Plotinian insight (seen in Plotinus's own discussions of intelligible matter) that all reality—including the Intellect at the heart of being and human being—is rooted in matter, as he also amplifies this insight through a description of reality in terms of a series of descending matters emanating one from the next. Starting with *al-'unṣur al-awwal* (first matter, first element, or, as I have translated it elsewhere, the material Grounding Element)[14]—itself portrayed as the first product of God's own hidden essence—Ibn Gabirol weaves a discourse of matters upon matters not, as I have argued elsewhere, as a cosmological-ontological description of reality, but rather, as an apophatic way of engaging the infinite gap between unity and plurality. Reflecting on the impossibility of bridging the gap between beings and unity, Ibn Gabirol crafts a discourse that emphasizes the impossibility of God's unfolding (as the impossibility of the compresence of unity and plurality—an impossibility that I have elsewhere called the Neoplatonic Paradox of Divine Unity) by emphasizing God's emanation first and foremost as the birth of one material ground(less ground), then another, and then another.[15] In his talk of "layers of matter," Ibn Gabirol, reflecting Plotinus's own talk of the matter at the core of being, constructs a mythic discourse in which nothing (God's essence) gives way to nothing (the material Grounding Element, followed by a string of consecutive matter-nothings). In what we may call his onto-story, or rather his hylology—or better still, his hylomythy—Ibn Gabirol traces the origin of being and human being to nowhere, unsettlingly settling on the anarchic ground of being and human being in a material not-yet, nowhere, nothing that announces itself multiply and iteratively throughout the cosmos. Subject to this uniquely hylomythic form of Neoplatonic apophasis, God is not simply (as in Denys) hyperpredicated or hymned; he is, rather, displaced by an emphatic focus instead on iterations of materiality.

In (un)speaking open a spaceless space as the anarchic ground(less ground) of being and human being, Ibn Gabirol—and the Islamo-Judeo-Greek tradition of which he is a part—may be said to highlight a khora-of-khora: a material ground(less ground) that amplifies—and indeed, exceeds—the arresting call of even Timaean khora. Whereas Plato's khora marks the anarchic ground of bodies (as one finds when considering the full context of the *Timaeus*), the Islamo-Judeo-Greek khora-of-khora—grounded in Plotinus's intelligible matter and reverberated through the Islamo-Jewish Neoplatonic tradition of the material Grounding Element—anarchically grounds being itself, thought itself, and—as such—the human subject in an ultimate moment of displacement. (For materialist or immanentist readers, or any readers suspicious of a mind-body distinction, who are inclined to privilege a khora tradition over a khora-of-khora tradition, bear in mind that within Plato's own Pythagorean Timaean context, khora is at best the placeless place of bodies, with the intelligible realm arguably safe from any khoric disruption; within a discourse of mind-body duality [construed mythically within Timaean and Neoplatonic traditions], it is arguably the khora-of-khora tradition that is more radical, naming matter at the core of form [and, as such, matter at the core of intellect and being], and as such, arguably going more readily to where Derrida wishes to go with Timaean khora).

Couched within an apophatic discourse of emanation, Ibn Gabirol hylomythically pictures God's first manifestation in the material Grounding Element itself giving way to a series of further material emanations, and eventually giving way a number of iterations "down the chain," we might say, to the Platonic khora.[16] In this sense, we may speak of Ibn Gabirol's material Grounding Element—and Plotinus's intelligible matter—as khora-of-khora.

Khoric Opening, 3: Matter and Messianicity

Coupled with this apophatic hylomythic reflection on anarchic grounds, Ibn Gabirol, again mirroring Plotinus, emphasizes the nothing-space of khora-of-khora not simply in its impossibility (as the impossible first site, so to speak, of unity's giving way to plurality), but also in its messianistic desire after a goodness that can itself never be possessed—a goodness that is, in other words, always yet to come. In this context, talk of divine disclosure is made equivalent to talk of a pure unity and goodness that erupts forward into plurality not simply as a powerful flow of water or light (the image most often associated with Neoplatonism) but as a flow that demands a recipient who is at the same time interrupted and constituted by desiring after that (unattainable) goodness and not being able to receive it. The unfolding of unity/God/goodness, in other words, is found only and always in/as the disruption of a material Grounding Element at the heart of Intellect—which is to say, a material not-yet at the heart of being and human being.

Moving beyond even a picture of a supraessential hyperreal goodness-above-being (as we find in Dionysian mystical theology) that unfolds into a material receiver that is too weak to receive its abundant flow (as is commonly the picture associated with Neoplatonism), we instead find in the complex apophatic rhythms of khora-of-khora emanation discourse an even subtler sense of goodness and being mutually manifesting in the former's constitution *and* (or: *as*) rupture of the matter—which is the say, the desiring-not-yet-anythingness—of the latter. In this regard, Plotinus and Ibn Gabirol emphasize being's root in khora-of-khora, a material "site" that awaits disruption (and as such constitution) by the radical otherness of an undefinable, unfindable, infinite goodness that is apophatically / hylomythically less defined—infinitely less defined—than a logotic or anthropotheological God of Revelation. This is what is signaled by the talk of a material Grounding Element as the first product of God / good at the core of being / Intellect.

On the messianistic theme of being's constitution-as-interruption in and through a material desire for unattainable goodness, we find Plotinus's own subtle exploration of the material (khora-of-khora) moment at the heart of being and Intellect—a dynamic that can be felt at the core of Ibn Gabirol's matter-apophasis and which is evidenced more generally throughout Ibn Gabirol's overall Theology of Desire.[17] Reflecting on Intellect (the fullness not only of self and knowing but of being), Plotinus—in what is a thematic at play in a range of Islamic and Jewish Neoplatonists—describes "two motions" or "moments" of *to noein*.[18] On the one hand, Intellect is theorized as looking inward, a kind of looking by which "it sees the things in itself" (τα ἐν αὐτῷ βλέπει); on the other hand, Intellect is theorized as looking upward / outward / other-ward, a kind of looking "by which [it sees] the things that are beyond it (τα ἐπέκεινα αὐτοῦ) by a direct awareness (ἐπιβολῇ) and reception (παραδοχῇ)." Most arrestingly, Plotinus goes on to describe Intellect's inward looking as "the contemplation of Intellect in its right mind" (ἡ θέα νοῦ ἔμφρονος) and Intellect's upward / other-ward looking as "Intellect in love, when it goes out of its mind 'drunk with the nectar,'" a reference to the drunkenness of Poros (Plenty, the father of Eros with Penia / Poverty) in Plato's *Symposium*.[19] Here, the moment of the "Godward / goodward / other-ward gaze" toward a radically other and undefined goodness that can never be located or received is reflected in a paradoxical state of present-absence in the seeking subject. On the one hand—in its description as a moment of reception / *paradoche* of "the things that are beyond it"—Intellect (and by extension, being and human being) here emerges as / in a moment of emptiness, as it also and at the same time emerges as / in a moment of fullness (in mythic relation to Poros / Plenty). We might say that in the atheological messianistic promise of a goodness that not just *has* not, but *can* not be received, being and human being are exposed in a material eros—in a searching that never finds and in a desire that is never satisfiable.

And it is, ultimately, in this impossible relation between an infinite goodness / unity and an infinite khoric ground(lessness) (and moreover, in the further impossibility of this impossible relation constituting being and human being) that we can begin to sense a dynamic of disruption, interruption, and rupture. Signaled in the *Symposium*'s mythic description of the birth of Eros in a founding rupturing (of Plenty *by* Poverty), we find an express link between the unfulfilled khoric longing for a goodness that exceeds, and a traumatic breaking open by the very excess of that goodness. Couched within his overall emanative Plotinian context, this sentiment emerges quite dramatically in Ibn Gabirol's own disruptive depiction of creation: *"ve-qara el ha-ayin ve-nivqa"* (And He called out to the nothing and it split open).[20]

Using the Hebrew *"ayin"* (nothing) to refer to the material Grounding Element, Ibn Gabirol describes divine disclosure in terms of a yearning material rupture at the heart of being—an unfolding in which a desiring not-yet is broken open by a goodness that exceeds, and as such anarchically constitutes and (dis)orients, being.

Hylomythy as Refusal to (Merely) Unspeak God

In contrast to Denys who (un)speaks God through hyperpredication-as-praise, Ibn Gabirol—within the tradition of Islamo-Judeo-Greek hylomythic emanation—(un)speaks God through hylomythic discourses on layers of matter, starting with the material Grounding Element as khora-of-khora. This suggests a self-reflective attention not only to the failures of language to speak God but to the failures of apophasis to unspeak God. In this sense, we find Islamo-Judeo-Greek hylomythy's subtle methodological awareness of the failures of apophasis itself (an awareness that we have seen to be a hallmark of Derridean deconstruction). We can discern this meta-sensitivity in at least two ways.

First, in focusing his attentions downward on matter-talk—what we may describe ultimately as a hylo-grammatology—beyond any God-talk, Ibn Gabirol enacts a uniquely Plotinian, khoric, atheological space of discourse. Moved by the impulse to talk God, Ibn Gabirol writes matter instead and as such occupies his theological desires through atheological encounters with a "nothing" (viz. matter) that is neither talk "to God" (the aspect of prayer in—or alongside—the Dionysian hymnic), or talk "about God" (which Derrida links to a degree of divine attribution at play in the Dionysian performance of hymn).[21] In Ibn Gabirol, God as subject is displaced entirely in the very writing of matter, after matter, after matter.

Second, in replacing God-talk with hylo-grammatology, a writing of matter in layers and layers (itself, we might say, as a "hylomania" sensitive to avoiding "theomania"), and in particular in replacing God-talk with khora-beyond-khora, Ibn Gabirol focuses, in his turn away from God to matter, on the other traditional philosophical marker for "nothing."[22] As we have seen, however, in this double turn away from God (i.e., from unspeaking God in hyperpredication or praise, to unspeaking God by speaking/writing khora-of-khora instead—a move I have elsewhere called "doubly apophatic"), Ibn Gabirol is attuned (with, we might say, an indeterminate directionality that does not know and knows it can never know the object of its attunement) to an undefined goodness, in this way sharing an optics with Levinas and Derrida in their own different but related logics of messianicity.[23]

Different from the performativity of language in a Dionysian hymn, here the performativity of language arises in a disruptive, "doubly apophatic" turn from the expected (non)subject of mystical atheology (viz. G̶o̶d̶-as-nothing) to the unexpected (non)subject of khoric atheology (viz. m̶a̶t̶t̶e̶r̶-as-nothing). In turning away from God doubly (in a downward, hylic turn removed not only from God but from G̶o̶d̶), khoric apophasis avoids the hymnic determinations of an anthropotheological God of Revelation as it at once reveals its own sense that to unspeak God, we must change the subject entirely. While hyper-predication suggests, in its very structure, the hope of untalking God by talking-(or-praising)-God-via-hyper-predication, khoric hlomythy more fully wears on its sleeve the very limits of negative theology: We cannot even unspeak God, so we speak unspeakable matter instead—an unspeakable matter that beckons to a disruptive (and always disrupted) desire-for-goodness at the heart of language, thought, and being.

In khoric apophasis, we do not pray to or praise God. There is, rather, something more deeply apophatic in the apophatic motion at play. In emphasizing this point, I do not mean to overlook the concomitant necessity (or, unavoidability) of a kataphatic moment; I mean only to obviate the need for a kataphatic moment that beckons to the divine through a specifying/determining act of divine attribution; in its downward directed hylo-grammatology, khoric apophasis redirects entirely—and in this way critiques—our desire to desire after God: khoric apophasis, while perfomative in its own right, is in this sense the antihymn. I might add that while khoric apophasis avoids divine affirmation, it does not avoid—and indeed goes hand in hand with—affirmation as a form of life. What we have in hylomythy is not an affirmative form of theology but an affirmative (in contrast to nihilistic) form of life dedicated to decision and action (or as I have put it elsewhere, a life dedicated to retrieving something of the goodness of God).[24]

Verily I Am Matter

We might add that khoric hylomythy "unspeaks matter" through disruptive-because-nonconventional uses of indicative, attributive language claims about matter (and self) that fly in the face of ordinary Platonic and Aristotelian claims about matter (and self). This includes hylomythic talk of the root of being and self in matter in decided contrast to conventional Greek philosophical identifications of being and self with form. This is the logic of Ibn Gabirol's and Plotinus's khoric apophasis, given to voice in hylomythic metaphysical-sounding (but in no way straightforwardly metaphysical) claims about "matter beyond matter at the heart of intellect" that Ibn Gabirol in particular further draws out (in a performative hylomania-that-displaces-theomania) through a hylo-grammatology of "layers" of material (non)disclosures at the (anarchic) ground of all beings and at the (anarchic) ground of human being.

Constituted by the eruption of a goodness that can never be found and a desire-for-goodness that can never be fulfilled, I am rooted in a nothing, born of nothing, itself born of nothing further still. Consider Derrida's own reflection on the dual opening of self in a singularity that is at once a division: "The singularity of the 'who' is not the individuality of a thing that would be identical to itself, it is not an atom. It is a singularity that dislocates or divides itself in gathering itself to answer to the other, whose call somehow precedes its own identification with itself."[25] And, connecting the undercurrent of this insight to themes of exile, Wolfson speaks of "the singularity of oneself insofar as one is otherwise than oneself" in terms of "the homelessness that alights the way back home in the foreboding night of our solitude."[26] Tracing the reverberations of these very insights within the forgotten khoric apophasis of Islamo-Judeo-Greek Neoplatonism, we are reminded of Ibn Gabirol's own reflection on the creation of being and human being in an eruptive opening, a groundless space where I await my ownmost constitution through nothing less than a splitting open that divides me. As the subject that is always not yet, "Verily I am matter . . . and you not I my maker."[27]

Levinasian Traces in/of/and Hylo-Grammatology

In the Islamo-Judeo-Greek tradition of khora-of-khora we must also speak of having found an apophasis of the trace—an apophatic construction (of mythic landscapes filled with material groundless grounds) that arrestingly bears witness at once to the ground(less ground) of being and human being in impossibility, and to the being who occupies that homeless no-place as oriented (in a disruptive desire) toward—because constituted (in a traumatic rupture) by—a goodness that can never be known or received but to which all is indebted.

We can in this sense hear the resonance between Ibn Gabirol's material apophasis and the signifyingness of the trace in Levinas:

> The other proceeds from the absolutely absent. His relationship with the absolutely absent from which he comes *does not indicate, does not reveal* this absent; and yet the absent has a meaning in a face. This signifyingness is not a way for the absent to be given in a blank in the presence of a face—which would again bring us back to a mode of disclosure. The relationship which goes from a face to the absent is outside every revelation and dissimulation, a third way excluded by these contradictories. . . . Within being, a transcendence revealed is inverted into immanence, the extra-ordinary is inserted into an order, the other is absorbed into the same. In the presence of the other do

we not respond to an "order" in which signifyingness remains an irremissible disturbance, an utterly bygone past? Such is the signifyingness of a trace.[28]

Sharing a logic with khora-of-khora, Levinas does not himself seem aware of this tradition as evidenced in his own reference to matter as the foil to, as opposed to an opening for, his view. Speaking of insomnia as an "opening that is prior to intentionality, a primordial opening that is an impossibility of hiding . . . in oneself"[29] in which the restful totality of sameness is disturbed by the Other,[30] Levinas notes:

> Here we find a passivity of inspiration, a passivity lacking a taking charge, or the subjectivity of a subject sobered out of its perseverance in being. The formalism of this insomnia is more formal than that of the form that encloses in a presence; this is a formalism of the void, a formalism of a piercing or fission. This is because the insomnia, or the awakening without intentionality, the disinterested awakening (in the etymological sense of the term: dis-inter-estedness), <u>is not an appeal to a form (it is not a materiality calling for form)</u>. And here form does not arrest its own design as a form, any more than it encompasses its content; instead, this form signifies the absolutely noncontained (or the *infinite*).[31]

Levinas disambiguates the passivity of insomnia from the passivity of matter; the passivity in which he is interested is not, as he notes, "an appeal to a form." But while, to be sure, the passivity of insomnia—its being hollowed out by an Other—is not anything like the matter-seeking-after-form that we find across most of the history of Western philosophy (rooted primarily in an Aristotelian hylomorphism with resonances too in at least certain traditions of Platonic khora), it is on the contrary quite like the khora-of-khora matter at play in our forgotten Islamo-Judeo-Greek tradition, a matter-desire-nothing at the heart of being, thought, and self which does not primarily seek after the fulfilling completions of form (a search in terms of which one might, pace Derrida, even read the Timaean khora). On the contrary, khora-of-khora seeks first and foremost after the absolutely other, infinitely unattainable undefined and undefinable goodness-without-form that can never be received.[32]

For Ibn Gabirol, the claim that there are layers of matter before/beyond/within beings—his hylomythy above and beyond any ontology, morphology, onto-story, or even hylology—is a reflection on the anarchic (un)rootedness of being, thought, and self in a khoric atopia, a placeless nothing that cannot be found, and which messianistically desires—without determinate direction—after a nondisclosing (because excessive) good that breaks in, constituting being and human being in and through a chasmic opening in desire that is nothing like a constitution (in the sense of a perfection or completion) by way of form (as one finds in standard Aristotelian hylomorphisms). Exhibiting the Levinasian dynamic of an insomnia that signals the splitting open of Same by Other, khora-of-khora at the heart of being does not primarily seek after the disclosing, completing motion of forms—for Ibn Gabirol and Plotinus, forms come "after" khora-of-khora, as well as "after" the infinite goodness that khora-of-khora seeks. In the Plotinian talk of intelligible matter as in Ibn Gabirol's Islamo-Judeo-Greek talk of a material Grounding Element, khora-of-khora is broken into by—and desires after—Goodness, the ultimate Other that exceeds all form (and hence is ultimately unreceivable). In the language of Levinas, here we find "a passivity of inspiration, a passivity lacking a taking charge, or the subjectivity of a subject sobered out of its perseverance in being."

Reflecting more fully on the link with Levinas, it is true that the Islamo-Judeo-Greek tradition of khora-of-khora does not focus in particular, as does Levinas, on the human other (as face) in the eruptive (not-yet) disclosure of transcendent goodness. That said, the khora-of-khora tradition does focus strongly on the anarchic interruptive ground of being and human being in the radical otherness of an undefined, formless goodness. We may in this sense say that the Islamo-Judeo-Greek tradition of khora-of-khora and Levinas share an optics. And, in its emphasis on a goodness that can never be had but which operates through the logic of trace, we may also say that the khora-of-khora's apophatic matter-discourse shares an optics with Levinasian and Derridean logics of messianicity. In this sense, we move from a metaphysics of matter, as a crude version of unreflective ontotheology, to a matter-discourse—or hylo-grammatology—which testifies to nothing less than a messianisitic opening.

Closing Thought: On a New Islamo-Judeo-Greek Khoric and Kenotic History of "Negative Theology"

Indeed, in this opening, we have perhaps struck upon a way to bridge the gap—arguably unbridged by even hymnic readings of Denys—between negative or mystical theologies and Derrida. As we have seen, Derrida sees "risk" in thinking together the khora with the *"es gibt* which always summons negative theology in its Christian history." In arguably related fashion, Derrida—while arguably unaware of the khora-of-khora tradition we have been exploring[33]—divides the history of Christian apophasis from the history of Islamic and Jewish apophasis. After expositing Christian apophasis (with a focus on Denys, as well as Augustine and Eckhart) in "How to Avoid Speaking," Derrida begins the third and final section of his essay as follows: "I thus decided not to speak of negativity or of apophatic movements in, for example, the Jewish or Islamic traditions. To leave this immense place empty, and above all that which can connect such a name of God with the name of the Place, to remain thus on the threshold—was this not the most consistent possible apophasis?"[34] Reflecting on Derrida's own distinction between Christian and Judeo-Islamic apophasis,[35] it seems that Islamo-Judeo-Greek hylomythy—from among all other moments in the history of "negative theology"—most fully stands together with Derrida in an apophatic speechlessness at the threshold.

We might in this regard also see Islamo-Judeo-Greek hylomythy as filling the gap described by de Vries between historical negative or mystical theologies and Derrida. Reflecting jointly on the importance of the khoric motif in Derrida, and the absence of that motif in the most well-cited examples of medieval apophasis (such as Denys), de Vries identifies what is "arguably the greatest challenge for any interpretation of Derrida's work that would wish to situate him in an unbroken lineage of apophatic discourse, whether of negative theology, mysticism, or both."[36]

It seems that it is precisely our forgotten Islamo-Judeo-Greek khora-of-khora—with its express focus on an anarchically grounding matter-desire-nothing at the root of being and human being—that might at least tentatively be called upon (and arguably, in any case, more so than the hymnic in Denys) as a possible way to maintain an "unbroken lineage" from ancient-medieval apophasis to Derridean messianicity.

The "doctrine" for which Ibn Gabirol has been lambasted in the history of philosophy (Ibn Gabirol is depicted for his "universal hylomorphic" claim that "even intellects have matter" as a bad reader of Aristotelian hylomorphism) now emerges as the site of a forgotten deep apophatic opening in the history of philosophy in which Ibn Gabirol—following Greek-into-Islamic Plotinian tradition—hylomythically writes matter-and-matter-and-matter in a performative apophatic encounter with the anarchic ground of being and of self in a desire which messianistically reaches for a goodness that is not yet arrived and is always yet to come. Unlike other apophatic traditions in which negation centers on (even as it in some sense decenters) God, the Islamo-Judeo-Greek hylomythic tradition focuses instead on a disruptively constituting khoric desert "from 'before' . . . any revelation" at the heart of life.

Might we not in this regard also take ourselves to have found a shared space between the logic of the Islamo-Judeo-Greek khoric apophasis and the logic of kenosis? Commenting on the paradox of the pure gift in theology, and reflecting on God Beyond Being's giving Himself in/as Being, de Vries talks about the unavoidability of the idolatry of ontotheology, drawing a connection in particular between the "emptying out" of Christian kenosis and the Levinasian and Derridean "*adieu.*" As de Vries notes: "There is no better figure for this paradox or aporia than the New Testament notion of the kenosis, reclaimed, like the *adieu*, first by Levinas and then by Derrida: a movement of passage, of emptying out, of making oneself (and one's word and thoughts) nothing, leaving everything behind and gaining everything in its place. This, nothing else, is the paradox of faith, its reversal, inversion, conversion."[37]

While kenosis is indeed one textual eruption of this paradox of faith—as the paradox of an emptying out which is a "gaining everything"—we have, it seems, uncovered another figure for this paradox, namely the Islamo-Judeo-Greek khora-of-khora as placeless place of desire and rupture, and as opening to the not-yet of goodness at the core of being and human being that, as site for nothing and everything, at once disrupts and orients. While we might note in the khora-of-khora tradition a more sustained emphasis—in the very contours of a matter discourse—on the "not-yet" (as opposed to the "gaining everything") in resonance with discourses of liminality and exile (something we might describe as a move from "hope" to "difficult hope"),[38] we can indeed find in this tradition a faithful focus on the compresence of emptying and gaining, as for example in our earlier consideration of Plotinus's own paradoxical depiction of the subject's "other-ward" turn as at once a moment of emptiness and fullness.

And we may speak of the kenotic opening provided by Islamo-Judeo-Greek hylomythy more broadly: where iterations of matters upon matters provide an insistent focus on a "pleromatic abyss"[39] of not-yet expectancies at the core of being, we have uncovered the root of self in a khoric "not-site" that is itself the sacred bursting open of all life.

Notes

1. I have in mind the sense of "pure messianism" or "messianicity without messianism" of which Derrida speaks; see Derrida, "Faith and Knowledge: The Two Sources of 'Religion' at the Limits of Reason Alone," in *Religion*, ed. J. Derrida and G. Vattimo (Stanford, CA: Stanford University Press, 1996), 17. I will use the terms "messianicity" and "messianistic" in this chapter in that spirit. For a compelling overview of messianicity without messianism in five succinct bullet points, see Robert Gibbs, "Messianic Epistemology," in *Derrida and Religion*, ed. Yvonne Sherwood and Kevin Hart (New York: Routledge, 2005), 120; see too John Caputo's commentary in *Deconstruction in a Nutshell: A Conversation with Jacques Derrida*, ed. John D. Caputo (New York: Fordham University Press, 1997), 156–180; on messianicity in Levinas, see, for example, Robert Bernasconi, "Different Styles of Eschatology: Derrida's Take on Levinas' Political Messianism," *Research in Phenomenology* 28, no. 1 (1998), 3–19; Bettina Bergo, "Levinas's Weak Messianism in Time and Flesh, or the Insistence of Messiah Ben David," *Journal for Cultural Research* 13, nos. 3–4 (2009), 225–248.

2. Jean-Luc Marion, "In the Name: How to Avoid Speaking of 'Negative Theology,'" in *God, the Gift, and the Postmodern*, ed. John D. Caputo and Michael J. Scanlon (Bloomington: Indiana University Press, 1999), 20–53, at 31–32.

3. I am thankful to the anonymous reviewer who reminded me to note that there are plenty of Jewish thinkers (Rosenzweig, Fackenheim, et al.; and I might add, plenty of Islamic thinkers) who also uphold the "anthropotheological God of Revelation" that Derrida deconstructs, and which I will in this chapter be contrasting with the more fluid sense of "God/good" in the Islamo-Judeo-Greek Neoplatonic tradition. I might also note that while my emphasis on the "Islamo-Judeo-Greek" is in part aimed against Marion's sense of "Greek versus Christian" apophasis and Derrida's sense of "Greco-Christian versus Islamic and Jewish" apophasis, one might supplement my own sense of "Islamo-Judeo-Greek versus Christian" apophasis with strong connections between the Jewish and the Christian in a host of other social and theological contexts. I might also note that not all Christian theologians view Plotinus (as does Marion) as theologically secondary to Christian thought. Tillich, for example, talks in rather exalted terms of Plotinus opening the way for much of what is most important in later Christian thinkers such as Denys. While demarcating Christian elements that differ from the Greek, Tillich—in his chapters on Plotinus and Dionysius in his *A History of Christian Thought*—presents a much more fluid interface between Greek and Christian Neoplatonisms.

On the other hand, we should note that Derrida is open, in other contexts (e.g., in his treatment of *Matthew*) to reading Christian texts in terms of excess and essential instability and as such reading Christianity as aporetic and as "an hyperbolic, never-ending, internal critique," see Tyler Roberts, "Sacrifice and Secularization: Derrida, de Vries, and the Future of Mourning," in *Derrida and Religion*, 263–282, at 268–272. Even so, Derrida remains cautious about resurrection, about Denys's account of a hymnic encounter with a trinitarian God, and about Marion's emphasis on the role of baptism in denominalization; on this, see Derrida, "How to Avoid Speaking: Denials," trans. Ken Frieden, in *Derrida and Negative Theology*, ed. Harold Coward and Toby Foshay (Albany: State University of New York Press, 1992), 73–142, esp. 111; Derrida, "Response to Jean-Luc Marion," in *God, the Gift, and the Postmodern*, 46. For additional complexities in Derrida's relation to Christianity on the one hand and to the Christological character of Marion's phenomenology on the other, see Elliot R. Wolfson, *Giving beyond the Gift: Apophasis and Overcoming Theomania* (New York: Fordham University Press, 2014), 448n202.

4. Emphasizing the inability of any "negative theology" to escape presence, Wolfson notes that "a vestige of theism remains and . . . it is not possible to think the unthought otherness without being caught in the paradoxical labyrinth of contemplating the other as precisely what is not the same and therefore the same other" (Wolfson, *Giving beyond the Gift*, 258) and de Vries notes that "the ontotheological mistake, its fatal idolatry and blasphemy, is . . . by no means either accidental or avoidable" (Hent de Vries, *Philosophy and the Turn to Religion* [Baltimore, MD: The Johns Hopkins University Press, 1999], 115).

5. Jacques Derrida, "Khōra," trans. Ian McLeod, in *On the Name*, ed. Thomas Dutoit (Stanford, CA: Stanford University Press, 1995), 89–127, at 96.

6. Derrida, "Faith and Knowledge," 21.

7. Derrida, *Rogues: Two Essays on Reason*, trans. Pascale-Anne Brault and Michael Naas (Stanford, CA: Stanford University Press, 2005), xiv; cited in Hent de Vries, "'Et Iterum de Deo': Jacques Derrida and the Tradition of Divine Names," in *Trace of God: Derrida and Religion*, ed. Edward Baring and Peter E. Gordon (New York: Fordham University Press, 2015), 13–38, at 36.

8. Derrida, "Khōra," 94. On khora in Derrida more broadly, see also Derrida, "Faith and Knowledge," 21, sec. 25; Caputo, *Deconstruction in a Nutshell*, 71–105; and de Vries, *Philosophy and the Turn to Religion*, 108–115.

9. Jacques Derrida in conversation with Richard Kearney, "Terror, God and the New Politics," in *Traversing the Imaginary: An Encounter with the Thought of Richard Kearney*, ed. John Manoussakis and Peter Gratton (Lanham, MD: Rowman and Littlefield, 2004), 26; cited in Richard Kearney, "Deconstruction, God, and the Possible," in *Derrida and Religion*, 297–307, at 297.

10. John D. Caputo, "Deconstructing God," *New York Times, Opinionator*, March 2, 2014, http://opinionator.blogs.nytimes.com/2014/03/09/deconstructing-god/?_r=0.

11. John D. Caputo, *Philosophy and Theology* (Nashville, TN: Abingdon Press, 2014), 64.

12. I have in mind the Timaean khora on the one hand, and Aristotelian prime matter on the other. The differences between these need not concern us here; for our context, the point is that each operates, in its respective system, as the philosophical foundation of corporeality (not of intelligibility).

13. For background on Ibn Gabirol's Neoplatonic system of emanating matters, as well as fuller bibliographical details on the Ps. Empedoclean tradition, the Judeo-Arabic, Latin, and Hebrew text additions of Ibn Gabirol's *Fons Vitae (Fountain of Life)*, as well as Hebrew and English versions of his poetry, see Pessin, *Ibn Gabirol's Theology of Desire: Matter and Method in Medieval Jewish Neoplatonism* (Cambridge: Cambridge University Press, 2013). On intelligible matter (in relation to indefinite dyad) in Plotinus, see John Dillon, "Solomon Ibn Gabirol's Doctrine of Intelligible Matter" in *Neoplatonism and Jewish Thought*, ed. Lenn E. Goodman (Albany: State University of New York Press, 1992), 43–59, and John M. Rist, "The Indefinite Dyad and Intelligible Matter in Plotinus," *Classical Quarterly* 12, no. 1 (1962): 99–107; for overview, see Pessin *Ibn Gabirol's Theology of Desire*, appendix A5, 172–173. In Plotinus, see *Enneads* 2.4.1–5; 5.4.2, 5.5.4; see, too, 3.8.11 and 5.3.11 (*Plotinus*, vols. I–VII [Loeb Classical Library], trans. A. H. Armstrong [Cambridge: Harvard University Press, 1966–1988]).

14. On the material Grounding Element, see Pessin, *Ibn Gabirol's Theology of Desire*, and "Solomon Ibn Gabirol," in *The Stanford Encyclopedia of Philosophy*, ed. E. N. Zalta, September 23, 2010, http://plato.stanford.edu/entries/ibn-gabirol.

15. Pessin, *Ibn Gabirol's Theology of Desire*, esp. chapter 8.

16. Neoplatonic emanation should not be confused, as it is by many, with a doctrine of causal mechanism; this error can be seen, for example, in Solomon Munk's contrast of "emanation" with a "doctrine of creation" (Munk, *Philosophy and Philosophical Authors of the Jews: A Historical Sketch*, trans. Isidor Kalisch [Cincinnati, OH: Cloch and Co., 1881]); this error can also be seen, for example, in Gilles Deleuze's presentation—in his analysis of the history of expression/immanence—of "emanation" as the conceptual foil to his (and

Spinoza's) view (Deleuze, *Expressionism in Philosophy: Spinoza*, trans. Martin Joughin [New York: Zone Books, 1990]).

17. On this "theology of desire," see Pessin, *Ibn Gabirol's Theology of Desire*.

18. On Intellect, see Plotinus, *Enneads* 6.7.35. The section of Plotinus's *Enneads* that I am here invoking as part of my analysis of a Plotinian-Gabirolean conceptual space is not currently known to have been available in Arabic. That said, we must bear in mind that the basic *themes* contained in these Plotinian passages—even if not the terms "intelligible matter" or "Grounding Element" per se—do indeed occur across a number of Arabic Neoplatonic texts. For example, while none of Farabi, Avicenna, or the *Theology of Aristotle* talks directly of intelligible matter (or of a material Grounding Element), each of them talks overtly of Intellect's complex inward/upward/outward turnings (a theme also pursued in *Enneads* 5.2.1), as they each also talk overtly of a desire at the heart of being. Once we understand the logic of Plotinian intelligible matter as an engagement with being's restless desire for a goodness that exceeds it (an idea directly at play as well in both an emphasis on Intellect's complex turnings and in an emphasis on cosmic eros), it becomes methodologically unnecessary (and unhelpful) to limit our talk of a khora-of-khora tradition to only those texts that overtly talk in terms of an "intelligible matter," a material "Grounding Element," or some other overt term for a matter that resides at the core of being and Intellect. Turning, for example, to the *Theology of Aristotle* (to which we have good reason to say Ibn Gabirol had access), while it does not overtly talk of a matter at the core of being, we do find—in relation to *Enneads* 5.2.1—an overt description of Intellect's turning, and "becoming filled with the light of God" (see Pessin, "Piety, Love, and Emanation in Islamic and Jewish Neoplatonism: Intermediation with Divine Presence and Other Implications of Apophatic Dialectic," in *Philosophy in Islamic Lands*, ed. Therese-Anne Druart [Washington, DC: Catholic University of America Press, forthcoming]); see *Theology of Aristotle*, chapter 10; for English, see *Plotiniana Arabica (including the Theology of Aristotle)*, trans. G. L. Lewis, in *Plotini Opera*, *Plotini Opera, Tomus II: Enneades IV–V*, ed. Paul Henry and Hans-Rudolf Schwyzer (Paris and Brussels: Desclée de Brouwer, 1959), 291–293; for Arabic, see *Plotinus Apud Arabes, Theologia Aristotelis et fragmenta quae supersunt*, ed. A. Badawi (Cairo: Maktabat an-Nahda al-Misriya, 1955), 135, lines 11–12. This set of descriptions—especially within the broader *Theology of Aristotle* dynamic of emanation, desire, and the excess of an uncontainable and unknowable goodness—is, I would argue, very much a part of the khora-of-khora tradition, even absent particular talk of "intelligible matter" or "Grounding Element."

19. On this drunkenness, see Plato's *Symposium* 203b5 (*Plato, with an English Translation* [*Loeb Classical Library*], vol. 5, Lysis, Symposium, Gorgias, trans. W. R. M. Lamb [London: Heinemann, 1925]).

20. Canto 9 of Ibn Gabirol's celebrated Hebrew poem, *Keter Malkhuth* (*Kingdom's Crown*); for Hebrew, see *Hebrew Poetry in Spain and Provence* (*Ha-shīrah Ha-'ivrīt Bi-Sefarad ū-be-Prōvans*) (Jerusalem: Mosad Byalik, 1954), 262, line 82; for English, see Cole, *Selected Poems of Solomon Ibn Gabirol* (Princeton, NJ: Princeton University Press, 2001), 149. For further treatment of this line, see Pessin, *Ibn Gabirol's Theology of Desire*, 113–117.

21. On Derrida's distinction between "pure prayer" and hymn in his analysis of Denys, see his "How to Avoid Speaking," 111.

22. I am here referring to Martin Buber's sense of "theomania" in *I and Thou*, trans. Walter Kaufmann (New York: Touchstone, 1970), 164.

23. For more on the "doubly apophatic," see Pessin, *Ibn Gabirol's Theology of Desire*, 131–139.

24. On Ibn Gabirol's Neoplatonic dedication to living toward goodness, see *Ibn Gabirol's Theology of Desire*, esp. 28–40, 116–117, 133–139, 149–159, and 160–163. For a sense of what I mean by an "affirmative" form of life, see Paul Franks on perfection in "Desdemona's Lie: Nihilism, Perfectionism, Historicism," *Journal of Nietzsche Studies* 44, no. 2 (2013): 225–245; Elliot Wolfson on the relation between mysticism and morality in *Venturing Beyond: Morality and Law in Kabbalistic Mysticism* (Oxford: Oxford University Press, 2006); de Vries on the relation of mystical apophasis and morality in *Religion and Violence: Philosophical Perspectives from Kant to Derrida* (Baltimore, MD: The Johns Hopkins University Press, 2002); and Tyler Roberts on decision and action in "Sacrifice and Secularization: Derrida, de Vries, and the Future of Mourning," in *Derrida and Religion*, 263–282.

25. Derrida, "'Eating Well', or the Calculation of the Subject: An Interview with Jacques Derrida," in *Who Comes after the Subject*, ed. Eduardo Cadava, Peter Connor, and Jean-Luc Nancy (New York: Routledge, 1991), 100.

26. Wolfson, *Giving beyond the Gift*, xiv.

27. Excerpt from a Hebrew poem by Ibn Gabirol (my translation), original in *Hebrew Poetry in Spain and Provence*, ed. Chaim Schirmann, 4 vols. (Jerusalem: Bialik Institute, 1960), 236, poem 96.

28. Emmanuel Levinas, "The Trace of the Other," in *Deconstruction in Context: Literature and Philosophy*, ed. Mark C. Taylor (Chicago: The University of Chicago Press, 1986), 345–359, at 355; author's emphasis.

29. Emmanuel Levinas, "In Praise of Insomnia," in *God, Death, and Time*, ed. Jacques Rolland, trans. Bettina Bergo (Stanford, CA: Stanford University Press, 2000), 208–209.

30. Ibid., 209.

31. Ibid., 210; *Levinas* in the original; my underlining for additional emphasis.

32. Speaking further of insomnia along these interruptive lines, Levinas notes: "Insomnia—the wakefulness in awakening—is disturbed in the core of its formal or categorical *sameness* by the *other*, which tears away at whatever forms a nucleus, a substance of the same, identity, a rest, a presence, a sleep. Insomnia is disturbed by the other who breaks this rest, breaks it from this side of the state in which equality tends to establish itself"; "God and Philosophy," in *Collected Philosophical Papers*, trans. Alphonso Lingis (Pittsburgh: Duquesne University Press, 1998), 156. In this regard, Levinas speaks of the self's being "interrupted by the unincludable" (ibid. 160), an image that he further describes in terms of a trauma (161). See too Simon Critchley, "The Original Traumatism: Levinas and Psychoanalysis," in *Ethics-Politics-Subjectivity: Essays on Derrida, Levinas, and Contemporary French Thought* (London: Verso, 1999), 183–197.

33. Derrida makes passing reference to Augustine's tradition of spiritual matter in "How to Avoid Speaking: Denials," 120, in the "Greco-Christian" part of his treatment. While not unrelated, Augustine's spiritual matter—absent the fuller discourse of a God who

relates to all beings via *emanation*—is not best seen as part of the Neoplatonic apophatic tradition of khora-of-khora being described in this chapter.

34. Derrida, "How to Avoid Speaking," 122.

35. Ibid., 121–122. One finds throughout Derrida the term "Greco-Christian" as one finds in this essay too a reminder that the Christian apophatic paradigm does not "ceas[e] to be Greek" (122).

36. de Vries, "Derrida and the Tradition of Divine Names," 36.

37. de Vries, *Philosophy and the Turn to Religion*, 115–116.

38. I plan in future work to address this notion of "hope versus difficult hope"—and the relation of these ideas to competing (though often complementary) discourses of "redemption versus exile." In this regard, consider Gibbs who, speaking of the "messianic epistemology" of Derrida, notes that a "formal structure of the future of the past *does not transform us* and charges us to hold open the future" (Gibbs, "Messianic Epistemology," in *Derrida and Religion*, 127; my italics); while I am not suggesting an impasse between this point in Gibbs and de Vries's insight, the difference in their locutions might point to something of the difference in emphasis—between exile (as "difficult hope") and redemption (as "hope")—to which I am beckoning. Along similar lines—though perhaps here indeed signaling an impasse—compare Marion's talk of transformation with Gibbs's emphasis on a formal structure that "does not transform" (a point perhaps related to his asking whether the radical messianicity of Derrida—as a promise that is never fulfilled and is always only yet to come—might be seen "as a rejection of the incarnation of God in Christ" [120]). On exile and related themes, see, for example, Edith Wyschogrod, "Autochtony and Welcome: Discourses of Exile in Lévinas and Derrida," in *Derrida and Religion*, 53–61, and "Crossover Dreams," *Journal of the American Academy of Religion* 54 (1986): 543–547.

39. I am here drawing on Wolfson's turn of phrase; see Wolfson, *Giving beyond the Gift*, xxvii, where he speaks of "a more far-reaching apophasis, an apophasis of the apophasis, based on the acceptance of an absolute nothingness—to be distinguished from the nothingness of an absolute—that does not signify the unknowable One but the manifold that is the pleromatic abyss at being's core."

NINE

Negative Dialectics, Sive Secular Jewish Theology: Adorno on the Prohibition on Graven Images and Imperative of Historical Critique

IDIT DOBBS-WEINSTEIN

> The cognitive Utopia would be to use concepts to unseal the non-conceptual with concepts without making it their equal.
> —*Negative Dialectics*, 10

> What clings to the image remains idolatry, mythic enthrallment.
> —*Negative Dialectics*, 205

Just as Adorno opens up the preface to *Negative Dialectics* with the bold claim that "negative dialectics is a phrase that flouts tradition" (*verstösst gegen die Überlieferung*), so do I wish to begin my considerations of negative dialectics, the book as well as model of philosophy it practices and proposes, with the bold claim that negative dialectics as a secular or (*sive*) Jewish negative theology is a phrase that flouts tradition.[1] But, what does flouting tradition mean? Why and how flout it? And, more important for this essay: whose tradition? These questions are not *mere* provocations although they certainly aim to provoke. That Adorno closes the preface with the anticipation of "attacks to which *Negative Dialectics* will expose him," that this anticipation proved to be "prophetic," and that, irrespective of their diversity, both the attacks and defenses often have an ad hominem component and manifest a need to distance him from or draw him to Judaism indicate the need to ask these questions. And, as will become evident, the question of tradition will also become the question of what is meant by "tradition." Since there is an unbridgeable abyss between the two traditions at the heart of these debates, an abyss willfully invisible to one, all too visible to the other, and since I wish to propose a critical model of the relation between "negative dialectics" and "theology" that flouts the one generally agreed upon by both opponents and exponents of Adorno, I must first briefly but critically engage the model of religion and theology prevalent in the debates about Adorno.

I: A Detour into History: The Hyphen

In the opening paragraph of a chapter titled "The Hyphen,"[2] J. F. Lyotard "speaking as a novice," takes a risk "of approaching a suffering of the breath and of the flesh, of the two together, a suffering that is perhaps the most impenetrable abyss within Western thought. I will be speaking of a white space or blank [*blanc*], the one that is crossed out by the *trait* or line uniting Jew and Christian in the expression 'Judaeo-Christian.'"[3] As Lyotard's poignant opening lines succinctly indicate not only is the Judeo-Christian tradition Christian, but its mode of being Christian constitutes the violent theologico-political history of Western thought as well as its politics.

Unlike Lyotard, I am not a novice, although I did not discover the term or concept "Judeo-Christianity," let alone as a single religious tradition common to Jews and Christians, until I was an adult, nor could it have been discovered until relatively recently. More importantly, neither the term nor the concept "Judeo-Christian" would have been coherent to the foremost medieval Jewish philosopher, RaMBaM or Moses Maimonides, in contrast to Judeo-Arabic, for example, the language in which he composed his philosophical and scientific works. I choose Maimonides as exemplar judicially since he was simultaneously a radical Aristotelian philosopher and the strictest advocate of negative predication of the divine names, arguing that the relation between all biblical attributes predicated of both God and humans is one of pure equivocation—a purely logical homonym. It cannot be overemphasized, however, that Maimonides's strict insistence of negative predication is strictly philosophical rather than mystical; subsequent appropriations by some Kabbalists notwithstanding. Moreover, Maimonides was the most esteemed medieval Jewish philosopher in the Christian, Latin west and his influence upon Christian philosophers was most extensive, including *inter multi alii*, St. Thomas Aquinas and Meister Eckhart, two Christian philosophers presented as practitioners of apophatic philosophy.

Just as Judeo-Christianity is a Christian mode of erasing the Judaic by incorporation through supersession, so is the incorporation of Jewish "theology" into the apophatic tradition. I must admit that I am, at best, hard pressed to understand what Habermas or Finlayson, the exemplary negative and positive interpreters of Adorno's purported mysticism, mean by Jewish thought and/or sources.[4] Ironically, Habermas's and Finlayson's philosophical evaluations of the apophatic, respectively negative and positive, determine their respective evaluations of Adorno's Jewish affiliation. Whereas Habermas acknowledges Adorno's Jewish milieu and influences, Finlayson is at great pains to deny these. And, it is poignantly ironic that it is precisely the elements that Habermas identifies as Jewish in Adorno's (and Horkheimer's) thought that he also condemns as irrational, contradictory, or bad philosophy. Conversely, and against Habermas *et idem alii*, Finlayson rescues Adorno as a philosopher by baptism, immersing him as it were in the waters of the Christian apophatic tradition of the Pseudo-Dionysus and Meister Eckhart, a tradition which at its most consistent requires not only negation but also remotion.

More importantly, I find especially troubling not only in Habermas and Finlayson, but also in the general literature about Adorno, the fact that what is identified as Jewish is almost entirely restricted to Kabbalah, or some cognate form of mysticism, rather than philosophy, literature, music, etc. Against this prevalent reading I wish to emphasize the facts that, in addition to the proximity and intimacy between Adorno, Benjamin, and Horkheimer, personal as well as philosophical, Adorno writes on Kafka, Bloch, Schoenberg, Kraus, Heine, Lucaks, Mann, Proust, Mahler, *et alii*. Among his collaborators as well as fellow émigrés are Marcuse, Pollock, Löwenhal, Krakauer, Eisler, Mann *et alii*. That Adorno was certainly intimately familiar with German Jewish philosophy, in general, the Marburg Neo-Kantian school, in particular, is clearly evident from the 1934 correspondence with Benjamin about *theology*. In this light and in the context of the question of tradition, it cannot be overemphasized that the foremost Marburg Neo-Kantian of the first part of the twentieth century, Herman Cohen, was especially concerned with the relation between reason and revelation, especially Judaism, and that several of his writings on religion attempted to synthesize Kant and Judaism, just as his preeminent predecessor Maimonides attempted to harmonize Aristotle and Hebrew scripture. Exemplary among these are *Religion of Reason out of the Sources of Judaism* (1919) and "An Analysis of Maimonides' Ethics" (1908).[5] Finally, Adorno was certainly familiar with Scholem's interpretation of the Kabbalah.[6] No less importantly, Adorno was keenly aware of the abyss between Christian mysticism and Kabbalah.[7]

Be that as it may, the "Meditations on Metaphysics," at the end of *Negative Dialectics*, makes clear the fact that "after Auschwitz," Adorno fully identified himself as a Jew, compelled as he was by material history. For, indeed, Auschwitz embodied the diabolical execution of the Jewish matrilineal law of descent, a law governing four generations. As Adorno states or confesses, "it may have been wrong to say that after Auschwitz you can no longer write poems. But it is not wrong to raise the less cultural question whether after Auschwitz you can go on living—especially whether one who escaped by accident, one who by rights should have been killed, may go on living." Presenting such survival as ridden by drastic guilt, Adorno characterizes the response to it as a nightmare atonement: he who was spared "will be plagued by dreams such as that he is no longer living at all, that he was sent to the ovens in 1944 and his whole existence since has been imaginary, an emanation of the insane wish of a man killed twenty years earlier."[8]

Rather than go into too great detail arguing against the prevalent discussions of Adorno's negative theology, I shall very briefly outline the major differences between the two traditions with respect to what is named "negative theology," a Christian naming, and subsequently discuss what all ignore, and thereby occlude, which ignoring also entails a misreading of the utopian moment in Adorno's thought or the standpoint of redemption, "whose reality or unreality hardly matters."[9]

Insofar as the majority of the literature discusses Adorno's "negative theology" in relation to the prohibition against graven images (*Bilderverbot*), I must begin with this rather telling association. When negative theology is considered in the light of medieval philosophy or theology, the underlying premise, explicit or implicit, informing the association between the negation of divine names and the ban on graven images is that the analogy of predication is the expression of the analogy of being. This is anachronistic even in the Christian tradition, certainly in the case of Aquinas,[10] and it is false in the Judeo-Arabic context. Nonetheless, this worry makes evident one of the major differences between the two traditions. An analogy of being in the Christian context is a worry precisely because "God became man." It is an ontotheological,[11] strictly Christian worry that gives rise to indefinitely many forms of nominalist-realist debates but, ironically, is of little interest to either philosophical or theological versions of medieval negative theology, be they rationalist or mystical. In the context of the debates about Adorno, the worry is about the relation between word and image or language and representation. More precisely, against both nominalists and realists Adorno first and foremost seeks to dissociate the immediate relation between consciousness and thing, or *material object*, the condition for both affirming and denying an immediate relation between word, image, and thing. Not only is the thought not the image of the thing *or* an unmediated fact of consciousness, but also, and more importantly, there can be no representation without reflection, in other words, mediation. As Adorno points out, "it is only in the *absence of images* that the full object could be conceived."[12] Thus, ironically Adorno's negative dialectics is a version of, or intervention in the nominalist realist debate after Leibniz, Kant, and Brentano,[13] again, a decidedly Christian, ontotheological worry. Nonetheless, insofar as one of Adorno's central concerns is the presentation of what is in excess of the concept, as well as the violence wrought by the concept, a concern that earns him (and Horkheimer) Habermas's vitriolic and spiteful attacks,[14] the association is understandable but wrong and misleading.

In contrast to the Latin Western presentation, which conflates the ban on images with the ban on uttering the divine names, and transforms them into a single ban, it is important to underscore the fact that in their Hebrew form the two prohibitions are against (1) *making* graven images and (2) bearing God's name *in vain*. That is, the first prohibition concerns the worship of idols, a worship that in that concrete historical context required human sacrifice; the second prohibition concerns bearing false witness or lying. Ironically, whereas in the Christian philosophical context of the nominalist-realist debate, the question is never about the possibility of divine knowledge, in fact, the idea of God is the ground of knowledge, in the Jewish context, especially in its Maimonidean form, it is divine knowability that is not merely in question but is denied. As an orthodoxy, the Christian concern with dogma focuses on ontotheology, whereas Judaism, as an orthopraxy, properly speaking, has no theology. It is not surprising, therefore, that for Maimonides both in the case of graven images and in the case of divine names the foremost concern is political rather than ontotheological. According to Maimonides, the purpose of the entire Torah and the raison d'etre of all the commandments and prohibitions is the eradication of idolatry. That is why even though he devotes almost all of *Guide of the Perplexed*'s book 1 to the negation of all divine predicates and argues for their strictly equivocal nature, at the very end of the *Guide*, in the penultimate paragraph of book 3, 54, Maimonides makes one concession to positive predication of the three major attributes characterizing divine action, namely, *Hesed, Mishpat, u-Z'Dakah*, "loving-kindness, righteousness, and judgment," since these are actions worthy of imitation. *Imitatio dei* for Maimonides is thus strictly political. The reason for obedience to the law is the pursuit of justice rather than salvation. Or, happiness, understood as *"eudaimonia"* can only come about in a just polity; where there is no justice, there can be no salvation, irrespective of how "salvation" is understood. The absence of "mercy," a divine attribute or name central to the Christian understanding of the divinity, is thus worth noting; for, mercy, properly speaking, is a violation of justice or the law. (Mercy is not equity, *epieikeia* in the juridical sense).[15] The Jewish community is a law-governed, political community rather than a community of believers, an orthopraxy rather orthodoxy.

In contrast to the association of the two prohibitions informed by the Christian tradition, in the Jewish tradition, precisely because it is the tradition of a political community, the prohibition against graven images is fundamentally linked to the antimessianic prohibition against preparation for the messianic age, that is, against the future orientation of history and politics and/or the future understanding of redemption. Understood in terms of concrete material history and politics, Adorno's strict adherence to the prohibition against "graven images" is formed and informed by his conversation with Benjamin about history and against Kant's and Hegel's teleologically oriented philosophy of history. Likewise, as will become evident in the following section, for Adorno, after Auschwitz, the prohibition against images, especially in a destitute world, must be read together with the prohibition against preparation for the messianic age, in other words, against a future orientation of either theory or praxis and must be given a stringent secular turn, stripped of any association with divine sanction, in fact belying it. Negative dialectics is thus a radical overturning (or overcoming) of theology, and in a significant way, especially of negative theology or Christian mysticism. In this light, I wish to insist that the utopian moment in Adorno's thought can be understood only in terms of the political status and inseparability of these two prohibitions.

II: Adorno: Negative Dialectics as Inoculation against Idolatry

In 2005, Adorno states, "I see no other possibility than an extreme ascesis toward any type of revealed faith, an extreme loyalty to the prohibition of images, far beyond what this once originally meant."[16]

What is, perhaps, most "infuriating" to traditional philosophy about *Negative Dialectics* is that, from beginning to end, its mode of flouting tradition, a mode characterized by Adorno as an "antisystem," resists any attempt at unification as a method. From beginning to end, Adorno provides different definitions or descriptions of negative dialectics many of which are negative, in other words, they state and elaborate either what it is not conceptually or what it is opposed to concretely, that is, objectively. Only at the end of the book, in the very last fragment of "Meditations on Metaphysics," does Adorno provide something akin to a "comprehensive" but strange definition of negative dialectics as a secular form of negative theology, situating negative dialectics in a material relation to redemption *or* the utopian moment in thinking, which definition, perhaps may account for the distinct definitions *or* descriptions scattered throughout the book. "It lies in the definition of negative dialectics that *it will not come to rest in itself*, as if it were total. *This is its form of hope.*"[17] A definition (*Bestimmung*) that is anything but a "common" philosophical definition; for neither can it function as a definition from which anything can be deduced, nor can it say anything about *what or how* negative dialectics *is*. Rather and instead, it provides a strange negative statement about what it ought not to *do*. The very formulation in the future tense takes the form of a wish, which wish is then presented again as a "form of hope," a form of the prophetic future? Perhaps. And, like a prophetic future, negative dialectics concerns practice *or* resistance in the present.

That is not to say, however, that *Negative Dialectics* lacks philosophical rigor or consistency, on the contrary, it rigorously resists reduction or unification and abstract conceptualization and instead insists on the primacy of the object, the individual, the material or what cannot be subsumed by the concept or, more precisely what *transcends* it. This is the only transcendence recognized by Adorno. As a secular *or* Jewish form of negative theology, the only transcendence possible is "vulgar," ontic, in other words, concrete, material, historical, the inverse of the mystical, spiritual, ahistorical transcendence characteristic of Christian mysticism.

While both forms of negative theology seek to transcend the concept, the secular (*or* Jewish) form returns thinking to bodies and suffering, to objective unfreedom, whereas the mystical, Christian one seeks to escape the latter through a flight out of politics and history and thereby at best trivializes suffering or becomes totally indifferent to it.

Negative Dialectics's strict adherence to the two "jewish" bans is an expression of a historical materialism informed by and echoing Benjamin's thought, of which the most important for this chapter are the writings on Kafka and the "Theses on the Concept of History," including the "Paralipomena to the 'Theses,'" theses that begin with the power of occult wizened theology and end with the prohibition against preparation for the messianic age—here as the prohibition against inquiring into the future—and instead calls for remembrance. "This disenchants the future" according to Benjamin, or in the language of *Dialectic of Enlightenment* breaks its spell, or in *Negative Dialectics* appears as the "Disenchantment of the Concept." It is these writings that belie the extensive and common reading of Benjamin as a messianic thinker as well as the common readings of "redemption" or reconciliation in Adorno. Rather than enter into an extensive polemos here, suffice it to underscore the fact that, much as she may wish to redeem the past, let alone usher in future happiness, even the angel of history cannot do so. And, if the angel of history cannot, then surely nor could a messiah, who, in the Jewish tradition, is but a man. Instead by disclosing the past as wreckage, insisting on remembrance, the angel can expose the present in all its indigence. It is this indigence that negative dialectics seeks to both expose and protest.

The proximity to Benjamin is nowhere more evident than in Adorno's insistence on the unconceptual, the individual, the immersion in detail, in the disjecta of history or more precisely of historicism. Rather than abandon a concern for truth, against the necessary truth of historicism both Benjamin and Adorno insist on the historical and transitory nature of truth. Benjamin's response to Gottfried Keller's claim that "the truth will not run away from us" is equally apt for Adorno, for it crystalizes the thoroughly historical nature of truth against historicism. Indeed, according to Benjamin, historical materialism pierces through historicism's timeless image. "For, it is an irretrievable image of the past which threatens to disappear in any present that does not recognize itself as intended in that image."[18] Thus understood, the ban on images is a ban on images as timeless rather than a ban on name or word provided that we insist on the gap between words and things, a gap marking the "history congealed in things." Just as Benjamin's historical materialism pierces through historicism's timeless image, so does negative dialectics penetrate the hardened objects so as to expose in them possibility "a possibility of which their reality has cheated the objects and which is nonetheless visible in each one."[19]

Against a logical or epistemological understanding of possibility, Adorno, following Benjamin, situates it historically. Insofar as *Negative Dialectics* begins with the question of the possibility of philosophy, it posits philosophy as an "object" of historical inquiry, an "object" like any other object whose lost possibility negative dialectics seeks to penetrate. Indeed, it is in terms of lost possibility that Adorno frames the question of philosophy today. As the opening sentence of the Introduction succinctly states, "philosophy, which once seemed obsolete, lives on because the moment to realize it was lost."[20] Viewed in this light, philosophy is a historical disjecta, either destitute or transformed beyond recognition into something use-full. Situated historically, the question of philosophy becomes a question of the relation between tradition and knowledge. And, according to Adorno, the mark of modern philosophy, whose patriarchs are Descartes and Bacon, is to radically dehistoricize the contents of thought, to render it timeless, to transform the object into an immediate, that is, fully present, datum. And, in the case of Bacon, most explicitly, to render philosophy into a use-full science. Ironically, the liberation of thought from history, originating in the insistence on the autonomy of inquiry against ecclesiastical-political authority that resulted in the rejection of all tradition as superstition, reinstated superstition in a more insidious, because occult, manner. The pure presence of all creation to the divinity, the identity between presence and present that constituted eternity, has now been transposed into the enthralling idol of a pure present. Thus, if *Dialectics of Enlightenment* critically traces the way in which "myth is already enlightenment, and enlightenment reverts to mythology,[21] *Negative Dialectics* critically traces the way in which Idolatry is already modern science (*scientia*) and philosophy,[22] and modern philosophy reverts back to idolatry. Against this form of idolatry Adorno insists on the intratemporal nature of all thinking and on its mediation by tradition. Critique is immanent precisely insofar as tradition is what mediates between known objects. Lest the question of idolatry become abstract, Adorno succinctly but precisely presents the concrete historical specificity of the inseparable relation between subject and object, in other words, forms of consciousness and objective material conditions. "A knowledge conforming wholly to *the idol of that purity, (dem Idol jener Reinheit)* of total timelessness—a knowledge coincident with formal logic—would become a tautology; there would be no more room in it *even* for transcendental logic. Timelessness, the goal which the bourgeois mind may be pursuing in order to compensate for its own mortality, is the acme of its delusion *(die Höhe von dessen Verblendung).*"[23] Modern science is also if not more totalitarian and authoritarian than was the medieval ecclesia against which it was first developed. Indeed, idolatry is a historical form, and hence the ban on images has to respond to its specific manifestation. It is not surprising, therefore, that in the last fragment of *Negative Dialectics* one of the definitions offered by Adorno concerns delusion. As he states, "Dialectics is the self-consciousness of *the objective content of delusion*; (*des objektiven Verblendungszuzammenhangs*) it does not mean to have escaped from that context. Its objective goal is to break out of the context from within."[24]

Recognizing the theologico-political origin and occult as well as distorted form of an ideal knowledge purportedly freed of tradition, Adorno recalls Benjamin's form of immersion in the details of tradition as a paradoxical critique of the autonomy of the subject. "Benjamin . . . strictly foreswore the *ideal* of autonomy and submitted his thought to tradition—although to a *voluntarily installed, subjectively chosen* tradition that is as unauthoritative as it accuses the autarkic thought of being."[25] Rather than abandon tradition as if that were possible through a transcendental leap, the critical relation to tradition transforms rather than escapes it. Philosophy's methexis in tradition, in the books that it criticizes, is transformative precisely because it is negative. It denies their authority rather than begrudges their importance. That is why, with Benjamin and Kafka, Adorno's model of the relation between philosophical books and their interpretation is exegesis rather than hermeneutics, originating as it does in the Jewish exegetical tradition, a tradition whose primary concern is transmissibility rather than truth or a tradition in which Haggadah can always raise a mighty paw against the Halakhah or a tradition that is nothing other than interpretation.[26] The historical core of truth is its transmissibility. Indeed, as the Sages of the Talmud have stated: *"Dibrah Torah Kilshon B'nei Adam"* or the Torah speaks human language, and elsewhere *"Shiveem Panim la-Torah"* or the Torah has seventy faces. Thus, although it may be possible to argue for a certain similarity between Halakhic interpretation and legal hermeneutics at the formal level, there is an abyss between exegesis of Hebrew scripture and Christian biblical hermeneutics, whose Protestant origins are not only concomitant with philosophical modernity, but also are motivated by the same rejection of ecclesiastical authority or tradition. In an all too brief a word, hermeneutics is overtly or covertly anagogically or escathologically oriented.[27] Indeed, Adorno's presentation of exegesis is "Jewish" *or* secular. After he establishes the commensurability between philosophy and tradition Adorno states, "This justifies the move from philosophy to exegesis, which exalts neither the interpretation nor the symbol into an absolute but seeks the truth where thinking secularizes the irretrievable archetypes of sacred texts."[28]

Adorno links the hostility to tradition to the hostility to rhetoric and to any linguistic expression that is not strictly significative, that is, extrahistorical. If the focus of the discussion of the relation between philosophy and tradition was the concern with the emptying of philosophy of mediation by the idols of positivistic science and pure presence, the concern of the discussion of rhetoric is the reduction of all meaning to signification, absolute precision and, more important, to the nominalist reduction of all meaning to signification in the name of demythologization, a reduction against which no rhetoric or dialectics can be mustered. Viewed in this light, Adorno's insistence on the historical core of truth is an intervention in the nominalist-realist debate, wrenching it free of Christology or in its Hegelian form restitution of conceptual realism. This is a critical intervention against doctrine. As Adorno states, "A genuine critical philosophy against nominalism is not invariant: it changes historically with the function of skepticism. To ascribe any *fundamentum in re* of concepts to the subject is idealism. Nominalism parted company with it only where idealism made objective claims. The concept of a Capitalist society is not a *flatus vocis*."[29] At its best, critically or exegetically understood, transmissibility is a matter of content rather than form. For, only as transmissible is truth not doctrine, the prohibition against thinking otherwise.

Against the philosophical hostility to rhetoric, which indeed can be usurped for merely practical, persuasive ends, Adorno argues not only that the rhetorical side of philosophy is dialectic but also, and more important, that "it is in the rhetorical quality that culture, society, and tradition animate the thought; a stern hostility to it is leagued with barbarism, in which bourgeois thinking ends."[30] Against the tyranny of form, mutual to idealism and nominalism, as well as late bourgeois thought, Adorno proposes a dialectic that attempts to rescue the rhetorical element of philosophy, linking thought and its "object" through language, a link that philosophy either trivializes or disempowers, that is, depoliticizes. As Adorno argues, against popular opinion, or *endoxa*, the rhetorical element in dialectics inclines to content, precisely because content is not closed, in other words, it is thoroughly historical and political. As a protest against form, dialectics is a protest against mythology, against the oppressive myth of the ever same, which, properly, that is materially, understood is a taboo against the concrete possibility that there *could be* a society without beggars. It is a protest against the promise of happiness in the midst of unhappiness. Against the insistence on form Adorno states, "to want substance in cognition is to want a utopia. It is this consciousness of possibility that sticks to the *concrete*, the undisfigured. Utopia is blocked off by possibility, never by immediate reality; that is why it seems abstract in the midst of extant things."[31] Negative dialectics brings into sharp relief the falsity insisted upon by an appeal to the necessity of what is presented as the unchangeable status of immediate reality, its eternal immutability. But, were there a right state of things, were there a society free of beggars, there would be no suffering and hence no need for utopia. That is why today, "the freedom of philosophy is [or should be] nothing but the capacity to give voice to its unfreedom."[32] Conversely, in a society where there are beggars, a society governed by use-value, the value governing the law of identity, "the ineffable part of utopia is that what defies subsumption under identity . . . *is necessary* anyway if life is to go on at all, even under the prevailing circumstances of production.³³ Against the necessity that constitutes the eternal immutability that justifies suffering now for the sake of universal salvation, Adorno presents the only necessity and hence "utopian" possibility in concrete, historical terms, namely in the face of life under conditions of oppression.

Adorno's writings on music, especially on Mahler and Schoenberg, confront the ban on images at its aesthetic core as well as underscore their Jewish form. Against the ahistorical edifying claims for both absolute music and modern music as expressions of the ever same,³⁴ new or avant-garde music deprives the hearer of the familiar, of consolation, repudiating the humanity of which they saw themselves as expressions, albeit in different ways, and thereby making manifest the inhumanity of the insistent claims to music's liberating ability in the midst of oppressive, totalizing institutions. The truth of avant-garde music resides in the absence of meaning, an absence that thereby repudiates the meaning of organized society. The doubled denial has no positive counterpart: in the current historical, political, material context, music is limited to determinate negation.³⁵ That Adorno describes the opposition to Mahler's and Schoenberg's music as an expression of antisemitism as early as 1930 is worth noting. Adorno's articulation of the anti-intellectual form of the hostility is especially striking since it makes evident the manner in which negative dialectics as a Jewish negative theology is a response to the barbarism at the heart of culture manifest in antisemitism. I shall, therefore, quote at length.

> whole groups of formulae are common to the fight against Schoenberg and against Mahler—*the Jewish intellectual whose deracinated intellect ruins oh-so beneficient Nature*; the despoiler of venerably traditional musical goods, which are either turned into banalities or corroded pure and simple; the abstract fanatic with the will discovered by Reimann "to accomplish something unheard of," who is burning down the lovely greensward all around us, on which, *everyone else feels so good*. Mahler, like Schoenberg, is the butt of all these accusations as if the radical dialectical rupture of the newer music did not fall between them.³⁶

"The abstract fanatic Jew" who indeed is "unlike everyone else," the "critical intellectual," is the always already one who seeks to demythologize the Romantic myth of beneficent nature that covers over a society that "feels so good" by ignoring suffering. Ironically, and dialectically, the diatribe against the Jew is not entirely untrue for, what is attributed to the "abstract" Jew and is rejected is the capacity for critical self-reflection, which capacity is predicated upon the rejection of graven images, reconciliation, and the promise of future happiness in the face of suffering, a capacity blocked off by the pacifying myth of beneficent nature. As Adorno states, "dialectics is a protest against mythology,"[37] whether it is critically expressed in music or philosophy and is understood as negative dialectics. And, as protest, it is a political intervention.

Finally, one of the most vivid, distilled monadic constellations of protest against the persistent and insistent humanist claims of art, an aesthetic expression of negative dialectics, is found in "Toward Understanding Schoenberg." After he notes that Schoenberg's music denies the listener everything to which she has been accustomed, in other words, a link to the traditional, to image and consolation, *or* to the possibility of reconciliation, Adorno states: "In an era of music's emancipation it claims to be nothing more than the voice of truth. Without crutches of the familiar, but also without the deception of praise and *false positivity*. The strength to do this, not illusion, is what is consoling about it. One could say that Schoenberg translated the Old Testament ban on images into music. This alienates us, where tone is concerned."[38] Art's relation to philosophy as a negative, radical Jewish *or* secular face (*species*) of negative theology is best summarized by the succinct claims that "art stands tensed in opposition to the horror of history" and that "it stands opposed to mythology" in *Philosophy of New Music*, the book described by Adorno as a third "detailed excursus to *Dialectic of Enlightenment.*"[39]

Notes

Significant portions of this chapter were published in Dobbs-Weinstein, *Spinoza's Critique of Religion and Its Heirs: Marx, Benjamin, Adorno* (Cambridge: Cambridge University Press, 2015).

1. Theodor Adorno, *Negative Dialectics*, trans. E. B. Ashton (New York: Continuum, 1999). The intransitive verbal formulation: *"verstösstwesen gegen"* commonly means to offend or violate—that is, it has a negative, or destructive aspect. When italicized, I use the term "or" in an inclusive sense, dialectically *or* as it is deployed in Spinoza's *Ethics*, for example, *Deus sive Natura*.

2. I borrow the provocative and very apt subtitle for this polemos from Jean François Lyotard and Eberhard Gruber, *The Hyphen: Between Judaism and Chrisianity*, trans. Michael Naas (Amherst, NY: Humanity Books, 1999). Although I have strong reservations about Lyotard's *reading* of Adorno and focus on a different interpretative approach to Hebrew scripture than he does, I agree with his presentation of the nature and scope of the abyss between Judaism and Christianity.

3. Lyotard and Gruber, *The Hyphen*, 13.

4. I limit myself to Habermas and Finlayson because they are exemplary of two sides of the debates about "negative theology" in Adorno's thought. Jurgen Habermas, "Theodor Adorno—The Primal History of Subjectivity—Self-Affirmation Gone Wild," in *Philosophical-Political Profiles*, trans. Frederick Lawrence (Cambridge, MA: The MIT Press, 1987). Habermas repeats the thesis and conclusions of this profile in multiple other

works. Gordon Finlayson, "On Not Being Silent in the Darkness: Adorno's Singular Apophaticism," *Harvard Theological Review* 105, no. 1 (2012): 1–32. The literature addressing theological motifs in Adorno is rather extensive. Finlayson provides a good bibliography of this literature.

5. *"Charakteritik der Ethik Maimunis."* The title is often mistranslated as "The Ethics of Maimonides."

6. Habermas acknowledges Adorno's Jewish context in the most appalling, negative description of Adorno's and Horkheimer's time warp after they returned to Germany in Jurgen Habermas, "Dual Layered Time: Reflection on T. W. Adorno in the 50s," in *The Logos Reader*, ed. Stephen Bronner (Lexington: University Press of Kentucky, 2005), 75–80. At best, his description is a barely disguised expression of resentment toward the German Jewish intellectual milieu. There can be no philosophical response to this vulgar display of envy and *freudenschade* and *I* certainly cannot offer one.

7. At the end of *Negative Dialectics*, Adorno points out that Kabbalah means tradition. Adorno, *Negative Dialectics*, 372; [GS, Band 6, 365] "Kabbala, the name of the body of Jewish mysticism, means tradition. In its farthest ventures, metaphysical immediacy did not deny *how much of it is not immediate*."

8. Adorno, *Negative Dialectics*, 362–363.

9. Theodor Adorno, *Minima Moralia*, trans. E. F. N. Jephcott (London: Verso, 2005), 247.

10. See E. J. Ashworth, "Analogy and Equivocation in Thirteenth Century Logic: Aquinas in Context," *Medieval Studies* 54 (1992): 94–135.

11. Although "ontho-theology" is a term coined by Kant in reference to Anselm's argument for God's existence, its origin precedes Anselm and, more important, in relation to Anselm, it applies more aptly to his *Cur Deus Homo* than to the *Proslogion*.

12. Adorno, *Negative Dialectics*, 207. My emphasis.

13. In other words, in the light of the transformation of the concept into an object constructed by reason *or* rather the turn to the sovereignty of the subject with its disdain for the empirical object.

14. I can think of no more reductive, trivial, and misleading a presentation of Adorno's *Negative Dialectics* and *Aesthetic Theory* and of Horkheimer and Adorno's *Dialectic of Enlightenment* than that found in Lectures III and V of Jurgen Habermas, *The Philosophical Discourse of Modernity* (Cambridge, MA: The MIT Press, 1990). Rather than engage it or respond to absurd claims such as the accusation of skepticism and a blindness to "existing forms of communicative rationality" or "semantic potential in myth," I shall let Adorno respond: "Direct communicability to everyone is not a criterion of truth. We must resist the all but universal compulsion to confuse the communication of knowledge with knowledge itself, and to rate it higher, if possible—whereas at present each communicative step is falsifying truth and selling it out." Adorno, *Negative Dialectics*, 41. Against the charge of skepticism, or more precisely what Adorno presents as the "fear of skepticism" characteristic of "finite, *abstractly intellectual* thought," Adorno points out that a skeptical moment is an element of philosophy as dialectics, an element that does not remain *merely* negative. Adorno, *Negative Dialectics*, 16.

15. In fact, the demand for "equity" as a "correction of legal Justice" in the classical legal tradition, as well as in Aristotle, is similar to Adorno's insistence on what is always in

excess of the concept, on the concrete, historical, material individual that cannot be subsumed by the concept.

16. Theodor Adorno, "Reason and Revelation," in *Critical Models*, trans. Henry Pickford (New York: Columbia University Press, 2005), 142.

17. Adorno, *Negative Dialectics*, 406. My emphasis. GS, 398. "Es liegt in der Bestimmung negative Dialectik, dass *sie sich nicht bei sich beruhigt*, als wäre sie total. *Das ist ihre Gestalt von Hoffnung*." My emphasis.

18. Walter Benjamin, "Theses on the Concept of History," in *Selected Writings, Vol. 4: 1938–1940*, ed. Howard Eiland and Michael W. Jennings (Cambridge, MA: Belknap Press, 2006). Thesis V, 390–391.

19. Adorno, *Negative Dialectics*, 52.

20. Adorno, *Negative Dialectics*, 3.

21. Max Horkheimer and Theodor Adorno, *Dialectics of Enlightenment: Philosophical Fragments*, ed. G. S. Noerr, trans. Edmund Jephcott (Stanford, CA: Stanford University Press, 2002), xviii.

22. Where philosophy is understood as the construction of the object by the subject.

23. Adorno, *Negative Dialectics*, 54. GS, Band 6, p. 64. My emphases. The psychoanalytic tone of this depiction of the bourgeois mind or reified consciousness cannot be overemphasized. For, it is not merely an individual delusion that is highlighted but, more important, it also constitutes a very powerful superstition whose political implications are extensive.

24. Adorno, *Negative Dialectics*, 406; GS Band 6, 398. My emphasis.

25. Adorno, *Negative Dialectics*, 55. GS, Band 6, 64. My emphasis.

26. Walter Benjamin, "Letter to Gershom Scholem on Franz Kafka," in *Selected Writings, Vol. 3: 1935–1938* (Cambridge, MA: Belknap Press, 2006), 326.

27. Ironically, although premodern, ecclesiastically approved biblical interpretation is escathologically oriented, it still does not reduce interpretation into a single interpretation nor does it discard the historical "core of truth." See, for example, Augustine, *De Doctrina Christiana*, or Aquinas's biblical commentaries, including the commentary on Job on which, against St. Gregory's injunction to the contrary, he commented *ad litteram*.

28. Adorno, *Negative Dialectics*, 55. Cf. Benjamin, according to whom books have afterlives rather than lives where his model for the afterlife is indeed Hebrew scripture.

29. Adorno, *Negative Dialectics*, 49–50. My emphases. Adorno's use of Rocelyn's rather vulgar description of the relation between name and thing named is clear evidence that he was well versed in the history of the debate from its inception in the eleventh century and recognized its specifically Christian origin and nature.

30. Adorno, *Negative Dialectics*, 56.

31. Adorno, *Negative Dialectics*, 56–57. My emphasis.

32. Adorno, *Negative Dialectics*, 18.

33. Adorno, *Negative Dialectics*, 11. My emphasis.

34. As a critical historical evaluation neither Adorno nor I wish to extend the claim concerning the similarity between Mahler and Schoenberg back, on the contrary, for example, to Beethoven. Rather, the claim is that concrete, material history has belied the promise of absolute music. Absolute music is the aesthetic face *or* species of pure presence;

hence opposition to it is a form of the ban on images. Modern music, as a successor of ancient and medieval music, is a form of the promise of future happiness. Hence, opposition to it is a form of the prohibition against preparation for the messianic age.

35. I understand determinate negation in a Spinozian, antiteleological manner, namely, *"omnis determinatio est negatio."*

36. Theodor Adorno, "Mahler Today," in *Essays on Music*, ed. Richard Leppert, trans. Susan H. Gillespie (Berkeley: University of California Press, 2002), 603–604. My emphases.

37. Adorno, *Negative Dialectics*, 56.

38. Adorno, *Essays on Music*, 638. My emphasis. In anticipation of the question on a seeming contradiction with the insistence on philosophy as methexis in tradition, I respond, not at all. Rather, the claim to alienation is situated precisely in relation to tradition. This critical negative relation is especially evident in Mahler's deeply problematic, pastiche-like citations, or even ridicule of traditional romantic music. In this sense, this is commentary.

39. Adorno, *Philosophy of New Music*, trans. Robert Hullot-Kentor (Minneapolis: University of Minnesota Press, 2006), 5.

TEN

The Passion of Nonknowing True Oneness: Derrida and Maimonides on God—and Jew, Perhaps

MICHAEL FAGENBLAT

1. Dear Jacob (the Presumed Addressee of a Stray Judaism)

Imagine a bundle of letters, loosely wrapped in a parcel marked *Guide des égarés*, having arrived in Jacques Derrida's postbox. As he ponders the parcel, several "repressed memory traces, those of primeval experiences" that "remain unbound" stir within him.[1] It was to the *Lycée Maimonide* that the twelve-year-old Jackie Elie Derrida was sent when he was denied admission to his own school in 1942 on account of Aryanizing laws established by the Vichy government.[2] The young Derrida refused to attend the *Lycée Maimonide* and for a year secretly skipped class. Maimonides thereby marks Derrida's expulsion *into* and exile *from* the Jewish community:

> It was there [at the *Lycée Maimonide*], I believe, that I began to recognize—if not to contract—this ill, this malaise, the ill-being that, throughout my life, rendered me inapt for "communitarian" experience, incapable of enjoying any kind of membership in a group. . . . On the one hand, I was deeply wounded by anti-Semitism. And this wound has never completely healed. At the same time, paradoxically, I could not tolerate being "integrated" into this Jewish school, this homogeneous milieu that reproduced and in a certain way countersigned—in a reactive and vaguely specular fashion, at once forced (by the outside threat) and compulsive—the terrible violence that had been done to it. This reactive self-defence was certainly natural and legitimate, even irreproachable. But I must have sensed that it was a drive [*pulsion*], a gregarious *compulsion* that responded too symmetrically, that *corresponded* in truth to an *expulsion*.[3]

An expulsion into and from his *Judeité*, as he would later call it, in which the name Maimonides functions like a trace, like an "ashen name"—"something that erases itself totally, radically, while presenting itself."[4] Here, as far as I know, is the only mention Derrida makes of it directly, if parenthetically: "(By the way, have I ever told you about the *Guide des Égarés*—the *Perplexed*—that I opened and touched as an eight year old in my grand-father's glass-paneled library? Look up the words *égaré* [mislead, mislaid, distraught, astray], *s'égarér*, to do with getting lost, therefore, and *garer* [to park, to dock]. You'll find all you need to talk about journeying [du voyage], and about *my* journeys, including truths to be docked [*à garer*], to be kept [*garder*]—or not, so as to guard oneself from them or park them.)"[5] The ashes of the *Guide*, whereby a perplexing Judaism, misleading *and* mislaid, marks his stray experience of being Jewish:

> as I thought I perceived it during my adolescent years, when I was beginning to understand a little what was happening, this heritage [of Judaism] was already ossified, even necrotized, into ritual comportment, whose meaning was no longer legible even to the majority of the Jews of Algeria. I used to think then that I was dealing with a Judaism of "external signs." But I could not rebel—and believe me, I was rebelling against what I took to be *gesticulations*, particularly on feast days in the synagogues—I could not lose my temper, except from what was already *an insidious Christian contamination*: the respectful *belief in inwardness*, the preference for intention, the heart, the mind, mistrust with respect to literalness or to an objective action given to the mechanicity of the body, in short, a denunciation, so conventional, of Pharisaism. . . . One can imagine the desire to efface such an event or, at the very least, to attenuate it, to make up for it, and also to disclaim it. But whether the desire is fulfilled or not, the traumatism will have taken place, with its indefinite consequences, at once destructuring and structuring. . . . Where then are we? Where do we find ourselves? With whom can we still identify in order to affirm our own identity and to tell ourselves our own history? First of all, to whom do we recount it? One would have to construct oneself, one would have to be able *to invent oneself without a model* and *without an assured addressee*. This addressee can, of course, only ever be presumed, in all situations of the world. But the schemas of this presumption were in this case so rare, *so obscure*, and so random that the word "invention" seems hardly exaggerated.[6]

An insidious Christian contamination of inwardness, transmitted from that other North African with whom Derrida explicitly and intimately identified, Saint Augustine, is the self-authorizing explanation for his allergy to Judaism's ossified mechanicity. Astray to the point that he did not know and could not even imagine that *this very perplexity* has a tradition, that precisely through his conventional denunciation of gesticulated Pharisaism he was *participating* in a Judaism that was suspicious not only of literalness and mechanicity but also, as we shall see, of (Christian?) inwardness and (Greek?) abstraction. Astray to the point that he made nothing of the hypothesis that his own lack of history has a history, that his need to invent his own *Judeité* has a tradition, even if not a model, and that if such a heritage is indeed "so rare, *so obscure*," it is nevertheless as common and canonical as the name Maimonides into which he was exiled. For despite having no "*assured addressee*" for his invented, inward Judaism, Derrida was himself in salient ways the "presumed addressee" for whom Maimonides had written the *Guide* (which is not to say that Maimonides had the likes of Derrida "in mind"). His experience of an "ossified," "necrotized," "Judaism of 'external signs,'" denounced in the name of a putatively Christian inwardness, is the very experience that Maimonides addresses: "the human intellect having drawn him on and led him to dwell within its province, he must have felt *distressed by the externals of the Law.*"[7] Maimonides's presumed addressee, having been contaminated not by Christianity or Saint Augustine but by Plato and Aristotle, Alfarabi, Al Ghazali, Ibn Bajja, Ibn Sinna, or Ibn Rushd, is distressed, just as Derrida was, on account of a "respectful *belief in inwardness*, the preference for intention, the heart, the mind, mistrust with respect to literalness or to an objective action given to the mechanicity of the body, in short, a denunciation, so conventional, of Pharisaism." The unrealized alliance and the repressed friendship between Maimonides and Derrida thereby comes into view as a kinship in perplexity for the sake of a different Judaism—an obscure and invented Judaism, as Derrida imagined it would have to be—which does not easily coincide with the Judaism found in the synagogue, the school, and the community.

The ashen name of Maimonides, already scattered at the point of Derrida's "expulsion of 1942,"[8] haunts his self-confessed, crossed-out Marranoism: "I am one of those *marranes* who no longer say they are Jews even in the secret of their own hearts, not so as to be authenticated *marranes* on both sides of the public frontier, but because *they doubt everything*, never go to confession or *give up enlightenment*, whatever the cost, ready to have themselves burned, almost, at the only moment *they write under the monstrous law of an impossible face-to-face.*"[9] By this time, however, by 1991, Derrida's Marranoism had become a carefully crafted *avoidance* of the one Jew, the figure, friend or master, who in truth if not in fact accompanied him at almost every turn: *biographically, rhetorically,* and *substantively. Biographically,* for Maimonides was also, before the letter and in a far more dangerous context, a *marrano*, forced to adopt the religion of Islam, for years living under Almohad rule as a Jew in secret and, to pile secret on secret, when he moved to the more tolerant environs of Egypt and publicly reverted to his Jewishness, obliged to keep his forced conversion to Islam utterly secret—though on one occasion he was openly denounced—for in Egypt to be a Jew was tolerated but to have renounced Islam was a capital offense;[10] *rhetorically,* for Maimonides is, first and foremost, perhaps more than any other Jew, the one who *wrote,* who stylized his *Guide, under the monstrous law of an impossible face-to-face* with God; and *substantively,* for Maimonides (or a certain interpretation of Maimonides, which Derrida could surely have drawn out), is the exemplary premodern figure of the Jewish thinker who *doubted everything* and *gave up enlightenment*—even the enlightenment of nonliteral inwardness that constitutes the "insidious Christian contamination."

In this way one can imagine that had Derrida opened the mail and unbound the bundle of postcards he might have found traces of his own fingerprints all over it. Everywhere, on every page, what this elaborate letter says, what it seems to say, how it says it, and how it avoids saying it, resembles and in some ways even *amounts to* what Derrida had been saying and how he was saying it. Consider: the methods of commentary rather than the treatise; admiration for "what the philosophers say," which nevertheless differs with and always defers "our position"; rigorous arguments coupled with demonstrations of their principled incompleteness; the employment of apostrophes addressed to the reader and of periphrases that wind their way through thickets of preconceptions and misconceptions; citations that are used in novel contexts that release intentions that will have been original; the crafts of iteration and its qualifications, of negations and their negations, of parables and imagery that at once—that is, in the course of subsequent readings—convey, suggest, and conceal meanings; and above all a "passion for non-knowing," as Derrida calls it,[11] an intimation of singularity that is without intuition or concept, thus a passion that is neither experience nor idea but more like a secret that cannot be known as such and therefore can neither be kept to oneself nor shared, or a wager that can neither be won nor lost but only endured. In such ways the ashen name of Maimonides presents itself throughout Derrida's corpus.

2. How to Avoid Saying *Kaddish* for Ya'kov Elie ibn Georgette Sultana Esther Derrida

Even so, these letters, postmarked Fustāt (old Cairo) circa 1190, remained memorialized behind a glass paneled bookshelf in Derrida's memory. By what right then can we now open the mail of a dead man, much less simulate his reading of it? He had his time and declined his chances. In a lecture in Jerusalem, where the matter was almost unavoidable, he spoke—in a footnote! did he *say* it? I imagine him muttering this note to himself, like the prayers of a drunk woman—of his "lack of capacity, competence, or self-authorization" that made him unable "to speak of what my birth, as one says, should have made closest to me: the Jew, the Arab."[12]

But he traced his Marranoism to another Mediterranean Arab, Saint Augustine, calling himself "a sort of *marrane* of French Catholic culture," with his "own" "Christian body, inherited from SA in a more or less twisted line, *condiebar eius sale* [seasoned with his salt]."[13] For Augustine, the salt refers to Christ and his being seasoned with Him fresh from the womb. For Derrida, it is a case of his "Christian body"—that space of interiority in which "he" speaks with "himself"—being seasoned by the salt of Augustine, whose thought, as is well known, played a decisive role in hollowing out this space of interiority from which the problematics of "identity"—the problem of the relations between "mind" and "body," "spirit" and "letter," "intention" and "act," and, no less crucially, of the relations between "me" and "we," "I" and "you," and indeed "speaking" and "writing," *la voix* and *le phénomene*—draw their apparently endless reserves. The thought echoes Jeremiah 1:5, "Before I formed you in the womb I knew you, and before you were born I consecrated you," which anticipates or perhaps even radicalizes the idea of a relation with an Outside that constitutes one's innermost identity and reverberates through one's ownmost interiority; the *voice* with which one talks to oneself, seasoned with someone else's salt or known by some other before I myself am formed. "You, more intimate to me than I am to myself," is how Augustine puts it (*Confessions* III vi 11). This is the scene that Descartes will fashion into an ontological argument, where the veracity of God's external presence guarantees the inward experience of the *cogito*. It is the scene that Heidegger will secularize in the form of a general, fundamental ontology that disperses, decapitalizes, and thereby decapitates the inward voice of the external other; whether as the undifferentiated voice of *das Man* or the singular voice, "the voice of a friend whom every Dasein carries within it," this listening that "constitutes the primary and authentic openness" of being-there *is* the form and mode of the "Christian" interiority by which Derrida speaks with himself *as* a Jew.[14]

Now Derrida's problem, which he shares with Plato, Augustine, and in a certain way with Maimonides (among others, such as Levinas or Marion, but not Heidegger, who dismisses it too hastily, almost dogmatically stipulating that it is "the voice of being"), can be stated as follows. How could one *know* that this presence, "more intimate to me than I am to myself," is You God, and not some Other? How could one know which you, what voice, name, or sign, it is that calls and demands to be addressed? The reason why Derrida so cherished Augustine's question—*What do I love when I love God?* or in Maimonidean parlance, *To what or to whom do I pray to when I pray to God?*—is because it problematizes the proper name to which one is responding, searching for *the one* wherever or in *whatever speaks* more intimately to me than I speak with myself. The proximity of deconstruction to certain apophatic traditions is due not only to their skepticism over attempts to close the gap between the meaning and reference of "God" but equally to the application of this skepticism to one's own knowledge of oneself, to the voice by which one speaks with oneself. Since this voice is more intimate to me than I am to myself it marks or traces the unrepresentability by which I represent myself to myself, without properly yielding its proper name, if it has one—like *his* eponymous Jacob, who demanded to know the name of the enigma with which he wrestled until dawn but was only given his own name, modified and wounded, in return.

There he was, in Jerusalem, speaking so as to not-speak (*ne pas parler*) of the unspeakable and unrepresentable, of "God, under this name or another," and he finds that what *"should have"* been *"closest"* to him, more intimate to him than himself—more intimate than his *cogito* or "consciousness," than his memory and his unconscious, than "all of my [J.D.'s] foreign languages: French, English, German, Greek, Latin, the philosophic, metaphilosophic, Christian, etc."—is not God and not You, not the voice of the Other or of Being, but—"the Jew, the Arab." Years later, he said that "the word *jew*" is "deeper and more profound in me than my own name, more elementary and more indelible than any other in the world, . . . closer to my body than an article of clothing, than my body itself."[15] What remains of Derrida when his accumulated ways of being, his *Ganzseit*, are negated, is not an experience of authentic selfhood but on the contrary his rudimentary foreignness with himself as Jew, as if *"judéité"* marked the place or the Place that would remain if he ever exhausted what he might say—to others, or to himself—about himself. Hence the address he delivered on *comment ne pas parler*, in which he avoided speaking of "the Jew, the Arab" that he himself is, was paradoxically but quite literally "the most 'autobiographical' speech" he "ever risked." Autobiography as apophasis, in which one speaks one's truth in the extreme of one's ownmost anonymity and passion for nonknowing who one uniquely is.

This is how to make sense of Derrida's complex *judeité*, which is what becomes of "Jewish identity" when the passage from theological to autobiographical negation of the voice through which one speaks with oneself is rigorously undergone. Derrida, who no longer held fast to Judaism in any form, not even in the secret of his own heart, who did not circumcise his two sons, excluding them from his broken alliance, and whose intentions were fulfilled—he who showed how intentions could never be fulfilled!—when he was buried without anyone saying kaddish, for *this very* Derrida there were only two words, "God—and *Jew*," which *guarded* the "determined silence" of an intimacy more intimate than he was with himself and that words such as "Judaism" *and* "atheism" both violate. This intimacy is "a silence that one protects and that protects," but for Derrida, whether by decision or by fate, it was also a secret that is kept *from* Judaism while keeping a certain Jewishness in play.[16] The secret is of a certain Jewishness and of the word God, but not a secret that Judaism can guard. By what right this priority of Jewishness over Judaism in the order that guards the secret? The question is not addressed. But from this it follows that *only in death* could "he" have opened Maimonides's letter. For in life, words such as "religion," "faith," "Judaism," and "atheism" crumbled in his hands, whereas "God—and Jew" were like the spaces between his fingers, into which his mortal hands have themselves decayed. Perhaps then only in becoming radically desubjectified in death, in becoming unlike unto himself in the absoluteness of death, could he draw nearest to the "closest," to that determined silence of those two words that were more intimate to him than he was to himself, God—and Jew. "All the apophatic mystics can also be read as powerful discourses on death . . . of what carries away, interrupts, denies, or annihilates its speaking as well as its own *Dasein*."[17] Here, in the place of death, that "ahuman and atheological location that opens the place well beyond any negative theology," that *khōra* that he once called "foreign to the God of the Jews and to the history of the law,"—precisely *here* two words abide, "God—and Jew." It was only when he negated himself to the point of radical desubjectification, resembling perhaps only his own death, did he discover that *khōra* "can still keep a deep affinity with a certain nomination of the God of the Jews," since "He is also The Place."[18] Derrida thereby marked a "deep affinity" between, on the one hand, the dispersal of death and the disunity of *khōra* and, on the other hand, his two most basic words, "God—and Jew." What to make of this deep affinity? How to avoid Judaizing Derrida without denying what was closest to him, God—and Jew? How to refuse to say kaddish without denying God—and Jew? *Il faut ne pas parler le kaddich pour Derrida*, one must unsay kaddish for Derrida.

To avoid Judaizing Derrida without denying what is closest to him, God—and Jew, one must then pass through the negation of all the predicates, dogmas, doxas, and, above all, identities that inhere in Judaism. Derrida argued that this *via negativa* was based on a distinction between Judaism and *"judeité,"* a distinction he developed by way of Freud and Yerushalmi, who proposed that Jewishness was interminable and infinitely malleable, while Judaism was terminable and restricted to certain institutions and dogmas.[19] Summarizing the point made in *Archive Fever*, Derrida notes that "jewishness seems to be able to emancipate [*affranchir*] itself, indeed, from tradition, from the promise and the election proper to judaism."[20] But on this late occasion, Derrida acknowledged that the emancipation of Jewishness from Judaism oscillates about an *"obscure and uncertain experience of heritage"* that would be the *"ultimate guardian"* of that *"jewishness that is allegedly without Judaism."*[21] In other words, the emancipation of Jewishness from Judaism requires an *experience of the very heritage* from which it has been liberated, the heritage of Judaism, now experienced *as obscurity and uncertainty*. For this to be possible there must be some way of reversing Yerushalmi's position by transposing the alleged surplus of Jewishness over Judaism into a heritage of Judaism that does not confine but releases novel and unforeseen forms of Jewishness. This "ultimate guardian" *keeps open* the gates of the obscure uncertain heritage of Judaism by virtue of whom Jewishness cannot be exhausted by the dogmas and institutions of Judaism.[22]

3. The Cindering Spirit of Rabbi Moyses

Someone else, an ultimate guardian, who might have kept the gates of Judaism open for new *judeités* that go beyond all dogma and institutional identities:

> There is always someone else, you know. The most private autobiography comes to terms with great transferential figures, who are *themselves* and themselves *plus* someone else.... In order to speak of even the most intimate thing, for example one's "own" circumcision, one does better to be aware that an exegesis is in process, that you carry the detour, the contour, and the memory inscribed in the culture of your body, for example. Here's an example among thousands of others, and which I've never talked about: a coming to terms with Meister Eckhart, who reported what Maimonides said on the subject.... Don't ask me why, in a detour from all these detours, Heidegger, who read Eckhart throughout his life as a master, never speaks of either circumcision or Maimonides; that's another story.[23]

Maimonides is here mentioned in an example that uses Eckhart "plus someone else" to suggest that "the most private autobiography" requires cultural inscriptions and their exegesis and that "the most intimate thing" has a history. Maimonidean ash in the Heideggerian archive discovered by Derrida. One could begin to think about this in relation to Bernard McGinn's thought, developed in detail by Yosef Schwartz, that "no Christian author of the Middle Ages . . . knew Maimonides better or reflected greater sympathy for his views than did Meister Eckhart."[24] But don't ask me why Derrida, who read Heidegger who read Eckhart who read Maimonides throughout his life, never speaks of Maimonides.

Except once. In a discussion of Hermann Cohen's *Deutschum und Judentum*, Derrida remarks on Cohen's provocative idea that "Maimonides exemplifies the spirit of Protestantism in medieval Judaism." Cohen's idea is that the spirit of Protestantism, like Maimonides, puts "no trust" in the authority of clerical institutions but only in "conscience's own labor" (*allein die eigene Arbeit des Gewissens*).[25] It is this spirit of Protestantism that imbibes German philosophy in the course of time. Cohen sketches a twisted line from Maimonides through Cusanus to Leibniz, omitting, as Derrida notes, Spinoza, but also, as Derrida does not note, Meister Eckhart and all that he became in German mysticism and philosophy. Cohen's Maimonides stands for a labor of conscience (Luther) that becomes historically informed by the demands of reason (Kant)—a critique of sensualist immediacy and a determination of the idea *as* hypothesis (thus placing Plato at the hearth of

German Idealism). For Cohen, the Reformation is an essentially philosophical project involving what Derrida glosses as the "cult of doubt, suspicion toward dogma (and if you prefer also toward *doxa*) and of institutions based on dogma, a culture of interpretation but of *free* interpretation, one which, in its spirit, at least, tends to liberate itself from an institutional authority."[26] And unlike the French *Lumièrs*, the "idealism" of this Reformation "does not go against faith" but "at one and the same time frees and encumbers religious thought."[27] The "spirit of Protestantism" that Maimonides exemplifies is thus characterized as the internalization and appropriation of the Logos, defined not as a positive or positivist object of faith but as an Idea (at once hypothesis, as per Plato, and purely regulative, as per Kant), thereby strictly *opposed to all dogma for the sake of faithfulness to the divine truth*. Maimonides the Protestant stands for an iconoclastic fidelity to the truth of God as it passes through "a certain communication between knowledge (*Wissen*), science (*Wissenschaft*), conscience (*Gewissen*), self-consciousness (*Selbst-bewusstsein*) and certainty (*Gewissheit*)."[28] For Cohen, the spirit of Protestantism, of Maimonideanism, of Platonism, and of Kantianism are one—each in its own way historicizes the spirit of the One, the very One of which prophetic Judaism speaks. Derrida summarizes Cohen's reading of Maimonides as "a grand, rigorous rationalism. It is in the name of reason that he [Cohen's Maimonides] founds the Jewish Reformation."[29]

This rigorous rationalism, however, stands in a certain tension with Maimonides's negative theology, just as Derrida's preference for inwardness and intentionality stands in tension with his critique of the transparency of consciousness. Given his sustained attention to negative theologies and his awareness that his familiarity was restricted to their Greco-Latin idioms, it is surprising that Derrida consigned Maimonides to a rationalism that entirely neglects his sustained and influential critique of the possibility of knowledge (*Wissen*) of God, of a science (*Wissenschaft*) of theology, of the conjunction of conscience (*Gewissen*) with divine will, and of self-consciousness (*Selbst-bewusstsein*) as the space in which God comes to pass. For among the ashen letters that Maimonides wrote to a presumed addressee perplexed much as Derrida was, there cinders an apophatic Judaism that, like those he read assiduously,

> render[s] itself independent of revelation, of all the literal language of . . . eventness, of the coming . . . , of the dogma . . . etc. An immediate but intuitionless mysticism, a sort of abstract kenosis, frees this language from all authority, all narrative, all dogma, all belief—and at the limit from all faith. At this limit, this mysticism remains, after the fact, independent of all history . . . *absolutely* independent, detached even, perhaps absolved, from the idea of sin, freed even,

perhaps redeemed, from the idea of redemption. Whence the courage and the dissidence, potential or actual, of these masters (think of Eckhart), whence the persecution they suffered at times, whence their passion, whence this scent of heresy, these trials, this subversive marginality of the apophatic current in the history of theology."[30]

Think not only of Eckhart but of the "plus someone else" who accompanied him, helped paved his way, toward this intuitionless mysticism without event or dogma, without narrative or belief, redeemed of redemption and smelling of heresy. In Maimonides's critique of the very rationalism and representationalism that he commonly adopts, we find an "obscure and uncertain experience of heritage" that guards open that which Derrida sought, a "jewishness that is allegedly without Judaism," "more obscure than what preceded."[31] If Derrida had encountered this obscure Maimonidean Judaism, devoid of dogma, skeptical of narrative, and redeemed from the idea of redemption, he would virtually have come full circle. For here, the Jewish "Pharisaism" that Derrida repudiated, *as much as* the Jewish Reformation he doubted, the Judaism of gesticulations as much as the Judaism of a grand, rigorous rationalism, gives way to a Judaism that might have been, and perhaps already is, a Judaism of "the destruction, not the demolition but the de-sedimentation, the deconstruction, of all the significations that have their source in that of the logos."[32] And if there were such an obscure, uncertain Judaism, we could say, without irony or apology, not that "deconstruction is a Jewish science," but that the true science of Judaism, the true *Wissenschaft des Judentums*, is a deconstruction.[33]

4. "An Immediate but Intuitionless Mysticism": Maimonides as a Guide for the Deconstruction of "Negative Theology"

From the outset, Derrida acknowledged that what he was doing was "occasionally . . . indistinguishable from negative theology."[34] The structural and tactical similarities made it all the more important to distinguish deconstruction from negative theology in order to clarify their quite different implications. In the course of time, Derrida marked at least four objections to negative theology corresponding to four ways by which deconstruction differs from the negation of theological predicates. Examining these in turn will clarify the extent to which Maimonides's view belongs within the tradition of "negative theology" that Derrida ultimately rejects, as well as the stakes of Derrida's avoidance of Maimonides and the possibilities it still harbors for a deconstruction of Judaism. It is a matter of doing Maimonides the justice Derrida would have, if only he had been capable, as he denied being.

Derridean Objection 1: The Metaphysical Hypocrisy of Negative Theology. Does not Maimonides betray a metaphysical hypocrisy that denies God "only in order to acknowledge His superior, inconceivable, and ineffable mode of being"?[35] Think of the adept in the sultan's palace, the one able to draw toward *"the presence of the ruler,* see him from afar or from nearby, or hear the ruler's speech or speak to him."[36] Like its Neoplatonic and Christian counterparts, Maimonidean negative theology would fail to do what it says it does because it denies "existence" only to assert "the immediacy of a presence."[37] Its denials would therefore be merely veiled affirmations of a concept of God as absolute, incorrigible positivity, which Derrida locates in both Plato's idea of the Good beyond being and Christian derivations, most notably that of Saint Thomas. The problem with both the Platonic and the Thomistic accounts is that each "maintains a sufficiently homogeneous, homologous, or analogous relationship between Being and (what is) beyond Being, in order that what exceeds the border might be compared to Being."[38] The correlate of "negative theology" would be a "hyperousiology" that "does not interrupt this analogical continuity" between being and beyond-being but on the contrary "assumes it."[39]

Maimonidian Response 1: "Know that likeness is a certain relation between two things and that in cases where no relation can be supposed to exist between two things, no likeness between them can be represented to oneself" (*Guide* I 56, 130). A mustard seed is like the sphere of the stars; the heat of warm wax is like that of burning fire. Like Derrida, Maimonides emphasizes the "analogical continuity" of *likeness* precisely in order to caution against it, for the relation between God and what is other than God "is considered as nonexistent" (ibid.). The words and, more importantly, the thoughts we have of God's essential attributes—living, powerful, knowing, and willing—must be understood "in a purely equivocal way," as pure homonyms that "have in common only the name and nothing else" (131). Maimonides thereby *avoids saying* that God exists in some eminent sense of the word "existence"; his denegations do not assume the hyperousiology of divine existence.

Derridean Objection 2: Negative Theology Implies Predication. If Maimonides avoids *saying* that God exists, does he not *imply* "that God exists," even merely by virtue of the *form of address* he employs. The *Guide* opens with a citation—"Cause me to know the way wherein I should walk, / For unto Thee have I lifted my soul" (Psalms 143:8)—and Maimonides begins by addressing himself, by means of another citation, to his disciple—"Incline thine ear, and hear the words of the wise, / And apply thy heart unto my knowledge" (Prov. 22:17). The entire *Guide* thus unfolds its radical negativity like a prayer in which the destination is ontologically implied in advance—to God, *for* the perplexed Jewish reader, in this respect comparable to works by Christian "negative theologians." Derrida is sympathetic to the idea that an address does not always know what it addresses. As Aristotle already said, "a prayer is a sentence, but is neither true nor false" (*De Interpretation* 17a, 1–5), since at issue in prayer, as in apophatic discourse, is not the propositional content of the utterance but its form as address. But Derrida insists that the form of a prayer as an address does not entirely suspend its implied content conveyed as praise. If prayer is an address to "I know not what," in the praise which inevitably accompanies prayer we find what Grice called "implicature": predicates or attributes implied by the very utterance of prayer, even if only the predicate "exists." Though a *pure* prayer may be neither true nor false, in fact prayer is always accompanied by implied predicates that *are* subject to truth values.[40] This formal division between the apostrophic and predicative mode of prayer is radicalized in discourses of negative theology. Maimonides, for example, deplores the fact that "poets and preachers or such as think that what they speak is poetry" have "predicated attributes of Him and addressed Him in all the terms that they thought permitted and expatiated at such length . . . that the utterances of some of them constitute an absolute denial of faith, . . . such rubbish and such perverse imaginings as to make men laugh . . . and to make them weep when they consider that these utterances are applied to God" (*Guide* I 59, 141). But Derrida's point is that rejecting explicit predication does not allow us to deny the implied predication which "adjusts discursive asceticism, the passage through the desert of discourse . . . by addressing itself from the start to the other, to you."[41]

Maimonidean Response 2: Maimonides does not balk at the *impurity* of language. Rather than devise some allegedly pure form of discourse that would be an unalloyed address devoid of predication, he accepts that even the purest address implies predication and to that extent is a misleading, compromised discourse, a "loosening of the tongue with regard to God" that is akin to "acts of great disobedience" like *speaking ill* and *defamation*. The predicative implications of prayer, Maimonides says, are *lashon ha'rah*, gossip, and *hotza'at shem ra'*, evil speech, about God![42] Far from contesting Derrida's objection to the idea of a pure prayer or pure apophatic discourse, Maimonides unhesitatingly endorses it. The legitimacy and even the necessity of prayer, on his view, derives not because it is a form of speech purified of predication but from its expedient instrumentality, for it serves the anthropocentric needs of human beings. Were anthropocentrism to be overcome—but in his view this can never happen on a mass scale—then even the highest form of discursive address, the purest prayer, ought to be replaced by nondiscursive "meditation."[43]

Derridean Objection 3: The Duplicity of Silence. Does not response 2 return us to objection 1 in a more ethereal but also more insidious mode? Does not Maimonides's concession to the impossibility of a nonpredicative discourse lead him to embrace nondiscursive states of mind, pure meditations, or acts of intellect, as the most desirable way of knowing God? This is a common way of understanding the passage from negation to silence, as when Maimonides says that "the most apt phrase concerning this subject is the dictum occurring in the *Psalms, Silence is praise to Thee* [Psalms 65:2]"; that "silence and limiting oneself to the apprehensions of the intellects are more appropriate—just as the perfect ones have enjoined when they said: *Commune with your own heart upon your bed, and be still. Selah* [Psalms 4:5]."[44] So too in III 51, in concluding and summarizing his views, Maimonides compares the passionate love (*'ishq*) for God to a condition in which "no thought remains that is directed toward a thing other than the Beloved" (p. 627).[45] Modern scholars, some emphasizing the Sufi, Neoplatonic, and Isma'ili background to Maimonidean silence, have concluded that "he is indeed in the company of Plotinus," that he guides toward nondiscursive "intuitive illuminations," toward a state of "post-cognitive, profound silence," "the silence of awe" "overwhelmed not by the emptiness of God, but by God's fullness."[46] Although he was commenting on Pseudo-Dionysius, Derrida might equally have had *this* Maimonides in mind when he expressed his "uneasiness" at the putative passage toward "that pure intuition of the ineffable, that silent union with that which remains inaccessible to speech" and "corresponds to a rarefaction of signs, figures, symbols—and also of fictions, as well as of myths or poetry."[47] As he noted, the tropes and strategies of negative theology are frequently governed by the promise of a nondiscursive, silent beholding of the presence of God. Is this not what Maimonides effectively promises when extols how "apprehension turns into incapacity" and "all eloquence turns into weariness," namely, the abiding in contemplative silence or intuitive flashes of nondiscursive theological truth?[48]

Maimonidean Response 3: Not necessarily. Josef Stern provides a recent and systematic interpretation of Maimonidean silence that provides a way of handling this objection. Stern argues that for Maimonides the *only* mechanism for securing *reference* to the objects of thought is through representation, which takes the form of mental soliloquy or inward speech. As such, representation has the *form of language*. Representations are bound by syntax just like spoken speech or writing; they are "syntactically complex like the sentences of external speech."[49] "The representations of inner speech are not just simple intelligibles but syntactically composite propositions that involves structured relations between subjects and predicates. This kind of linguistic structure presupposes metaphysical distinctions (for example, between substance, or substratum, and attribute) that violate the absolute simplicity required for representations of absolutely simple beings."[50] On this view, knowledge is constrained by the representational form it inevitably assumes. In Maimonides's words, "there is no oneness at all except in believing that there is one simple essence in which there is no complexity or multiplication of notions . . . either in the thing as it outside of the mind *or as it is in the mind* " (*Guide* I 51, 113 emphasis added). The representational structure of silent thought involves a major constraint on Maimonides's account of silent contemplation of God: "In knowing a truth, *how* one knows it—how one represents it to oneself—is no less significant than *what* one knows."[51]

On the one hand, then, an utterance bears only as much truth as the belief on which it is based, and beliefs are that which are "represented in the soul" (*Guide* I 50, 111). Here is the Maimonidean move to the inwardness of faith that seeks to *redress* the gesticulated Judaism that left Derrida *égaré*—perplexed in the dire sense, as in Esther 3:15, where it means confounded and afflicted. But on the other hand, the turn to the inwardness of representation is nevertheless syntactically composite; even negative predications in which it is denied that God is, say, not-ignorant or not-dead, involve the divisibility of the subject from its predicates and hence "do not give us knowledge in any respect whatever of the essence the knowledge of which is sought."[52] Maimonides here makes the very point Derrida will emphasize, namely, that negative predication involves a syntax that remains bound to the anthropomorphic structure of a subject with predicates (attributes) and is therefore a necessary but insufficient way of deconstructing the errors of predication. His resort to negative predication is accompanied by a critique of the epistemic value of the *via negativa*. In other words, Maimonides not only denies positive attributions but also "deconstructs grammatical anthropomorphism."[53] Theology (or metaphysics) is *necessary*, for without the inwardness of representation, Judaism risks congealing into perplexing gesticulations that lead one astray (*égaré*), but theology is also *impossible*, for even negative theology does not yield knowledge of "God's being One by virtue of a true Oneness" (*Guide* I 50, 111). Maimonides's recourse to philosophical negation therefore does not culminate in mystical intuition or silent contemplation but articulates a *critique of negative theology*, if by that is meant *knowledge* of God by negation, or it articulates a form of *negative theology as critique*. It thereby attests to what Derrida calls "an *excessively* philosophical gesture: a gesture that is philosophical and, at the same time, in excess of the philosophical."[54] The "true oneness" that "gives the mind the correct direction toward the true reality" (I 57, 133) is neither a thought predicating categorical negation nor silent intuitive knowledge of God. This amounts to the "intuitionless mysticism" that Derrida locates in "pure prayer," prayer that lacks the predicative implications of praise.

Recall that Derrida describes this "intuitionless mysticism" as "a sort of abstract kenosis." This compares favorably with Maimonides's account of prayer as oriented toward self-emptying. For Maimonides, the *kavannah*—intention or, better, "correct direction"—of prayer requires that a person "empty his soul," *yifaneh libo*, hence an *intuitionless* silence refrains from false representations, including negative predications, and therefore, as Stern explains, involves no "union" with God.[55] The silence to which Maimonides guides is not a fullness of divine presence but an empty or "skeptical" silence oriented toward "true oneness," one that can neither be intuited nor thought, and therefore cannot be *known*.[56]

Since a proper prayer, oriented in the "correct direction," empties the soul of all representation, both the one who prayers and the who that is receiving the prayer remain unknown.[57] For both Maimonides and Derrida, prayer aspires to a type of Pyrrhonian skepticism or *epoché*, to a mode of address in which knowledge of oneself as the one praying and knowledge of the one to whom one is praying are bracketed. Maimonides enjoins us to "refrain and hold back" from "corrupt imaginings" and other "points appearing as dubious,"[58] while Derrida says: "When I pray, I am thinking about negative theology, about the unnamable, the possibility that I might be totally deceived by my belief, and so on. It is a very skeptical—I don't like this word 'skeptical,' but it will have to do—prayer. And yet this 'skepticism' is part of the prayer. Instead of 'skepticism,' I could talk of *epoché*."[59]

Answering the objection of the duplicity of silence, however, does not mean that Derrida and Maimonides experienced the truth of negative theology in the same fashion. On Stern's view, Maimonidean experience yields a detached *shalom* (following the paradigm of Maimonides's Rabbi Aqiba, who alone entered the *pardes* and came out *shalom*), a "peace of mind or tranquility" that "cures us of our epistemic unhappiness" by demonstrating the equipollence (*isostheneiai*) of opposing metaphysical convictions while ridding us of dubious beliefs and imaginings.[60] For Derrida, however, the *epoché* of theology, the approach to the space between God (true oneness) and the name of God (syntactic predication), yields an unlimited restlessness, an "interminable" oscillation of experience edged between the absolutely singular and the generally intelligible. The experience of prayer, of theology as skepticism or *epoché*, would not be an experience of tranquility, as Stern thinks it was for Maimonides, but *a disorienting experience*—one thinks again of Hannah (1 Samuel 1)—incessantly reorienting the space of representation toward the (next) absolutely singular.

Had Derrida opened those letters addressed by Maimonides precisely to him, he would surely have found the skeptical experience described in the *Guide* to be interminable, restless, passionately, incurably nontranquil. This brings us to a final objection, perhaps the most serious, which Derrida would doubtless have raised against Maimonidean negative theology.

Derridean Objection 4: The Radical Conservatism of Negative Theology. The discourse of radical negation, Derrida points out, is often complicit with the most conservative traditionalism, and not by chance. Those who renounce what they know of God invariably do so by consecrating their own canons as privileged sites of negation that thereby *foreclose* the possibility of novel, multiple, disruptive experiences of the unknown God. In aiming at a specific, circumscribed discourse in order to negate it, such as a particular historical revelation or determined canon, traditional apophaticisms consecrate such canons as exclusive sites of divine negativity. Since radical negativity has nothing to rest on besides the presumption of a revelation that has always been and a tradition that is always already authorized, the more radical a negative theology becomes the more "coextensive" and "confined" it will be "to the same quantity of discourse" it contests.[61]

This coextensivity of radical critique and radical conservativism is clearly seen in Maimonides's defense of Rabbi Haninah's rejection of liturgical innovation. Maimonides warns against waxing lyrical with one's prayers, for "when you make an affirmation ascribing another thing to Him, you become more remote from Him." One must therefore *"draw a line* at using these expressions and not apply them to Him except only in reading the *Torah"* and "when saying our prayers."[62] Since ordinary language is both semantically and syntactically unable to speak of God, Maimonides concludes that only *the sacred institution* of prayer has theological legitimacy—not because of its semantic content or syntactic structure, since these are as conventional as all languages, but because it accords with tradition and the institutional authority of "the men of the Great Assembly." The radicalism of Maimonidean negation thereby bears a profoundly conservative, ultimately uncritical or even dogmatic function, since it approaches the unknowability and incomprehensibility of divine uniqueness only to the extent that it presupposes, nominates, and stipulates its own institutionalized discourse, its own canons, revelations, and traditions, as the exclusive site of divine truth.

Moreover, this radical conservativism is not an accidental feature of Maimonidean negative theology, for the experience of theological *epoché* under the law of an impossible face-to-face rejects all appeal to representation (to a concept of divine oneness) and presentation (an intuition of oneness). Denying every thought or experience of that which solely gives theological authority effectively forecloses in advance *the very possibility of an alternative* representation or presentation of theological truth. The critical function of Maimonidean negative theology with respect to the dogmas of Jewish faith is entirely *internal* to the discourse in which it circulates. The very same conservatism was manifest in Yeshayahu Leibowitz's use of Maimonidean negative theology, which in the end amounted to an iconoclastic Halakhic behavioralism. The attempt to render negative theology systematic and develop a pure theological discourse, immunized from the falsities of positive predication, lays claim *in advance* to the exclusive authority of *the same* sacred institutions, Scripture, liturgy, and authorized commentaries whose semantic content it denies. As Derrida points out, such a negative theology "cannot contain within itself the principle of its own interruption. It can only indefinitely defer the encounter with its own limit."[63] A radical form of negative theology such as Maimonides's (and the same can be said of Pseudo-Dionysius[64]) *destroys* conceptual dogmas *to the very extent that it guards* the institutions that preserve them. This is no doubt what Derrida had in mind when late in life he recalled his experience as an eight-year-old viewing the *Guide des Égarés* behind his grandfather's glass-paneled shelves, for here the *égaré* and *s'égarer*, the perplexing and straying truths of negative theology become *garer* and *garder*, docked and guarded. "Look up the words *égaré, s'égarer*, to do with getting lost, therefore, and *garer*. You'll find all you need to talk about journeying, and about *my* journeys, including truths to be docked [*à garer*], to be kept [*garder*]—or not, so as to guard oneself from them or park them."[65]

Is there a Maimonidean riposte to this Derridean objection? It is by no means evident that Maimonides would have shirked the charge of radical conservatism, though the irony would not have been lost on him, great reformer that he tried to be.[66] Even so, in a certain way Maimonides leaves open the gates that his own negative theology guards. Moreover, he does so in Derridean fashion, by the mode of writing with which he communicates the "secrets" to which he guides the reader. Much has been said about Maimonides's concealment of secrets, but our concern is with his account of the truth of divine oneness in the chapters on negation (*Guide* I 50–63). What is striking about this writing, in which Maimonides negates all conceptual predication of God, is how the passage toward "God's being One" is *reiterated in four different ways*. The true oneness that Maimonides has in view is approached and denoted in four different ways, whose sense or meaning cannot, as a matter of principle, be self-evidently identified with the one referent. The multiplication of four different ways of indicating true oneness opens a cleavage, a unity that separates, between the sense and reference of God.

The first way by which the *Guide of the Perplexed* approaches "God's being One" is as "the existent of necessity," an Avicennan term referring to God's existence as uncaused and not dependent on any parts, which Maimonides understands as a homonym, such that God's "existence" is unrelated to the multiple senses of existence we routinely employ. The second way of approaching true divine oneness is as *'anniyya*, an undecidable term with multiple meanings—*being, that, I-ness, indeed*—each of which designates God without recourse to the subject-predicate structure[67] The third way is afforded by the Tetragrammaton—a tautology in which the predicate refers to the subject. Finally, the fourth way of approaching true oneness is as the glory of God that can neither be seen nor represented.

Maimonides's use of multiple strategies to designate true oneness implicates him in a performative impasse that jeopardizes the monotheism he is attempting to radicalize. Since none of these ways of indicating true oneness amount to a description or takes the form of a syntactical representation, there is no criterion for identifying one with the other. In no case can a principle like the identity of indiscernibles be applied, since there is neither property nor predicate nor subject nor object that could be compared. But for the same reason, these four ways of indicating true oneness also fail to yield a dissimilarity based on their diverse properties, for they have no properties. It follows that it is impossible *for Maimonides himself* to determine in what respect these various names identify the one same true God. Of this "dissemination" at the heart of true oneness, Derrida might have said what he said of Austin and Searl: the intention to refer to the one (true oneness) can only make sense, even to the one who "has the intention," by means of graphemes, material conventions, and contexts that determine its referent. It is not the four terms, or the thought of any one of them, that individuates their referent as the one true God but the context in which they might be invoked. Accordingly, the fulfillment of Maimonides's intended meaning depends entirely on its reception—by Maimonides himself, by other Jews, by "the community," by non-Jews (Aquinas, Eckhart, or any other). Maimonides's *own* capacity to refer to the one true God depends not only on his capacity to negate false meanings but above all on the reception of these indicative orientations of true oneness insofar as their already differentiated notations are reproduced, maintained, or recontextualized *by others*. Instead of closing theology down by reducing it to the truth of a determined silence or nondiscursive illuminations, Maimonides guides theology to the potentially endless recontextualization of its ultimate term. The most "confined" of the four reductions, that to the Tetragrammaton, should therefore be rendered in its most open sense: not as the determined "I am that I am" (as Pines translates it) but as *one yet to be* determined, "I will be as I will be," or even "I will be as I will have been," since determining the identity of this true oneness depends on repeating it in contexts that no one, not even God, can control.

Maimonides seems to recognize this very problem in discussing the unique referential capacity of the Tetragrammaton in *Guide* I 61. There he states, "*Perhaps* it [the Tetragrammaton] indicates the notion of a necessary existence, according to the [Hebrew] language" (I 61, 148; my emphasis). I take Maimonides to be making not only a point about the corruption of our knowledge of the Hebrew language, such that were we in our full linguistic powers we could establish that the Tetragrammaton clearly refers to "necessary existence," but that this identification is a matter of conjecture in the best of cases. After all, how could one *translate* that which no representation can think and no syntax can structure? The recourse to *perhaps* goes further than a speculative identification of the Tetragrammaton with Necessary Existence because it avoids the alternatives of being and nonbeing altogether, exposing the structure of anticipation to uncertainty, nonknowing and nonidentification—"I will be that which I will be." As it happens, that is how Derrida came to understand the function of the "perhaps" and to differentiate it from the "maybe." The latter, on his stipulated view, refers to what will possibly occur, whereas the former refers to an event that never coincides with an occurrence since it does not present itself as such to consciousness: "the category of the perhaps is perhaps the best category to refer to what remains to come."[68] "With regard to the 'perhaps,' moreover, there exists a theological vein, in the work of Bohme, Bruno, Nicholas de Cusa, that defines God not as being—and precisely for which fact they break with what Heidegger calls the 'ontolotheological tradition'— but defines God as 'before' and outside of being, *without being*. They define God as 'perhaps.' God is the perhaps."[69] Maimonides's four ways of indicating God's true oneness endure this equivocation, for one can only presume or speculate, under the sign of a "perhaps," if Necessary Existence is "the same" as the Tetragrammaton.

Maimonides touches on this again when he proposes that Glory *"sometimes"* refers to the "essence and true reality" of God while at other times refers only to derivative actions of God (*Guide* I 64, 156). The implication is that sometimes God signifies as the Name, but *sometimes, it happens that*, God signifies as the glory that fills the earth. So too, *sometimes it happens* that the "one by virtue of a true Oneness" signifies one way, as 'necessary existent,' while sometimes it signifies otherwise, by *that* (*'anniyya*). Indeed chance or happenstance are involved in every attempt to affirm that the manifold of nonconceptual, intuitionless onenesses are in fact one: "the attributes of negation do not give us knowledge in any respect whatever of the essence the knowledge of which is sought, *unless this happens by accident*" (I 58, 135). The enigmatic space of Maimonides's various designations for the "true oneness," of which there can be no concept, is held together by contingent, nondemonstrable relations. What do you pray to, Rabbi Moses, when you pray to *the Name*? How do you know it is *the very one* as the "necessary existent"? How do you know this Name is *That*, *'anniyya*? How do you know that these are the effects of the Glory that fills the earth? There are no conceptual criteria for identifying these respective uniquenesses. The multiple iterations of "one by virtue of a true oneness" "give the mind the correct direction" (I 57, 133) by orienting, or rather, disorienting the mind. Moreover, each of these singular terms orients or disorients the mind in quite distinct ways: existence of necessity orients the mind toward the impossibility of a concept of God; *'anniyya* involves an intrinsic ambiguity of a term without subject or predicate; the Tetragrammaton orients the entirety of Scripture and liturgical life toward its conceptual void; but Glory disseminates this confounding experience throughout all manifest forms of life. Do all these singular terms refer to the "one true oneness"? Perhaps, by chance, sometimes—but the identity of these signs can neither be known nor represented as such. This shared passion for nonknowing feigns to speak a royal Greek, the logos of being as unity.[70] It does not, however, prostrate silently and tranquilly before the King but, like Ehud in the presence of King Eglon (Judges 3), left-handedly evades the guards of the true oneness, imperils its Sovereignty and disseminates its royal blood.

A spilling of Sovereign blood through a left-handed assault on the unity of true oneness can be justified if, as the Zohar puts it, the blood of God consists of *each and every soul*.[71] For in that case, the dissemination of the unity that negative theology relentlessly has in view would amount not only to theological modesty but also to a possible divinization or glorification of any singularity whatsoever. *Whatever* passes for God betrays the absolute singularity of the unrepresentable. This was precisely Derrida's point in deconstructing negative theology, for every absolute singularity exempts itself from the concept one makes of it and gives rise to its own alterity in unpredictable contexts: "God or *no matter who*, precisely, *any singularity whatsoever*, as soon as every other is wholly other (*tout autre est tout autre*) . . . where the other loses his name or is able to change it in order to become no matter what other."[72] In this way, deconstruction is like a "generalized apophaticism"—but an apophaticism of the intuitionless (non-Neoplatonic) kind, passing through representation in order to deconstruct its grammatical anthropomorphisms, a "skeptical" and, if you like, a generalized Maimonidean apophaticism, a perplexing, obscure, uncertain experience that can be traced through a certain heritage of Judaism to the point of breaking with all history, all community, and all identity. In this way the ashen name of Maimonides, having been erased totally from Derrida's archive, presents itself in its specific non/Jewish form.

Notes

1. Jacques Derrida, *The Postcard: From Socrates to Freud and Beyond*, trans. Alan Bass (Chicago: The University of Chicago Press, 1987), 353.

2. Jacques Derrida and Maurizzio Ferraris, *A Taste for the Secret*, trans. Giacomo Donis (Cambridge: Polity Press, 2001), 37–39

3. Jacques Derrida and Elizabeth Roudinesco, *For What Tomorrow . . . : A Dialogue*, trans. Jeff Fort (Stanford, CA: Stanford University Press, 2004), 111, cited by Benoît Peeters, *Derrida: A Biography* (Cambridge: Polity, 2012), 21.

4. Cf. Jacques Derrida, "On Reading Heidegger: An Outline of Remarks to the Essex Colloquium," *Research in Phenomenology* 17 (1987): 177, cited by Ned Lukacher in Jacques Derrida, *Cinders* (Lincoln: University of Nebraska Press, 1991), 1.

5. Jacques Derrida and Catherine Malabou, *La Contre-allée* (Paris: La Quinzaine Litteraire/Louis Vuitton, 1999), 263; translation modified from *Counterpath: Traveling with Jacques Derrida*, trans. David Wills (Stanford, CA: Stanford University Press, 2004), 267.

6. Jacques Derrida, *Monolingualism of the Other; or, the Prosthesis of Origin*, trans. Patrick Mensah (Stanford, CA: Stanford University Press, 1998), 54–55 (my emphases).

7. Moses Maimonides, *Guide of the Perplexed*, trans. Shlomo Pines (Chicago: The University of Chicago Press, 1963), introduction, 5 (my emphasis); see also I 31, 67.

8. Derrida and Ferraris, *A Taste for the Secret*, 39.

9. Jacques Derrida and Geoffrey Bennington, *Jacques Derrida (Circonfession)*, (Chicago: The University of Chicago Press, 1993), 170–171 (my emphasis).

10. Joel Kraemer, *Maimonides: The Life and World of One of Civilization's Greatest Minds* (New York: Doubleday, 2008), 116–124; Amir Mazor, "Maimonides Forced Conversion to Islam: New Evidence," [in Hebrew] *Pe'amim* 110 (2007), 5–8.

11. Derrida, *Cinders*, 75.

12. Derrida, "How to Avoid Speaking," *Derrida and Negative Theology*, ed. Howard Coward and Toby Foshay (Albany: State University of New York Press, 1992), 66n13.

13. Derrida and Bennington, *Jacques Derrida*, 170. On p. 173 of the Derrida and Bennington text, the full sentence from the *Confessions* (I xi 17) is given: "Fresh from the womb of my mother, who put much hope in Thee, I was marked with the sign of His cross and seasoned with His salt." Augustine's salt may refer to a eucharistic surrogate for catechumens who were "of-but-not-in" the Christian community, a status that may also have applied to infants; James O'Donnell, *Augustine* Confessions: *Volume 2: Commentary, Books 1–7* (Oxford: Oxford University Press, 2013), 67.

14. Martin Heidegger, *Being and Time*, translated John Macquarrie and Edward Robinson (London: Blackwell, 1962), 206.

15. Derrida, "Abraham, the Other," in *Judeities*, ed. Bettina Bergo, Joseph Cohen, and Raphael Zagury-Orly (New York: Fordham University Press, 2007), 9.

16. Derrida, "Abraham, the Other," respectively 10, 6.

17. Derrida, *On the Name*, ed. Thomas Dutoit (Stanford, CA: Stanford University Press, 1995), 44.

18. Derrida, "Abraham, the Other," 33.

19. Derrida, *Archive Fever: A Freudian Impression*, trans. Eric Prenowitz (Chicago: The University of Chicago Press, 1996).

20. Derrida, "Abraham, the Other," 32.

21. Derrida, "Abraham, the Other," 32–33 (my emphases).

22. Maimonides comes close to saying as much in *Guide* II 25 when he remarks that the gates of figurative interpretation are not closed, except that he has the opposite purpose in mind: his aim there is to keep the gates of dogma open so as to foreclose the need to modify practical forms of Jewishness. We will return to this later.

23. Derrida, *Points . . . Interviews 1974–1994*, ed. Elizabeth Weber (Stanford, CA: Stanford University Press, 1992), 353 (interview with François Ewald, *Le Magazine littéraire*, March 1991).

24. Bernard McGinn, *Meister Eckhart: Teacher and Preacher* (Mahwah, NJ: Paulist Press, 1986), 17. For a thorough elaboration of this topic, see Yossef Schwartz, *"To Thee Is Silence Praise": Meister Eckhart's Reading in Maimonides' Guide of the Perplexed* (in Hebrew) (Tel Aviv: Am Oved Publishers, 2002).

25. Derrida, "Interpretations at War: Kant, the Jew, the German," in *Acts of Religion*, ed. Gil Anidjar (Stanford, CA: Stanford University Press, 2001), 160.

26. Derrida, "Interpretations at War," *Acts of Religion*, 156.

27. Ibid., 160.

28. Ibid., 160–161.

29. Ibid., 163.
30. Derrida, "Sauf le nom," in On the Name, 71.
31. Maimonides, Guide, I 57, 132; I 58, 134.
32. Derrida, Of Grammatology, trans. Gayatri Chakravorty Spivak (Baltimore, MD: Johns Hopkins University Press, 1997), 10.
33. Cf. Derrida, Archive Fever, 82–83; John Caputo, The Prayers and Tears of Jacques Derrida: Religion without Religion (Bloomington: Indiana University Press, 1997), 263–279.; Dana Hollander, "Is Deconstruction a Jewish Science? Reflections on 'Jewish Philosophy' in Light of Derrida's Judéités," Philosophy Today 50, no. 1 (2006): 128–138.
34. Jacques Derrida, "Différance," in Margins of Philosophy, trans. Alan Bass (Chicago: The University of Chicago Press, 1982), 6, cited by Derrida in "How to Avoid Speaking," 131–132n2.
35. Derrida, Margins of Philosophy, 6, cited by Derrida in "How to Avoid Speaking," 132n2.
36. Maimonides, Guide, III 51, 618; "in the presence of the king" translates the Arabic byn y'd'y, rendered by Friedlander as before the king, by Ibn Tibbon, Kafih, and Schwartz as lefnei ha'melekh, by Munk as se presenter devant le souverain; for an argument against reading byn y'd'y in terms of presence-to-consciousness or re-presentation, see Josef Stern, The Matter and Form of Maimonides' Guide (Cambridge, MA: Harvard University Press, 2013), chap. 7.
37. Derrida, "How to Avoid Speaking," 79.
38. Ibid., 102.
39. Ibid., 102; the critique of hyperessentiality goes back to "Différance."
40. Cf. "Epoché and Faith: An Interview with Jacques Derrida," in Derrida and Religion: Other Testaments, ed. Yvonne Sherwood and Kevin Hart (London: Routledge, 2004), 30. To the extent that discourse can be reduced to a pure form of address, to a pure apostrophe, Derrida is prepared not only to countenance prayer but indeed to generalize it and thus accept Levinas's view ("Is Ontology Fundamental?" in Emmanuel Levinas, Basic Philosophical Writings, ed. Adriaan Theodoor Peperzak, Simon Critchley, and Robert Bernasconi [Bloomington: Indiana University Press, 1996]): "This tie to the other, which does not reduce itself to the representation of the other but rather to his invocation, where invocation is not preceded by comprehension, we call religion. The essence of discourse is prayer" (7). But in "Violence and Metaphysics," in Writing and Difference, trans. Allan Bass (Chicago: The University of Chicago Press, 1978), Derrida cast doubt on the possibility of reducing discourse to a pure invocation, a point he made again against Jean-Luc Marion in arguing that the purest of prayers implies positive predication, if only that of existence.
41. Derrida, "How to Avoid Speaking," 110.
42. Maimonides, Guide, I 59, 141–142.
43. Cf. Maimonides, Guide III 32, 526; and see, among others, Ehud Benor, Worship of the Heart: A Study of Maimonides' Philosophy of Religion (Albany: State University of New York, 1995).
44. Maimonides, Guide I 59, 139–140.
45. See Steven Harvey, "The Meaning of Terms Designating Love in Judaeo-Arabic Thought and Some Remarks on the Judaeo-Arabic Interpretation of Maimonides," in

Judaeo-Arabic Studies: Proceedings of the Founding Conference of the Society for Judaeo-Arabic Studies, ed. Norman Gold (Amsterdam: Harwood Academic Publishers, 1997), 175–196, esp. 190–194.

46. Respectively, Alexander Altmann, "Maimonides on Intellect and the Scope of Metaphysics," in *Von der Mitteralterlichen zur modernen Aufklärung* (Tübingen: Mohr Siebeck, 1987), 122; Yair Lorberbaum, "On Contradictions, Rationality, Dialectics, and Esotericism in *Maimonides'* Guide of the Perplexed," *Review of Metaphysics* 5, no. 4 (2002): 746; David R. Blumenthal, *Philosophical Mysticism: Studies in Rational Religion* (Ramat Gan, Israel: Bar Ilan University, 2006), 144; Diana Lobel, "'Silence Is Praise to You': Maimonides on Negative Theology, Looseness of Expression, and Religious Experience," *American Catholic Philosophical Quarterly* 76, no. 1 (2002): 46, 44. Kenneth Seeskin has developed an alternative approach to Maimonidean silence that avoids unitive implications and emphasizes the heuristic and moral telos of this *via negativa*; see, for example, his chapter in this volume and also "Sanctity and Silence: The Religion Significance of Maimonides' Negative Theology," *American Catholic Philosophical Quarterly* 76, no. 1 (2002): 7–23.

47. Derrida, "How to Avoid Speaking," 79.

48. *Guide*, I 58, 137. Derrida's profound sympathy for certain types of negative theology combined with his "uneasiness" concerning Christian Neoplatonic modes of unitive silence has prompted others to explore the affinity between Derridean nonmetaphysical negativity and Kabbalistic negativity. On this, see the stimulating work by Shira Wolosky, "An 'Other' Negative Theology: On Derrida's 'How to Avoid Speaking,'" *Poetics Today* 19, no. 2 (1998): 261–280; and Elliot R. Wolfson, *Giving beyond the Gift: Apophasis and Overcoming Theomania* (New York: Fordham University Press, 2014), 154–200. Though I approach Derrida's apophaticism from a Maimonidean rather than a Kabbalistic point of view, my conclusions are close to Wolfson's, namely, that for Derrida "The secret is not something than can be unveiled" (191).

49. Josef Stern, "Maimonides' Epistemology," in K. Seeskin, ed., *The Cambridge Companion to Maimonides* (Cambridge: Cambridge University Press, 2005), 123; see also Josef Stern, "Meaning and Language," in *The Cambridge History of Jewish Philosophy: From Antiquity through the Seventeenth Century*, ed. Steven Nadler and T. M. Rudavsky (Cambridge: Cambridge University Press, 2009), 237–244, and especially Stern, *Matter and Form*.

50. Stern, *Matter and Form*, 197.

51. Ibid., 198.

52. *Guide*, I 58, 135; cf. Stern, *Matter and Form*, 204–218.

53. Derrida, "How to Avoid Speaking," 79.

54. Derrida and Ferraris, *A Taste for the Secret*, 4. "Like a good skeptic, Maimonides argues with the philosophers on their own ground; he advances no positive thesis of his own" (Stern, *Matter and Form*, 234). On Derrida's relation to Pyrrhonian skepticism (which is the tradition within which Stern places Maimonidean skepticism), see Bob Plant, "Perhaps . . ." *Angelaki: Journal of the Theoretical Humanities* 11, no. 3 (2006): 137–156.

55. Maimonides, *Mishneh Torah*, Laws of Prayer, IV 16; see Stern, *Matter and Form*, 326–327.

56. For this reason, Stern declines to associate Maimonidean skepticism with mysticism: "There is no celebration of negation like we find in Neoplatonists or in mystical writings, the use of negation to overcome intellect and language to experience a divine presence beyond being. Maimonides' use of negation is restrained, calculated, and controlled" (205); "It is important to note that Maimonides' description of that experience can be understood entirely naturalistically. The lightning flashes need not be taken, as some scholars take them, to be supernatural revelations or interventions that go beyond the intellect. The focus is on *experience*, but it is not supernatural, transcendent, or 'mystical'" (292–293). When Derrida entertains an "intuitionless mysticism," he is thinking in similar terms. It should be noted that this distinction between a mystical and a skeptical negative theology was made at length by A. H. Armstrong in his extensive work on Neoplatonism and negative theology; on which, see John Peter Kenney, "The Critical Value of Negative Theology," *Harvard Theological Review* 86, no. 4 (1993): 439–453.

57. Derrida and Ferraris, *A Taste for the Secret*, 41.

58. Maimonides, *Guide* I 32, 70; cf. Stern, *Matter and Form*, 81–94.

59. Derrida, "Epoché and Faith," 30–31, where Derrida also says: "As you know, a prayer is something secret . . . absolutely secret. Of course there are public prayers. There are people in communities who pray together. And the first thing I will tell you is this: when I was young my first rebellion against my religious environment was to do with public prayer." Here again we find those perplexing verbal gesticulations that Derrida could neither renounce nor reclaim. "So my way of praying, if I pray, is absolutely private. Even if I am in public, even if I am in a synagogue and praying with others, I know that my own prayer would be silent and secret, interrupting something in the community."

60. Stern, *Matter and Form*, 185.

61. Derrida, "How to Avoid Speaking," 81.

62. Maimonides, *Guide*, I 59, 139, 140; my emphasis on "draw a line."

63. Derrida, "How to Avoid Speaking," 81. Cf. "Sauf le nom," in *On the Name*, 67–68.

64. Agamben argued that the unknowable God of Pseudo-Dionysus becomes "the invisible principle of power" that is "fully translated into a hierarchy" that governs in the Name of its impenetrable transcendence; Georgio Agamben, *The Kingdom and the Glory: For a Theological Genealogy of Economy and Government*, trans. Lorenzo Chiesa, with Matteo Mandarini (Stanford, CA: Stanford University Press, 2011), 154.

65. Derrida and Malabou, *La Contre-allée*, 263; translation modified from *Counterpath*, 267.

66. For an account of Maimonides's reformist methods and agenda see Moshe Halbertal, *Maimonides: Life and Thought* (Princeton, NJ: Princeton University Press, 2015), chap. 4 and 6.

67. Stern, *Form and Matter*, 225; on 'anniyya generally, see Warren Zev Harvey and Steven Harvey, "A Note on the Arabic Term 'Anniyya/'Aniyya/'Inniyya,'" *Iyyun* (April, 1989), 167–171.

68. Derrida, "Perhaps or Maybe: Jacques Derrida in Conversation with Alexander Garcia Düttmann," *Warwick Journal of Philosophy* 6 (1997): 1–2. On this, see also Plant, "Perhaps . . ." (see note 54).

69. Derrida, "Deconstructions: The Im-possible," in *French Theory in America*, ed. Slyvére Lotringer and Sande Cohen (New York: Routledge, 2001), 31.

70. Derrida, "Violence and Metaphysics," 89.

71. Zohar 1:264b–265a. The passage comes from *Zohar parashat Piqqudim*, which was most likely written by Moshe de Leon, one of Maimonides's most inspired readers.

72. Derrida, *On the Name*, 74 (my emphases). It is therefore not surprising, though it is indeed amazing, that Maimonides's closest, most loyal readers, those who most share his "passion for non-knowing," were among those most open to the pantheistic dissemination of divine glory (cf. *Guide* I 64), as, for example, Moshe Cordovero. On this, see Elliot Wolfson, *Aleph Mem Tau: Kabbalistic Musings on Time, Truth and Death* (Berkeley: University of California Press, 2006).

ELEVEN

Jewish Negative Theology: A Phenomenological Perspective

DAVID NOVAK

1. The Absence of God

A number of theologians in the three monotheistic religions of revelation—Judaism, Christianity, and Islam—have engaged in what is generally called "negative theology," in other words, speculating about what we cannot say about God. Much negative theology has been done over the centuries, though very little has been done in the past one hundred years or so (other than antiquarian studies of mediaeval philosophical-theology). This neglect seems to stem from the fact that *theology* as what we now call "God-talk," whether positive or negative, is taken to be a "mind-game," that is, speculation not originating in or having any application to any kind of human experience.[1] And, since Kant, almost all philosophers require any speculation to have these connections to some kind of human experience.[2] So, if any kind of theology is to be of modern philosophical interest, it must have some connection to the kind of experience in which God is the main concern therein, in other words, "religious experience." In order for religious experience to be worthy of philosophical reflection, it must be taken as what is to be explained, not to be explained away.

When any kind of experience is taken to be irreducible to any other kind of experience, but is taken prima facie, it seems that phenomenology is the philosophical methodology most able to take that kind of primal experience seriously in and of itself. It avoids taking the phenomenon before us to be the effect of some cause outside it. That is why phenomenology must not bring a discourse that emerges from one kind of experience and apply it (however skillfully) to its reflection on some other kind of experience. Instead, phenomenological reflection must enter the discourse that emerges from a specific kind of experience by learning to speak its language and then think in its categories. This linguistic acquisition is what enables those who have had this kind of experience to retain it, reflect on it, and communicate it to those who can only receive it secondhand. "Theology" is the name given to the discourse that emerges from religious experience, a discourse that comes through those who have experienced what was spoken to them in this revelatory event and thus attempt to understand it as best one can. Therefore, phenomenology that engages religious experience must appropriate its theological language and attempt to clarify its meaning as much as possible, yet without losing contact with the experience itself out of which that language emerges and to which it must regularly return for its vitality.

In order to appropriate theological language, phenomenology must be interested in irreducible religious experience. This is the kind of experience that cannot be explained away as epiphenomenal. It cannot be taken to be an illusion, in other words, it is not an unconscious projection of something we *want* to have experienced rather than a reflection on what we actually do experience. It is also not a causal inference from a more basic, irreducible experience.[3] That is, it is not like "natural theology," which infers divine causality *from* our experience of the hierarchal orderliness of the external world (which is quite different from our experience of the external world after Galileo, Newton, Darwin, and Einstein). Moreover, this religious experience is of unique historical events in which God makes His specific claims on the human subjects to whom he has revealed these claims. Since these events occur at a particular time, in a particular place, to particular people, they are not universally at hand for everybody, anytime, anywhere. There are only certain universally available, a priori preconditions that enable (but do not necessitate) people to have such religious experiences and be able to retain them for further reflection.[4] So, whereas one can affirm a universal propensity for the experience of such unique events, the events themselves are only experienced by members of particular communities, who speak of them in their own language, and who define themselves according to them. That is why I can only speak of negative theology in the context of the Jewish experience of divine negativity inasmuch as that experience is the only experience I as a Jew (who freely accepts his being historically situated in the Jewish tradition) could have, retain, and reflect upon. Christian and Muslim thinkers, it seems, are similarly limited. Hence our respective reflections on our particular religious experiences, which are our experiences of a unique revelation, can only yield analogies to one another. These reflections ought not presume that there is some prior generic experience of which our respective religious experiences are only subsequent specifications.

From this phenomenological perspective, there is positive God-talk/theology and there is negative God-talk/theology. Positive theology is concerned with divine immanence, which is the experience of God's presence. Negative theology is concerned with divine transcendence. But how do we experience what is beyond the horizon of our experience, which is what "transcendence" means: "going beyond" or "surmounting" (from the Latin *transcendere*)? Perhaps we could say that our experience, from which negative theology is derived, is our experience of the absence of God: when God is *away from us*, when *God is not here*. At the level of the God-talk that emerges from this experience, we cannot speak of who is not here with us; it can only allude to the God who had been here with us, but who is now absent. Nevertheless, we could not have such anguished experience if this God had never been with us here. Only a God whom we have experienced as present *to* us could now be experienced as being absent *from* us. Since we can speak of this once present God, negative God-talk presupposes positive God-talk in the same way absence presupposes presence. Yet unlike divine presence that does directly address us and that calls for our response, divine absence does not address us at all, but only elicits from us either our silent resignation or our often painful waiting for God to come back to us from out of His absence from us. In rabbinic parlance, this absence is called *hester panim*, literally "God's hiding His face," which is our experience of what seems to be God's indifference to our existential plight.[5]

Despite their essential difference, divine presence and divine absence are necessarily related in the God-human relationship. When they are not related, though, when divine presence is assumed without assuming even the possibility of divine absence, there is no one whom such an omnipresent God could confront any more than a whole could confront what is a part therein, or any more than a part could confront what totally *envelopes* it. There is no one *to whom* one could say: "Here I am" (*hineni*).[6] Omnipresence admits of no external relations, no live transactions *between* persons. It admits of no covenant (*brit*). Omnipresence admits of no transcendence; the omnipresent God is always at hand, always immanent. We can only allude to that radical transcendence of God's presence *to* us when God is absent *from* us.[7] Moreover, when divine absence is presumed to be permanent, when even the possibility of God's return to us is denied, we are left with the "dead god" of whom Nietzsche (although not the first) most famously spoke.[8] This is the authentic experience of an atheist: not the nonbeing of a god who never existed, but rather the absence of a god an atheist despairs will never return again.

2. Maimonides's on God-talk: Positive and Negative

As a tentative definition of what distinguishes positive from negative theology, let us look at how the greatest Jewish proponent of natural theology, Moses Maimonides, distinguishes between positive and negative God-talk. He writes, "Every attribute that is found in the books of God . . . is an attribute of His [God's] action and not an attribute of His [God's] essence."[9] Later, in the same work, he writes: "The expression [*kavod*] is sometimes intended to signify His [God's] essence and true reality . . . as when he [Moses] says: *Show me, I pray Thee, Thy* glory, and was answered: *For man shall not see Me and live*. This answer indicates that the *glory* spoken of here is His [God's] essence [*atsmo*]."[10] In other words, we can say what God *does*, but we cannot say what God *is*. But what is the difference between *being* and *doing*?

Let us now try to understand Maimonides's theory or "theo-logic" so as to draw out its ontological assumptions. We then need to decide whether these assumptions make sense in and of themselves. Moreover, are they adequate to the tradition of Jewish God-talk found in Scripture, Talmud, and Midrash? That means much more than locating counterexamples to Maimonides's theory of attribution in that vast traditional literature. Instead, we need to determine whether Maimonides's theory can be countered by another theory that is more adequate to the traditional data. No theory is without counterexamples among the data it attempts to explain; nevertheless, it seems that a theory having greater explanatory power than a competing theory will also face fewer counterexamples. In and of itself, though, by the criterion of Ockham's razor (*pluralitas non est ponenda sine necessitate*) a theory having greater explanatory power will also make fewer assumptions than its competitors.

Why does Maimonides refuse to say anything about *what God is*? Obviously, one cannot say God is *some thing*, for all things are finite bodies and God is infinite: limited by nothing; limiting everything.[11] But why not predicate some quality of God, such as saying "God *is* good"? After all, such qualities are not like finite bodies, because they admit of an infinite number of subjects of whom they can be predicated, in other words, they can be endlessly extended. However, if I understand Maimonides correctly, the reason why this divine predication/attribution is also unacceptable theologically is that Maimonides seems to assume that *goodness* names a reality (like a Platonic *idea*) in which an endless number of subjects could participate. So, even if God is "first among equals" (*primus inter pares*) as a subject/participant within this infinite reality, God would still be subordinate to it (like Plato's creator/god is subordinate to the idea: the Good).[12] That is because in this Platonic logic and ontology, qualitative adjectives such as "good" are hypostatized into substantive nouns such as "goodness."[13] As such, "good" no longer functions as an adjective that qualifies a subject and is thereby secondary to it. Instead, to say a subject is "good" is to say that this subject (even if this subject were God) merely instantiates a greater reality, named by the idea called "goodness." In other words, the real subject is subordinate to the real predicate that is greater than it. Thus *a* good person is less than *the* goodness he or she instantiates, and this is just as a finite being is less than infinite Being. But, surely for Maimonides as a Jewish theologian, nothing is greater than God.

All this notwithstanding, is Scripture not filled with such qualitative existential attribution? How does one explain that? Maimonides explains such attribution by assuming that such existential attribution expresses a double negative or a negation of a negation. Thus to say "God *is* good" is to say "God *is not* bad," that is, God is not not-good. A double negative (-1×-1) in arithmetic logic leads to an affirmation $(-1 \times -1 = +1)$ or, as the Talmud puts it: "from *no* you infer *yes*."[14] Yet

Maimonides does not infer from what we cannot attribute to God's being anything positive that we can attribute to God's being.[15] Why not? That is because to do so would put God into some category or other, even if we were to equate God and goodness. That would be like saying "God *is* goodness" (A = B) *or* "goodness is God" (B = A). But by making God's being utterable or effable, we would be enabling ourselves to subsume God in a category in which God is not the only member. Creatures too are called "good."[16] Thus God's ineffable transcendence is compromised. Therefore, our negative predication only serves to save God from falling below what we humans respect; it does not limit how far God goes beyond even what we most highly respect in the world. Negative predication, then, functions as the *conditio sine qua non* for God-talk, in other words, it eliminates what cannot and ought not be said of God. In a way, it is like the prohibition of idolatry, that is, one can say that any finite being is *not*-God, without having to say what God *is*.[17]

Following Maimonides's way of doing negative theology, what one cannot say of God does not lead us to infer anything positive about God. Even God's absolute perfection can only be spoken of as lack of any defects. Negative theology only postulates a reality of which humans cannot or could not ever say what it is, at least not in this world. (It is like Kant's postulation of the *Ding an sich* or "thing totally unto itself."[18]) But if we cannot say anything about this reality, why not follow Wittgenstein's rule: "What we cannot speak of, we must be silent about" (*wovon man nicht sprechen kann, darüber muss man schweigen*)?[19] Is not this insistence on silence the way Hume put down negative theology when he tried to show that not being able to say *any-thing* positive of God seems to be no different than speaking of *no-thing*, in other words, speaking of nothing is the same as not speaking at all?[20] Whatever one says here has no real referent at all, nor is it helpful for explaining what any real referent in the world actually does.

When, however, one takes a qualitative predicate such as "good" and takes it to be an adverb, that is, as a qualification of an act rather than the subordination of a person to some greater entity, as is the case when a qualitative predicate is taken to be an adjective and then hypostatized into a supernoun, one does not fall into the ontological trap of defining God. (To de-fine God is to limit God by something greater, thereby obliterating God's in-finity: *un Dieu defini, c'est un Dieu fini* as a French philosopher is said to have uttered.) Here, only an act is being qualitatively described, in other words, it is being evaluated, but its subject is not being subordinated to an entity greater than Himself. It seems this is what Maimonides means by his distinction between substantial attributes and attributes of action. Note how, in his discussion of moral qualities or characteristics [*middot*] attributed to God, he emphasizes that the acts they characterize do not proceed from some character or property of God's being per se: "The apprehension of these actions is an apprehension of His attributes [*te'arav*] . . . with respect to He is known. . . .

The meaning here is not that he possesses moral qualities [ba'al middot], but that He performs actions [po'el pe'ulot] resembling the actions that is us proceed from moral qualities—I mean from aptitudes of the soul [me-tehunot nafshiyot]."[21] Such essential attributes or characteristics cannot be attributed to God, though, because we do not know what God is. And that means that even if God might have such characteristics, knowledge of them is beyond even our highest apprehensions.

Since these attributes of actions are known to us (for Maimonides, through our reflection on the overall beneficence of the created natural order), we can assume they are made known to us by the same divine will that beneficently willed all creation. And, why does God make these qualities known to us? This is done so that we feel obligated to imitate this divine beneficent action and thereby participate with God in its furtherance in the world. In other words, their ultimate significance is not in what they describe but in what they prescribe (i.e., the "is" here is for the sake of the "ought"). Thus Maimonides concludes at the end of his philosophical-theological work, *Guide of the Perplexed*:

> It is clear that the perfection of man . . . is the one acquired by him who has achieved, in a measure corresponding to his capacity, apprehension of Him [hasagat ha-shem] . . . and who knows His providence [hashgahato] extending over His creatures as manifested in the act of bringing them into being and in their governance [ve-hinhigu otam] as it is. The way of life of such an individual, after he has achieved this apprehension, will always have in view *loving-kindness, righteousness,* and *judgment* (Jeremiah 9:23), through imitation of His actions [le-hidamot be-pe'ulot ha-shem].[22]

Writing in his great compendium of the Law, *Mishneh Torah*, where he is more beholden to the specific revelation of the Torah, Maimonides concludes: "As for [the people] Israel, to whom God has emanated [hishpi'a] the goodness [tovat] of the Torah by commanding them just laws and norms, they are compassionate [rahmanim] with all [of creation]. Concerning the qualities [be-middot] of God that He commanded us to imitate [le-hidamot bahem], it is said: *His compassionate acts extend over all His works* (Psalms 145:9)."[23] Now the beginning of the scriptural verse Maimonides has quoted states: "The Lord is good [tov]," in other words, God *benefits* all of creation. There are a number of rabbinic precedents which teach that to know God's beneficent qualities is so that we may imitate them by our own beneficent acts. As the rabbis teach: "Learning's greatness lies in its leading us into action [ma'aseh]."[24] For Maimonides, conversely, knowledge of God's being is not only not utterable in words, it is inimitable in deeds. Nevertheless, that does not means such knowledge is impossible, for we cannot presume to rule out that it does have a real object, yet who is only known through the type of prophetic apprehension that is ineffable. For Maimonides, such ineffable prophetic apprehension seems to have been Moses's alone.[25]

3. Being and Doing

Maimonides says that the difference between an attribute of action and an essential attribute is the difference between saying "Zayd carpentered this wall" and saying "Zayd is a carpenter."[26] Nevertheless, is not a "carpenter" somebody who "carpenters," in other words, somebody who builds things out of wood? Is there really a difference in kind between what one is and what one does? Is not the difference here one of degree: between what is done regularly and what is done irregularly? Is not a carpenter somebody for whom carpentering is a regular *activity*, whereas carpentering is a random *act* of somebody for whom something else (or nothing) is their regular activity? Thus the only difference I see here is, perhaps, the difference between a wall built by a professional carpenter with much experience in building walls and an amateur carpenter with little or no experience in building walls. Usually, we can tell the difference by looking at the quality of the wall: when it is of good quality, we can infer that it was built by an experienced professional; when the wall is of bad quality, we can infer that it was built by an inexperienced amateur (who usually builds bad walls). In that case, though, are not all personal attributes the attributes of actions (both regular activities and random acts being subsets of action)? The most we could say is that a professional carpenter has more capacity for building good walls than does an amateur. But a capacity is a preparation for action, of which a professional has more and an amateur less. It is not that the professional has it, but the amateur does not.

This preparation for action is what we call "thought" as when scripture speaks of "thoughtful work" (*mlekhet mahshavet*—Exodus 35:33). And, since *mahshavah* is attributed to God—"My thoughts [*mahshavotai*] are not your thoughts" (Isaiah 55:8)—even God's thoughts are God's plans for what God intends to be transitive action.[27] These thoughts are God's theoretical preparation for transitive action. Like human intention (*kavvanah*), these thoughts are the exercise of a capacity for intelligent action. The difference between God and humans, though, is not that humans plan transitive action and God does not; instead, the difference is that God can plan the type of creative acts that humans as creatures are simply incapable of. So it would seem that Maimonides's analogy of the difference between the carpenter and carpentering only indicates a difference of degree, whereas his metaphysical differentiation between action and being is supposed to indicate a more radical difference in kind. So, how can being be seen as essentially different from action?

Even Aristotle's God, who is "thought-thinking-itself" (*noēsis noēseōs noēsis*), is acting, though He is not "doing *anything*," in other words, God is not acting *on* what is not-God, that is, what is *other* than God.[28] This God is an intransitive rather than a transitive actor. Therefore, the difference between transitive and intransitive action is that transitive actors are involved in external relations, whereas intransitive actors are involved in internal relations. In the case of the transitive actor, the action intends an "other" as its object outside itself. In the case of the intransitive actor, the action is all self-contained inside himself.

Since Maimonides's God is the Creator, this God engages in transitive action: He acts *on* the universe as an efficient cause (*po'el*) acts on its end product.[29] So, only God's transitive action can be spoken of. To speak of God's being, though, involves the tautology: "God is what God is," or "God is Being."[30] To say a subject is identical with its predicate, when we do not know what that predicate means, is to say nothing *about* this subject. By speaking of God in the indicative voice, are not we only repeating God's name? That is different from evoking God so as to elicit some sort of response to our evocation of His proper name, which is asking God to *do* something good for us.[31]

4. Describable Divine Action

Before we can understand what it means to say we cannot say *what God is*, we need to see how Jews can actually say *what God does*. The place where God-talk functions most cogently in the Jewish tradition is in the liturgy (*avodat ha-qodesh*). Jewish liturgy takes its language from revelation recorded in Scripture and its tradition. Liturgy is the language of Scripture and tradition. We are required to regularly speak to God among ourselves by employing the language we are taught God spoke to us in. Accordingly, theology is beholden to liturgy as the spoken language it needs to always think in and thereby refine, yet never soar beyond.[32]

Liturgical God-talk is conducted along two lines: *hoda'ah*: acknowledging what God has done for us; and *baqashah*: requesting of God what we want God to do for us.[33] In both cases, the common denominator is that we are either acknowledging what God has done *for us*, or we are requesting God to do something *for us*. This "for us" means that our *hoda'ah* is actually a "thanksgiving" (as in *todah*), that is, a "thank You" that more readily leads to a "please" (like *be-vaqashah* in modern Hebrew) than does the merely verbal "acknowledgment." Thus in the liturgical order of morning worship (*shaharit*) and evening worship (*arvit*), we begin by praising God for *what* God has done for us, that "what" being our evaluative attribution of these acts. Immediately thereafter, as the Talmud puts it, "one is to juxtapose the mention of past redemption and the request for future redemption" (*ha-somekh ge'ulah le-tefillah*).[34] In other words, because God had benefitted us in the past, there is good reason to hope and pray in the present that God will benefit us in the future.

By citing these theological facts, our requests are more than the blind begging from an unknown benefactor, who could be anyone.[35] They are more than wishful thinking. Instead, our requests are directed to the One *from Whom* we have received benefits in the past, and who has promised even more benefits in the present and into the future (both near and beyond). As such, if we accept as true what God has done for us in the past, we have good reason to make our requests and direct them to the Lord God alone. And these requests must be consistent with the commandments (*mitsvot*) that constitute God's primary relationship with humans, and even more so with the elect people Israel. Indeed, Maimonides points out that the reason God has, does, and will benefit us, is ultimately to better enable us to keep His commandments.[36] In other words, God's greatest beneficence for us are the commandments we are to keep to benefit the cultivation of body and soul.[37] Therefore, any other benefits we request from God are, maximally to better enable us to keep the commandments; minimally, they are not to impede our keeping of the commandments.

One might also add that this is especially the case regarding those commandments that constitute the divine-human relationship (*bein adam le-maqom*) which, as emphasized in Kabbalistic and Hasidic theology, is something done for God's sake insofar as God desires the intimacy *with* us (*it'aruta de-l'eila*) because we desire intimacy with Him (*it'aruta de-le-tatta*), which the *mitsvot* enable both God and humans to enact together.[38] This tells us why we humans need to acknowledge/praise God, and why God needs to hear that acknowledgement/praise from us. But all this only takes place with the covenantal relationship between God and His people. Outside of that covenantal relationship, human praise of God seems to be a useless activity: both *by* humans and *for* God. Who needs it? Inside that relationship, however, both humans and God do need for God to be praised by these human members of the covenant. As we shall now see, the humans need to remind God of His promises to them so that they can have hope for their future, and God needs to be shown that His human covenant partners remember what God has promised them and what God has commanded them to do now in remembrance of God's fulfillment of some of promises in the past.[39]

However, are we not violating the widely accepted philosophical prohibition (most famously enunciated by Hume) of deriving an "ought" from an "is"?[40] For we are not just requesting what God *will* do, but what God *shall* do, based on what God *has* done. Just because God has benefitted us in the past, does that entail that God *ought* to benefit us in the future? Nevertheless, the way out of this conundrum is to note that our very description of what God has done for us in the past is itself a description of an "ought." It is God's partial fulfillment in the past of the promises (*shevu'ot*) God Himself has made by Himself, *autonomously*, to benefit us in the present and the near future, and to completely fulfill His promise in the end-of-days (*aharit ha-yamim*). In making these covenantal promises, God has obligated Godself by taking an irrevocable oath.[41] (That is the only autonomy that a traditional Jew can affirm in good faith.) Accordingly, our descriptive praise of God is our *reminding* God of *how* God has kept His promises in the past. This "reminding God" like all "reminding" (*zakhor*), in other words, causing someone to remember to do what they are obligated to do, is not like reminding someone of a memory they have forgotten. It is thus more than simply "calling-to-mind." (Indeed, how could that be in the case of God, since reminding God to cognize what God has forgotten would imply that God has the cognitive defect of forgetfulness?) Instead, reminding is reminding someone, even reminding yourself what he or she ought to *attend to*, based on what that person has been *obligated to do* in the past.[42] For us as creatures, the obligation of which we are reminded is heteronomous: it is the claim God has made upon us, sometimes directly, sometimes through other creatures. In God's case alone, the obligation is autonomous: it is self-imposed. Reminding God, then, is holding God to God's own revealed word.[43]

That is what *the* covenant (*ha-brit*) primarily means. In the covenant God promises what God shall do for us, and we promise what we shall do for God. Yet unlike the kind of conditions involved in ordinary contracts, the covenant is unconditional; it has no termination clauses. Hence noncompliance on either side is only cause for complaint, which is each side *reminding* the other what is yet to be done. When we humans are noncompliant, not having kept our covenantal promise or oath, repentance (*teshuvah*) here and now is the prescribed remedy. When God seems to be noncompliant, not having kept His covenantal promise, we humans then have the right to call upon God to remember to do what He has promised to do for us, even though more often than not we do not see much divine fulfillment in this world, but have to wait for it to come in another world that is beyond even our highest horizon.[44] Thus we are entitled to say: "I know my Redeemer lives, though He be the last to arise on earth; and after this has been marked in my flesh, only then will I behold God" (Job 19:25). Jewish worship, therefore, is an unending dialogue between God and His people Israel (even though that dialogue is only mutually and simultaneously conducted when it is conducted between God and a prophet). And, as regards both sides (albeit functioning asymmetrically), that dialogue involves *transactions between* the two parties to the covenant: divine and human. Unlike commercial trade-offs, though, both parties to the covenantal transactions want the same thing, which is the relationship itself, not what the relationship could yield for each of the parties to it.[45]

Nevertheless, as regards the God-human *dialogue*, I cannot accept the well-known view of Martin Buber, in his version of negative theology, we can only speak *to* God (*ansprechen*), but not *about* God (*aussprechen*).[46] But *what* is the content of our speaking to God; *what* do we talk with God about? So, I differ with Buber because in Jewish liturgy our speech *to* God (*tefillah*) does have content: it is reminding God of *what* He has done for us in the past, thus requesting that God do it again for us in the present and in the future. That enables our requests made *to* God to have grounds upon which they can be made. (By the way, the problem of what would be the content of "humans' speaking/praying to God," according to Buber, is similar to the problem of what would be the content of "God's speaking-to/commanding" humans, according to Buber.[47]) One could say our prime request of God in Jewish liturgy is for God to enable us to keep His commandments that constitute our relationship *with* God together. By so doing, we are asking God to help us activate our potential to keep our covenantal promise. So too, do we ask God to activate God's own potential to keep His covenantal promise, indeed, to finally and totally fulfill it.

In the liturgy, the beneficial deeds of God on our behalf which we can recount (*zakhor*) are of two kinds: God's beneficence done *through* nature; and God's beneficence done *in* history. Now the theological advantage of emphasizing God's beneficence done through nature is that it is regularly experienced by everyone. As the liturgy puts it, "God beneficently renews [*ha-mehadesh*] creation every day continually."[48]

There are two theological disadvantages to this kind of God-talk though. First, God's causality *of* nature is not directly experienced, but only inferred by some sort of "argument from design." (Let us recall that the argument from design was the one argument for God's existence that Kant did not regard to be inherently irrational, just scientifically superfluous.[49]) Second, since no prophet has informed humankind in general (those who can experience through natural phenomena some sort of divine grace) just *how* God has chosen to benefit humankind *through* natural events, we have no retort to the charge that such benefits could simply be accidental, in other words, we have no way of showing that they were actually benefits personally intended to be *directly for us*. (The same charge could be made against those who see intended divine punishment being wrought through natural events; this too could be accidental, i.e., without any personal intent at all.)

That is why, it seems to me, the liturgy primarily celebrates what God has done for Israel His people directly, that is, what God has done for His people directly in *their* history. Unlike nature, which is universal, history is particular. There is no universal history experienced by all humans equally; conversely, universal nature is experienced equally by all humans. (That is why mathematics qua *mathesis universalis* is the language of natural science throughout the world, whereas the history of each people can only be told in the sagas of their own language.) God's beneficence, then, is not known by any inference from natural phenomena, but rather *through* the revelation of God's practical intentions by a prophet. These historically known benefits are what Scripture call the "mighty acts of God" (*gevurot ha-shem*) or "miracles" and what Nahmanides called "public supernatural divine manifestations" (*nissim mefursamim*).[50] In fact, even when in the liturgy (whose paradigm of God-talk comes mostly from the psalms) God is praised for His creation of natural phenomena, this is usually background for praising God for what God has done for us and, therefore, that we can have justifiable expectation God will do for us in the future similarly.⁵¹ In other words, only the Creator of the entire natural order could insert Himself into that order at will, anytime anywhere, in order to use that order to either bless us or curse us, benefit us or punish us—both of which are designed to bring us back into covenantal intimacy with God.

Another important difference between natural and supernatural beneficence described by the liturgy is that natural beneficence is usually physical, that is, the fulfillment of our bodily needs. Thus the blessing said after full meals (*birkat ha-mazon*) begins with acknowledging God "who feeds the world" (*ha-zan et ha'olam*), something which, by the way, is not the unique experience of the Jews.⁵² But then the blessing quickly moves on to speak of "the good land which He [God] has given you" (Deuteronomy 8:10).⁵³ Now what is the difference between the gift of food and the gift of the land of Israel? The difference is that food comes to us *through* the natural or physical world, whereas the land of Israel is given to us directly *in* history. The gift of the land of Israel is a *political* fact that occurs in history. The connection of the people Israel to the land of Israel is not a physical fact, for Scripture clearly teaches that the people of Israel are not indigenous to the land; we are not the land's aboriginal natives. The land is a gift from God.⁵⁴ Thus we move from the needs of the body to the needs of the body politic. Moreover, the fulfillment of the needs of the body are only the necessary condition for the fulfillment of the needs of the body politic, hence the raison d'être of the body politic is much more than being the collective instrument for fulfilling the economic needs of the body. For Jews, the purpose of our "body politic" or communal life and continuity is to be the historical and geographic site of the covenant, plus being the launching pad for the messianic consummation of the promises God made when electing Israel.⁵⁵ The fulfillment of these promises will include the entire world.⁵⁶

Nevertheless, what these two gifts, the one given indirectly and the other given directly, have in common is that in neither case are the human recipients of these gifts their passive recipients of them. In each case, the human recipients must actively *take* these gifts in a prescribed way. In each case, that active taking is structured by commandments. In the case of food, Jews are required to thank God for the food given to them, both before and after partaking of it.⁵⁷ In the case of the land of Israel, Jews are required to actively settle the land and develop there a society worthy of being the main site of the covenant between God and his people.⁵⁸ Thus it could be said that all God's gifts, whether directly or indirectly given, are given in order that Jews might live the covenantal life with God that is constituted by the good deeds (*ma'asim tovim*) prescribed by divine commandment to be done by us. And in both cases, Jews are required to speak to God of what God has done for us in the past, of what God commands us to do in the present, and to remind God what God has obligated Godself to do for us (and all the world along with us) in the future.

5. Divine Transcendence

Only when we understand to a certain extent *what* our experience of the acts of God is, and *how* we are to respond to these acts, are we in a position to begin to understand what it means to say *that* God transcends His transactions *with* us and *for* us. Thus we need to understand *why* we cannot describe what God is doing apart from our experience of what God has done for us in this world (*ba'olam ha-zeh*). But, when doing this kind of negative theology, we now need to ask whether God's acts are beyond our actual experience in this world, but that they are still what we could imagine to be our possible experience in this world were we able to be there when God made it. Or, are there acts of God that are even beyond anything we could ever imagine in any world like our own?

Scripture speaks of two kinds of divine transcendence: first, there are acts of God that are beyond our experience in this world, but which we could actually experience nonetheless, and second, there are acts of God that we could never experience. The former acts of God, which are spoken of in human language (*ke-lashon bnei adam*) are, therefore, tangible transitive acts of which we humans can speak.[59] The latter acts of God, though, are acts of which we have not been told anything; therefore we cannot imagine what they are. We cannot even imagine what this absent God is doing when He is not involved with us in our world. Now there seem to be two kinds of human responses to this divine absence.

The first human response to this divine absence is most clearly enunciated by the prophet Habakkuk when he said: "The Lord is in His holy precinct [*be-hekhal qodsho*], keep away from Him in silence [*has mi-panav*] all the earth" (Habakkuk 2:20). Because humans hear nothing about what God is doing there, they could not possibly speak of it. Reverential silence seems to be the only proper response from humans hearing *that something rather than nothing is happening there*.[60] The problem is, though, that such silence implies human resignation to the absence of God *here*. But should the absence of God elicit longing, even protest, from the humans experiencing this absence? In fact, in Scripture this is expressed thusly: "My God, my God, why [*lamah*] have You forsaken me; why is my deliverance so far off [*rahoq*] from my groaning?!" (Psalms 22:2). "Why [*lamah*] are You like a transient [*ke-ger*] in the land, like a guest who only stays over for a night . . . so, if You are in our midst, since we are called by Your name, do not leave us [*al tan-ikhenu*]?!" (Jeremiah 14:8–9). And this is expressed in the prayer that for many Jews is the most important part of the liturgy, repeatedly recited in it, called kaddish.

There we Jews say: "May Your kingdom come soon during the lifetime of all Israel!"

When we think of God as absent from our world, we do not say that God is doing nothing. Total inaction is death, but the Lord God is "the living God" (Deuteronomy 5:23). Surely, God has a life totally apart from His relationship with us in the world. So, as we move from phenomenological reflection to ontological speculation, it is correct to infer that there is an internal divine relationality in which God engages when God is absent from us. This move from phenomenology to ontology is required by our theological reflection, insofar as the God who presents Himself to us in revelation is the God who breaks through the horizon of our worldly experience from beyond, locating us rather than our locating Him on our own horizon.[61]

The difference in external and internal divine relationality has been insightfully shown by Franz Rosenzweig's novel suggestion of the meaning of "metaphysics." Whereas in the Western philosophical tradition since Aristotle, "metaphysics" (a term Aristotle himself did not use) has come to designate that realm of being that goes beyond (*meta*) physical nature (*ta physika*) and actually undergirds it, Rosenzweig takes the "physics" in *metaphysics* to refer to "nature" or "essence," in other words, the nature or essence or "whatness" of God. By creating the world God comes out of his self-enclosed being, out of His absolute perfection, and engages in a real relationship with *who* is not-God.[62] For Rosenzweig, the freedom of God to be whatever, whenever, and wherever God wants or does not want to be (God's *da-sein*) seems to require that we at least postulate a realm where God is totally apart from any external relations. That is something that could not ever be said of any creature, even the human creature created in the image of God. But can we postulate more than that and still not describe what God is?

It is not enough to say that God apart from any external relations is *Being*, a point that began when the Septuagint translated God's retort (*ehyeh asher ehyeh* [Exodus 3:14]) to Moses's asking the name or essence of God: "I am Being" (*eimi ho ōn*), a point reiterated by Maimonides and by Thomas Aquinas (following the Vulgate: *ego sum qui sum*) among others.[63] Franz Rosenzweig and Martin Buber, proceeding from a very different ontology, translate it as *ich werde dasein als der ich dasein werde* "I will be there whenever I will be there," which is a statement of God's free relationality (*da-sein*): to be present whenever and wherever God wants to be present; conversely, to be absent whenever and wherever God wants to be absent, that is, by Godself.[64] This is not a statement of God as Being (*Sein*) or omnipresence. Indeed, only the truly free God has the choice to be either present or absent at will, which omnipresence as an ontological necessity denies. As such, "being" is not a predicate, but is rather a relation between two distinct parties. This relation connects them, but does not contain them.[65] The relation serves the parties; the parties are not subservient to the relation. Thus "being" is *how* the two parties affect each other, in other words, it is what they *do to, for, or with* each other. Hence to say "God is king" must be completed by an answer to the question "king of whom?" To say "God *is* king" is to say what God *does*: "God *rules* His people." And to say "the Jews *are* God's people" is to say "the Jews *are to serve* God." Accordingly, we should not equate God with a relation, since a relation connects two parties, thus serving them rather than being served by them. "I am the Lord; there is no god besides Me . . . there is none but Me" (Isaiah 45:21). A relation is certainly not divine, even though it is what enables God to be *for* humans and humans to be *for* God *with* each other.[66]

To postulate that God has an inner life, and that God's inner life consists of inner relations, means that we can no longer agree with Maimonides, who holds that to say "the Lord is One" (*ha-shem ehad*) is to say that God is a singularity without the multiplicity of internal relations, even when God is considered totally apart from any relation to what is not-God.[67] But does not postulating such singular divine simplicity imply the defect of divine poverty rather than the superabundance of divine richness? Does not the capacity to engage in multiple and different external relations or transitive acts imply some multiplicity in God Himself?[68] Indeed, this is what the Kabbalists did when they posited the tenfold multiplicity of the *sefirot* as being what comprises the inner life of God.[69] However, by not only positing that inner multiplicity but actually describing *them* and *their* operations, and by assuming that all external human relations in the world are really participations in the inner life of God already, the Kabbalists broke down the real difference between God and the created world that is so emphasized by Scripture and the rabbinic tradition. Thus it seems correct *that* the inner life of God has been affirmed, but it seems quite problematic to thereby constitute what that life is or does.

If negative theology functions like Kant's *Grenzbegriff* ("border concept"), telling us what we cannot say about God, then is it not subject to Wittgenstein's criticism of this notion of Kant's: How can we say something is limited unless we know *what* is limiting it from the other side?[70] Perhaps the answer is eschatological: we can hope to see what this inner life of God is if and when we ever reach the world-beyond (*olam ha-ba*). That totally other world is still yet to come; hence it is temporal though unending, but not eternal, unchanging, and primordial. That is not only something we have not experienced, it is something we could not ever experience in this world at all. In other words, negative theology tells us what we cannot say here and now, but that we might be able to say it in a world that "no eye but God's has yet seen" (Isaiah 64:3).[71] Since we are told that God *has seen* this other world, we can believe we are affirming something that actually exists, and that it exists in a definite way. Yet here and now we cannot say *what* that way *is*. We can hope for it, maybe we even hope to participate in it and not just behold it from without. Therefore, we can hope *for* more than we can actually express in words. "O' that I had faith [*lul'ei he'emanti*] to see the goodness of the Lord in the land of the living; so hope for the Lord and fortify your heart—hope [*qavvei*] for the Lord!" (Psalms 27:13–14).[72] Faith (*emunah*) relates us to God's presence; hope (*tiqvah*) enables us to wait for God to overcome His absence.[73] Hence negative theology is hopeful, so while it does not enable us to say what God is per se, it does enable us to say more than God *simply* exists.

Notes

1. "Theology," which literally means "God-talk" (*theologikē*) is a term coined by Aristotle (*Metaphysics*, 6.1, 1026a20–24) to denote what we call "ontology," whose chief concern is with "the divine" (*to theion*). Since, for Aristotle, *the divine* is the acme of Nature qua cosmic order, Aristotle can be considered to be the founder of "natural theology."

2. So Immanuel Kant writes in *Critique of Pure Reason*, B619, trans. N. Kemp Smith (New York: Macmillan, 1929), 500: "Reason . . . stretches its wings in vain in thus attempting to soar above the world of sense by mere power of speculation." Like Kant, Bertrand Russell writes in his essay, "Acquaintance and Description," in *The Problems of Philosophy* (Oxford: Oxford University Press, 1959), 48, "All our knowledge, both knowledge of things and knowledge of truths, rest upon acquaintance as its foundation." Neither Kant nor Russell (et alia) is interested in biblical revelation, the prime source of Jewish (and Christian) God-talk, for they (et alia) think that the name "God" has no real referent. As such, revelation is an imaginative construction, not a type of authentic, irreducible experience that can be directly theorized by means of intellectually constructed categories. Hence biblical revelation is most often dismissed as an illusion, either the projection of one's unconscious wish or a deliberate hoax that panders to the unconscious wishes of others. See Sigmund Freud, *Future of an Illusion*, trans. W. D. Robson-Scott and J. Strachey (Garden City, NY: Doubleday, 1961), 49–52. On the other hand, when the God of biblical revelation is taken to be a conscious theoretical construct, a theology of revelation is dismissed as a theory having no heuristic value to explain any type of authentic experience. For a critique of this rather narrow notion of experience, see Karl Jaspers, *Kant*, ed. Hannah Arendt, trans. R. Manheim (New York: Harcourt, Brace, and World, 1962), 141–142.

3. This is well expressed by the French phenomenologist, Maurice Merleau-Ponty, who wrote in the preface to his *Phénoménologie de la perception* (Paris: Gallimard, 1945), i: "Qu'est que la phénoménologie? . . . C'est l'essai d'une description directe de notre expérience telle qu'elle est, et sans aucun égard à sa genèse psychologique et aux explications causales que le savant, l'historien ou le sociologue peuvent en fournir."

4. See David Novak, *Jewish-Christian Dialogue* (New York: Oxford University Press, 1989), 129–138.

5. Hagigah 5a–b regarding Deuteronomy 31:17 and Rabbenu Hananel and Rashi, s.v. "eino mehem" thereon; also, Mararsha, *Hiddushei Aggadot* thereon regarding Numbers 6:26, and Berakhot 20b regarding Deuteronomy 8:10; *Beresheet Rabbah* 36 regarding Job 34:29.

6. For human *hineni*, see, for example, Genesis 22:1, 11; Exodus 3:4; I Samuel 3:16; Isaiah 6:8. For divine *hineni*, see, for example, Genesis 9:9 and 17:4; Exodus 33:21; Isaiah 52:6; Jeremiah 44:26; Ezekiel 34:10.

7. Note the French-Jewish phenomenologist, Emmanuel Levinas, who wrote in his *Totality and Infinity*, trans. A. Lingis (Pittsburgh, PA: Duquesne University Press, 1969), 77: "Transcendence is to be distinguished from a union with the transcendent by participation."

8. Note *Also Sprach Zarathustra* 3 in *Friedrich Nietzsche: Werke in Zwei Bänden* (Munich: Carl Hanser Verlag, 1967), 1:549: "Und Zarathustra sprach also zum Volke ... Einst war der Frevel an Gott der grösste Frevel, aber Gott starb, und damit starben auch diese Frevelhaften." For the notion that blasphemy (*Frevel* in German) is the explicit wish that God be dead, see *Mishnah*: Sanhedrin 7.5; Sanhedrin 56a regarding Leviticus 24:16.

9. Moses Maimonides, *Guide of the Perplexed*, trans. S. Pines (Chicago: The University of Chicago Press, 1963), 1 53, 121.

10. Maimonides, *Guide*, 1 64 regarding Exodus 33:18, p. 156.

11. *Commentary on the Mishnah*: Sanhedrin chap. 10 (Heleq), principle no. 3, ed. Kafih, p. 141; *Mishneh Torah*: Yesodei ha-Torah, 1.8–8; *Guide*, 1 26–27, 55.

12. Plato, *Timaeus*, 29A–D.

13. Plato, *Republic*, 507B.

14. Nedarim 10a.

15. *Guide*, 1 26, 58. For Jewish precedents to Maimonides's notion of divine transcendence, see Saadiah, *Emunot ve-De'ot*, 2.8; Bahya ibn Pakudah, *Hovot ha-Levavot*, 1.10; Judah Halevi, *Kuzari*, 2.2. For non-Jewish precedents (though probably unknown to the preceding Jewish theologians), see Plotinus, *Enneads*, 5.6; Pseudo-Dionysius, *De Divinis Nominibus*, chaps. 1 and 5. For its subsequent influence, see Thomas Aquinas, *Summa Theologiae*, 1, q. 13, a. 5. See also, David Novak, "Maimonides' Theory of Religious Language," *Law and Theology in Judaism* (New York: KTAV, 1976), 2:28–37, where other texts from the *Guide* are cited and analyzed, in which Maimonides does affirm several important truths about God.

16. See Genesis 1:4, 12, 18, 21, 31.

17. See David Novak, "Defending Niebuhr from Hauerwas," *Journal of Religious Ethics* 40 (2012): 288–292.

18. Kant, *Critique of Pure Reason*, A29.

19. Ludwig Wittgenstein, *Tractatus Logico-Philosophicus*, 7, trans. D. F. Pears and B. F. McGuiness (London: Routledge and Kegan Paul, 1961), 150–151.

20. David Hume, *Dialogues Concerning Natural Religion* (New York: Hafner, 1948), pt. 4, 31.

21. Maimonides, *Guide*, 1 54, 124.

22. Ibid., 3 54, 638.

23. *Mishneh Torah*: Avadim, 9.8 regarding Psalms 145:9.

24. Kiddushin 40b and parallels.

25. *Commentary on the Mishnah*: Sanhedrin, chap. 10 (Heleq), principle no. 7, ed. Kafih, pp. 142–143; Maimonides, *Guide*, 1 39.

26. Maimonides, *Guide*, 1 52, 118–119.

27. See Exodus 31:2; Betsah 13b and parallels; *Mishnah*: Kelim 26.8, Makhshirin 6.1.

28. *Metaphysics*, 12.7, 1072b14–30.

29. Maimonides, *Guide*, 2 13 regarding Genesis 21:33 and 14:22.

30. Maimonides, *Guide*, 1 53 regarding Exodus 3:14.

31. See Rosh Hashanah 17b regarding Exodus 34:6, where the repetition of the Tetragrammaton is to be used evocatively in supplication.

32. See Berakhot 28b.

33. *Mishnah*: Berakhot 9.3 and Maimonides, *Commentary on the Mishnah* thereon; Avodah Zarah 7b regarding Psalms 142:3; Maimonides, *Mishneh Torah*: Tefillah, 1.2.

34. Berakhot 4b.

35. It is emphasized that the first time the people Israel cried out for deliverance from Egyptian bondage, their cry was a supplication consciously directed to the God of Abraham, Isaac, and Jacob. See *Shemot Rabbah* 21.5 regarding Exodus 14:10 and 2:23.

36. *Commentary on the Mishnah*: Sanhedrin, chap. 10 (Heleq), ed. Kafih, p. 138; *Mishneh Torah*: Teshuvah, 9.1.

37. Maimonides, *Guide*, 3 27; also 2 40.

38. Zohar: Vayehi, 1:135a regarding Ezekiel 37:9 and Tazri`a, 3:45a–b; also, Moses Cordovero, *Pardes Rimmonim*, 8.20; Levi Isaac of Berdichev, *Qedushat Levi*: Eqev regarding Deuteronomy 10:12, ed. M. Dembaremdiger (Brooklyn, NY: Makhon Qedushat Levi, 1995), 1:214.

39. There is an essential difference between human needs (what the Kabbalists call *tsorkhei hedyot*) and divine needs (what the Kabbalists call *tsorkhei gevoah*). Human needs are necessary insofar as they claim us, our only choice being how to either fulfill them or suppress them; but we cannot eliminate them by pretending to live in a time before they claimed us, or in a time after we have transcended their claims upon us. Divine needs, though, are themselves chosen, in other words, God has the freedom to become involved or not become involved with us in a mutually erotic relationship in which the two parties are both effective and affective, active and passive simultaneously. Thus God's choice to elect Israel for a covenantal relationship is thereby God's choice to need His people, while Israel's need for God is not an option to be chosen or not chosen. The human need for God is ubiquitous. But God has a life both before humans came into the world and after we have departed the world (see Isaiah 43:10, 44:6), hence God's need for us is not ubiquitous. God transcends us, whereas we cannot transcend God. See Nahmanides, *Commentary on the Torah*: Exodus 29:46; Meir ibn Gabbai, *Avodat ha-Qodesh*, 2 2, 7; David Novak, *The Jewish Social Contract* (Princeton, NJ: Princeton University Press, 2005), 179–181.

40. Hume, *A Treatise of Human Nature*, 3.1.1, ed. L. A. Sleby-Bigge (Oxford: Clarendon Press, 1888), 455–470. Cf. David Novak, *Covenantal Rights* (Princeton, NJ: Princeton University Press, 2000), 21–25.

41. Berakhot 32a regarding Exodus 32:13. For the irrevocability of Israel's covenantal obligation stemming from God's election of this people, see Sanhedrin 44a regarding Joshua 7:11; Shevuot 39a regarding Deuteronomy 29:13; David Novak, *The Election of Israel* (Cambridge: Cambridge University Press, 1995), 189–199.

42. Note Menahot 43b: "Remembering [*zekhirah*] brings one to action [*asiyyah*]." See Pesahim 106a regarding Exodus 20:8; Megillah 18a regarding Deuteronomy 25:17, 19.

43. *Shemot Rabbah*, 44.7 regarding Exodus 32:13.

44. Kiddushin 39b (the view of Rabbi Jacob).

45. Cf. Plato, *Euthyphro*, 13A–15B.

46. Martin Buber, *I and Thou*, trans. W. Kaufmann (New York: Charles Scribner's Sons, 1970), pt. 3, 123–124.

47. Ibid., 159–160.

48. In the morning liturgy (*shaharit*), this phrase is at the conclusion of the first section before the recitation of the *shema*, which celebrates God's beneficence in nature. The last section, which follows thereafter speaks of God's loving election of the people Israel, which occurs in history. See any traditional prayer book (*siddur*).

49. Kant, *Critique of Pure Reason*, B655.

50. *Commentary on the Torah*: Genesis 46:15. See David Novak, *The Theology of Nahmanides Systematically Presented* (Atlanta, GA: Scholars Press, 1992), 61–75.

51. Note, for example, Psalm 95, where the psalmist easily moves from praise of God's work in nature into praise of God's work in history.

52. See *Beresheet Rabbah* 43.7 regarding Genesis 14:19.

53. *Tur*: Orah Hayyim, 187.

54. Genesis 17:8.

55. See David Novak, *Zionism and Judaism: A New Theory* (Cambridge: Cambridge University Press, 2015), 139–152.

56. See Isaiah 2:1–4; Zephaniah 3:9; Zechariah 14:9.

57. Berakhot 21a and *Yerushalmi*: Berakhot 7.1, 11a regarding Deuteronomy 8:10.

58. Numbers 33:53.

59. Maimonides, *Guide*, 1 26.

60. Ibid., 1 59 regarding Psalms 65:2 and 4:5.

61. See *Beresheet Rabbah* 68.9 regarding Genesis 28:11.

62. Franz Rosenzweig, *Star of Redemption*, trans. B. E. Galli (Madison: University of Wisconsin Press, 2005), 22–25.

63. Maimonides, *Guide*, 1 62–63; *Summa Theologiae*, 1, q. 13, a. 11. This LXX translation marks the beginning of natural theology by Jews (and Christians).

64. Martin Buber and Franz Rosenzweig, *Die Fünf Bücher der Weisung* (Cologne, Germany: Jakob Hegner, 1954), 158. See *Shemot Rabbah* 3.6 regarding Exodus 3:14.

65. This is different from Kant (*Critique of Pure Reason*, B626) who takes "being" to be a copula that situates or subsumes a percept within an appropriate concept.

66. In German, one would say the relationship between God and Israel is a *Beziehung*, not a *Verhätlnis*, in other words, it brings the parties together; it does not situate them in a field that encloses them.

67. *Commentary on the Mishnah*: Sanhedrin, chap. 10 (Heleq), principle no. 2 regarding Deuteronomy 6:4, ed. Kafih, p. 141; Maimonides, *Guide*, 3.45 regarding Deuteronomy 6:4.

68. The rabbis, however, did speak of tensions between the divine characteristics (*middot*) of justice (*middat ha-din*) and mercy (*middat rahamim*). See, for example, Berakhot 7a; *Beresheet Rabbah* 12.15 regarding Genesis 2:4. This seems to be the way the rabbis thought how God deliberates before choosing to act, which is not quite assigning any actual faculties

to the divine mind, though this does at least imply they were thinking of some sort of inner divine multiplicity. Nevertheless, unlike Maimonides's view that attributes such as "just" and "merciful" only apply to God's actions *ad extra*, which affect others but are not affected by them, the *middot* the rabbis imagine are *responsive*, that is, they are affected by the actions of others *ad intra*. Divine justice is affected by and responds to human injustice, and divine mercy is affected by and responds to human supplication. Both modes function *ad extra* and *ad intra*. This indicates two very different ontologies between the rabbis and Maimonides (et alia). For the Kabbalists, all divine relations are *ad intra*, and all human actions are participations *in* the inner life of God. Theirs is a third ontology, different from that of the rabbis and that of Maimonides.

69. See Gershom Scholem, *Major Trends in Jewish Mysticism*, 3rd rev. ed. (New York: Schocken, 1961), 206–209.

70. Wittgenstein, *Tractatus Logico-Philosophicus*, 5.61, contra Kant, *Critique of Pure Reason*, B311.

71. This follows the interpretation of this verse on Berakhot 34b.

72. See Berakhot 4a.

73. Berakhot 4a.

TWELVE

Mysteries of the Promise: Negative Theology in Benjamin and Scholem

AGATA BIELIK-ROBSON

> Schier vollendet bis zum Dache
> Ist der grosse Weltbetrug.
> Gib denn, Gott, dass der erwache,
> Den dein Nichts durchschlug.
> So allein strahlt Offenbarung
> In die Zeit, die dich verwarf.
> Nur den Nichts is die Erfahrung,
> Die sie von dir haben darf.
> —Gershom Scholem, a poem on Kafka's *Trial*[1]

> The difference between "not," "nothingness," and "none" is of great importance for philosophy. The Kabbalah contains the fundamental notion (which reappears in Hermann Cohen) that God is nothingness. . . . Idols are called "nothing," while God is called "nothingness" (which is entirely un-Christian).
> —Gershom Scholem, Diary entry from February 22, 1918[2]

In my essay I will approach critically the idea of the "hidden God," which figures very strongly in the writings of Gershom Scholem and Walter Benjamin and comes to the fore most intensely in their famous correspondence on Franz Kafka.

In *Old Mirrors, New Worlds*, Moshe Idel claims that this emphasis on negativity, so fashionable in the intellectual milieu of the German philosophical Jewry (not just Scholem and Benjamin, but also early Lukàcs, Ernst Bloch, and Jacob Taubes) is, in fact, not very Jewish at all, rather strongly influenced by the German-Protestant notion of *deus absconditus*, and deeply entrenched in reformed Christianity, from Luther via Kierkegaard to Barth.[3] There is more than a grain of truth in this accusation. Indeed, while reading Scholem and Benjamin's correspondence, particularly their reflections on Kafka (where the celebrated phrase of *Nichts der Offenbarung* appears), one may have an impression that their divine negativity is of an uneasy, mixed origin, and that Idel is right when he criticizes the German Jews for falling too much into a Protestant account of negative theology, deriving from Kierkegaard, Schelling, and Barth. Yet, I would not go as far as to adopt Idel's unambiguously *kataphatic* and positive image of the Jewish God as "fully revealed in the Torah," which supposedly has nothing in common with any negative theology, this lofty science of God of Philosophers, usually Christian and Muslim, but rarely Judaic. Idel may be right in pointing to the Kierkegaardian-Barthian influence, but in the case of Scholem and Benjamin this influence, though palpable, is nonetheless not *all-consuming*. The language in which they talk about God's hiddenness may indeed be to some extent foreign, but the theological meanings that they try to create in this partly alien medium do not belong to it originally; they suggest a different notion of divine negativity that Harold Bloom calls simply "the Jewish negative."[4] The aim of this essay will be to distill from their writings *the clinamen on the divine negativity* which, once disentangled from the conflation with the Christian notion of God's concealedness, should reveal aspects unique to the Jewish tradition.[5]

Idel's critique is, in fact, an ironic reversal of Scholem's own frequent objections against those representatives of modern German Jewry who, in their eagerness to "sound modern," would draw heavily on the Protestant theological idiom-of-the-day, thus throwing away all the achievements of the Judaic tradition that are resistant to such attempts at quick modernization. Idel's irony—operating under the principle of "first heal yourself, doctor!"—accuses Scholem of falling exactly in the same trap that he saw as crippling the thought of Hans-Joachim Schoeps, Ernst Bloch, or the young Jacob Taubes. In the open letter to Schoeps, the author of *Jüdischer Glaube in dieser Zeit* (from August 15, 1932), Scholem protests against his approach to Judaism as too strongly tinged with Protestant categories, deriving directly from Kierkegaard and Barth. And while he sides with Schoeps in his effort to ignore the apologetic element in Jewish thought, which he also sees as dated and *unecht* (inauthentic), he nonetheless does not want to allow for the concept of modern "authenticity" that would indicate a possibility of facing the word of revelation itself in its *absolute Konkretheit* (absolute concreteness) without any mediation of the tradition. Scholem thus rejects Schoeps conviction that "with the process of emancipation, Halachah has lost its theological meaning for us and that we must now return to the biblical revelation itself."[6] Scholem perceives such a suspiciously "modernizing" maneuver as nothing more than an unconscious recurrence of a very old Jewish heresy, Karaitism, which "is always the most modern, whether in the tenth century as Mutasilite, or in the twentieth century as Kierkegaardian," yet, precisely because of that, "does not give the Jewish existence a long lasting breath" (ibid. 470). Not only does the Neo-Karaite move not renew and authenticate Jewish belief, but it destroys the most characteristic Jewish difference that lies precisely in the dialectical mediation of the absolute concreteness of the given, in other words, the word of revelation itself: "[Revelation] is the absolute that gives meanings but itself remains meaningless as the interpretable (*das Deutbare*) which shows itself only in time thanks to the mediation of the tradition" (469).

But that is not all. Apart from accusing Schoeps for falling into the oldest "modernizing" blunder of Judaic heterodoxy, he also reproaches him for not understanding properly the Jewish concept of *Nichts Gottes*, "the nothingness of God," which, according to Scholem, has nothing to do with the holy terrors of the Kierkegaardian-Barthian abyss of transcendence (*der Sprung in Nirgendwo* [the leap into nowhere], [467–468]). Scholem's conviction that the Jewish concept of negative theology, which identifies the most secret name of God with *ayin*, is absolutely unique, appears at the very early stage of his intellectual biography, and remains intact until the end. "Idols are called 'nothing,' while God is called 'nothingness' (which is entirely un-Christian)," notes Scholem in his diary in 1918, and this belief—in the radical difference between Jewish and Christian ways of approaching the divine concealedness—can indeed be said to have fueled his life-long theological pursuits. And these, as Idel rightly observes (though with a critical intention in mind) should not be simply reduced to the work of a disinterested historian. They have an agenda—the exposition of the unique Jewish *clinamen* within negative theology.

The Deactivated God

But before we get to the Jewish *clinamen* of the divine hiddenness, we must first understand the dominant idiom from which it consciously deviates: the Protestant discourse of *deus absconditus*.

Deus absconditus, the hidden and distant God of Calvin and Luther, is utterly removed from the world because of its contrast with the God of incarnation, the close and palpable Jesus Christ. Unlike the Son, the truly revealed God—where revelation, *die Offenbarung*, means, as in Hegel's idea of Christianity, *die offenbarte Religion* (laying out all clear)—God the Father hides in the mist of unapproachability as an uneasy remnant of the Old Testament that needs to be acknowledged but also superseded by the New Covenant. From the beginning, therefore, the Jewish God becomes a part of the dialectical dynamics, already implied by Paul's notion of *kathargein*, which Luther translates as *Aufhebung* and Hegel later elevates to the heights of his philosophical dialectics. He is made remote and concealed due to the maneuver of deactivation, just like his Law becomes deactivated for the sake of Love and Grace. He is made inoperative, leaving all revelatory activity to His Son, now understood as God the Redeemer: the one who comes to elect, exonerate, and save. His, therefore, is the hiddenness of a shadowy remnant that stays behind the only *truly active* God, the Second Person of the Trinity.

As all shadowy remnants, the Jewish God is ambivalently poised between good and evil; later on, in Schelling, even *beyond good and evil*, imagined as a "dark ground of existence" (*der dunkle Grund der Existenz*). His concealedness tends to be understood as an impenetrable withdrawal, violent self-contraction that stands in stark contrast to the revealedness of incarnation. Hence it becomes susceptible to all those elements of Marcionite Gnostic dualism, which *nolens volens* pervade all Protestant thought only to find its culmination in the openly Marcionite climate of the Weimar period and the theologies of Adolf von Harnack and Karl Barth.[7] Take, for instance, this quote from Feuerbach's highly illuminating essay, "The Essence of Faith According to Luther": "'The God in Himself, God beyond Christ'—Luther says—'is a terrible and terrifying God.' And what inspires terror and fright, is an evil entity. God in Himself, the divine 'majesty,' differs only in name and in our imagination from the essence of the devil. . . . The only real God, the only object of Lutheran and Christian faith is Christ."[8] And indeed, in Kierkegaard and Barth, God the Sovereign, Lord of Creation, the hidden God of the created cosmos, is the one who inspires "holy terror" and—as Ernst Bloch put it apropos Kierkegarrd's *Fear and Trembling*—makes one wonder whether the divine is not confused here simply with the demonic.[9] Bloch is absolutely right. The Marcionite mistrust toward the God of Creation, so palpable in all Lutheran and post-Lutheran writings, lends itself immediately to even more archaic overtones, associating the hiddenness of God the Father with the pagan dark mysteries of nature itself, which, as in the famous saying of Heraclitus, "likes to hide" (*physis kryptestai philei*).

In *The Veil of Isis*, Pierre Hadot sketches a two-millennia-long history of this pagan motif of hiding nature, *Isis abscondita*, which according to him culminates in the theosophy of Schelling.[10] In Schelling, we find a truly modern syncretic combination of the pagan-masonic image of the veiled Isis-Jehovah, the Pietist vision of Angry God, deriving mostly from Jakob Boehme, as well as a peculiar echo of the Kabbalistic motif of *tsimtsum*, which Schelling interprets in his own way, very far indeed from the manner of Isaac Luria himself and his twentieth-century German-Jewish followers: Scholem, Benjamin, and Kafka.

The theosophy of Schelling, especially when interpreted by Hadot, constitutes a *symmetrical case of influence* where the Lurianic concept of divine contraction becomes accommodated to the Protestant vision of *deus absconditus*. Here, *tsimtsum* is imagined not as a gentle self-withdrawal, a loving act of giving space for creation, but as an "angry" (*zornig*) self-condensation that gives the hidden God his solid dark ground of existence and constitutes the violent origin of his inscrutability. In Schelling's vision, "development presupposes envelopment" (ibid. 301), which means that being, when regarded in itself, is originally in the state of contraction, producing a dense and opaque "dark ground" that "loves to hide" and resists any attempt of penetration. By conflating the God of Moses, who says of Himself "I am that I am," with the principle of self-contracting being, Schelling perceives the divine reduction as an act of what Levinas later could have called "the ontological egoism": *tsimtsum* here is an indirect manifestation of "the blind, obscure, and inexpressible side of God" (ibid.). God as the principle of being, delivering the dark ground of "the hidden mystery of existence" (302), is thus also an object of a sacred terror and anguish, which befalls every living thing. Hadot quotes Schelling: "Anguish is the fundamental feeling of every living creature, and all that lives is born and greeted only in the midst of a violent struggle" (ibid.). Delivering the dark canvas for everything that exists, contracted in wrath and inner struggle, the Schellingian *deus absconditus* is at the antipodes of love that can come only with his second manifestation, the God of revelation and redemption, "the pure essence" of Christ. The hidden God, therefore, stands here for "that which terrifies: *a power and a blind force*, a barbaric principle that may be transcended but never canceled, and which is the basis of all that is great and beautiful' (303); all majestic, unapproachable, sublime, ultimately mysterious, unfathomably sovereign. As Hadot rightly observes, the Schellingian vision of God is deeply *tragic* (302): the darkness, which surrounds God's foundational act of being, can never be dispelled. While the angry God remains an impenetrable mystery to Himself, this blindness must impart itself to all being as such; it is precisely in this violent blindness that revelation must meet its tragic limits.

This hidden God, identified as the principle of being in itself, is a very far cry indeed from the Lurianic God of *tsimtsum* that our twentieth-century "Kabbalists" will interpret in terms opposed to tragic, videlicet, in *messianico-antinomian* terms—as a gesture of withdrawing *from* being, contrary to the gesture of establishing ontological foundations *for* the created world. It will be one of the tasks of this essay to expose the main difference between Christian (especially Protestant) and Jewish modes of perceiving the divine concealedness as organized around a distinction between the *tragic* and the *messianico-antinomian* vision of divine transcendence. While the tragic mode of hiddenness, quite aptly associated by Benjamin with Christianity,[11] addresses God as the eternally dark principle of created being, the antinomian mode of hiddenness adopted by the "Kabbalists," addresses God as a *Gegenprinzip*, a counterprinciple to being, which can manifest itself in the creaturely realm only in an indirect, partial, and subversive manner.[12] While the tragic mode of hiddenness smuggles into its *deus absconditus*, a pagan notion of inscrutable and essentially unchangeable Fate, the antinomian mode of hiddenness locates itself at the antipodes to fatalism by remaining faithful to the messianic reversal that leads to a future *apocalypsis*, videlicet, the possibility of seeing God without veils and secrets: not *hester panim*, but finally "face to face."

Perhaps, the best way to illustrate this difference is to recall a thirteenth-century student of Abraham Abulafia, himself a representative of the ecstatic Kabbalah, Rabbi Nathan ben Sa'adyah Harar, who taught the mysteries of the *messianic reversal*:

> During the time of the Exile the activity of the names has been obliterated, and prophecy has been cancelled from Israel, because of hindrance of the attribute of judgment. The state will go on until the coming of him whom God has chosen, and his power will be great because of what has been transmitted to him. . . . Then he will stand against the attribute of judgment . . . and the attribute of mercy will guide him. *The supernal entity will become lower, and the lower will become supernal, and the Tetragrammaton, which has been concealed, will be revealed, and Adonay, which was revealed today, will be concealed.* Then it will happen to us what was written: "For they shall all know me from the least of them to the greatest of them." Then the natural, philosophical sciences will be cancelled and concealed, because their supernal power was cancelled, but the science of names and letters, which are by now unknown to us, will be revealed, because their supernal power is gradually enhancing.[13]

This is not a static image of the Divine Sovereignty, as in Karl Barth's diathesis. The Tetragrammaton, the hidden God behind the revealed Adonai, is not the God of mastery and judgment, but the God of eternal life and mercy—precisely the other way round than in the Christian vision of the concealed Sovereign and the revealed Christ. Since the messianic reversal, which already had happened in Christianity, has not yet happened here, the game of good and evil, love and justice, law and mercy, hope and obedience, is still in play, not fully "layed out." But one thing is sure. The messianic reversal will one day result in the divine exchange of places: the Lord, Adonai, will become concealed, while the Tetragrammaton, the Living God, will finally be revealed.

It is, therefore, not God the Sovereign who "likes to hide" his somber face, but a God of Life, the merciful lord of the world to come, which will know only the concrete "science of names and letters," doing away with the abstractions of the Law. It is not the terrifying Master of Creation, which constitutes the dark abyss of "nothingness" behind the revelation of Christ the Redeemer—but a God of Sabbath, a still hidden and unrealized possibility of the divine itself: the *not-yet* of God, his own pregnant *nothingness* shining through his so far manifest revelation. Not the deactivated God of the Old Testament, but a not-yet-activated God of *olam ha ba*.

The Nothingness of Revelation: Procuring the Messianic Reversal

It is only in this context that we should approach the famous phrase uttered by Gerschom Scholem in his correspondence with Walter Benjamin over the works of Franz Kafka: *der Nichts der Offenbarung*, "Nothingness of revelation":

> You ask what I understand by the "nothingness of revelation"? I understand by it a state in which revelation appears to be without meaning, in which it still asserts itself, in which it has validity but no significance. A state in which the wealth of meaning is lost and *what is in the process of appearing (for revelation is such a process) still does not disappear* [das Erscheinende, wie auf einen Nullpunkt des eigenen Gehalts reduziert, dennoch nicht verschwindet (und die Offenbarung ist etwas Erscheinendes)], even though it is reduced to the zero point of its own content, so to speak. This is obviously a borderline case in the religious sense, and whether it can really come to pass is a very dubious point. I certainly cannot share your opinion that it doesn't matter whether the disciples have lost the "Scripture" or whether they cannot decipher them, and I view this as one of the greatest mistakes you could have made. When I speak of the nothingness of revelation, I do so precisely to characterize the difference between these two positions.[14]

We shall yet go back to this formulation: *what is in the process of appearing (for revelation is such a process) still does not disappear*, which, I think, constitutes the gist of Scholem's argument. The choice of the word here, *das Erscheinende*, is highly significant: as a *gerundivum*, an active verbal adjective that condenses in itself—as indeed in the Lurianic image of *tsimtsum*—the activity of revelation, it presents this activity as congealed in the participial form and thus held in suspense. Before we lay out Scholem's message, suffice it to say that it is not purely negative. "Nothingness of revelation," far from suggesting some dead remainder of a once living religion, contains a component of a future-oriented promise: of something truly living, expectant, still in the process of revealing itself, slowly (though not at all surely) coming to the fore.

First, however, we must turn toward Benjamin's interpretation of Kafka, the crux of which is the position of the Law, so fiercely criticized by Scholem. For Benjamin, the Kafkan universe is perfectly lawless: *nothing* separates law from life, which means that scripture has simply become life. Law, therefore, is no longer a structure giving meaning to life, but life itself, the meaningless force of *flux*: entropy and dispersion. For Scholem, on the other hand, law is still separated from life, though as if by the intangible film of *nothing*: the fact that *nothing* separates them is experienced precisely as a cause of a sacred alarm, a sign of the deepest and most sinister distortion, which, felt as such, still maintains its validity, though without suggesting any directive. For Benjamin, God the Legislator withdraws, leaving a complete vacuum of "mere life" (*blosses Leben*) with its senseless flow-and-fall, unable to produce "one grain of meaning." For Scholem, however, this withdrawal is dialectical: the more God disappears from the world, the more the world is in need of revelation, which, in the end, becomes a *new* form of revelation characteristic of a "religious nihilist" or a "pious atheist": *Nur den Nichts is die Erfahrung, / Die sie von dir haben darf* (Only nothingness is the experience we are allowed to have of you).[15] Thus, while Scholem concentrates on the *Nothing* itself, expecting from it a renewal of revelation, or a messianic reversal occurring within the Godhead itself, preparing to leap into a new manifestation (thus, we can say, *reculer pour le mieux sauter*[16])—Benjamin is ready only to rely on the "weak messianic force"[17] of the abandoned creatures who must procure the messianic reversal themselves:

> You take—he replies to Scholem—the "nothingness of revelation" as your point of departure, the salvific-historical perspective of the established proceedings of the trial. I take as my starting point the small, nonsensical hope, as well as the creatures for whom this hope is intended and yet who on the other hand are also the creatures in which this absurdity is mirrored. . . . Whether the pupils have lost it [the scripture] or whether they are unable to decipher it comes down to the same thing, because, without the key that belongs to it, *the Scripture is not Scripture, but life*. Life as it is lived in the village at the foot of the hill on which the castle is built. It is in the attempt to metaphorize life into Scripture that I perceive the meaning of "reversal" [*Umkehr*], which so many of Kafka's parables endeavour to bring about . . . Kafka's messianic category is "the reversal" or the "studying" (Letter 63, 135).

For Scholem, the formula *Nichts der Offenbarung* is reversible: it is just as well "the revelation of Nothingness," which maintains its validity—the power of hope and expectation—despite the zero point of its content (despite, or precisely *because* of that). But not so for Benjamin and Benjamin's Kafka, where nothingness, not to be capitalized, appears only from the "nether side," as a simple, nondialectical nullification of transcendence: "I endeavored to show how Kafka sought—on the nether side of that 'nothingness,' in its inside lining, so to speak—to feel his way toward redemption. This implies that any kind of victory over that nothingness, as understood by the theological exegetes around Brod, would have been an abomination for him" (Letter 59, 129). This is not what Scholem expects—not the victory over nothingness that would lead to a positive restoration of the Law—so it is a bit unfair of Benjamin to use this argument against his friend, which would put him in the naively pious company of Max Brod. What they truly quarrel about is the *dialectics of nothingness*, not its positive overcoming: whether it is necessary to stay on the nether side of nothing, or whether it is possible to wrench from it a new form of revelation.[18] Or, yet in other words: whether the fading of the Law, its receding into nothing, ends the story of revelation (so Benjamin)—or whether it merely marks a point of erasure, yet another *tsimtsum* of God, which also bears a hope of the revelatory renewal (so Scholem). Filled with a definite "sense of an ending," Benjamin says:

> For the work of the Torah—if we abide by Kafka's account—has been thwarted. And everything that Moses accomplished long ago would have to be reaccomplished in our world's age (Letter 63, 135; second sentence added by Benjamin in his notes).

To which Scholem obstinately replies:

> I am still firmly convinced that a theological aspect of this world, in which God does not appear, is the most legitimate of such interpretations [of Kafka]. . . . *The existence of secret law foils your interpretation*: it should not exist in a premythical world of chimeric confusion, to say nothing of the very special way in which it even announces its existence. *There* you went much too far with your elimination of theology, throwing the baby out with the bathwater (Letter 57, 122–123; my emphasis).

In a moment we will return to the "chimeric confusion" Scholem attributes to Benjamin on the basis of his "dangerous" fascination with Bachofen. Even if Scholem agrees to a point with Benjamin that "the work of the Torah . . . has been thwarted," he nonetheless would not go as far as to assume a complete disappearance of the *shadow* of the Law and thus a full regression to the "premythical world" that had not yet known the light of revelation. He thus constantly admonishes his friend for neglecting the "numinous shadow" that is still present in the fading of the Torah: "You stubbornly persist in viewing [the Law] only from its most *profane* side . . . and one finds your silence about it quite puzzling" (Letter 58, 127). God may be dead, Law may be finished—but we still have not cast away their shadows, their persistant *reshimu* (remnants) still floating about in the voided world. Thus, when Nietzsche complains in *The Gay Science* about the still hovering presence of the dead God over us,[19] for Scholem this haunting remnant serves as a positive point departure.

The discussion, therefore, oscillates between the *dysfunctionality* of the Law, which nonetheless still remains the Law, and the *dissolution* of the Law into the hetaeric universe of bare life, the Bachofenian plasticity of *blosses Leben*: just being there, profligating and growing, incapable of stopping in its senseless *flux* and producing a new, stable meaning, structure or form. For Scholem, the alarmingly naked "nothing of revelation" calls for the absent meaning—while for Benjamin, the very issue of meaning may no longer emerge; it may not even be "askable" in the strange twilight of the life in the village at the foot of the hill. *Nothing remains of revelation*: yet, either it is a *mesmerizing* nothing, nothing itself as a remnant, poising in front of us one big distressing question mark and putting all being into doubt without delivering any counteranswer—or indeed, nothing as a simple nullity, no remnants at all, where the whole job of Moses would have to be done again completely from the premythic scratch.[20] It is, after all, a question of viewing the history: in Scholem, firmly linear, under "the salvific-historical perspective of the established proceedings of the trial" (as Benjamin sarcastically reproaches his friend for sticking unreflectively to the Schillerian *dictum*, according to which *Die Weltgeshichte ist das Weltgericht*[21])—while in Benjamin, fragmented and prone to temporal disturbances, where the revelation can indeed be lost without a trace.

At this point, we should resist the temptation to follow Giorgio Agamben who, siding with Benjamin, claims that Scholem's defense of the *shadow* of the Law boils down to the preservation of *the naked structure of sovereignty*.[22] It is, in fact, just the opposite: Scholem rather wishes to maintain *the antinomian lesson of the Jewish Law* (precisely for this reason not to be conflated with any "profane" law), now reduced only to the mystifying "nothing" that cannot mean anything in the world dominated by mere life, fully consummated by its "deceit," but still can retain its resistant and vestigial validity. In Kafka, he maintains, there still remains the vestige of the Law, already dysfunctional and emptied, which nonetheless constitutes the *trace* of the antinomian message that had failed to reach us and transform world-being into redemptive history. Just like the Kafkan message from the Emperor, lost in the infinite chain of Chinese whispers that twist and distort its original meaning, this antinomian lesson came to earth disfigured beyond recognition. It may now masquerade as a hollow shell of pure sovereignty, which gives no account of its claim to power, but it is not how it keeps its significance; the question of meaning, of what it was *meant for* in the first place, has not departed from it completely. It still hovers there in a spectral manner, like the ghost of Hamlet in Derrida's interpretation of the revolutionary teaching of Marx, which also underwent a historical distortion.[23]

This is precisely why Scholem protests so strongly against leveling the Kafkan world back to the Bachofenian hetaeric universe of absolute beginnings (or the Goethean *Urmütter*) where no issue of Law can even be raised: "You don't manage—he scolds Benjamin—without doing flagrant violence to the text; you are constantly obliged to interpret in defiance of Kafka's own testimony, not only in the matter of the Law . . . , but also in that of women, whose function you construe so masterfully, but from a totally one-sided Bachofean perspective, which runs counter to the most obvious evidence. . . . If it were a primal world, then what need would there have been to make the women's relationship to it into a riddle?" (Letter 66, 141). To which Benjamin retorts that in this true and absolute nothingness of revelation, to which the Kafkan world regresses, there is only bare life—flowing, self-proliferating, "sinking back into itself" (precisely as in Scholem's poem: "no life can unfold / that doesn't sink into itself": *Preisgegeben an Gewalten, / die Berschwörung nicht mehr zwingt, / kann kein Leben sich entfalten, / das nich in sich selbst sinkt*). In this world of the deepest oblivion, the only messianic hope lies in the fully immanentist maneuver, in other words, the reversal of studying: *stopping the flow*, which for Benjamin is always paramount to *stopping the fall*. For it is only studying, taking life for its object, that can create meaning without the props of tradition that can no longer teach how to get out from the snares of being. Torah has been thwarted (in its antinomian attempt to revolutionize being), the Tradition "sickened," the Law completely forgotten—so the only way to procure the messianic reversal is to "metaphorize life into Scripture" by studying. To which Scholem says, again: fine, let us grant that this reversal will be fully immanent this time, but why do it at all? If this truly were the primal world of the Bachofean *Mutterrecht* without the trace of the vanished revelation, why would we bother at all rather than just live in the lap of our *Urmütter*? Why would anything pose itself as a "riddle": a question mark, a pressing problem?

This, indeed, is a valid point. But Benjamin has an answer for that objection too. For in his interpretation of Kafka, it is only a revelation in form of the Law–the Torah, which has been "sickened" and nullified beyond any redemption; despite the regression to the hetaeric universe, there still hovers a memory of this regression, preserved in the only *form* that is truly opposite to life's chaotic flow: the narrative, the story, *that-which-progresses* by its very nature. In the later letter to Scholem from June 1938, Benjamin explains:

> Kafka's work represents a sickening of tradition. Wisdom has sometimes been defined as the epic side of truth. Wisdom is thus characterized as an attribute of tradition; it is truth in haggadic consistency. This consistency of truth has been lost . . . Kafka's genius lay in the fact that he tried something altogether new: *he gave up truth so that he could hold to its transmissibility, the haggadic element*. His works are by nature parables. But their poverty and their beauty consist in their need to be *more* than parables. They don't simply lie down at the feet of doctrine, the way Haggadah lies down at the feet of Halahkah. Having crouched down, they unexpectedly cuff doctrine with a weighty paw.[24]

Already in his early talk on Kafka in German radio, from July 1931, Benjamin sees the antagonistic use of the Haggadic element against the Halakhic order as the most distinctive feature of Kafkan parables: "Like the haggadic parts of the Talmud, these books, too, are stories; they are a Haggadah that constantly pauses, luxuriating in the most detailed descriptions, in the simultaneous hope and fear that it might encounter the halachic order, the doctrine itself, on route. . . . The fact that the Law never finds expression as such—this and nothing else is the gracious dispensation of the fragment" (*Selected Writings* 2:496, 497). The kinetic character of this imagery is very telling. Benjamin pictures the Law as a "burden" that weighs upon life and stops its flow by freezing life's chaotic movement; it gives life an order, but it does not give it a meaning. The meaning is promised by the Haggadic storytelling, which aims at easing and dissolving the heavy load of the Law by the narrating "procrastination" (496). By studying attentively all the details and pausing at seemingly irrelevant *peripeteia*, the Haggadic parable chooses the longest, most winding route possible in order to avoid the encounter with the order: the totalistic sovereign authority of Halakhah. We have thus three elements here, bestowed with three kinds of motions: bare life which flows; the Law which stops; and the story which both progresses and procrastinates. The latter two oppose the messy *flux* of life, but in a very different way: while the Law orders life, it also kills it; whereas the Story, less interested in ordering, aims at wrenching from life a meaning, a *sense*, that is, "orientation" and "direction," and at the same time delays the moment of the ossifying ordering. The Tradition is thus seen here as divided between the "Letter that kills" (Benjamin would not have minded this Paulian association) and the spirit of a pure *transmissibility* whose only purpose is a sense-giving and formatting of the movement of life or reversing its inertial tendency toward dispersion.

The Law, therefore, is nothing but the hunch of the hunchback, which can only be lightened by the movement of storytelling whose vector is not exactly opposite, but tangential to the weighing down force of law (*force de loi*);[25] this means that when you move with a great speed forward, you feel less the burden pressing down on you (it is not just Kafka's physics!). Narration plays then the role of Scheherazade who delays the verdict of death: the encounter with the lethal-legal doctrine.[26] But there is also another movement of narration: the studying, which implies the reversal of the flow of unreflected life. These two movements of storytelling may seem at first glance contradictory—running forward faster than life and stopping the flow of life by a hindsight—but, in fact, they share the same vector of antinomianism, pressing against the inertial flux of the hetaeric *Vorwelt*. For Kafka, as for Benjamin, the Law is like the Sinai mountain that YHVH threatens to throw at Israel, unless it accepts His teaching: it is indeed a hill, a burden, a hunch, which weighs down on the believers, paradoxically thwarting their attempt at Exodus.[27] For, although God presents his Law as the help and guidance in the process of Exodus, without which it would not be possible to leave Egypt and begin a new life in the desert, it is, in fact, a ruse which aims at aborting the exodic movement and reestablishment of the Egypt-like legalistic arrangement of life.

For Benjamin, therefore, Kafka's works reflect the pure structure of Haggadah whose paradigmatic instance is precisely the story of Exodus from Egypt. There lies for him the only hope for the exit from bare life: not in the traditional *content* of the exodic story, but in the *form* itself, which now is supposed to fare better than the message it had so far conveyed. The weighty paw of Haggaddah, which focuses on the motif of Exodus, rises against Halachah because of the latter's betrayal of *yetziat mitzrayim* in the rigid and mortifying doctrine of the Law. The feud between Haggadah and Halakhah, which Benjamin found in Kafka's parables, may thus be understood as the opposition of the still valid project of Exodus (though preserved only in a vestigial form of a pure narrative) and the compromised legalistic doctrine that lost its antinomian touch and fell back into the realm of being.[28]

The Exodic Storytelling

The difference between Scholem and Benjamin would thus appear to be even more subtle, now circling around the issue of the *antinomian trace*. While for Scholem, it would still be the shadow of the Jewish Law, waging war against the laws of nature—for Benjamin it would only be the liberated form of the exodic narrative: the very movement of storytelling. For Scholem, the antinomian trace would still hide in the retreating *nothing* of revelation; for Benjamin, it would merely stay in the pure form of the exodic story, which, relieved from the traditional content, now also tells *nothing*. Their debate is not about the Messiah versus the Sovereign (so Agamben in *Potentialities*), nor about the profanation versus the secularization (so Agamben in *Profanations*), but about two *nothings*, two "zero point contents," which preserve the antinomian intuition of the radical "otherwise than being": the nothing of the nullified, no longer significant Law—and the nothing of the liberated exodic narrative. These two "nothings" are also the respective *loci* where Scholem's and Benjamin's *dei absconditi* reside.

Yet, the common point of the discussion is the motif of distortion, which Benjamin developed in his essay on Kafka. While Scholem believes that it is possible to revert the distortion of the teaching of the Law and go back to its antinomian-messianic origins, Benjamin believes in the powers of the narrative, capable of disentangling the distorted fragments of life and reverting them, via *en geringes Zurechtstellen*, "a small adjustment," to the right form of the living. Life "assumes [the distorted form] in oblivion,"[29] and it is only a story that can retrieve it from the abyss of forgetfulness. In another essay on Kafka, "Franz Kafka: *Beim Bau der Chinesischen Mauer*," Benjamin signals the enormous difficulties that lay in front of every attempt at such reversal, where any "description" can work as a double agent, only deepening the distortion:

> Kafka's work is prophetic. The precisely registered oddities that abound in the life it deals with must be regarded by the reader as not more than the little signs, portents, and symptoms of the displacements that the writer feels approaching in every aspect of life without being able to adjust to the new situation. His only reaction to the almost incomprehensible distortions of existence that betray the emergence of these new laws is a sense of astonishment, mixed with elements of panic-stricken horror. *Kafka is so possessed by this that he is incapable of imagining any single event that would not be distorted by the mere act of describing it* . . . Kafka's fixation on the sole topic of his work—namely the distortion of existence—may appear to the reader as obsessiveness (*Selected Writings* 2:497; my emphasis).

As we have already said, the proper story of exodus-reversal cannot move in accordance with the "normal" flow of life. In his theory of the messianic narrative, Benjamin would come up with many versions of counterrythmic rhetorical devices or "conversation stoppers." Thought-image, dialectical image, gesture, isolated quotation—all function here as figures of a counterarticulation, or *die gegenfügige Strebung* in the field of articulating practice, which, as Sigrid Weigel observes, avails itself of *die entstellte Ähnlichkeit*: "distorted imitation of particular figures of thought, often in completely changed thematic contexts."[30] It is, therefore, the distortion, *Entstellung*, this essentially Freudian category, which governs the dialectics of the Benjaminian tropes of counterarticulation. For "distortion" itself is a hyperdialectical notion: it is a double-edged sword that points to the "right" hidden origin of all these distortive *clinamena*, but also simultaneously shows how far it is and how difficult it is to reach. Distortion, therefore, is at the same time a form of oblivion and a form of memory: "the forgotten [i.e., distorted] always touches on the best, for it touches on the possibility of redemption" (*Illuminations* 136).[31]

Not only does it remember, distortion also protects, for it hides the Messianic Idea from the onslaughts of the mythic forces of "what is." Kabbalistically speaking, it gives a masking cloak to the Angels of the realm of Yetzirah, so they can go unnoticed in the hostile world of Assiyah, and appear as the parodic opposite of their fiery power, for instance, as a grotesque Odradek or a helpless *Gehilfe* (or, going straight into Frankism, a scandalous Messiah incarnated into a son of a prostitute). *To hide means also to protect.* One can do it as Rosenzweig did in *The Star of Redemption*, when he wished to hide the messianic prophecy in the storage of the religious unconscious, as a safely deposited *Niederschrift*, with which no one will tinker and expose it to the dangers of repaganization. Or one can do it in the Benjaminian way, that is, by allowing for symptomatic, necessarily distorted, expressions of the messianic *Niederschrift*, always trying to deceive the surface consciousness and assuming the manner of the Freudian symptomatic speech. But such protecting through hiding remains a risky method for it may lead to a quite straightforward *oblivion*: the complete irrelevance of a God who is now so well hidden that he no longer bears on our lives. Thus *to hide means also to risk losing by forgetting*; to bury things too deeply in the oblivion, beyond the reach of any mnemotechnics. Hence, one should rather tell stories by knowing that every word is but a symptom or a knot on a handkerchief, only pointing toward something we forgot, but were not supposed to have forgotten.

Weigel sums up this dialectics nicely by saying: "Distortion is *the* form in which lost similitude is both concealed and yet at one and the same time becomes perceivable" (ibid., 136). But this dialectic develops even further in what she rightly calls "the reversal of revelation into the messianic" (139), which constitutes yet another dimension of this massively overdetermined word, *Umkehr*: "the remoteness from revelation reverses into a Messianic figure: into redemption" (140). When revelation becomes completely nullified, the only messianic force can be found in the redemptive form of a narrative that will look for immanentist distortions and their "lost similitudes." For Benjamin, therefore, "nothingness of revelation" means that there is no longer hope (at least, not for us) of the revival of revelation, or looking for *the signs of transcendence*; once the attempt to rekindle the transcendent perspective, undertaken by Benjamin in his work on *Trauerspiel*, failed, all that remained is to watch for *the redemptive indices* within the realm of abandoned immanence, pointing obliquely where to go to realize the messianic ideal of a happy, undistorted life.

It is in the context of the interplay between oblivion and distortion as the disfigured form of memory that we should look at Benjamin's use of Bachofen's concept of the "hetearic world," which so much irritated Scholem. In fact, they—again—are not so far from one another, also on this point. Just like in his essay on the Kafkan story on the Chinese Wall, Benjamin praised its author for prophetic powers, also in his piece from 1935 called "Johann Jakob Bachofen," he begins by extolling the "prophetic side of Bachofen" (*Selected Writings* 3:12). He is fascinated with the Bachofenian primal world of hetaeric fluidity where life and death do not yet form an opposition, which he also associates with the matriarchal form of early communism. The Kafkan women, promiscuous and seductive, rolling in the deep night of creation, are the true rulers of this anarchic world without rulers, where all the *Behörde* had been put into a sleep of oblivion. Yet what clearly attracts Benjamin in the vision of the premythic stage of mankind is not the narcotic universe of

Mutterrecht itself but only its *distorted similarity* to the messianic age; the disfigured image of a "happy, lawless life" that cannot be saved *as such*, but can nonetheless be saved dialectically as the bearer of the distorted redemptive spark that it contains.

But this is also where Benjamin's and Scholem's ways truly part. While for Benjamin, more radical in this respect, the "nothingness of revelation" means that it can no longer be renewed or retrieved, and all that is left is a search for the indices of redemption, contracted in the immanent distortion—for Scholem, "nothingness of revelation" means that revelation itself goes into hiding and retreats into original "meaninglessness" from which it can spring again reinvigorated. While Benjamin's way is strictly "horizontal," investing in a complex kinetics of the messianic narrative—Scholem's expectation remains "vertical," firmly convinced that "what is in the process of appearing (for revelation is such a process) still does not disappear."[32] For Scholem, therefore, the modern world, although naturalized and nihilized, still presents itself as an arena of a potential powerful revival of religious intuition. In his eulogy of Franz Rosenzweig from 1930, he thus says:

> There is no doubt that we had lost sight of the traditional objects of theology, yet they still remain as hidden lights, which radiate from the inside, invisible from the outside. . . . But is that true that He does not reveal himself at all? Perhaps, this last contraction of His is simultaneously His last manifestation? Perhaps, His regression to the point bordering on nothingness was a matter of the highest urgency, according to the wisdom that His Kingdom may be revealed only to such radically voided world? For "I am sought of them that asked not for me; I am found of them that sought me not" (Isaiah 65, 1).

Power versus Promise

The excursion into Scholem-Benjamin correspondence on Kafka was meant to raise once again the issue of the Jewish *clinamen* on the Protestant theme of *deus absconditus*, with which I began this essay. Pace Idel (though also partly in agreement with him), I wanted to demonstrate that there is more to the debate on the *Nichts der Offenbarung* than just a repetition of the well-known German-Protestant motives coming from Kierkegaard, Schmitt, and Barth. In the concluding section, I would like to sum up these differences and put them in even stronger relief: as a salient distinction between *the negative theology of power* and *the negative theology of promise*.

The Protestant hidden God of the unreachable beyond is always the God of the sovereign power. But not so the Lurianic God who figures so strongly in the Scholem-Benjamin exchange in which both friends develop two complementary aspects of Luria's metaphysics: while Scholem elaborates on God's "second *tsimtsum*" or his withdrawal into the transcendent "nothingness of revelation," Benjamin focuses on his vestigial presence as hidden-in-the-world, immanently distorted and weakened, thus even more radically breaking with the mythic image of lordship. Both Scholem and Benjamin would agree that there is, in fact, nothing inconceivable or deeply mysterious about divine sovereignty—as long as it is, simply, sovereignty. *Power holds no mysteries*; quite to the contrary, it is the most self-evident of all earthly things, the very essence of the most manifest mythic immanence. In their polemic against the dubious *mysteries of sovereignty*, which so strongly dominated Protestant negative theology, Benjamin and Scholem firmly unite: Benjamin in his deconstruction of the holiness of power in the *Trauerspiel* book, and Scholem in his alternative interpretations of the divine "meaninglessness." As Scholem says, *Es gibt Geheimnis in der Welt*, but this mystery is *not* the mystery of a hidden might; it is always and only the mystery of the unknown God who *promises* the ultimate messianic transformation of the power-dominated life into life liberated, happy, and blessed, beyond any dominion of sovereignty. It is not power that is concealed and radically transcendent—but only life, the "mysterious hidden life of God." God, therefore, reveals himself as indeed meaningless—but not as a Nothing-of-Meaning or the capriciously inexplicable power issuing "commands that command nothing,"[33] but as an autotelic Pleroma of eternal Sabbath, delighting in its own absolute uniqueness.[34]

But this *reversal of divine concealedness* is not Benjamin's or Scholem's own invention; it derives from the Kabbalstic teachings much earlier than those of Isaac Luria. Already in Zohar, which was Scholem's first Kabbalistic love, we find a dismissive treatment of the Divine Sovereignty (as merely human projection) in favor of the absolute mystery of the All-Hidden One who, not incidentally, appears also to be the joyful God of Sabbath: the other, nonsovereign and nonjudgmental God of the "bundle of life." Thus even YHVH, who makes Himself manifest as the active principle of creation, is called "Small Countenance," and only "in the last [order of manifestation], in Sovereignty, he calls himself King"[35]: "Man dares project one sole conception of the Holy One, be blessed, that of his sovereignty over some one attribute or over the creation in entirety. But if he be not seen under these manifestations, then there is neither attribute, nor likeness, nor form in him. . . . Neither shape nor form has he, and no vessel exists to contain him, nor any means to apprehend him" (ibid. 52–53). But there is just one hint with which the human mind can begin to approach the All-Hidden Ancient One: it is not, as in the ascetic practices of Christian negative theology, a rigorous *via negativa*, but the joys of the Sabbath:

> On each of the six days of the week, at the hour of the afternoon prayer, the force prevails of the unmitigated judgment, and retribu-

tion stands by. Not so on the Sabbath. When the hour of the Sabbath afternoon prayer has come, regnant are the benign influences, the lovingkindness of the Holy Ancient One is made manifest, all punishments are restrained, and joy and satisfaction are everywhere. In this hour of satisfaction and grace, the holy, faithful prophet Moses departed from this world, so that it might be known that he was not taken away through judgment, but that his soul ascended in the hour of grace of the Holy Ancient One, to be hidden in him. Hence, "No man knoweth of his sepulchre unto this day" (Deuteronomy 34:6). Thus, as the Holy Ancient One is the All-hidden, unknowable to those above and those below, so also was the soul of Moses hidden, in the revelation, as the Sabbath afternoon prayer, of God's grace. *Of all hidden things in the world, this soul of Moses is the most hidden, and cannot come under judgment* (Zohar 59; my emphasis).

There are no mysteries of power, for power lies always on the surface: it is the most crudely visible and open feature of the immanent life. There is also nothing enigmatic about guilt and judgment, despite the Christian emphasis on the unfathomable depths of *hamartia*, the tragic guilt, then only slightly modified by Augustine and turned into the concept of "original sin." What is truly cryptic, always in-the-hiding, is only the *promise*: the nothingness of *not-yet*, releasing from all guilt and judgments, all covenants and oaths, pointing out of its virtual nonexistence toward a "sabbath-like" possibility of life.[36] And just like, according to the *Pesach Haggadah*, the whole world is Moses's grave, the whole world is also filled with his "hidden soul": the scattered spark of grace that can nonetheless be found v the distortion.[37]

The Scholemian formula of *Nichts der Offenbarung* shimmers with all these alternative meanings that have nothing to do with the traditional negative theology, especially in its Nominalist-Protestant variant, enquiring into inscrutability of God's transcendent power. While it releases from the grips of the Law, as the only Jewish manifestation of the Divine Sovereignty, it does not show a mysterious *nothing* behind it, from which there spring God's capricious decisions and verdicts. It rather shows an originating matrix of an ever-renewable promise of which we cannot talk openly and have to remain prudently silent.[38] Or, just hint at it, pause at it, and luxuriate at its possibility, as according to Benjamin, all Haggadic narratives do by cherishing their own version of the hidden God.

Nothing perhaps sums this discussion better than the remark made by Paul Celan in *The Meridian*. Celan, who read Scholem and Benjamin carefully, saw himself as a poet continuing the Haggadic storytelling, trying to find ways out from the Egypt of the post-Holocaust world. Equally committed to seeking the possibility of the "messianic reversal" in the midst of the Egyptian *Engführung*,[39] Celan never abandoned hope into what he called the hidden God of the poem and his still concealed poetic powers of future expression: "one makes something understandable through non-saying; the poem knows *argumentum ex silentio*. There is an ellipse which one should not confuse with a trope or a simple stylistic sophistication. *The God of the poem is undoubtedly a deus absconditus*."[40]

Notes

1. "The great deceit of the world / Is not consummated. / Give then, Lord, that he may wake / Who was struck through by your nothingness. / Only so does revelation / Shine in the time that rejected you. / Only your nothingness is the experience / It is entitled to have of you." In *The Correspondence of Walter Benjamin and Gershom Scholem. 1932–1940*, trans. Gary Smith and Andre Lefevre (New York: Schocken Books, 1989), 125.

2. Gershom Scholem, *Lamentations of Youth: The Diaries of Gershom Scholem, 1913–1919*, ed. and trans. Anthony David Skinner (Cambridge, MA: Harvard University Press, 2007), 208.

3. See Moshe Idel, *Old Worlds, New Mirrors: On Jewish Mysticism and Twentieth-Century Thought* (Philadelphia: University of Pennsylvania Press, 2010), 111. Another critic of the "hidden God" motif in the context of Jewish thought is Hans Jonas who comes from a completely different background than Idel. In his famous essay, "The Concept of God after Auschwitz" (in *Mortality and Morality: A Search for the Good after Auschwitz*, trans. Lawrence Vogel [Chicago: Northwestern University Press 1996]), Jonas says:

> The *Deus absconditus*, the hidden God (not to speak of an absurd God) is a profoundly un-Jewish conception. Our teaching, the Torah, rests on the premise and insists that we can understand God, not completely, to be sure, but something of him—of his will, intentions, and even nature—because he has told us. There has been revelation, we have his commandments and his law, and he has directly communicated with some—his prophets—as his mouth for all men in the language of men and their times: refracted thus in this limiting medium but not veiled in dark mystery. A completely hidden God is not an acceptable concept by Jewish norms (140).

On the issue of the influence of Karl Barth on his Jewish readers, see most of all Benjamin Lazier, *God Interrupted: Heresy and the European Imagination between the World Wars* (Princeton, NJ: Princeton University Press, 2012), especially the chapter "Romans in Weimar."

4. See Harold Bloom, "Freud," in *The Strong Light of the Canonical: Kafka, Freud and Scholem as Revisionists of Jewish Culture and Thought,* City College Papers 20 (New York: City College of New York, 1987), 32. Bloom talks about the specificity of the Jewish Negation that issues from the iconoclasm of the Second Commandment and creates "a certain curious sense of interiority," characteristic only of a Jewish psyche that "represses all images." This negativity has nothing to do with the "Hegelian mode of negative thinking" (following

the Protestant dialectical logic of *kathargein*) but "always reenacts the ambiguities of the Second Commandment": the prohibition of figuration that only intensifies *the desire to see*, to confront God one day "face to face" (ibid. 34). On the ambiguities of this "desire to see," compare also the magisterial study of Elliott Wolfson, *Through a Speculum that Shines: Vision and Imagination in Medieval Jewish Mysticism* (Princeton, NJ: Princeton University Press, 1997).

5. I take the term *clinamen* also from Harold Bloom, who in his *Anxiety of Influence* calls by it the first stage of poetic revision. In my usage *clinamen* indicates the revisionary effort of Jewish thinkers trying to deviate from the Protestant canon of negative theology. See Harold Bloom, *The Anxiety of Influence. A Theory of Poetry (With a New Preface on Shakespeare)* (New Haven, CT: Yale University Press, 1997).

6. "Offener Brief an den Verfasser der Schrift *Jüdischer Glaube in dieser Zeit*, von Dr. Gerhard Scholem, Universität Jerusalem," in Gershom Scholem, *Briefe I, 1914–1947*, ed. Itta Shedletzky (Munich: Verlag C. H. Beck, 1994), 469.

7. In Barth's own words: "I was puzzled, on reading the earlier reviews of Harnack's book, by the remarkable parallels between what Marcion had said and what I was actually writing": Karl Barth, "Preface to the Second Edition," in *The Epistle to the Romans*, trans. Edwyn C. Hoskyns (Oxford: Oxford University Press, 1968), 13.

8. Ludwig Feuerbach, *Das Wesen des Glaubens im Sinne Luthers: Ein Beitrag zum 'Wesen des Christentums,'* in *Gesammelte Werke*, Band 9, ed. Werner Schuffenhauer (Berlin: Akademie Verlag, 1967–2007), 392 (my translation).

9. See Ernst Bloch, *Atheism in Christianity*, trans. Peter Thompson (London: Verso, 2009), 37.

10. Pierre Hadot, *The Veil of Isis: An Essay on the History of the Idea of Nature*, trans. Michael Chase (Cambridge, MA: The Belknap Press of Harvard University Press, 2006).

11. See Walter Benjamin, "Capitalism as Religion," in *Selected Writings. Volume 1: 1913–1926*, ed. Marcus Bullock & Michael W. Jennings (Cambridge, MA: The Belknap Press of Harvard University Press, 1996).

12. This term is used by Jacob Taubes in his *Abendländische Eschatologie*; Jacob Taubes, *Occidental Eschatology*, trans. David Ratmoko (Stanford, CA: Stanford University Press, 2009), 15.

13. Idel, *Old Worlds, New Mirrors*, 129.

14. Gershom Scholem to Walter Benjamin, Letter 66, September 20, 1934, in *The Correspondence of Walter Benjamin and Gershom Scholem: 1932–1940*, trans. Gary Smith and Andre Lefevre (New York: Schocken Books 1989), 142; my emphasis. In the original, this fragment runs: "Ich verstehe darunter einen Stand, in dem [die Offenbarung] bedeutungsleer erscheint, in dem sie zwar noch sich behauptet, in dem sie *gilt*, aber nicht *bedeutet*. Wo der Reichtum der Bedeutung wegfällt und das Erscheinende, wie auf einen Nullpunkt des eigenen Gehalts reduziert, dennoch nicht verschwindet (und die Offenbarung ist etwas Erscheinendes), da tritt sein Nichts hervor. Es versteht sich, dass im Sinn der Religion dies ein Grenzfall ist, von dem sehr fraglich bleibt, ob er realiter vollziehbar ist": *Walter Benjamin, Gershom Scholem. Briefwechsel 1933–40*, ed. Gershom Scholem (Frankfurt am Main: Suhrkamp, 1980), 157.

15. The idea of a religious nihilist as someone capable of "walking a thin line between nihilism and religion" appears first in Scholem's letter to Salman Schocken from 1937 and then becomes repeated in his *Ten Unhistorical Theses on Kabbalah*, characteristically—apropos Franz Kafka: Gershom Scholem, "Zehn unhistorische Sätze über Kabbala," *Judaica* (Frankfurt am Main: Suhrkamp Verlag, 1973), 3: 271. The name of a "pious atheist" also refers originally to Kafka: "The emptying of the world to a meaningless void not illuminated by any ray of meaning or direction is the experience of him whom I would call *the pious atheist*. The void is the abyss, the chasm or the crack which opens up in all that exists. This is the experience of modern man, surpassingly well depicted in all its desolation by Kafka, for whom nothing has remained of God but the void—in Kafka's sense, to be sure, the void of God": Gershom Scholem, "Reflections on Jewish Theology," in *On Jews and Judaism in Crisi:. Selected Essays*, ed. Werner Dannhauser (New York: Schocken Books, 1976), 283.

16. Irving Wohlfarth, combining Scholemian-Lurianic metaphysics with Benjamin's later metaphor of the chess-playing, cunningly hidden Theology, will call it a *theologischer Schachzug*, a theological chess gambit in which God retreats into a new *tsimtsum* in order to spring anew from his nothingness: Irving Wohlfarth, "Haarscharf auf der Grenze zwischen Religion und Nihilismus: Zum Motiv des Zimzum bei Gershom Scholem," in Peter Schäfer and Gary Smith, eds., *Gershom Scholem: Zwischen den Disziplinen* (Frankfurt am Main: Suhrkamp, 1995), 236–237.

17. This term will appear just few years later in Benjamin's *Theses on the Philosophy and History*, clearly anticipated in Benjamin's reflections on Kafka.

18. We could thus say that in this debate Scholem occupies a position with which Benjamin toyed in his *Ursprung des deutschen Trauerspiels*, but abandoned, precisely because of its nondialectical impasse in which he could not secure the "transcendent leap" on the grounds of the isolated immanence. The argument was to work along the now-Scholemian lines of "the more isolated, the more open to transcendence," but Benjamin must have found it ultimately unconvincing. Stephane Mosès summarizes this strategy very aptly: "Gershom Scholem had a lifelong fascination with Franz Kafka's *oeuvre*, in which he saw a paradigmatic image of the spirit of our age: the meticulous presentation of a world void of the idea of the divine, yet one in which immanence itself must be read as the inverse of a lost transcendence.... The deterioration beyond repair Scholem detected in that world, recalling Benjamin's description of the world of Baroque, is that of a corrupt universe beyond salvation": Stephane Mosès, "Gershom Scholem's Reading of Kafka: Literary Criticism and Kabbalah," in "German-Jewish Religious Thought," ed. Leora Batnitzky, Peter Eli Gordon, and Jonathan Skolnik, special issue, *New German Critique* 77, (Spring–Summer, 1999): 149, 162, respectively. A similar interpretation of Scholem as oscillating between nihilism pure and simple, self-content and self-enclosed and in the disenchanted modern reality, and a "religious nihilism" that turns the experience of *Nichts Gottes* into a springboard of a potential revelation appears also in the already quoted Irving Wohlfarth's essay, "*Haarscharf auf der Grenze zwischen Religion und Nihilismus*": "Where Benjamin expects a profane-messianic salvation from the materialistic transformation of theology, Scholem insists on the potentiality to wrench the messianic directly from the process of secularization, the numinal from the loss of aura, and God from his self-withdrawal," 182.

19. See the aphorism 108 called "New Struggles."

20. As Robert Alter put it in his commentary on the "Kafka debate": "At first blush, the difference between the two positions may seem hairsplitting, but it will be worth pondering what might be at stake in the opposition between an absent and an unintelligible revelation": Robert Alter, *Necessary Angels: Tradition and Modernity in Kafka, Benjamin, and Scholem* (Cambridge, MA: Harvard University Press, 1991), 103.

21. "The history of the world is the trial of the world": this phrase, later borrowed by Hegel, appears originally in Friedrich Schiller's poem, *Resignation*.

22. See Giorgio Agamben, "The Messiah and the Sovereign: The Problem of Law in Walter Benjamin," in *Potentialities: Collected Essays in Philosophy*, trans. Daniel Heller-Roazen (Stanford, CA: Stanford University Press, 2000), 162. In the later essay from *Profanations*, Agamben will even strengthen his critique of Scholem and, once again leaning toward Benjamin, reproaches Scholem for maintaining the rhetoric of secularization that blocks the modern idiom of profanation, the only one capable of truly casting off the transcendent "shadow."

23. See Jacques Derrida, *Specters of Marx: The State of Debt, the Work of Mourning, and the New International*, trans. Peggy Kamuf (New York: Routledge, 1994).

24. Walter Benjamin, *Selected Writings*, vol. 3, 326 (my emphasis).

25. On the heavily material aspect of the force of law and the mystical foundation of authority, see Jacques Derrida, "The Force of Law," in *Acts of Religion*. Derrida may be also said to speak in favor of Haggadah as the narrative alternative form of revelation in the conclusion to his *Mal d'archive*, where secret, nothing, and literature belong together; see Jacques Derrida, *Archive Fever: A Freudian Impression*, trans. Eric Prenowitz (Chicago: The Chicago University Press, 1996).

26. As presented by Benjamin in his essay "The Storyteller: Observations on the Works of Nikolai Leskov," *Selected Writings*, 3:154. In his interpretation of Leskov, Benjamin depicts the art of storytelling as offering the "epic side of truth," which he calls "wisdom,"—and this balance between truth and wisdom is precisely what has been lost in a now deeply disturbed relationship between Halachah and Aggadah. Here Benjamin clearly follows Bialik's essay, "Halachah and Aggadah" (1916), which he read at the time of writing his text on Kafka, and in which Bialik states sarcastically that "now we are privileged to live in an age of pure Aggadah, both in literature and actual life. The whole world is but Aggadah within Aggadah; of Halachah, in whatever sense, there is no trace and no mention": Haim Nahman Bialik, "Halachah and Aggadah," in *Revealment and Concealment: Five Essays* (Jerusalem: Ibis Editions, 2000), 83. Yet, as Stephane Mosès rightly observes, even in the midst of this gravely "sickened tradition," "Kafka's *oeuvre* is a testimony to the survival of a certain manner of 'telling the tale'": Mosès, "Gershom Scholem's Reading of Kafka," 165.

27. This is how the Talmudic tractate *Shabbath* (88a and 88b) interprets the moment in the exodic story of Israel when "they stopped at the foot of the mountain" (Exodus 19:17): "Rav Abdimi bar Hama bar Hasa has said: This teaches us that the Holy One, Blessed be He, inclined the mountain over them like a tilted tub and that He said: If you accept the Torah, all is well, if not here will be your grave." The "mountain threat" is also the topic of Emmanuel Levinas's second Talmudic reading, "The Temptation of Temptations," whose

conclusions are—needless to say—very opposite to Benjamin's perception of the Law as a useless burden. See Emmanuel Levinas, *Nine Talmudic Readings*, trans. Annette Aronowicz (Bloomington: Indiana University Press, 1990), 30–50.

28. On the salvific powers of the narrative in Judaic tradition, one can also refer to Wohlfarth who, followingYoseph Hayim Yerushalmi's *Zakhor*, stresses the role of memory playing itself out in storytelling. Convinced that Scholem finally took to heart his friend's "mystique of story-telling," Wohlfarth analyzes the conclusion of Scholem's *Major Trends in Jewish Mysticism*, which reminds readers of the Hasidic story according to which "we can no longer make the fire, we can no longer pray, we no longer recognize the place, but we can still tell the story about it"—and says: "This would also be the moral of the whole story: that telling of the story itself is a religious act. Scholem accepted this moral in turning it into his own art of a critical retelling of the Jewish history": "*Haarscharf auf der Grenze zwischen Religion und Nihilismus*," 180.

29. Walter Benjamin, *Illuminations: Essays and Reflections*, trans. Harry Zohn (New York: Schocken Books 1968), 133. Benjamin says of the hunchback, the emblem of the distorted life: "This little man is at home in *distorted life*; he will disappear with the coming of the Messiah, of whom a great rabbi once said that he did not wish to change the world by force, but would only make a slight adjustment in it" (134).

30. Sigrid Weigel, *Body and Image-Space: Re-Reading Walter Benjamin*, trans. Georgina Paul (London: Routledge 1996), xi. Benjamin in *Berlin Childhood around 1900*, trans. Howard Eilan (Cambridge: Cambridge University Press, 2006), 59: "Ich war entstellt von Ähnlichkeit" (I was distorted by resemblance).

31. Distortion in this sense is thus akin to repression in Bloom's interpretation of the essentially Freudian "Jewish Negative," for it touches on the specificity of "Jewish memory." Bloom says: "Freudian memory is Jewish memory, and Freudian forgetting is yet more Jewish" (*The Strong Light*, 36), which suggests that both remembering and forgetting are dialectically intertwined in one operation of repression-distortion, *Verdrängung-Entstellung*.

32. Gershom Scholem, "Gedenkrede auf Franz Rosenzweig," in Franz Rosenzweig, *Der Stern der Erlösung* (Frankfurt am Main: Suhrkamp, 1988), 533.

33. See Agamben, *Potentialities*, 163.

34. Scholem writes about this delight and joy apropos one of his favorite Kabbalists, Israel Saruk from the Lurianic school around 1600: "He explains the beginning of the speech movement, originating in the infinite essence of the Godhead, by pointing to the joy, delight and pleasure—in Hebrew *shi'ashu'a*—which creates the first stirring within the *Ein-Sof*": Gershom Scholem, "Die Sprachtheorie Isaak des Blinden," in *Judaica* 3:53. This beautiful image very aptly sums up Scholem's positive and affirmative understanding of God's nothingness and meaninglessness as a spontaneous self-expression of the original pleromatic joy.

35. *Zohar: The Book of Splendour*, trans. and ed. by Gershom Scholem (New York: Schocken Books, 1995), 54.

36. This Scholemian-Benjaminian motif of getting beyond the mysteries of power will then continue in Jacques Derrida's reflections on the death/withdrawal of God who dies/withdraws in order to release us from all forms of validity and guilt, *Geltung-Gültigkeit*. In

the exchange with Yvonne Sherwood, Kevin Hart, and John D. Caputo, called "Epoche and Faith," Derrida says: "One has to dissociate God's sovereignty from God, from the very idea of God. We would have God without sovereignty, without omnipotence": in *Derrida and Religion: Other Testaments*, ed. Yvonne Sherwood and Kevin Hart (New York: Routledge, 2005), 42.

37. For Ernst Bloch (whose *Spirit of Utopia* was highly appreciated by Benjamin, though less so by Scholem), this is yet another instance of the theological superiority of Haggadah over Halachah and its "redacted Scripture," for it pardons and exonerates Moses instead of supporting the image of YHWH as an angry, all-powerful and punishing God; see Ernst Bloch, *Atheism in Christianity*, 75. Bloch follows Bialik's famous opening of his essay: "Halachah wears a frown, Aggadah a smile. The one is pedantic, severe, unbending—all justice; the other is accommodating, lenient, pliable—all mercy. . . . On one side there is petrified observance, duty, subjection; on the other perpetual rejuvenation, liberty, free volition": Bialik, *Revealment and Concealment*, 45. But unlike Bialik, who believes that there is a constant communication between the two and "a living and healthy halachah is an aggadah that has been or that will be—and the reverse is true also" (ibid. 47), Bloch, similarly to Benjamin, emphasizes the antagonism between them and opts for an alternative theology issuing from the Haggadic narrative.

38. Already in his short essay on "Lamentation and Dirge" from 1918, Scholem talks about the "unfallen silence," which retained its purity despite the fall of all languages. Scholem never abandoned his belief in silence and its unfallen quality, still containing the promise hidden in *Nichts der Offenbarung*. See Gershom Scholem, "Über Klage und Klagelied," *Tagebücher nebst Aufsätzen und Entwürfen bis 1923*, vol. 2: *Halbband 1917–1923* (Frankfurt am Main: Jüdischer Verlag, 2000), 133.

39. One of the most famous Celan's poems, *Die Engführung*, takes its title from the Hebrew meaning of Egypt as *mitzrayim*, "the narrow place": the place of suffocation and death.

40. Es gibt . . . ein dem Gedicht und nur ihm eigenes Sprach-Tabu, das nicht allein für seinen Wortschatz gilt, sondern auch für Kategorien wie Syntax, Rhytmus oder Lautung; vom Nichtgesagten her wird einiges verständlich; das Gedicht kennt das *argumentum ex silentio*. Es gibt also eine Ellipse, die man nicht als Tropus oder gar stillistisches Raffinement missverstanden darf. *Der Gott des Gedichts ist unstreitig ein deus absconditus*: Paul Celan, *Der Meridian: Endfassung—Entwürfe—Materialien*, ed. Heino Schmuhl and Bernhard Böschenschein (Frankfurt am Main: Suhrkamp, 1999), 86–87.

THIRTEEN

Can Halakhah Survive Negative Theology?

DAVID SHATZ

By now it is a commonplace that metaphysics and what Heidegger called "onto-theology" are dead. But what follows from this thesis as regards religion? A standard response is that religion—more accurately, philosophy of religion—has to shift focus. Thus, Avi Sagi, in his tellingly titled *Jewish Religion after Theology*, writes: "This book . . . points to a post-theological trend that shifts the focus of discussion from metaphysics to practice and examines the possibilities of establishing a religious life centered on immanent-practical existence."[1] Subsequent chapters of Sagi's book discuss different aspects of this shift. A straightforward example of the shift is Rabbi Joseph Soloveitchik's call to shy away from the question "Why is there evil?" and instead ask "What [halakhic] obligation does suffering impose upon man?"[2] The most vociferous (indeed, cantankerous!) Jewish opponent of religious metaphysicizing was Isaiah Leibowitz, and he, as per the pattern just noted, made halakhic commitment central to his conception of Judaism.[3] Indeed, following Halakhah[4] is, for Leibowitz, what Judaism is *entirely* about.[5]

In reflecting on such aversions to metaphysics, we should note several points. First, there is a difference between trying to *understand* religion (or a religion) in terms of practices and trying to *justify* the religion so understood—that is, trying to justify the practices. Sometimes the distinction gets lost—authors sometimes stress understanding and neglect justification. By contrast, Daniel Rynhold, for example, engages in both understanding and justification, arguing that rather than inquire into reasons for the *mitzvot*, Jewish thought should accept the "primacy of practice" as the justification for observing Halakhah.[6] A second point is that the shift to practice can be argued for even without regarding theology as a pursuit doomed to failure and/or irrelevance. Theology might be possible and yet not worth an investment of time and resources, or someone might argue that authoritative texts of his or her religion show that God wants practice and minimizes the value of theology. Third, the shift that thinkers commend is not always from antimetaphysics to praxis; sometimes the movement is from anti-metaphysics to a focus on religious experience. Such a move was anticipated, or charted, by Kierkegaard and others. Here, however, we will focus on practice.[7]

The question pursued in this essay can be formulated as follows. As will become clear, I do not think there are convincing arguments for rejecting theology and/or the religious pursuit of theology in principle. But are the above-mentioned authors correct that *if* "negative theology" is correct (how the term is defined will be explored later), an appropriate response to its demise is highlighting practice? *Or would negative theology, on the contrary, spell trouble for commitment to Halakhah?* Our question is not *de facto* but *de jure*. De facto, through the centuries many adherents of Halakhah have subscribed to some form of negative theology: from rationalists to mystics, from Maimonides to Rabbi Abraham Isaac Kook, and to Leibowitz himself, who is neither rationalist nor mystic. So negative theology and Halakhah have often lived in peace. But to *justify* this living arrangement requires work. Notwithstanding the compatibility implied by the "religion after theology" project, negative theology is sometimes thought to *logically* undermine halakhic commitment, despite the fact that many thinkers embrace both. Whereas it is precisely because of negative theology that thinkers often say, "Forget knowledge of God. You can't attain it. Focus instead on religious action," we need to consider the charge that not only is this argument a non sequitur, but the opposite inference is correct: "Forget knowledge of God. You can't attain it. So there's no good reason to follow Halakhah." Thus the prevalent combination of negative theology and halakhic commitment is precisely what critics find indefensible.[8]

Daniel Statman makes this claim, focusing on Leibowitz's thinking. In reading the following passage, bear in mind (to grasp the context) that Leibowitz denied that practicing *mitzvot* serves any human purpose or goal but instead involves acquiescence to demands.

> It is bad enough if the commandments do not lead to any earthly achievement, such as harmony of the soul, stability of society, or intellectual perfection. But if they do not even realize a religious goal, what is the point—the *religious* point—in observing them? To this Leibowitz replies as follows: The aim of proximity to God is unattainable.... What, then, is the substance and import of the performance of the mitzvot? It is man's *striving* to attain the religious goal.

Statman continues:

> At this point, one naturally asks: why is keeping the laws of kashrut or of Shabbat the right way to "strive to attain the religious goal?" To this Leibowitz would presumably reply by saying that these laws are God's commandments, hence observing them is the only way to express one's effort to attain the religious aim. Yet, this answer is not easy to reconcile with Leibowitz's claim that "God revealed Himself

neither in nature, nor in history." If nothing positive can be said about God, in particular if it cannot be said that at some time and place He delivered His law to some human beings, then the divine origin of the Torah becomes somewhat problematic. Furthermore, I mentioned above that on Leibowitz's view, religious believers, *qua* believers, are committed to no special propositional beliefs, hence they can accept any scientific theory without religious reservation. Now let us imagine that historians of ancient Israel discover new and overwhelming evidence that the book of Leviticus was edited by a person who utilized extracts of the local laws of his society and other familiar traditions in creating that book. According to Leibowitz, there would be no religious impediment for believers to fully accept this scientific discovery. But if they did, could they still maintain that by observing the laws of Leviticus they are *worshipping* God, or striving to attain a *religious* aim?[9]

Statman cites a celebrated article by the eminent historian, Haym Soloveitchik, in which Soloveitchik seeks to explain (in Statman's words) the "increasingly strict loyalty" to the laws of halakhah in contemporary society. In the closing sentence of his article, Soloveitchik makes the point this way: "Having lost the touch of His presence, they seek now solace in the pressure of His yoke."[10] Statman sees a similar development with regard to the decline of theology. But if Statman is right, the trend is problematic—psychologically prevalent, but logically hard to defend.

I will argue in this essay for four propositions. First, that arguments on behalf of *sweeping* forms of negative theology (both arguments that have been proposed and arguments that might be proposed) are unconvincing. More cautiously put, sweeping forms of negative theology may be legitimate *options* for a religious thinker—but they are no more than options. Second, that acceptance of sweeping forms of negative theology is compatible with commitment to Halakhah. Third, that, although there is a way in which a nonsweeping form of negative theology—to wit, the claim that we are ignorant of God's *intentions* and *purposes* (as opposed to God's nature)—might be thought to impact adversely on Halakhah by casting doubt on the rationality of halakhic decision making in a perhaps wide range of cases, halakhic decision making can be defended even if we lack knowledge, or some knowledge, of God's intentions and purposes. Fourth and finally, that there is another way in which a form of negative theology might appear to undermine Halakhah. This restricted form, I will argue, does pose a genuine problem; that problem, though, is not truly about negative theology but about mistaken theology.

To frame matters another way, there are three forms that the challenge of negative theology to Halakhah can take: (1) A sweeping negative theology, (2) a negative theology only about intentions and purposes, and (3) a negative theology about specific theological claims that ground specific *halakhot*.

The Varieties of Negative Theology

Let us begin by asking what negative theology *says*. I would have liked to quip that negative theology can be characterized only by saying what it is not, but alas we have all too many ways to say what it is.

Epistemological Formulations of Negative Theology

> Epistemological thesis 1: As per classic Maimonidean teaching (says this thesis), we cannot know God's attributes of essence—what God is in Himself; but we can know His attributes of action. The epistemological claim that we cannot know His attributes of essence is inferrable from an ontological thesis—that God has no attributes of essence at all.[11]

Maimonides' view has a further dimension, about the *meaning* of God-talk. Statements that seem to ascribe psychological predicates to God, i. e. anthropopathic statements, notably the predicates included in the *yod-gimel middot*, the Thirteen Attributes (Exodus 34:6–7), are to be translated into statements about God's actions. Statements that ascribe knowledge, will, power, knowledge, existence and other attributes, are to be translated into statements of the form "God is not not-X," where the latter is understood to negate the application to God of any and all categories.

> Epistemological thesis 2: We cannot know any of God's attributes, not even attributes of action.
> Epistemological thesis 3: We *can* know God's attributes—we are not *of necessity* limited—but in point of fact we do not. The sense of "necessity" used here needs clarification.
> Epistemological thesis 4: There are no credible statements about God in religious traditions.
> Epistemological thesis 5: We cannot have metaphysical knowledge at all.
> Epistemological thesis 6: We can know some or all of God's *attributes*, but we cannot know all (or any) of His *purposes and intentions*. Thus, we cannot know matters such as the following: why He created the world, why He chose Abraham and His descendants, why He allows evil, why He gave *mitzvot* at all, and why He gave the specific *mitzvot* that He did.[12] (This thesis will be the sole survivor of the criticisms of arguments for negative theology advanced in this section; the problems it causes will emerge later.)

Ontological Formulations of Negative Theology

Ontological thesis 1: God has only attributes of action but does not have attributes of essence.

Ontological thesis 2: God has neither attributes of action nor attributes of essence. (God, according to this thesis, does not do anything, in addition to having no intrinsic properties.)

Ontological thesis 3: There are no facts about God.

Ontological Thesis 4: God does not exist.

Ontological Thesis 5: There are no metaphysical facts at all.

Deontic and aretaic formulations of negative theology

Deontic thesis: It is wrong to explore God's attributes.

Aretaic thesis: One who explores God's attributes exhibits defects in religious character.

With this taxonomy in place, we face two questions. First, why believe any of these epistemological, ontological, deontic, or aretaic formulations? Are there good arguments for them? Second, if we accept one or more of these theses, would that undermine commitment to Halakhah?

Must We Accept Negative Theology?

Whereas negative theology is de rigeur in circles of Continental philosophy, philosophers in the analytic tradition conspicuously devote tomes upon tomes and articles upon articles explicating the divine attributes. That God, if He exists, has attributes and that, with sufficient thinking and prodding, we can understand these attributes, is taken for granted in these discussions. Strikingly, there is little or no echo of the sorts of problems that preoccupy Continental theology and are often taken for granted in Jewish discussions. There is no small irony in the contemporary analytic/Continental divide. For it is precisely in analytic philosophical circles that there arose decades ago the notion that metaphysical (including theistic) statements are cognitively meaningless. That notion has long since been abandoned. Why, given its history, analytic philosophers now look favorably on metaphysics, but in Continental circles metaphysics is still resisted, is an intriguing question. One philosopher attributes the shift in analytic philosophy to the death of logical empiricism and the flowering of alternative theories of knowledge that make room for religious knowledge.[13] Whatever the explanation, the fact that philosophers are not unanimous about the death of metaphysics suggests that the claim must be scrutinized. Why accept negative theology?[14]

It is not feasible for me to here engage in a knock-down, drag-out, exhaustive dialectic to assess the arguments I will consider. Nor will I go through the various versions of negative theology seriatim. But the remarks that follow should create doubt over considering negative theology as anything more than an option.

Let me first state, following Aaron Segal, that claims in ethics and political philosophy, as well as, say, claims in the area of mind-body, are not easier to establish than claims in theology.[15] Whatever difficulties we encounter in pursuing "positive" theology, we should keep perspective: this is the nature of philosophy. Proponents of negative theology may well agree and therefore may extend their analysis to other areas such as ethics, political philosophy, and the mind-body problem. But once it is extended to other areas, negative theology is no longer a claim about theology per se. And would champions of negative theology genuinely advocate "negative" versions of ethics, political philosophy, and theories of mind? And if they would, must their opponents follow suit?

Moreover, it is not clear whether negative theology is intended as a philosophical thesis drawn from outside traditional religion or whether it is an explication of traditional religion (or traditional Judaism), a legitimate interpretive option within traditional religion (or traditional Judaism). The latter route seems unpromising. The Bible says too much about knowing God and about His attributes to make negative theology a plausible, let alone preferred, option within it. The fact that the Bible sets limits to human understanding (as in Isaiah 55:8, Job and rabbinic statements that we cannot fully understand God) does not impugn this claim any more than our knowledge that there are limits to what we can know about history implies that we can have no knowledge of history at all. Granted, endorsers of negative theology may not be interested in working within religion, but only outside, but others do not have to make this same decision. They may work from inside.[16]

Let us nonetheless turn to philosophical arguments for negative theology. Maimonides's version of negative theology boasts no persuasive arguments on its behalf. Maimonides's arguments are largely (though not exclusively) based on the problem of compositionality. God is one; He therefore has no multiplicity; but even possession of a single predicate violates unity.[17] Now is this Maimonidean fear of multiplicity and compositionality warranted? The entire notion that there can be no multiplicity in God will strike some as rooted in an outmoded medieval tradition. And even if simplicity is not a problematic concept in itself, it can be questioned whether having properties violates simplicity.[18] Furthermore, Gersonides lodged two cogent criticisms of Maimonides:[19] (1) Maimonides's negative theology cannot explain why the Torah uses certain attributes and not others—anything anyone feels like saying about God could be translated to imply that no determinables apply to God. (2) If we do not know what terms mean when applied to God, theological inferences are impossible—yet Maimonides himself makes inferences.[20] In response to (1), the advocate of Maimonidean negative theology may argue, that the Torah chooses which adjectives apply to God using political considerations[21] and in response to (2) may embrace the thesis that, indeed, all theological inferences are vitiated. But as I wrote earlier, even if negative theology is kept alive as an option by means of these responses, rejecting those arguments is also an option. (Gersonides mentions the first response.) Being dissatisfied with the replies to Gersonides's objection is certainly reasonable. And Gersonides would not only be rejecting Maimonides's arguments; he would be establishing the need for "affirmative" theology.

The most obvious casualty of our critique of Maimonides's arguments, setting aside Gersonides's attempt at refuting negative theology itself, is the attempt to establish ontological theses 1–3. However, insofar as Maimonides denies the possibility of knowing God's essence because he endorses the rejected ontological theses, *epistemological* theses 1, 2, and 3 will lack support. Since we can know about God, epistemological thesis 5 is objectionable too. As for epistemological thesis #4, that view is not rejecting the possibility of positive theology, it is rejecting particular metaphysical claims. Atheists are not negative theologians.

But cannot other arguments be given for versions of negative theology? The most obvious one appeals to a Kantian epistemology, in which human beings have no metaphysical knowledge at all, this as a result of the fact that certain conceptual structures are needed for us to have cognition at all, and those structures are applicable only to objects of experience. But it is by no means clear that one cannot infer the existence of a nonphysical being from objects of experience. Yes, there are problems with standard arguments for the existence of God, but the arguments themselves do not seem out of court, and now enjoy an impressive revival. Moreover, if it is Kant we are worried about, we have got a lot more to worry about than just not knowing God; we are ignorant of all things-in-themselves. Given that, invoking Kant would prove what many would regard as too much. We could even end up negating ontology and not just theology. (So how could we even know that we are torturing *a person* or seeing DNA?) It may be that, in spite of these difficulties, a proponent of negative theology rejects ontology in the sense outlined. But, first, any implication that the case of God is special then falls by the wayside; second, some philosophers would argue that it is justifiable to reject Kant's epistemology because of its untoward results.[22] Add to this that Kant may have been more epistemically permissive about belief in God than is commonly thought.[23]

What about discrediting metaphysics by invoking a verificationist criterion? To do so would require grappling with the numerous difficulties that beset such criteria; in addition, those who use such criteria to discredit metaphysics cannot summarily dismiss arguments for God's existence that are claimed to provide the demanded verification. There is also in the negative theology camp the idea that God is "too high," as it were, to be captured in human categories. But this assertion is precisely what needs backing, so the claim is question-begging, and even if we want to preserve some inaccessibility for God, the claim that He cannot be captured exhaustively in human categories does not entail that He cannot be known *at all* to human minds. (One of the things we may know about Him is that He revealed the Torah. And that justifies—or requires—obeisance to Halakhah.)

Perhaps negative theology is understood by its contemporary adherents in such a way as to not need argument, because it is just supposed to capture in part what they mean by "God." In other words, it is not that they start with some other conception of God—whether philosophical, scriptural, or otherwise—and then try to argue that we cannot know/say anything about God-so-understood. Rather, they just think it a straightforward conceptual truth that nothing to which we could correctly (or knowingly) apply our terms/concepts could be God.[24] How one could argue for this supposed conceptual truth is unclear. Absent good reasons for adopting negative theology, rejecting it on religious grounds seems reasonable.

What about the deontic and aretaic formulations? Merold Westphal, elucidating Heidegger, maintains that it is presumptuous to investigate God: "What we lack [goes the argument] is not so much the power to pull off this project (though, of course, we do) as the right to attempt it."[25] But why would we lack this right? Is not knowledge of God a worthy ideal, as Maimonides averred (albeit this was in tension with his negative theology)? What if God gives us "the right" to study Him? It could be asserted—and here it is the negative theology advocate who is working from within—that mystery is an important element to preserve in religious life. John Hick has effectively rebutted such arguments, however,[26] and even if mystery is desirable, there are plenty of ways in which God could be (and is) mysterious without being totally opaque to human cognition. Perhaps the most basic point, however, is that even if it is wrong to investigate God, the question whether halakhic commitment can be justified without someone violating some deontic or aretaic constraint is not the same as whether it can be justified, period. (Perhaps someone who does not attempt to understand God out of deontic and/or aretaic considerations will not personally be justified, but this is a different question.) It could further be said in support of negative theology that knowledge of God in the Bible is knowledge by acquaintance, not by description. But the case for a single-model view (acquaintance) needs to be made, and it is not an easy one to construct given the occurrence of rational arguments in the Bible.[27]

The pro-negative theology arguments have other defects. In assessing whether we have knowledge of God, the arguments for saying we cannot know God's attributes (or this-or-that about God) would probably show at most that we cannot have knowledge of God's attributes *using methods other than revelation*. But given that the conclusion should include this proviso, what justifies the move to the *unqualified* claim that one cannot have knowledge of God's attributes, period?[28] Why would we need to be able to know God's attributes independently—why cannot we work from within and know God's attributes by revelation? Why cannot we use revelation and scripturally licensed attributions? To be sure, a key question will be what the scriptural terms that we possess *mean*. If we do not know what they mean, we do not know what we are saying. But why assume we *do not* know what they mean—once arguments for negative theology have proved unpersuasive? Granted, I can think up arguments trying to show that we do not know what they mean (e.g., "clearly some statements about God are conceded to be nonliteral, so maybe all are"). But at least revelation tells us what words can aptly be used to capture God's attributes, and that puts constraints on interpretation. Moreover, there might be reasons for favoring one interpretation over another.

One might counter—and this point draws upon Statman's critique—that the statement, "God revealed what His attributes are" has no clear meaning. But it seems more accurate to say that, for the believer, the interpretive difficulty is about *how* revelation takes place, not about *whether* God revealed Himself. *In whatever manner it took place, says the believer, it has resulted in a list of attributes and a body of laws.* Even Maimonides views the *mitzvot* as effects of divine action without knowing what it means for God to reveal Himself. Knowing the effects would seem to suffice, for Maimonides, to justify and obligate a mitzvah-filled life.[29] And with that last in hand, halakhically committed individuals need not fear negative theology, though they still need to confront other objections to their claims.

Next, consider one attribute: perfection. God (if He exists) is perfect. If that is so, then all we need to know in order to know God's nature is which value judgments are correct. Our value judgments as to what constitutes perfection "reveal" what God is. If negative theology proponents deny that we can say God is perfect, there is no need for their critics to go along with that.

Another effort to ground negative theology is to invoke Kabbalah. Kabbalists would insist that we cannot know what God is. Rabbi Abraham Isaac Kook goes so far as to say that "from the standpoint of the Ein Sof, there is no difference between formulated faith and heresy."[30] But is it obligatory to accept Kabbalah? And is not speaking of the *Ein Sof* at all a kind of positive theology?

A final attempt at establishing a sweeping negative theology is to use enumerative induction, showing one by one that none of the candidates proffered as attributes of God apply to God. This would bring us into the debates between theists and atheists about the coherence of descriptions of God. But the conduct of those debates about particular attributes strongly suggests that atheists do not maintain that ascribing attributes to God is *in and of itself* is problematic.

In short, the denial of the possibility of metaphysical knowledge is a dogma. We have in negative theology a powerful trend, but merely a trend. The various versions of negative theology arise from giving reflexive credence to thinkers such as Heidegger, Kant, and Maimonides, a credence whose basis is weak. Hence, one option for preserving halakhic commitment is to question why we should accept negative theology.

But even if a sweeping negative theology is true, it does not follow that halakhic commitment falls by the wayside. After all, there are numerous other rationales besides Leibowitz's that have been proposed for performing *mitzvot*—social and cultural ones, for example, and Rynhold's primacy-of-practice argument. For present purposes, I cannot engage these other rationales, so it will have to suffice to point out that their existence casts substantial doubt on the move from a sweeping negative theology to the conclusion "no halakhic commitment." From these rationales, one may not get the idea of obligation, but one may derive the thesis that it is rational to perform *mitzvot* (not just that it is not irrational to do so, but that it is positively rational). We do many things that are not obligatory but are rational, and, moreover, the interpersonal ethical duties in the Torah may be obligatory even by extrareligious criteria. One might reject this response because of Leibowitz's thesis that human interests have no place in religion (which for Leibowitz precludes both appeals to humanistic values and appeals to utility for society). But arguing against the response in this way makes things too easy for a critic of halakhic commitment. A defender of Halakhah can discard Leibowitz's thesis that religion has no room for human interests, thus keeping the road open for justifications of halakhic practice that do not advert to revelation.

For the most part, I have not argued against negative theology, but rather against arguments for establishing it. Negative theology is an option, perhaps, but so is its denial. I have, however, pointed out some considerations that make the denial of negative theology more plausible from within a tradition, and I suggest that critics will have to rule out other rationales for *mitzvot* in order to argue that, due to negative theology, halakhic commitment makes no sense. One version of negative theology has been left standing, however: to wit, epistemological thesis 6—that although we can know some or all of God's *attributes*, we cannot know all (or any) of his *purposes and intentions*. The argument to consider next is not that commitment to Halakhah is impugned by epistemological version 6, but that the ability of human beings to make halakhic decisions is seriously undermined. I will argue that the assertion of ignorance has to be qualified, and more importantly, that such ignorance does not impugn the possibility of halakhic decision making.

Divine Intentions and Halakhic Commitment

Even if sweeping versions of negative theology have failed to persuade, so that halakhically committed Jews need not face the question of how we can claim to know anything about God or how we can assert that revelation occurred, they do have to face the question of how human beings can penetrate God's intentions and purposes; more precisely, how they can *know* they have penetrated God's mind successfully. Questions about God's intentions and purposes include why God created the world, why he chose Abraham and his descendants, why God allows evil, why God allows the righteous to suffer and the wicked to prosper, but also—most important for us—why God gave *mitzvot*. In our context, this means not, or not primarily, why did he give *mitzvot* at all, but why He gave this particular corpus, that is, what ends was He trying to achieve by individual *mitzvot* or groups of *mitzvot*. (Why these *mitzvot*, why not others?) Or did He perhaps have no end in mind other than habituating us to submit to His will? It is perplexing to find the confidence, even certainty, with which medieval thinkers posited answers to these questions, all the more so because they knew that other interpreters had posited other reasons. Rabbi Dov Linzer would seem to be correct that "a simple comparison on a random selection of *mitzvot* between the explanations of Rambam, Ramban, Chinnukh, Maharal, Ramhal, Rav and Rav Hirsch will demonstrate how subjective and speculative this attempt is." Linzer continues: "Given the lack of any objective criteria to determine that we have identified the correct underlying principle, how could we not be hesitant to use it to determine the scope of a mitzvah?" He calls this "the confidence concern."[31]

Compounding the difficulty, Talmudic sages maintained that some commandments (known as *hukkim*) have no obvious reasons—a fact that would make it difficult to determine the precise application of a law by reference to its rationale.[32] No doubt rabbinic authorities knew as well that the details of certain *mitzvot* whose rationale may seem obvious do not conform to the ostensible reason for the commandment. A good example revolves around the twofold idea common among medieval commentators that laws against causing pain to nonhuman animals are intended to refine human character, and that laws prescribing *shehitah* (slaughtering of animals) reflect this objective.[33] Among the requirements for valid *shehitah* is that the animal be slaughtered at the throat rather than the neck. If the reason for cutting by the throat is concern for human character, we would expect that eating the meat of an animal that has died of natural causes would be unproblematic and indeed preferable. Instead, eating such meat is specifically prohibited by the Torah. In addition, there is no requirement to follow laws of ritual slaughter when the animal is being killed for some purpose other than eating, for example, to provide garments.[34]

In modern discussions of *ta'amei ha-mitzvot*, in contrast to medieval ones, it often is clearly recognized that judgments about reasons for *mitzvot* are *in some way* subjective. We must ask: Is ignorance of God's intentions and purposes a problem for believers? The answer, it could be argued, is yes, because ignorance of God's intentions and purposes would make halakhic decision making very difficult. Knowing the purpose of a law would seem to be an important condition for making good decisions in cases when there is no precise precedent. As Rabbi Yitzchak Blau argues:

> Do grounds exist for assuming that teleology should exert some impact on halakhic thought? The overwhelming majority of traditional authorities assume that mitzvot reflect Divine wisdom and not just Divine will. That is, each individual mitzva attempts to bring about a particular good. If so, we would imagine that the legal details of these mitzvot should be arranged in a way that helps promote these goals. It is true that legal systems have a tendency towards general rules, even if such generalization means that the teleology of those rules is not realized in individual exceptional circumstances. . . . However, granting the need for general principles, if the gap between the purpose of the law and the detailed working out of the law grows too wide, we would have to question the wisdom of the system. In the same way, a law that builds upon the wisdom of the Divine surely must be constructed in a manner that specific legal details help bring about its desired goals. From this perspective, it makes sense that understanding the rationale for commandments would aid halakhic analysis. In other words, how could Halakha promote certain ideals if the legal development of Halakha pays no attention to those ideals?[35]

Blau points out, additionally, that "a widely accepted view contends that the Torah represents values and ideals, and that there is a 'spirit of the law' above and beyond formal requirements." He notes that "this contention depends upon viewing individual halakhot as sources for particular values" and that "such a process becomes easier when we ask questions about the teleology of mitzvot." Rabbi Emanuel Rackman states that a *posek* must ask: "What are the ends of the law that God or nature ordained and how can we be guided by these ideas in developing the law?" Rackman identified three responsa of Rabbi Joseph B. Soloveitchik ("the Rav") that, while unpublished, had been shown to him by their author. According to Rackman these responses illustrated Soloveitchik's own commitment to a teleological approach. Soloveitchik rejected this attribution, characterizing his own approach as "eidetic-normative."[36] That aside, the question of whether *teloi* should be considered in decision making seemingly should be answered in the affirmative.

But as Linzer and Blau point out, there seems to be no sure way to know what those values are.[37]

Here, then, is the rub: on the one hand, the enterprise of finding *ta'amei ha-mitzvot* seems subjective and speculative; on the other hand, repudiating claims to read God's mind as regards *mitzvot* hampers decision making because it precludes our knowing certain things that jurists, or jurists with certain philosophies of law, would normally want to incorporate (viz. considerations about the purpose of a law, and ethics).[38] Halakhic decision making would have to be based on grounds too narrow to create a sufficiently broad domain in which decisions could be made. Granted, even if lack of knowledge about God's reasons (the form of negative theology now under discussion) does pose a problem for the justification of halakhic practice, it still may be the case that, as Daniel Rynhold has argued and was mentioned earlier, a theory of *mitzvot* need not and should not be predicated on finding theoretical principles that justify Halakhah. Instead it can be founded on "the priority of practice." What justifies a practice is participating in it.[39] Other rationales for observance have been given, and perhaps create obligations. But even so, legal decision making will have to address situations not covered by existing practices and precedents.[40] Making these decisions without knowing the reasons behind the law would be a stab in the dark.

Are there *halakhot* about using purposes in decision making? That is, does Halakhah itself require knowing God's reasons as a basis for *pesikah* (halakhic decision making)? In the Talmud, Rabbi Judah and Rabbi Shimon debate whether "*darshinan ta'amei di-kera*"—whether we utilize the reasons for a commandment in deciding the law.[41] Rabbi Judah maintained no, Rabbi Shimon yes. Despite the seeming acceptance of Rabbi Judah's view by many post-Talmudic authorities, and despite the refusal on the part of some rabbinic authorities to rule on halakhic matters by invoking reasons for the commandments,[42] Blau is able to marshal example after example of rabbinic decisions that did draw on teleology (my shorthand for: the teleology of particular commandments). If we cannot fathom God's intentions and purposes, the logical admissibility of this actual practice of authorities is cast into doubt, and with it their rulings. We would be left arguing from is to ought, the actual practice of decisors to the logical tenability of their decisions.

The challenge just outlined seems formidable: We need teleology but cannot have it.[43]

And yet, responses are available, as emerges from Blau's article. First, some rulings are uncontroversial because they utilize reasons that the Torah itself had given. We know something of the divine intent, the parts God clues us in on.[44] Second, in some cases, the reason was obvious and undisputed. Recall that the name of the game, as it were, is finding reasons that would manifest divine wisdom, and in some cases this is possible. Third, it is plausible to accept teleology as support for a ruling when the ruling would be stringent rather than lenient.⁴⁵ But even in other cases, the decision could be driven by teleology.⁴⁶

For cases that do not fall under the foregoing categories, another option exists: be a formalist *about those cases*. Now the school of Talmudic analysis known as the "Brisker" school, associated with Rabbi Hayyim Soloveitchik (1853–1918) famously maintains as an across-the-board principle that Talmudists/Halakhists should deal only with the "what" (the derivation of laws from other laws) and not the "why" (the reason behind the laws). Reasons are irrelevant to *pesikah*. Blau explains: "The Brisker may claim that he agrees to all of the above [i.e., to Blau's arguments for using teleology to make halakhic rulings] but the teleology must come from within the Halakha and not from our limited human understanding of the Divine word."⁴⁷

This Brisker position does not have to derive from agnosticism about God's reasons, but could result simply from a formalistic approach to law of the sort familiar in general legal philosophy. Either way, Blau notes that: "One difficulty with this position is that it may depend upon expanding the amount of received tradition in the Oral Law and minimizing the element of human interpretation. To the degree that the received tradition consists of a system for human interpretation rather than concrete details, Chazal ["Our sages of blessed memory"— the sages of the Talmud and Midrash] would find it more difficult to reconstruct teleology from the given information."⁴⁸ It is possible that in some cases a formalist approach is well suited for the task of arriving at a ruling. Blau affirms that a large number of decisions proceed formalistically.⁴⁹ There is room for admitting formal considerations into determination of the law and ways of arriving at a ruling when teleology cannot be identified. (Jewish law would not be worse off than secular ethics, which has problems of its own in generating correct decisions.)

However, perhaps the most important counter to the attempt to undermine Halakhah via the alleged inscrutability of God's reasons is that it does not matter if God's true reason differs from the one we construct. It makes no difference if we come up with the wrong reading of the divine mind. What slogan about halakhic decision making is better known to contemporary readers than "The Torah is not in Heaven"⁵⁰? Or a close second, "A judge has only what his eyes see"?⁵¹ The sages' rulings are binding even if they fail to accurately grasp God's thoughts. Writes Abraham Maimonides, the son of Rambam:

> The general principle is this: I maintain that a judge who in his rulings exclusively follows that which is written and explicit is weak and timid. For such a course results in the abandonment of the rule "a judge has only what his eyes see." This is not as it ought to be.⁵²

And Maharal (Rabbi Betzalel Loewe of Prague) states:

> The sage has only to consider what his intellect apprehends and understands from the Talmud, and if his understanding and wisdom mislead him, he is still beloved by God when he decides in accordance with his mind's decrees, for a judge has only what his eyes see.[53]

To be sure, one might posit a distinction between, on the one hand, invoking the principles "the Torah is not in Heaven" and "a judge has only what his eyes see" to justify making a legal judgment about how certain putative precedents and analogies are to be applied or not applied, and, on the other hand, invoking those principles to justify using a personal "factual" judgment such as "God has purpose X in giving this commandment." Maybe there is no truth of the matter in the former instance but there is a truth of the matter in the latter case—so the principles in question do not apply to the second case. Recall, for example, the position in secular philosophy of law that judges create law rather than discover it. Rabbinic decisors are not engaging in fact-finding when they reason from legal data at hand, but they are doing so when they seek to identify the divine purpose, and for that reason appear to be on weaker ground. Nonetheless, while such a distinction *could* be drawn, it does not *have to be*: if God leaves legal judgments about precedents, analogies, and textual interpretations in human hands, He might also leave factual judgments in their hands. In fact, this is certainly so. For almost all legal decisions depend upon factual judgments about what circumstances obtain, judgments that in particular cases may be contested, as per the expression *"mahaloket* in *metzi'ut,"* a dispute about what the facts are.[54]

A final comment to fine-tune what I have just argued: There are two things that could be meant by saying that ta'amaei ha-mitzvot are subjective. One we can call *subjective hypothesizing*, the other *subjective response*. In subjective hypothesizing, one tries to figure out the true reason for a commandment—God's reason—but acknowledges that he or she could be wrong, that others may come up with different readings of the divine intent, and so forth. But in his articulation of subjectivity of the second kind, Rabbi Soloveitchik suggests something broader: that the whole enterprise of figuring out God's reasons is a waste, and that all we should do is figure out how one can best assimilate a mitzvah into his or her consciousness.[55] I have been speaking of subjective *ta'amei ha-mitzvot* only in the sense of subjective hypothesizing, not subjective response.

Theological Claims and Halakhah

Numerous halakhot are based upon theological ideas. Louis Jacobs assembled many such laws in a book titled *Theology in the Responsa*, albeit the title is misleading because he expressly uses the term "theology" in a manner I would call loose.[56]

Correct theologies are needed, at the very least, to set up categories of heresy, which in earlier times and far less so today have practical halakhic import. But determinations of heresy are not the only instances where *halakhot* are explicitly based upon theological claims. Hence, one could argue that not knowing what theology is correct should have barred rabbinic authorities from deriving certain *halakhot* that they in fact did derive. We can distinguish barring inferences based on speculations about reasons for *mitzvot* from barring inferences that are based upon other, wider theological assertions. Perhaps the latter is problematic even if the former is not.

Many examples of theologically grounded *halakhot* involve claims about divine providence. Certain levels of risks may be undertaken because "the Lord watches over the simple";[57] other risk levels should not be undertaken because "we do not rely on miracles."[58] Rabbi Moshe Feinstein, one of the most famous of twentieth-century rabbinic authorities, uses this latter principle to permit buying a life insurance policy, as opposed to expecting that God will provide for loved ones. Buying the policy, like working for a living, would not show lack of trust in God.[59] Some rabbis argue, though, that one must put only minimal effort into one's source of earnings, since God will provide the rest.[60] Noam Zohar shows how theological ideas drive decisions and disputes in medical ethics.[61] To take another example, according to rabbis who opposed Zionist activity in the nineteenth century and beyond, Jews must not try to hasten the messiah's arrival by practical means because God and God alone will bring the messianic age.[62] An interesting example in the Talmud involves a property owner and a tenant-farmer: whether the farmer may deduct from his rent when a field has been devastated depends upon whether the devastation is due to bad luck or divine decree.[63]

Now, what problem are such sources thought to generate? Apparently, the problem is that we cannot know which theologies are true. But once again an appeal to "the Torah is not in Heaven" and "a judge has only what his eyes see," would seem to remove the problem. To say that we must despair about taking a stance on the extent of divine intervention just because different authorities will have different theologies does not strike me as cogent. Different authorities may have different theories of metaphysical concepts such as identity across time, or different positions on ethics or politics, or on human nature, but this is hardly a reason to doubt that authorities can take positions based on their views about the relevant questions.[64] A dispute about how God acts in the world indeed can be waged rationally, using both authoritative texts and philosophical arguments. Subjective understandings of God and His interventions are no worse than other subjective elements in decision making, and their use is therefore admissible.

If there is a problem with determining laws by theology, the problem does not seem to flow from negative theology. It flows rather from what some might regard as a *wrong* positive theology. For example, one who believes that God "runs" the world by natural laws and not by direct intervention will find some of the cited cases problematic (albeit he or she will find others benign and correct).[65] The critic of the decisions under discussion will lapse into incoherence if he or she claims that we cannot know about God while at the same time expressing the view that the world is run naturalistically. In addition, despite the fact that numerous examples may be cited in which theology determines the law, such cases are hardly ubiquitous. We are dealing with a manageable set of *halakhot*, not an overwhelming phenomenon.[66]

Conclusion

In this chapter I have examined numerous ways to construe negative theology and several ways in which negative theology might be thought to undermine Halakhah. I have argued that sweeping versions of negative theology do not undermine halakhic commitment because those versions have to be established by argument, and the arguments commonly given fail. Negative theology is at best only an option. A nonsweeping version of negative theology is the version that states we cannot know God's intents and purposes in giving the law. Without an accurate teleology of *mitzvot*, one may ask, how could we apply *halakhot* to new situations? My main answer was based on the principle that when cases arise in which the teleology is unclear, halakhic decision-makers are licensed to either judge based on what they *believe* is a law's telos, or to arrive at a decision formalistically. Finally, commitment to *specific halakhot* might be undermined not by negative theology but by what strikes an observer as wrong theology. This, however, is a different problem from negative theology. And so, in sum, Halakhah can survive negative theology.[67]

Notes

1. Avi Sagi, *Jewish Religion after Theology* (Boston: Academic Studies Press, 2009), viii.

2. Rabbi Joseph B. Soloveitchik, *Fate and Destiny*, trans. Lawrence Kaplan (Jersey City, NJ: Ktav, 2000) (a translation of *Kol Dodi Dofek*), 7–8; compare the different argument for what I believe is roughly the same conclusion in Soloveitchik, "A Halakhic Approach to Suffering," in *Out of the Whirlwind: Essays on Suffering, Mourning and Human Condition*, ed. David Shatz, Joel B. Wolowelsky, and Reuven Ziegler (New York: Toras HoRav Foundation, 2002), 86–115. For discussion of *Kol Dodi Dofek*, see Moshe Sokol, "Is There a 'Halakhic' Response to the Problem of Evil?," in his *Judaism Examined: Essays in Jewish Philosophy and Ethics* (New York: Touro College Press, 2013), 67–82.

3. The best resource in English for things Leibowitzian is the anthology *Judaism, Human Values, and the State*, ed. Eliezer Goldman, trans. Yoram Navon, Zvi Jacobson, Gershon Levi, and Raphael Levy (Cambridge, MA: Harvard University Press, 1995). See especially chapter 1, "Religious Praxis: The Meaning of Halakhah," 3–29.

4. I capitalize "Halakhah" when referring to the corpus of Jewish law as a whole, but use lowercase when referring to individual laws (*halakhot*).

5. Eliezer Goldman took a related albeit distinct position. See (for a quick sample) Goldman, "On Non-Illusory Faith," in *Faith: Jewish Perspectives*, ed. Avi Sagi and Dov Schwartz (Boston: Academic Studies Press, 2013), 123–136. For critical assessments of Leibowitz by Goldman, see the three essays in Goldman, *Mehkarim ve-Iyyunim: Hagut Yehudit be-Avar u-ba-Hoveh*, ed. Daniel Statman and Avi Sagi (Jerusalem: Magnes Press, 2007), 234–261. See also Avi Sagi, *Tradition vs. Traditionalism* (Amsterdam: Rodopi, 2008), chap. 4.

6. Daniel Rynhold, *Two Models of Jewish Philosophy: Justifying Practice* (New York: Oxford University Press, 2005), esp. chaps. 4–7; Rynhold, "Letting the Facts Get in the Way of a Good Thesis: On Interpreting Rabbi Soloveitchik's Philosophical Method," *The Torah u-Madda Journal* 16 (2012–2013), 52–77 (see especially 56–57).

7. For discussions of the "religion after metaphysics" theme that are not specifically about Judaism, see Mark Wrathall, ed., *Religion after Theology* (New York: Cambridge University Press, 2003).

8. What is widely called orthopraxy would be untenable.

9. Statman, "Negative Theology and the Meaning of the Commandments in Modern Orthodoxy," *Tradition* 39, no. 1 (Spring 2005): 64. Leibowitz is somewhat evasive about whether the metaphysical statement "God exists" is meaningful. His language and certain aspects of his conceptual framework at times suggests it is. In the interviews he gave to Michael Shashar, when asked if the sentence "I believe in God" has any meaning, he answered: "I do not understand these words if they are divorced from the obligations that derive from them . . . faith in God is not what I know about God, but what I know about my obligations to God." (Yeshayahu Leibowitz, *Al Olam u-Melo'o, Sihot im Michael Shashar* [Jerusalem: Keter Publishing House, 1988], 97). As Daniel Rynhold wrote to me, "Make of that what you will!! It seems to me, though, that he has to believe in God, or else how can he have obligations to Him or make his whole distinction between *avodah lishmah* and *shelo lishmah* (worship for its own sake and worship not for its own sake)?"

10. Haym Soloveitchik, "Rupture and Reconstruction," *Tradition* 28, no. 4 (Summer 1994): 103.

11. One puzzling facet of Rambam's treatment of *mitzvot* is this. The most relevant attribute to *mitzvot* is wisdom; he says this often (see, e.g., *Guide of the Perplexed*, 3:25–28, 31). But he places wisdom among the attributes of essence (in 1:58). One would think that God's wisdom should be *explicated* on the model of 1:54, as (this is not an actual quotation from Maimonides, but my mimicking of his analysis) "God does acts such that were a human to do them, that person would be called wise." He was, I think, boxed into placing wisdom outside the attributes of action because he restricted the attributes of action to the thirteen given in Exodus 34:6–7. He did this, I think, because in turn he needed the narrative in Exodus 33 to fit with the idea that Moses needed to know something about God, and that the thirteen are all he was entitled to know ("Your ways" as opposed to "Your glory"). But if we set that consideration aside, it would have been best for him to view wisdom as

an attribute of action, and to view both laws of nature and Torah law as reflections of that. ("Glory" and "ways" appear in the Shlomo Pines translation of *Guide for the Perplexed* [Chicago: The University of Chicago Press, 1963]).

12. Maimonides implies such ignorance in *Guide of the Perplexed* 2:25 and 3:13. But, as in so many other areas, his statements with regard to these questions are prima facie not consistent and require interpretation.

13. Nicholas Wolterstorff, "How Philosophical Theology Became Possible within the Analytic Tradition in Philosophy," in *Analytic Theology*, ed. Oliver Crisp and Michael Rea (Oxford: Oxford University Press, 2011), 155–168.

14. Interesting examinations of the Continental-analytic divide in the philosophy of religion include Rea's introduction to *Analytic Theology* and Nick Trakakis, *The End of Philosophy of Religion* (London: Continuum Books, 2008).

15. In a paper titled "Contemporary Jewish Thought and Metaphysics," delivered at the Tikvah Graduate Seminar in July 2009.

16. On the legitimacy of theology viewed from both inside and outside, see Aaron Segal, "A Religiously Sensitive Philosophical Theology," *Torah u-Madda Journal* 16 (2012–13): 186–200. (The article is a review essay of Ezra Bick, *In His Mercy: Understanding the Thirteen Midot* [Jerusalem: Maggid Books and Yeshivat Har Etzion, 2011].)

17. For an intensive examination of this argument as it functions in *Guide of the Perplexed*, see Josef Stern, *The Matter and Form of Maimonides' Guide* (Cambridge, MA: Harvard University Press, 2013), chap. 6.

18. Cf. the defense of simplicity in Jeffrey E. Brower, "Simplicity and Aseity," in *The Oxford Handbook of Philosophical Theology*, ed. Thomas E. Flint and Michael Rea (New York: Oxford University Press, 2009), 105–128. (My thanks to Aaron Segal for the reference and for discussion that is reflected in the text.)

19. Gersonides, *Milhamot Hashem*, 3:3. The work was translated by Seymour Feldman, appearing as *Wars of the Lord* (Philadelphia: Jewish Publication Society, 1987). The critique of Maimonides is in volume 2, 107–115.

20. For example, for Maimonides, it follows from God's being one that God is not a body and has no affirmative attributes, and it follows from certain premises that God exists. These inferences would be vitiated by the complete equivocity and unknowability Maimonides assigns to attributes of essence that the Bible ascribes to God.

21. See *Guide* 1:26, 1:46 (at pp. 98–100 of the Shlomo Pines translation [Chicago: The University of Chicago Press, 1963]).

22. Admittedly, this formulation requires expansion; it touches on basic issues about philosophical method.

23. For a careful examination of what the historical Kant did and did not show, see Andrew Chignall, " 'As Kant Has Shown . . .': Analytic Theology and the Critical Theology," in Rea and Crisp, *Analytic Theology*, 116–135.

24. Aaron Segal suggested to me this understanding of the basis for negative theology, without endorsing it.

25. See Merold Westphal, *Overcoming Onto-Theology: Toward a Postmodern Christian Faith* (New York: Fordham University Press, 2001), chap. 1, and Michael Rea's discussion

of Westphal's critique in *Analytic Theology*, 9–11. On responses to the charge of religious presumptuousness, see Segal, "A Religiously Sensitive Philosophical Theology."

26. See John Hick, *Evil and the God of Love*, rev. ed. (New York: Harper& Row, 1978), 6–11. For more on mystery, see William Wainwright, "Theology and Mystery," in Flint and Rea, *Oxford Handbook*, 78–102. I believe that mystery is more of an element in Christianity than in Judaism.

27. See the examples in David Shapiro, "The Rationalism of Ancient Jewish Thought," *Tradition* 5, no. 2 (Spring 1963): 205–224.

28. My thanks to Aaron Segal for suggesting this formulation.

29. I set aside here thorny issues raised by Maimonides's interpreters about the role of human beings in producing Torah legislation.

Would the negative theologian's argument be that the revelation would need to be proved divine, but we cannot know the revelation is divine, and that is why we should be proponents of negative theology? If so, that is a lot different from skepticism about metaphysics or theology per se.

30. Rabbi Avraham Isaac Kook, *Orot ha-Emunah* [Lights of faith] (Jerusalem: Mossad HaRav Kook), 23–24.

31. Dov Linzer, "Tza'ar Ba'alei Chaim: A Case Study in Halakah and Values," in *Mishpetei Shalom: A Jubilee Volume in Honor of Rabbi Saul (Shalom) Berman*, ed. Yamin Levy (New York: Yeshivat Chovevei Torah Rabbinical School, 2011), 399–400.

32. See Babylonian Talmud (hereafter BT), *Yoma* 67b.

33. See, for example, Moses Nahmanides, commentary to Deuteronomy 22:6, and in particular his interpretation of *Genesis Rabbah* 44:1. Kant gave the same explanation of why we should not be cruel to animals, in response to the fact that nonhuman animals could not act from application of the categorical imperative.

34. See J. David Bleich, *Contemporary Halakhic Problems* (New York: Ktav and Yeshiva University Press, 1989), 3: 205–217. Rabbi Bleich writes: "Yet, as is well known, the ramifications and applications of Jewish law in fulfilling any specific commandment frequently are not coextensive with the rationale underlying the precept. Thus, it cannot be assumed that other modes of killing animals are proscribed by Jewish law particularly if the method is painless" (217). One may ask *why* the rationale is not applied fully, and why the detail that seems contrary to the assumed rationale does not undermine the claim to have found the correct rationale.

35. Yitzchak Blau, "Ta'amei Ha-Mitzvot, Halakhic Analysis, and Brisker Conceptualization, "in *That Goodly Mountain*, ed. Reuven Ziegler, Shira Schreir, Dov Karoll, and Yitzhak S. Recananti (Alon Shevut, Israel: Yeshivat Har Etzion, 2012), 199. See also Moshe Lichtenstein, "'What' Hath Brisk Wrought: The Brisker Derekh Revisited," *Torah u-Madda Journal* 9 (2000): 1–18.

36. For a close analysis of the Rackman-Soloveitchik material, see Lawrence J. Kaplan, "From Cooperation to Conflict: Rabbi Professor Emanuel Rackman, Rav Joseph B. Soloveitchik, and the Evolution of American Modern Orthodoxy," *Modern Judaism* 30, no. 1 (2010): 46–68.

37. Linzer, "Tza'ar Ba'alei Chaim," 400.

38. Even Leibowitz invokes values, as when he argues for changes in the status of women. Not knowing God's reasons for allowing evil could lead human beings to distrust their own ability to recognize an adequate justification. In turn this would impede moral decision making. But the existence of halakhic rules can greatly mitigate this concern. See Ira M. Schnall, "Sceptical Theism and Moral Scepticism," *Religious Studies* 43 (2007): 43–69.

39. Rynhold, *Two Models*, chaps. 5–7.

40. This uncodifiability thesis is argued for by Rynhold in *Two Models*, chap. 2.

41. See BT, *Shabbat* 128b, *Bava Metzi'a* 32a–33a.

42. The case over which Rabbi Judah and Rabbi Shimon disagree concerns the Torah's commandment to give relief to an animal that is suffering under its burden. Can we derive from this a general prohibition against causing pain to animals in any form?

43. As Daniel Rynhold suggested the challenge be formulated.

44. Examples: sitting in a *sukkah*; observing Shabbat. I suppose that in the abstract one could argue that the reasons should not be taken literally, or that the reasons were created by humans to justify existing practices. These responses are not tempting and are, to invoke my earlier category, merely options.

45. This last sentence may raise a red flag to some readers, especially those aware of Sidney Morgenbesser's quip about Jewish ethics: Jewish ethics says, "can implies don't." (This is a parody of Kant's "ought" implies "can.") Why accept a theory in which nay-saying is valued over leniency? Do we not learn that "the power of permitting is greater" (i.e., it is preferable to teach the extent of a leniency than of a stringency; *Berakhot* 60a)? So although the point captures some actual decision making, I decline to stress it.

46. See also Linzer, "Tza'ar Ba'alei Chaim," 388–390. Rabbinic figures such as Rabbi Moses Sofer (known as Hatam Sofer) and Rabbi Ezekiel Landau (known as Noda be-Yehudah) developed such criteria for applying reasons. Blau points out as well that sometimes authorities read a reason into the law post facto, after knowing what the law is.

47. Blau, "Ta'amei Ha-Mitzvot," 100.

48. Ibid.

49. See especially ibid., 108.

50. BT, *Bava Metzi'a* 59b.

51. BT, *Niddah* 20b, *Sanhedrin* 6b, *Bava Batra* 130b. This principle is noted by Linzer, "Tza'ar Ba'alei Chaim," 400.

52. "Responsa of Rabbi Abraham ben ha-Rambam," 97. This translation and the Maharal translation that follows are found in Jonathan Sacks, "Creativity and Innovation in Halakhah," in *Rabbinic Authority and Personal Autonomy*, ed. Moshe Z. Sokol (Northvale, NJ: Jason Aronson, 1992), 130–132.

53. Maharal, *Hiddushei Halakhot ve-Aggadot* to *Sotah* 22a.

54. The idea of leaving matters in human hands and letting judges see things through their own eyes coheres well with the fact that Judaism values and encourages *mahaloket* (dispute). See, for example, David Shatz, "Interpretive Pluralism," in *The Jewish Political Tradition: Volume One: Authority*, ed. Michael Walzer, Menachem Lorberbaum, and Noam Zohar, co-editor Ari Ackerman (New Haven, CT: Yale University Press, 2000), 339–344.

55. See Soloveitchik, "May We Interpret *Hukim?*," in *The Man of Faith In the Modern World*, adapted by Rabbi Abraham R. Besdin (Hoboken, NJ: Ktav, 1989), 91–99. Cf. the related discussion in Soloveitchik, *The Halakhic Mind* (New York: Seth Press, 1986), 91–99.

56. See Jacobs, *Theology in the Responsa* (London: Routledge and Kegan Paul, 1975), x. He uses "theology" to refer to beliefs, where the subject matter of the belief is defined broadly. Because of this broad definition many of Jacobs's examples are not truly as advertised.

57. See, e. g., BT, *Yevamot* 12b, *Shabbat* 129b. "The Lord watches over the simple" is in Psalms 116:6.

58. See, for example, BT, *Pesahim* 64b; Jerusalem Talmud *Shekalim* 6:3, and *Yoma* 1:4.

59. Rabbi Moshe Feinstein, *Iggerot Moshe, Orah Hayyim* 2, *responsum* 111; also ibid., 4:48,78–80.

60. Rabbi Eliyahu Dessler, *Strive for Truth*, ed. and annotated by Aryeh Carmell (New York: Feldheim, 1978), passim but especially 2:237–256. The book is a translation of *Mikhtav Me-Eliyahu* (Letter from Eliyahu).

61. See Noam Zohar, *Alternatives in Jewish Bioethics* (Albany: State University of New York Press, 1977).

62. See Aviezer Ravitzky, *Messianism, Zionism and Jewish Religious Radicalism*, trans. Michael Swirsky and Jonathan Chipman (Chicago: The University of Chicago Press, 1996), 1–144. A key text is a passage on *Ketubbot* 111a, discussed by Ravitzky, 211–234.

63. BT, *Bava Metzi'a* 106a. David Berger pointed out this example to me.

64. See Eli Hirsch, "Identity in the Talmud," *Midwest Studies in Philosophy* 23 (1999): 166–180. However, in "Contemporary Jewish Thought and Metaphysics" (n. 15 above), Aaron Segal argues that the Talmudic disputes that Hirsch is trying to explain are not disputes about metaphysics.

65. Maimonides spoke of divine action, but construed this concept naturalistically. See especially *Guide of the Perplexed* 1:54, 2:48.

66. Some rulings that seem to be driven by metaphysics could be approached by reductionism: simply translate the theological teachings into norms. The theological statement, "God watches over the simple" could mean "this is the norm: a person can assume a certain level of risk" (a vintage Leibowitzian position, by the way, as Daniel Rynhold noted to me). Whether or not it is cogent in the case at hand, reductionism will not work across the board.

67. My thanks to Yitzchak Blau, Daniel Rynhold, Aaron Segal, and Alex Sztuden for their comments on an earlier version of this essay, and to Michael Fagenblat for extensive correspondence during the planning stages.

FOURTEEN

The Stylus and the Almond: Negative Literary Theologies in Paul Celan

ADAM LIPSZYC

The experience of modernity generally, and the Jewish experience in particular, involves multiple transformations of the sacred that neither break with the religious elements of the past nor simply extend them. What we find in modernity, rather, is the presence of the sacred in multiple secular forms. As Carl Schmitt famously argued, modern political concepts such as the sovereignty of the state are one prominent way through which theological concepts live on in secular life without being clearly affirmed or denied.[1] There is something simplistic and ultimately misleading in Schmitt's view, however, insofar as it suggests that the historical passage from theology to politics seems to involve no great loss of meaning in the process of translation, as if politics were another language by which to speak theology and thereby convey the same meanings. Leaving aside whether this is a reasonable view of modern political concepts, is it the case for the passage from theology to literature? How does literature at once arrogate but also modify the sense of the sacred in modern Jewish experience? These are the questions I would like to approach through a reading of two poems by Paul Celan, for Celan's theologico-literary negativity allows us to contemplate some of what is at stake in the distension of God that marks modern Jewish experience. But to get this quasi-theological bearing on Celan's poems, let us look at two Jewish variations of the idea that modern literature neither breaks with nor extends theology but involves the transformation of the sacred in various secular forms.

Having had the publisher send a copy of his book on baroque to the author of *Political Theology*, in a respectful letter of December 9, 1930, Walter Benjamin wrote to Schmitt: "You will very quickly notice how much this book owes to you when it comes to the presentation of the seventeenth-century doctrine of sovereignty. Perhaps I am also allowed to mention that in your later works as well, especially in *Dictatorship*, I have found the adequacy of my approach to the philosophy of art confirmed by your philosophy of state."[2] In a curriculum vitae written at the beginning of 1928, Benjamin explained that in his analyses of literary works he wants to cross the borders between various disciplines and strive toward their "integration," in order to present the work under consideration as an expression of "the religious, metaphysical, political and economic tendencies of the age," and he explicitly pointed out that in this respect he partly follows Carl Schmitt whose efforts in the field of analysis of "political entities" Benjamin found analogous to his own project.[3]

Yet, Schmitt's project was more radically defined than the general notion of "integration" might suggest. Schmitt's idea was to contribute to the understanding of political notions by recognizing them as secularized categories of theology. When Benjamin points to the alleged parallelism between his own literary research and Schmitt's analyses of politics and refers to the notion of "integration" of disciplines, he avoids stating the full analogy between their projects—the analogy, which would rely on the very idea of analogy. The proper analogue of Schmitt's strategy in literary research would be a strategy that assumes the full analogy between literary creations and theological constructs, or, in other words, that recognizes literature as a secularized theology. This, however, is not a strategy that Benjamin adopts—neither in the book on baroque nor anywhere else. This is obviously not to say that theology does not play any role in his analyses of literature. On the contrary, it is crucial for them. This makes the difference between the deployment of theology by Schmitt and Benjamin all the more noteworthy. Schmitt draws clear-cut analogies between the omnipotent God and the political sovereign or between the category of miracle and the idea of exception—and so he replaces the coherent, closed world of theology with an equally coherent and equally closed world of despotic politics. By contrast, Benjamin describes literary works created in a torn world of secularization where the theological machines have stopped working properly and no longer give a sense of security. He does not regard works of literature as secular analogues of theological treatises, because this is something of which literature is not capable. And yet the full understanding of those works requires that we recognize them as creations that express the human condition in the world where theology is broken, where the answers are gone but the questions linger. Works of literature inherit the theological impulse—in particular, the dream of redemption—but they have no solutions at hand; rather, they document the collapse of those patterns, while at the same time looking for their own tentative, broken solutions. A theologico-literary perspective, modeled on Benjamin's actual approach, can never be fully analogous to the Schmitt's theologico-political perspective. It must account both for the partial survival and for the crumbling of the stable theological structures in the medium of literature. Let us see if we can make the idea of literary theology a bit more precise.

At a memorial service devoted to Franz Rosenzweig that took place in January 1930 in Jerusalem, Benjamin's friend Gershom Scholem tried to characterize the situation of theology at the time when *The Star of Redemption* was published. For our purposes, it is worthwhile to quote *in extenso* the most powerful passage of his talk:

> Theology is not a science of the essence of the divinity beyond creation but consists rather of the eternal questions of love and will, wisdom and ability, judgment and mercy, justice and death, creation and redemption. Theology has concrete questions. In time this theology took on an alien cast, in our times astoundingly abstract and pallid, as if abandoned by its subjects which went off in search of another field. . . . Is it at all surprising that with theology's status at its nadir, even problems no one could doubt belong to it have fled and have ensconced themselves in art and literature? Dostoyevsky was already well aware of this in *The Idiot*. And if we consider undertakings of a clearly theological nature such as Marcel Proust's *A la recherché du temps perdu* or Franz Kafka's *The Trial* and *The Castle*, it is amazing that the theologians had no feeling whatever of *tua res agitur*—that their concern is taken up here—but rather have allowed this discovery to be made by discerning critics. It is obvious, then, that in our time theological issues have vanished from sight, have become concealed—lights that cast their light inward and are not seen from outside. The divinity, banished from man by psychology and from the world by sociology, no longer wanting to reside in the heavens, has handed over the throne of justice to dialectical materialism and the seat of mercy to psychoanalysis and has withdrawn to some hidden place and does not disclose Himself. Is He truly undisclosed? Perhaps this last withdrawal is His revelation. Perhaps God's removal to the point of nothingness was a higher need, and He will reveal His kingship only to a world that has been emptied, in the sense of "I gave access to them that asked not, I was found by those who sought me not." That is the abandonment and the question from which *The Star of Redemption* appeared to Rosenzweig, and to him as a Jew it appeared in its Jewish form, as a Star of David.[4]

Scholem pictures the discipline of theology in its contemporary state as hollowed and dry, while actual theological problems seek their refuge in the element of literature. It is the job of the "discerning critics" to uncover them: the most prominent of them being, for Scholem, his friend Walter Benjamin who devoted much attention to the writers mentioned in the passage. But this is certainly not all. For this very shift between "genres"—the passage of the theological issues from official theology to literature—is now presented by Scholem as reflecting a far more dramatic change: not just a wandering, but a radical withdrawal of the divine. But if this is so, then two possibilities seem to open themselves before us. Scholem does mention both of them in the conclusion of the passage, but he is too careless or too sly to distinguish between them. One possibility is that the withdrawal of the divine, the disappearance of its traces from the empty world and human interiority, is a necessary moment of preparation for a new, perhaps more credible revelation. This seems to be the path of Rosenzweig himself who, in his great book, saw to it that the elements of his universe (God, world, man) should first sink into the nothingness of mutual separation and ignorance and only then turn toward each other. The other possibility is that the withdrawal itself is a kind of revelation. As far as the relations between literature and theology are concerned, it is crucial which path we choose. Namely, if we take the first path, then together with the revelation of the Star of David theology comes back to its own element, leaving literature behind as a temporary refuge. If we take the other path, literature becomes now the only element of the theological. But if Scholem is right in his suggestion that the passage from the theological to the literary reflects the general withdrawal of the divine, then the theology that critics may discern in literature must always be a more or less negative one.

Although he did not disclose his own feelings in his eulogy, Scholem was not convinced by Rosenzweig's revelation. He might have hoped that somebody—perhaps himself, perhaps Benjamin when brought to Palestine—would travel the first path more successfully. For the time being, however, he tried the second path and attempted to become "a discerning critic" in respect to one of the authors he mentions. The crucial result of the attempt is his famous idea of the "nothingness of revelation"—revelation as being valid but with no meaning—which both sums up his reading of Kafka's work and restates his vision of the presence of the divine in the contemporary world as sketched in the eulogy for Rosenzweig: the divine is present only in literature, but there also only as "nothingness."[5] It is not my intention to analyze Scholem's reading of Kafka and his famous debate with Benjamin on this point: this is the central topic of Agata Bielik-Robson's essay in the present volume. For our purposes—that is, in order to closer define the idea of "literary theology"—it is enough to remind the reader that after some preliminary hesitation Benjamin opted against the idea of the nothingness of revelation. He did not deny the theological dimension of Kafka's work, and yet he was convinced that Scholem's idea posits too strong a theological presence. In other words, if Scholem discerns in Kafka's work quite stable, even though very negative theology, Benjamin feels that this negativity should destabilize the very status of theology as such. Thus, if Scholem claimed that at the center of Kafka's work one can discern the indecipherable scripture, identical with revelation, which withdrew to the state of nothingness, Benjamin suggested that we should think of Kafka's work as presenting a universe where scripture is truly lost and what remains is only *a rumor* about the revealed truth, where truth can take only the form of a rumor about itself. Famously, Benjamin tried to present this state of affairs by referring to the concepts of Halakhah and Aggadah: Kafka's work is composed solely of the Aggadic element, the substance of rumor about the Law. This conceptualization can help us understand that Benjamin is *not* claiming that Kafka's work leaves theology behind and migrates into the sphere of the purely aesthetic. It remains Aggadic even if there is no revelation to comment upon or, more precisely, if there is only rumor about it. This is why Benjamin claims that Kafka's writings are "similar to literature."[6] In this overwhelmingly simple formula, he seems to be putting his finger precisely on what we are looking for in the present analysis. Kafka's writings are not coded theological treatises, nor are they simply literary works. They are only similar to literature. They are unable to lock themselves in the beautiful appearance of the literary work, for they keep reopening themselves in the Aggadic gesture of a commentary. They are not chained to revelation with an umbilical cord, but they do have a navel, a scar that prevents them from rounding up and turning into the purely aesthetic.[7]

With this Benjaminian correction of Scholem's reading in mind, we may now ask the general question about the nature of literary theology. Kafka famously claimed that writing is "a kind of prayer." This formula seems to correspond rather well to the almost equally well-known passage from the *Meridian* speech by Paul Celan, where one of the most central categories of poetic endeavors is identified as "attentiveness," which is then defined after Malebranche (quoted, as it happens, from Benjamin's essay on Kafka!) as "the natural prayer of the soul."[8] And yet it is crucial to point out that in one of the notes for the *Meridian* speech this very same Paul Celan rather ironically comments on Kafka's definition of writing as a kind of prayer: "Also this means, first and foremost, not *praying*, but *writing*: you cannot do it with your hands folded."[9] Kafka's formula read *together with* Celan's witty commentary—and *only* with this commentary—can become the motto for all literary theology that takes seriously its literary nature and does not want to be merely theology in disguise. When in his essay on Rosenzweig, Scholem complains about the sterility of the official theology and refers to literature as the refuge of true theological issues, he comes dangerously close to the claim that the true theology is present in literature in quite a solid form, even if it is the radically negative, Kafkan theology of revelation withdrawn to its nothingness. If we followed this path, we would end up with a rather precise literary equivalent of Schmitt's claims about politics. But Scholem's general claim about the relations between theology and literature remains in force if only we modify it in a way parallel to the Benjaminian correction of his reading of Kafka. Literature may be the continuation of theology by other means, but the very passage into the dense, inescapably ambiguous element of literature, into the medium where one cannot function with one's hands folded, must result in a very ambiguous, broken theology that comes into being only as the process of writing develops. The space of literary theology is the space where revelation can at best exist as a haunting specter, as a rumor about itself. In this space, the inherited forms of the contact with transcendence get lost, traditional solutions are gone, and the writer must do everything on his own. And yet what she does will indeed be a kind of prayer, it will never quite be literature but only *similar* to literature, it will be a literature with a navel. Literary writing cuts, questions, distorts, and spectralizes theological structures and then, moving among the ruins and specters, in the whirl of ironies and revocations, once again tries the impossible gesture of transcendence. And because the results of this operation must be different in every writer and in every single text, strictly speaking there is no literary theology. There are only literary theologies in the plural.

Having sketched this general framework I want to take a closer look at the negative literary theologies in the work of Paul Celan himself. It is quite evident that among the numerous and very divergent sources of inspiration for this work, theology played a key role. More precisely, it is various mystical theological ideas that Celan was inspired by, derived both from the Christian and Jewish mystical traditions. Most prominently, he would refer to Meister Eckhart and Angelus Silesius on the one hand, and to the Kabbalah as mediated through the writings of Gershom Scholem on the other. In this cluster of theological ideas, the tradition of negative theology seems to be particularly prominent. This is evidently true of the Christian line of influence on Celan and, only a bit less evidently, true of the Jewish one. There is quite a thick bundle of Kabbalistic concepts and images of enormous significance for Celan—among them the image of the tree of sefirot and sexual symbolism seem to be most important—that cannot be classified as belonging to the universe of negative theology without any reservations. And yet, the way they are used and purposely distorted in his poetry often reveals their negative lining or radically inverts them, so that if they suggest any presence at all, it is—at best—through negative images of separation and absence.

There are at least three good reasons for Celan's predilection for negative theology. We already know the first reason, as it has less to do with Celan himself than with the very nature of literary theology as defined herein. As we have seen, if theological issues are to be undertaken in the literary medium and if the traditional theological mechanisms of the positive contact with the divine are no longer visible, then every literary theology must be negative at least to some extent. Celan is very conscious of this when he writes in a note for the *Meridian* speech: "The poem knows the *argumentum e silentio* . . . God of the poem is unquestionably a *deus absconditus*."[10] But then it must be emphasized that no literary theology can be satisfied even with the inherited patterns of negative theology, either—just like Benjamin could not be satisfied with Scholem's reading of Kafka—and so we may say that from the literary-theological perspective, no negative theology can be negative enough. The second reason is an extension or historical concretization of the first one and it is still by no means specific to Celan. As both Scholem and Benjamin understood, the negativity of Kafka's residual theology can be seen as a reflection of his position vis-à-vis the Jewish tradition, as an expression of the deadly weakening of the authority of this tradition as such, at least in the specific German-Jewish milieu in which Kafka wrote and to which both Scholem and Benjamin belonged. Certainly, Celan—both by birth and by choice—was situated in the same line, one generation later and a few more steps deeper into the negative. But then, obviously, it is not just the question of quantitative difference: and this is what brings us to the third reason of his predilection for negative theology, the one that is much more specific for Celan himself. For it is almost trivial to notice that what defines Celan's universe is not only and not primarily the crisis of tradition losing its authority, but the radical break of the Shoah. Celan tries to find and write his way in the world after this break that questions the presence of the divine, the status of the human, and the possibilities of language in a new, unexpected way, which inevitably produces new forms of literary theology of a radically negative sort.

The presence of twisted and distorted theological patterns can be discerned in almost everything Celan wrote. Particularly clear references to Kabbalah appear, say, in a cycle of poems included in the *Fadensonnen* volume (1968), whereas Meister Eckhart's presence is particularly visible in the closing poems of the *Lichtzwang* volume (1970).[11] However, if one wants to enter the multiple world of Celan's negative literary theologies and begin studying its peculiarities, the obvious book to turn to is *Die Niemandsrose* (1963), which already in its title refers to the (possibly divine) Nobody or No-one and the rose of Angelus Silesius and/or the Kabbalistic rose that stands for the Shekhinah. Two poems from this collection present most of the problems and intricacies of Celan's literary-theological world in striking fashion. Here is the first one in the German original, followed by Michael Hamburger's translation:

Psalm
Niemand knetet uns wieder aus Erde und Lehm,
niemand bespricht unsern Staub.
Niemand.

Gelobt seist du, Niemand.
Dir zulieb wollen

wir blühn.
Dir
entgegen.

Ein Nichts
waren wir, sind wir, werden
wir bleiben, blühend:
die Nichts-, die
Niemandsrose.

Mit
dem Griffel seelenhell,
dem Staubfaden himmelswüst,
der Krone rot
vom Purpurwort, das wir sangen
über, o über
dem Dorn.

Psalm
No one moulds us again out of earth and clay,
no one conjures our dust.
No one.

Praised be your name, no one.
For your sake
we shall flower.
Towards
you.

A nothing
we were, are, shall
remain, flowering:
the nothing-, the
no-one's rose.

With
our pistil soul-bright,
our stamen heaven-ravaged,
our corolla red
with the crimson word which we sang
over, O over
the thorn.[12]

In the space of this famous but persistently mysterious poem, a highly ambiguous, negative literary theology crystallizes itself in the rhythm of maddening paradoxes. At the same time, it is also the space of reflection on the very condition of theology and literature—and on their possible relations—in the contemporary world. Let us see how it works.

Psalm is based on a conceit, a pun, which accounts both for its power and its weakness: it is a sort of a literary-theological joke. While we are reading it, nothing (literally, nothing) seems to be warning us that we are heading for a trap. The picture is bleak, but rather equivocal. Celan seems to lead the reader into a space where the history that began with the creation of man turned full circle and so we are lying now in and as dust; no one forms us again out of clay, no one makes us come to life again by means of his/her word and breath. We are less than golems: no word, no breath, but no shape either, only dust. It seems, then, that not only the whole work of Moses has been undone, not only is the Torah, the Law, the revelation gone, but even the creation of man has been revoked. But this particular novelty may be only apparent, if we assume what many have more or less implicitly suggested and what Hermann Cohen expressed most clearly when he defined revelation as the creation of reason.[13] If, as Cohen also assumed, rationality is bound together with language, then the true meaning of this elegant formula is that the moment God has breathed life into the nostrils of the human golem was also the moment when the ability to speak, think, and pass moral judgments was given to him—and so it should be seen as the moment of revelation, the revelation given to Adam, to use Rosenzweig's phrase.[14] But if this is so, then the disappearance of revelation and the disappearance of the human are just two aspects of the same event, summarized in the disappearance of the word as such. There is no one to change the situation.

The explosive pun comes with the first line of the second stanza. The *niemand*, "no one" of the first stanza turns into a possibly divine *Niemand* written with uppercase. This forces the reader to reread the first stanza as a positive statement about *Niemand* who does mold us again and does impart his creative word to us. But then again, no one (literally, no one) can stop us from reading the first stanza the way we read it first with *niemand* in lowercase in the second line of the first stanza. Thus, none of the readings of the first stanza is decisive, and so we must bear their aporetic coexistence.

There seem to be two paths that may lead beyond this impasse. If we were to walk the first, we would have to develop the following reasoning. In the first stanza, Celan does, indeed, invoke a world in which God has abandoned creation and revelation, a world almost completely devoid of the word. Almost: for there are the residual powers of language that the poet is carefully trying to make use of, beginning already with the first stanza. This can be observed in the subtle use he makes of the letter case. The uppercase of the *Niemand* in the first line of the first stanza is determined by its placement at the beginning of a grammatical sentence and so we cannot know if the word would be written with uppercase otherwise. The lowercase in the second line seems to confirm the guess that even the first *Niemand* was a pronoun rather than a name and hence, in itself, it is a lowercase word. This suggestion is, seemingly, not refuted by the uppercase in the third line of the first stanza, which forms a one-word sentence. But it is precisely the third line where the residual powers of language begin to work. For this isolated repetition of the grammatical subject of the first sentence (i.e., of the two first lines of the first stanza) prepares the chemical crystallization of the pronoun *niemand* into the name *Niemand*, the crystallization that will occur suddenly in the first line of the second stanza. Thus, under the cover of grammatical and typographical rules—and, indeed, making the guerilla, underground use of them—Celan is taking the step from absence to presence and recognizes *niemand* as the quite solid *Niemand*. And so, if in the third stanza we ourselves are called a "Nothing" that was, is, and will be, the rose of Nothing and No-one, then following the same line of reasoning we might say that the age-old rules of negative theology are at play here, intact after all the historical turbulences. We, the dust formed into a blossoming rose, the Nothing, stand vis-à-vis the big, divine No-one or Nothingness. This "standing" is sometimes pious and sometimes resistant, as we face the silent, mysterious divinity in the empty universe. We might add one more twist to this reading by suggesting a mystical union or identity between the two types of nothingness. Thus, the linguistic-theological process would result in our own divinity, a suggestion that we do find stated in negative theologians such as Meister Eckhart. The uppercase of the "Nothing" in the first line of the third stanza, as well as well the very possibility of reading the name *die Niemandsrose*, the Rose-of-No-One, as "the No-One blossoming *as* a Rose" rather than "the Rose belonging to No-One," might support this twist, but its validity would have to remain undecided. Be that as it may, on this reading as a whole, Celan's poem would be presenting us with a universe where, in line with Scholem's essay on Rosenzweig and his analysis of Kafka's work, absence can be discovered as presence and the nothingness of revelation looms over us, recognized and rediscovered thanks to the powers of language.

The second path that leads out of the aporia between the first and second stanza is much easier to describe. In this case, the argument would simply rest on the possibility that all this is just a macabre joke and that what is being ridiculed here is precisely negative theology itself. On such a reading, the rhetoric of negative theology is used in the poem only to stress the flatness of our abandonment and the impossibility of finding any meaning in it. No-one is no-one and nothing was, is, and will be a nothing whatever the case you write the words with. The title, the biblical references, the pious praise of the first line of the second stanza: all these are just elements of a bitterly sarcastic discourse. The image of the rose, so strongly embedded in the mystical and poetic traditions, would play the same role. For the rose is made of dust (*Staub*) and the dust still persists in its stamen (*Staubfaden*). The stamen is *himmelwüst*, heaven-ravaged or heaven-waste, which clearly suggests that the rose is sterile just like the empty heavens of this bleak universe, but also—possibly—that it is the rose of the desert (*Wüste*), which is not a flower at all, but a sand formation produced by wind. If the mechanisms of negative theology are based on the idea of inversion, the sly conceit of inverting the absence into a presence, then the ironic, inverted use of them prevents the inversion from happening and so the last mechanisms that might lead us out of the desert are simply disarmed.

I do not think it is very productive to follow either of these two paths to the end. The first reading reduces literature to (negative) theology. The second reduces it to antitheology. Instead of choosing either of these reductions, it is much wiser to stay between them. If we take this advice, we will see Celan leading us through a strange, unstable, ambiguous domain where the nothingness of revelation is not substantial enough to reconstruct the mechanisms of negative theology, but it is not absent enough to be seen as gone for good. It is also a space where we cannot be certain of our own existence: we might be nothing and we might be a Nothing that, moreover, praises no-one—or No-one—or stubbornly opposes the empty sky. But in the end *wir bleiben*, we remain, as the third line of the third stanza tells us, if only cut out from the grammatical clause it belongs to, a manipulation encouraged by the versification of the poem itself. Although only as a sterile rose made of dust, we do remain with our residual linguistic capabilities. And so out of the dynamic field of forces stretched between contradictory possibilities, there grows a complex and paradoxical, and yet consistent structure of the literary theology of the poem.

The key to this structure can be found in the fourth stanza. This key is the noun of the second line of the stanza, that is, the word *der Griffel*. In its botanical sense, it does mean the pistil of the flower, in this case the rose, but it also means the stylus, the writing instrument. Celan must have had this meaning in mind when writing the poem, as he had recently translated the *Griffel-Ode*, the *Stylus Ode* by Ossip Mandelshtam to whose memory *Die Niemandsrose* is dedicated.[15] Thus, in the desert where we, the biologically sterile dust-roses, remain with our remnants of linguistic capabilities—we write. Apart from all other meanings of this proclamation of the practice of writing, I think it should be read in the context of Celan's comment on Kafka's idea that writing is a kind of prayer. Thus, if one is praying here, or singing psalms, it is through writing only, which also means: independently of any traditional theological mechanisms. But what kind of writing is that?

The answer might be found in the two last lines of the poem. The fourth stanza uses the clearly Christological imagery of crown, purple, and thorn. But it would be a mistake to claim that by referring to this imagery Celan wants to restate the redemptive idea of the suffering God or even inscribe Jewish suffering of the Shoah into this pattern. Rather, by playing with the vision of Christ as the Word, Celan is developing his own literary-theological vision of linguistic practice. Thus, a Jewish literary theology springs from a deconstruction of the Christological pattern.

Celan develops the idea and practices it at the same time. For at the critical point he makes his language break in the painful caesura of the O appearing in the penultimate line of the poem. We write and sing just above the thorn, and so we make our language surround the point of pain with a circle of words, touch it for a moment and then break so that it forms a round crown soaked with purple blood. This redness does not make the rose more organic and less sterile—writing is *not* conception and stylus is *not* a phallus—but the caesura of O is not for nothing. Or it is—for Nothing. This writing practice, this literary-theological, natural prayer of the soul—the stylus is "soul-bright"!—culminates in the moment of attentiveness for the point of break in language, the actual *argumentum e silentio*, which makes our pain present in the silent caesura. It is here that Celan effectively goes beyond the infinite wavering between negative theology and its sarcastic refutation. Stepping beyond the perhaps all-too simple pun on the negative pronouns, which defines the desert-like field of forces, but does not offer any solution, he reaches the actual, though fleeting, negative transcendence in the break of language. Thus, he turns the poem into an ethical linguistic act of witnessing to pain: language realizes the remnants of its ethical possibilities where it tears itself apart, for otherwise it covers what should be witnessed for with its unholy positivity. The subject that *bleibt*, that remains, in Celan's universe is the witness who not so much redeems as he testifies to pain in the silent caesuras of language. And—according to Celan's famous formula from *Aschenglorie*—"No-one" bears witness for the witness himself.[16] The purposefully ambiguous formula expresses the absolute, desperate abandonment of the witness and yet confirms that his negative, silent testimony is able to cut or mark the sphere of immanence. This confirmation is highly paradoxical, for it is received at the price of giving up any stable theological guarantees: the testimony may hope to be effective only when it accepts its own groundlessness. And this literary-theological, perfectly singular, attentive act of witnessing to the singularity of suffering is the only act of transcendence—or should we rather say "of weak transcendence" or even "of non-immanence"?—that is possible in this world.

The literary theology of the second poem I want to discuss shows this perhaps even more clearly. It also tells us more about the nature of the literary-theological testimony by arranging a peculiar clash between the theological and the historical. Here is the German original, followed again by Michael Hamburger's translation:[17]

Mandorla
In der Mandel—was steht in der Mandel?
Das Nichts.
Es steht das Nichts in der Mandel.
Da steht es und steht.

Im Nichts—wer steht da? Der König.
Da steht der König, der König.
Da steht er und steht.

    Judenlocke, wirst nicht grau.

Und dein Aug—wohin steht dein Auge?
Dein Aug steht der Mandel entgegen.
Dein Aug, dem Nichts stehts entgegen.
Es steht zum König.
So steht es und steht.

    Menschenlocke, wirst nicht grau.
    Leere Mandel, königsblau.

Mandorla
In the almond—what dwells in the almond?
Nothing.
What dwells in the almond is Nothing.
There it dwells and dwells.

In Nothing—what dwells there? The King.
There the King dwells, the King.
There he dwells and dwells.

    Jew's curl, you'll not turn grey.

And your eye—on what does your eye dwell?
On the almond your eye dwells.
Your eye, on Nothing it dwells.
Dwells on the King, to him remains loyal, true.
So it dwells and dwells.

    Human curl, you'll not turn grey.
    Empty almond, royal-blue.

If we begin by looking only at the first two stanzas of the poem, we will be certainly struck by their ostensible simplicity: the sequence of questions and answers, the repetitions, the three nouns, the single verb (*stehen*, literally, to stand). The simple form seems to refer the reader to a nursery rhyme, to a child playing with words and making up a singsong. This "formal regression" is not unusual for Celan and, in particular, for *Die Niemandsrose*, which opens with the great poem *Es war Erde in ihnen*, written almost in a form of a song or a chant, including a sort of mock school exercise in conjugating the verb *graben* (to dig).[18] This should come as no surprise, if we remember from *Psalm* that the universe of *Die Niemandsrose* is a world—or an archipelago of worlds/poems of the volume—where the work of creation of the human might have been almost completely undone and language almost gone. Now, if possible, one has to find one's bearings in this reduced linguistic universe and, if possible, learn human speech anew. The child's singsong appears to be a natural form of such an enterprise.

The choice of the odd, fairytale-like nouns—the Almond, the Nothing, the King—is in perfect agreement with the form of children's songs, which tend to contain the most mysterious words and images. Thus, in the rhythm of questions, answers, and repetitions, the playful, but also very uncanny child reveals before us the simple structure of double containment: in the Almond there dwells ("stands") the Nothing, in the Nothing there dwells ("stands") the King. The figure of the almond is one of the key images in Celan's poetry. It brings together various meanings, but it is not difficult to see that, in one way or another, they usually refer to Judaism and Jewishness. The four main lines of such reference can be easily identified. One is based on the pun from Jeremiah 1:11–12 between the words *shaked* (almond) and *shoked* (I shall watch): "The word of the Lord came to me: 'What do you see, Jeremiah?' 'I see the branch of an almond tree,' I replied. The Lord said to me, 'You have seen correctly, for I am watching to see that my word is fulfilled.'" Celan relies on this pun openly in the early poem *Zähle die Mandel* where he opens with an address to a "thou," urging him or her to count the bitter almonds that kept one on watch—and ends with an urge to make himself bitter and count himself among the almonds.[19] The second line of the almond reference is based on the description of the Menorah from Exodus 25:31–35, where the almond blossom ornaments of the candlestick are described. Celan alludes to the opening of this passage in the poem *Vor einer Kerze*, where it is his mother who is said to have ordered him to produce the golden candlestick.[20] It is also in the same poem that the third version of the "Jewish almond" appears: the image of the almond-shaped eyes ascribed to a Jewess, an image that appears also in the poem *Andenken* in the phrase *das Mandelauge des Toten* (the almond eye of the dead one).[21] Finally, and perhaps most obviously, there is the name of Ossip Mandelstam, to whose memory, as mentioned, *Die Niemandsrose* is dedicated and who is referred to, more or less explicitly, in a number of poems throughout the volume.[22]

Against this background of the fourfold system of references to the "Jewish almond," it is interesting to note that the poem in which the image of almond is most prominent, that is, *Mandorla* itself, is also the only one based explicitly on Christian imagery. *Mandorla*, the Italian word for almond, is the name for the almond-like shape in which Medieval Christian painters often depict Christ in his glory, Christ as the King. Celan's notes for this poem explicitly suggest that he had this image in mind.[23] In the poem itself, Celan seems to superimpose this imagery with the meditation of Nothingness rooted clearly in the tradition of negative theology. Thus, similarly to the case of *Psalm*, we face the question of how seriously are we to treat this theology, to what extent are the mechanisms of this tradition truly reaffirmed and reapplied by Celan. The second question, which also has its parallel when it comes to *Psalm* and the Christological imagery of its last stanza, is how "Christian" this poem really is and does it really affirm its rootedness in the Christian tradition vis-à-vis the Jewish one.

One extreme position would be to give an unqualified positive answer to these questions. On such a reading, the formal regression of the poem would reflect the catastrophe of the human and the linguistic, as well as the withdrawal to the elements where the whole process of creation might be started anew. At the point of almost absolute withdrawal of meaning, Celan would find himself capable of reaffirming the divine origin of the world thanks to the mechanisms of negative theology that allow him to recognize nothingness as the site of the sacred. The supposed hollowness of the almond meditated upon in the first stanza reveals its dark substantiality and so the royal element contained even deeper within it can come to the fore. And once we have established this line of reading, we may continue it through the remaining three stanzas of the poem. True, the third stanza composed of the single line "Jew's curl, you'll not turn grey" is likely to destabilize the reading. For the time being, however, we might take it into account as introducing the question of cruel, premature death, which will still have to be addressed later in the poem. Thus, we might proceed to the fourth stanza, which introduces a new noun and a new position in the negative-theological game described in the first two stanzas: the position of the meditating eye. The eye dynamically (and not very grammatically) stands "toward" something, namely it stands vis-à-vis the almond and the Nothingness, and it "stands and stands" by the King, loyally dwells on him. Whereas in *Psalm*, the word *entgegen* (against, in both meanings of the word) seemed to suggest some kind of stubborn confrontation—either with the hollowed, disenchanted sky or with the divine No-one—here it seems to suggest more of a mystical concentration that, indeed, results in loyalty. It is this meditative loyalty to the King that leads to the final movement described in the last stanza, where the almond is empty again, but it is royally blue: now the King and the eye combine in the mystical union and disappear in blue Nothingness. The troubling question introduced in the third stanza reappears here in the universalized form ("human curl"), only in order to find its ultimate solution: even if the first meaning of not-turning-grey is the cruel, premature death, the repetition of the phrase, perfectly *rhymed* with the last line of the poem, reveals its second meaning, which is the cessation of time in the eternity of the empty, royally blue *mandorla*. Moreover, the passage from the Jewish to the human might be seen as parallel to the passage to the Christian imagery of the almond that Celan undertakes in this poem. Yet it is also interesting to note that when reading a few years later Gershom Scholem's book *Von der mystischen Gestalt der Gottheit*, Celan underlined the sentence reading "The righteous one stands in Nothingness" and explicitly linked it to his own *Mandorla*. This might suggest that he did try to include Jewish imagery in the mechanisms of the poem in a *post factum* gesture and sketch a Judeo-Christian negative theological pattern of passage to the eternity of the almond.

Internally, the reading appears to be rather sound. Yet, there is not much to prevent us from opposing it with a radically different one, which inverts its positive conclusions. Rather than affirming and applying the patterns of negative theology, we might see *Mandorla* as mocking them by their very confrontation with the cruelty of premature death. Thus, the clash of the theological structure sketched in the first two stanzas with the irreducibly historical event of premature death—possibly the death of Celan's mother who is identified as the one whose hair never turned gray in an early poem titled *Espenbaum*—inaugurates a dismantling of the theological.[24] The negative-theological mode of thinking is referred to again in the fourth stanza where the subject ("the eye") seems to locate himself nicely and loyally in the theological structure. However, the final stanza arranges the ultimate encounter between the theological and the historical, closed together in the confines of the rhyme, and so the prematurity of death, now recognized as universal in its contingency and brutality, hollows the almond again and leaves it empty, undoing the royal success of the second stanza and reverting the King to a faint blue halo. Flat emptiness is really very far from the divine Nothingness. The childish, singsong rhyme of the last stanza is an expression of pure sarcasm and so the ultimate meaning of the formal regression will be not so much a hopeful withdrawal to the theological origins, as a destruction of the theological at the hands of a very cruel child. Thus, ultimately, the particularity of Jewish suffering would effectively dismantle the whole machine of passage to eternity offered by Christian negative theology.

However, just as in the case of *Psalm*, I do not think it is wise to take either the route that reduces literature to theology or the one that shows literature as antitheology. Rather, it seems much wiser to read *Mandorla* as developing its own, broken literary theology, which *is* based on negative theological patterns, but results from their *partial* dismantling. Thus, referring to both patterns of reading sketched herein, but combining and replacing them with a third one, we should say the following. The dismantling is, indeed, introduced by the intervention of the historical in the third stanza: its very position as shifted to the right suggests the passage from the vertical movement toward transcendence to the horizontal movement of history. And it is not by chance that the position of the eye appears only after this intervention. Whereas the first two stanzas view the theological pattern from nowhere, the historical almost naturally produces the isolated subject confronted with the elements of the divine. It is at this point that we should take a look at an important, dense note for the *Meridian* speech, which reveals one more meaning of the image of almond. Celan writes: "Whoever is ready only to shed his tears and cry over the almond-beautiful one, he murders her one more time and buries her deeper in oblivion.—Only when you go with your own-most pain to the crooked-nosed, hunchbacked, jargon-speaking, disfigured dead ones of Treblinka, Auschwitz and other places, then you encounter also the eye and its *eidos*: the almond. Not the motif, but the pause and interval, the silent courtyards of breath, the rhetorical cola warrant in the poem for truth of such an encounter."[25] Let me explain right away: I do not think that the eye from this note should be identified with the eye from *Mandorla*. The eye in the poem is the eye of the subject facing nothingness, the subject that appears in the poem as a result of the passage to the historical. It is the eye of the poet as a witness. And it is this very eye that wants to encounter the eye of the lost ones whose hair will never turn gray, the contingent and particular lost ones "toward" whom the poet "stands" with his own-most pain. It wants to encounter the almond as the *"eidos"* of the eye.

Just like in *Psalm* the Christological imagery was deconstructed into a vision of writing that cuts immanence by marking the spots of pain, but does not leave any space for redemption, so too in *Mandorla* the Jewish "curl" disturbs the form of Christian negative theology. And yet this process of disturbing does not result in a total collapse of the theological as such. Celan works his way through Christian theology and ends with a negative literary-theological pattern that, with necessary reservations, can be seen as specifically Jewish. It does away with the image of the triumphant Christ, just as *Psalm* did away with the image of Christ who redeems through his suffering, and it comes as close as a post-Shoah literary theology can to the Jewish idea of each subject's redemptive task, the messianic responsibility toward the other. However, in Celan's world, the actual redemptive power is gone: what remains is only the power of witnessing. The movement of the poem replaces the vertical pattern of passage to eternity with a horizontal tension between the witnessing eye of the poet and those who are lost. If we are not to bury them deeper in oblivion, their "eyes" must appear only at the negative moments of break, in the intervals, in the silent courtyards of breath. Thus, this active form of attentiveness called writing must use its stylus in order to produce empty spaces in language, spaces that would reveal not the eyes themselves—they are gone—but, perhaps, their absence. Paradoxically enough, from the point of view of the writing witness, the *eidos* of the eye is its very absence: and so the ultimate image of *Mandorla* is the empty almond. The almond was finally hollowed by the contingency of death it encountered in the rhyme of the last stanza, so there is no resurrected, triumphant King in it anymore. Instead, there is the blue, royal afterimage, *the empty afterimage of the eye*. Much less substantial than the thick Nothingness of negative theology, this particular, empty almond, which is only locally sketched by the work of the stylus, is still the only cut in the immanence, the only moment of the weakened, testimonial, nonredemptive transcendence in this literary theology. Not because the eye of the lost one is the site of the divine, but because the very activity of such a writing is the only decent form of prayer in the hollowed world of Paul Celan.

Notes

For Paweł Piszczatowski of the Franz Kafka University of Muri, to whom I owe so much of what follows.

1. Carl Schmitt, *Political Theology: Four Chapters on the Concept of Sovereignty*, trans. George Schwab (Chicago: The University of Chicago Press, 2005), 36.

2. Walter Benjamin, *Gesammelte Schriften*, vol. 1 (Frankfurt am Main: Suhrkamp Verlag, 1974), 887.

3. Walter Benjamin, *Gesammelte Schriften*, vol. 6 (Frankfurt am Main: Suhrkamp Verlag, 1985), 219.

4. Gershom Scholem, "Rosenzweig and *The Star of Redemption*," in Paul Mendel-Flohr, ed., *The Philosophy of Franz Rosenzweig* (Hanover, NH: University Press of New England, 1988), 26–28.

5. *The Correspondence of Walter Benjamin and Gershom Scholem: 1932–1940*, trans. Gary Smith and Andre Lefevre (New York: Schocken Books, 1989), 142.

6. Walter Benjamin, *Gesammelte Schriften*, vol. 2 (Frankfurt am Main: Suhrkamp Verlag, 1977), 420.

7. I owe the image of the navel to Piotr Paziński of The Franz Kafka University of Muri.

8. Paul Celan, *Der Meridian: Endfassung–Entwürfe–Materialien* (Frankfurt am Main: Suhrkamp Verlag 1999), 9.

9. Ibid., 157.

10. Ibid., 87.

11. Paul Celan, *Die Gedichte: Kommentierte Gesamtausgabe in einem Band*, ed. Barbara Wiedemann (Frankfurt am Main: Suhrkamp Verlag, 2005), respectively, 251–254, 304–305.

12. Ibid., 132, and *Poems of Paul Celan*, trans. Michael Hamburger (London: Anvil Press Poetry, 1995), 175.

13. Hermann Cohen, *Religion der Vernunft aus den Quellen des Judentums* (Wiesbaden: Fourier Verlag, 1978), 84.

14. Franz Rosenzweig, "New Thinking," in Franz Rosenzweig, *Philosophical and Theological Writings*, ed. Paul W. Franks and Michael L. Morgan (Indianapolis, IN: Hackett Publishing Company, 2000), 130.

15. Paul Celan, *Gesammelte Werke in fünf Bänden*, vol. 5 (Frankfurt am Main: Suhkamp Verlag, 1983), 138–141.

16. Celan, *Die Gedichte*, 198.

17. Ibid., 142, and Hamburger, *Poems of Paul Celan*, 192.

18. Celan, *Die Gedichte*, 125.

19. Ibid., 53.

20. Ibid., 73–74.

21. Ibid., 79.

22. See especially the poem *Eine Gauner- und Ganovenweise gesungen zu Paris emprès Pontoise von Paul Celan aus Czernowitz bei Sadagora* (Celan, *Die Gedichte*, 135–136) and *Nachmittag mit Zirkus und Zitadelle* (ibid., 150–151).

23. Ibid., 690.

24. Ibid., 30.

25. Celan, *Der Meridian*, 128.

FIFTEEN

"Gods Change": The Deconstruction of the Transcendent God and the Reconstruction of the Mythical Godhead in Yehuda Amichai's *Open Closed Open*

TZAHI WEISS

> Otherness is God. Otherness killed Him
> הָאַחֵרוּת הִיא הָאֱלֹהִים. הָאַחֵרוּת הָרְגָה אוֹתוֹ
> —Yehuda Amichai

I.

The attitude of the poetry of Yehuda Amichai toward the image of God as well as other religious motifs has been the subject of much discussion in scholarship about his work.[1] The recurrent ironic rhetoric in Amichai's poetry that questions God has been interpreted as secularizing God by transforming religious concepts into humanistic, existential values. It is noteworthy that some scholars have pointed to a more complex attitude according to which the deconstructive operation applied to fundamental religious notions is accompanied by a reconstructive approach that resurrects these concepts in a modern idiom.[2] Nevertheless and despite the disparity between the various studies that have been dedicated to this subject, they all assume that there exists a clear concept of the Jewish God and that this is the God addressed in Amichai's poetry. In what follows, I start from a different point of departure and consequently present a different perspective concerning the attitude of Amichai's poetry to the figure of God. The analysis will focus on Amichai's final volume, *Open Closed Open*. This book, which has been described as Amichai's magnum opus, is elaborately engaged with the image of God and therefore serves well as a test case for this study.[3]

The basic assumption in the scholarship of Amichai's poetry, according to which there is a clear-cut image of God with which Amichai's poetry grapples, does not, in fact, correspond with the course of the historical development of Jewish thought. The rabbinical Jewish belief as it developed from late antiquity until today has never succeeded in offering clear theological dogmas. It appears that the basic structure of rabbinic Judaism, which based itself on ritual and Halakhic rules, paved the way and, in a sense, generated a free zone for the articulation of beliefs and thoughts. The image of God in Jewish rabbinic literature has taken on forms both various and contradictory, going between depictions of a transcendent God lacking all qualities and detailed mythical and physical depictions of supposedly the very same God. This understanding concerning the possibility of divergent images of the God invites and warrants an examination and definition of the image of God against whom Amichai rebels in his poetry and consequently the significance of this rebellion in regard to the image of God.

A note concerning the depth of the acquaintance of Amichai with Jewish sources and traditions should be stressed at this point. Amichai grew up in a German orthodox Jewish family and was acquainted with some biblical, rabbinical, and liturgical sources. Nevertheless, as Arnold Band notes, Amichai was not a scholar and the references to Jewish sources in his poems reflect no more than the knowledge of a modern orthodox high school student.[4] Hence, as we shall see, it seems that Amichai's search for an alternative Godhead does not derive from his personal journey through Jewish mythical and mystical sources as an adult but from his rebellion against the abstract God with which he was familiar with.

There is a development in Amichai's poetry of interest from a theological-literary perspective. As we will see, the ironic rhetoric employed by Amichai in his poetry is, like an arrow aimed at the image of God, directed at the specific image of God with which he was probably acquainted during his childhood: the Jewish God lacking physical attributes or qualities. In many respects, the God that Amichai ironically challenges is a folk version of the God of negative theology. But this very act of rebellion that Amichai realized in his poetry through a deconstructive process allows for the emergence of a different image of God possessing human, figurative, and mythical qualities.

II.

In a poem describing the differences among the Christian God, the Muslim God, and the Jewish God, Amichai complains about the abstract nature of the Jewish God. The comparison in the poem yields an interesting and paradoxical conclusion: the Jewish God is present in Christianity, where God is embodied in the flesh of an actual Jew. In the same vein, but in this case with no scriptural foundation, Amichai depicts the Islamic image of God as that of a Jew walking in the desert. In contrast, the Jewish God according to the poem is an abstract and distant figure lacking human qualities and therefore possessing no national attributes. The Jewish God is less Jewish than the God of Christianity or Islam God.

> The God of the Christians is a Jew, a bit of a whiner,
> And the God of the Muslims is an Arab Jew from the
> desert, a bit hoarse.
> Only the God of the Jews isn't Jewish.
> The way Herod the Edomite was brought in to be king of the Jews,
> so God was brought back from the infinite future,
> an abstract God: neither painting nor graven image
> nor tree nor stone.[5]

The Jewish God is described in this poem as an artificial God, distant in time and space, who has been "brought back from the infinite future." The Jewish God seems alienated, an absolutely transcendent God: "an abstract God: neither painting nor graven image nor tree nor stone." Beside the criticism expressed in the poem in regard to the distant Jewish God, one can hear a longing for a different God: whether Christian, Muslim, or imaginary—a human God, "one of us" as Jews and as human beings.

Another poem that illustrates Amichai's rebellion against the transcendent God concerns the Holocaust. The issue of theodicy is at the basis of any theological discussion pertaining to the Holocaust, an issue that becomes increasingly poignant in the case of an embodied image of God. It is exactly the mythic God, characterized by direct intervention in worldly matters as well as by personal providence, who can be held responsible for the destruction of his own people and the death of millions. In the poem that ends the series "Gods Change, Prayers Are Here to Stay," Amichai describes the God of the Holocaust as an abstract God lacking all attributes. In a skillful move, the poem accuses God not of responsibility for the events of the Holocaust but of detachment and indifference: the genocide of Jews in the Holocaust illustrates that God is unmoved and deaf to Jewish suffering. The numbers tattooed on the arms of victims are like the numbers of a disconnected telephone belonging to God who does not answer and has left no forwarding address. The disappearance of the Jews from the world symbolizes the Jewish God without a body. In those dark days of the Holocaust when Jews were truly in dire need of a father to protect them, they relied on an abstract God possessing only the name of the father but not being a father.

> After Auschwitz, no theology:
> From the chimneys of the Vatican, white smoke rises—
> a sign the cardinals have chosen themselves a pope.
> From the crematoria of Auschwitz, black smoke rises—
> a sign the conclave of Gods has not yet chosen
> the chosen people.

> After Auschwitz, no theology:
> The numbers on the forearms of the inmates of extermination
> are the telephone numbers of God,
> numbers that do not answer
> and now are disconnected, one by one.
>
> After Auschwitz, a new theology:
> The Jews who died in the Shoah
> have now come to be like their God,
> who has no likeness of a body and has no body.
> They have no likeness of a body and they have no body.[6]

To conclude this section, I would like to present two further examples that bear witness to Amichai's revulsion from the Jewish God lacking attributes and his longing for a more mythical Godhead. In a close scrutiny of these examples, we are confronted by a textual tension created by Amichai predicated on his reading of the Old Testament. Based on a panoramic survey, it would be very hard to justify a transcendent image of God in the Hebrew Bible. Listening carefully to the weekly portions reveals that in the *Torah* God has a figure and that He interferes in the world; God has feelings, He is angry or pleased, He rewards his people and punishes his enemies. As opposed to this vital biblical God with which he was most certainly acquainted, Amichai was inculcated in his childhood with the image of God who was abstract, distant, and lacking any real interest in the world. Thus Amichai depicts the tension between the two images of God:

> God's love to His people Israel is an upside-down love.
> First crude and physical, with a strong hand and an outstretched arm:
> miracles, ten plagues and ten commandments,
> almost violent, no a no-name basis.
> Then more: more emotion, more soul
> but no body, an unrequited ever-longing love
> for an invisible god in the high heavens. A hopeless love.[7]

Another example of the same sort is expressed in a poem that describes the historical highlight of the Jewish people, *Matan Torah*, as antithetically the very event in which God deserts them leaving them alone with the *Torah* or with the *Torah* alone:

> When God packed up and left the country, He left the Torah
> with the Jews. They have been looking for Him ever since,
> shouting "Hey, you forgot something, you forgot"

and other people think shouting is the prayer of the Jews.
Since then, they've been combing the Bible for the hints
of His whereabouts, as it says: "Seek ye the Lord while He may be found
call ye upon Him while He is near." But He is far away.[8]

Amichai's invocation of an abstract God also bespeaks a longing for a different God, one with a mythical character and human qualities. In what follows, I will attempt, on the one hand, to demonstrate the longing expressed in Amichai's poetry to this other God is more figurative, concrete, and anthropomorphized and, on the other hand, I will point to the legitimacy of those perceptions within certain Jewish theological trends that Amichai probably was not aware of or at least did not know well.

III.

As noted, in Amichai's poetry, the ironic rhetoric is aimed at the God and generates a reexamination of the meaning of words and phrases. It is this irony that leads him in some of his poems to attend to the fact that the name of the monotheistic Jewish God *Elohim* is in a Hebrew plural form. Thus he asks in one of his poems: "And why is *Elohim*, God, in the plural?"[9] and stresses in another poem: "Longings in plural masculine like God, *Elohim*."[10] In Hebrew, there are a few names of God that are grammatically in a plural form like *Elohim* or *Adonai*. These names most probably derived from ancient near eastern sources that were not monotheistic. Nevertheless, these appellations cannot be considered only as a residue of prebiblical traditions since nonmonotheistic traditions accompany Jewish theology from late antiquity through the Middle Ages. Thus, one finds *binitarian* traditions in Jewish sources of late antiquity concerning the existence of two authorities in heaven as well as medieval Kabbalistic sources that outline a detailed heavenly entourage composed of ten *Sefirot* or thirteen measurements of God. Some scholars have in fact raised the question whether the Jewish religion should be considered monotheistic.[11] It is doubtful that Amichai was acquainted with Jewish *binitarian* or Kabbalistic traditions. It is rather the very linguistic examination that is to be found in his poetry that uncovers the hidden significance and leads the author in his rebellion to the embrace of Jewish approaches different from those known to him.

An example of Amichai's examination of the limits of the belief in a transcendent God can be found in a poem that ponders what would happen were we to change the descriptions of the God such that God would be transformed from an invisible God into a visible one and from a seeing God to a blind one:

> I don't want an invisible god. I want
> a god who is seen but doesn't see so I can

> lead him around
>> and tell him what he doesn't see. and I want
>> a god who sees and is seen. I want to see
>> how he covers his eyes, like a child playing
>> blindman's bluff.[12]

This poem attests to Amichai's rebellion against the image of God known to him. His aim is to transform God from an abstraction, like the concept of omniscience, to a weak and dependent but concrete figure whose eyes are covered. Amichai might be considered an iconoclastic poet secularizing the most significant parts of Jewish theology. But my point here is that Amichai's "heresy" reverts to the common way in which God is depicted in other Jewish traditions, probably less known to Amichai. Figurative descriptions of God and His depiction as weak of character were widespread in Jewish traditions and hundreds of examples of these attitudes can be found in Jewish sources from rabbinic literature and onward.[13]

An interesting example for a depiction of God as a weak character can be brought from an interpretation that was quoted by the early sixteenth-century Kabbalist Rabbi Meir Ibn Gabai in which the image of God describes as a shadow of man:

> In the Midrash, [we learn] that the Holy One, blessed be he, said to Moses: "Go, tell Israel that my name is 'Ehyeh 'asher 'Ehyeh." What is the meaning of 'Ehyeh 'asher 'Ehyeh? Just as you are present with me, so am I present with you. Likewise David said: "The Lord is thy shadow upon thy right hand." What does "the Lord is thy shadow" mean? Like thy shadow: just as thy shadow laughs back when you laugh to it, and weeps if you weep to it, and if you show it an angry face or a pleasant face, so it returns, so is the Lord, the Holy one, blessed be he, thy shadow. Just as you are present with him, so is he present with you.[14]

In order to demonstrate the proximity between the "heretic" approaches that Amichai sketches in his poems and Jewish traditions of a mystical and mythical nature, I will examine two poems that describe the role of the worshipper and the role of God in the daily prayers. In the first, Amichai describes his father praying. According to this poem, it was not his father who swayed before God but rather it was God who swayed before his father—God prayed to his father:

> Even solitary prayer takes two:
> one to sway back and forth
> and the one who doesn't move is God.
> But when my father prayed, he would stand in his place,

erect, motionless, and force God
to sway like a reed and pray to him.¹⁵

A similar description is to be found in a poem that depicts Hannah's prayer before God in the tabernacle of Shilo. This very famous prayer, in which her lips moved and her voice was not heard receives a new interpretation in Amichai's poem:

> Development in the prayer of Hannah: From
> weeping out loud
> in bitterness for she had no son, to a silent weeping
> and from a silent weeping, to an audible prayer and
> from an audible prayer
> to a silent prayer, only her lips moved and she was drunk
> from the prayer inside her body, and the priest Eli thought
> she was drunk from wine. And a final development:
> she sits and God prays to her, the prayer of Hannah.¹⁶

The first part of the poem describes the prayer of Hannah in the tabernacle and the misconstrual of Eli who thought she was drunk. Nevertheless, the innovative part of this poem, which expresses its revolt against the well-known biblical narrative, is epitomized by its interpretation of the coupling in the prayer of Hannah. "The prayer of Hannah" according to the poem is not the prayer of Hannah to God but the prayer of God to Hannah.

Amichai presents a subversive alternative to the concept of prayer that possesses a humanistic character: it is not man in the margins who prays to God who is in the center, but rather God sways like a reed and prays to man. This humanistic theme of anthropocentric quality is not alien to Jewish traditions that represented the Jewish deity as a weak figure in need of His believers. Thus, for example, in one of the famous theurgic Midrashim in the rabbinic literature, it is told of Rabbi Ishmael the high priest who entered into the innermost part of the temple, the holy of holies, God's private room in order to beg for mercy for the people of Israel. A dramatic description ensues in the Midrash that depicts Rabbi Ishmael standing before God who is sitting on a high throne. In the very dramatic moment when Rabbi Ishmael looks at God and is about to make his request of mercy, God turns to him and asks Rabbi Ishmael to bless him:

> It has been taught on Tannaite authority: Said R. Ishmael ben Elisha,
> "One time I went in to offer up on the innermost altar, and I saw
> *Akhathriel Yah Adonai Tsevaot*, enthroned on the highest throne, and
> he said to me, 'Ishmael, my son, bless me.' I said to him, 'May it be

your will that your mercy overcome your anger, and that your mercy prevail over your attributes, so that you treat your children in accord with the trait of mercy and in their regard go beyond the strict measure of the law.' And he nodded his head to me."[17]

We do not have good reason to think that Amichai was aware of theurgical traditions such as can be found in the tale about Rabbi Ishmael ben Elisha, the high priest. It is also necessary to stress that the similarity between Amichai's poems and some Jewish mythical and mystical traditions is not precise, *verbum pro verbo*. Nevertheless, from an historical-literary point of view a more interesting process is at work. In this process Amichai rebels against the negative theological traditions with which he was acquainted and unknowingly returns to more mythical and mystical ones.

A poem on prayer presents us with another example of the similarity between the perceptions that are developed in Amichai's poetry and mythical and mystical Jewish traditions and at the same time allows us to determine that these perceptions were not directly drawn from those Jewish traditions. In this poem, the prayers of humans are described as having created God who in turn created humans who created the prayers. There is irony in this circular depiction that ridicules the need for prayers by which God is addressed for help while in fact it is the prayer itself enunciated by men that creates Him. It is worthy of note that a lack of logic such as we can find in this poem might be considered as the mystery that allows the believers to go beyond the order of the normative world.

> I declare with perfect faith
> that prayer preceded God.
> Prayer created God.
> God created human beings,
> human beings create prayers
> that create the God that creates human beings.[18]

In a similar manner to the poem's circular depiction of the relations between God and human being, we find in one of the most famous Midrashic depictions from *Bereshit Raba*, the description of God creating the world through reading the Torah, the very same Torah that depicts God as creating the world:

> the Torah speaks, "I was the work-plan of the Holy one, blessed be He." In the accepted practice of the world, when a mortal king builds a palace, he does not build it out of his own head, but he follows a work-plan. And [the one who supplies] the work-plan does not build out of his own head, but he has designs and diagrams, so as to know

how to situate the rooms and the doorways. Thus the Holy one, blessed be he, consulted the Torah when he created the world. So the Torah stated, "By means of 'the beginning' [that is to say, the Torah] did God create...." And the word for "beginning" refers to the Torah[19]

Describing God as being created by prayers or as creating the world by the book that He wrote may appear paradoxical given an assumption and consequent expectation that God be omnipotent, but it seems that this expectation was not common in many Jewish traditions that are similar to Amichai's "heretical" attitude.

Last but not least, I would like to discuss an interesting theological motif in Amichai's poetry that to the best of my knowledge has not been discussed by his commentators: the place of a Jewish feminine divinity hinted at in some of his poems. In *Open Closed Open*, Amichai does not explicitly raise the possibility that the Jewish God or its hypostasis possesses any feminine quality, but in some of his poems, he does give preference to the feminine rather than the masculine religious world. Thus unknowingly, he develops symbolic motifs that have in fact been connected with earlier Jewish traditions with regard to the feminine hypostasis of God, the *Shekhinah*. An example of this can be found in a poem in which the author expresses, through the eyes of a boy, the longing to leave the man's section (*Ezrath Gvarim*) in the orthodox synagogue and join the women and be assimilated in their section (*Ezrath Nashim*):

> I studied love in my childhood in my childhood synagogue
> in the women's section with the help of the women behind
>   the partition
> that locked up my mother with all the other women and girls.
> But the partition that locked them up locked me up
> on the other side. They were free in their love while I remained
> locked up with all the men and boys in my love, my longing
> I wanted to be there with them and to know their secrets
> and say with them "Blessed be He who has made me
>   according to His will" and the partition—
> a lace curtain white and soft as summer
> dresses, swaying on its rings and loops of wish and would
> *lu-lu* loops, lullings of love in the locked room.
> And the faces of women like the face of the moon behind the clouds
> or the foil moon when the curtain parts: an enchanted
> cosmic order. At night we said the blessing over
> the moon outside, and I thought about the women.[20]

The preference expressed in regard to the women's section in the synagogue is indicative of the rebellion at the heart of the patriarchal religious world and a predilection for the alternative world that seemingly exists in its margins. The world of the women is depicted as an alternative religious framework in which a different and a more humane religion can exist. The *Ezrath Nashim* as a physical space turns by way of a play on words to the theological help (*Ezra*) offered by the women to a sensitive child who prefers the soft cloth and the sweetness of the secrets in the closed room. The child in the poem feels excluded from this alternative religiosity and views the enclosure of women as well as their blessing: "Blessed be He who has made me according to His will," a land that he can see only from a distance, but cannot enter. From the perspective of the history of Jewish ideas, the alternative that the women's section offers to the child is not simply Amichai's wishful thinking but is a buried theological possibility that appears in the Jewish sources in the image of the *Shekhinah*. Moreover the motif of the moon mentioned in the poem is one of the well-known symbols of the *Shekhinah* in the Kabbalistic literature, while the blessing of the renewed moon every month designates the dynamic character of the feminine divinity.[21] The mixture between the synagogue and prayer, the image of women and the blessing of the moon, is also expressed elsewhere in some of Bialik's poems and Agnon's stories.[22] Despite the structural and symbolic similarity between Amichai's poem and the manner in which the image of the *Shekhinah* was formed in Kabbalistic sources and some Hebrew authors at the beginning of the twentieth century, in this case, too, I am of the opinion that Amichai was not directly influenced by any serious knowledge of the image of the *Shekhinah*. To put it slightly differently, although Amichai had probably heard of the *Shekhinah*, this poem, which has additional parallels in *Open Closed Open*, primarily expresses a rebellion aimed at the patriarchal religion that he knew well.[23] It does not seem to side with an alternative tradition. It is not the *Shekhinah* that drew him but rather his repulsion from the religion that was formed in *Ezrath Gvarim* at whose head was placed a single male God with no bodily representation.

IV.

Yehuda Amichai, a poet extremely sensitive to people and to words rebelled against the religious world in which he grew. But in the very act of rebellion and in his flight from the abstract negative beliefs of his Orthodox German upbringing, Amichai discovers and accidentally rediscovers the world of Jewish myth and mysticism. While not completely aware of the theological origins to which his poems redirect us, his astute and ironic sensibility understood the circular nature of his rebellion against God. He expressed this in a poem about Abraham's rebellion against the God:

We are all children of Abraham
but also grandchildren of Terah, Abraham's father.
And maybe it's high time the grandchildren did unto
their father as he did unto his
when he shattered his idols and images, his religion, his faith.
That too would be the beginning of a new religion.[24]

Notes

I would like to thank Bella Fuchs, Menachem Kellner, and Yakir Paz for their help in writing this chapter.

1. On the attitudes toward God in Amichai's poetry, see, for example: David Aberbach, "Religious Metaphor and Its Denial in the Poetry of Yehuda Amichai," *Judaism* 53 (2004): 279–292; Glenda Abramson, "Amichai's God," *Prooftext* 4 (1984): 111–126; Chana Bloch and Chana Kronfeld, "Amichai's Counter-Theology: Opening Open Closed Open," *Judaism* 49 (2000): 153–167; David Fishlove, "Yehuda Amichai: A Modern Metaphysical Poet," *Orbis Litterarum* 47 (1992): 178–191; Yoseph Milman, "Sacrilegious Imagery in Yehuda Amichai's Poetry," *AJS Review* (1995): 99–121; Miriam Neiger, "And I Didn't Say: A Vision for the End of the Days—Eschatology in the Poetry of Yehuda Amichai," [in Hebrew] *Jerusalem Studies in Hebrew Literature* 26 (2013): 311–338; Naomi Sokoloff, "On Amichai's El Male Rachamim," *Prooftext* 4 (1984): 127–140.

2. On this point, see, for example, Milman, "Sacrilegious Imagery."

3. Bloch and Kronfeld, "Amichai's Counter-Theology," 153.

4. Arnold J. Band, "Secularization of Sacred? Forms of Inter-textual Expression in a Poem by Yehuda Amichai," [in Hebrew] in *Creation and Re-Creation in Jewish Thought: Festschrift in Honor of Joseph Dan*, ed. Peter Schäfer and Rachel Elior (Tübingen: Mohr-Siebeck, 2005), 194.

5. Yehuda Amichai, "Gods Change, Prayers Are Here to Stay," no. 8, *Open Closed Open: Poems*, trans. Chana Bloch and Chana Kronfeld (Orlando: Harcourt, 2006), 41–42. All the references to Yehuda Amichai's translated poems to English will refer to this edition.

6. "Gods Change, Prayers Are Here to Stay," no. 23, 47.

7. "Gods Change, Prayers Are Here to Stay," no. 18, 45.

8. "Gods Change, Prayers Are Here to Stay," no. 5, 40.

9. "The Language of Love and Tea with Roasted Almonds," no. 1, 93; 'ומדוע אלהים הוא 'לשון בלשון רבים', 92).

10. Ibid., no. 017, 106 106 'עמ, 17 # בכל געגועים האשר מגע וטשטוש הכאב דיוק.

11. On this subject, see, for example, A. Peter Hayman, "Monotheism—A Misused Word in Jewish Studies," *Journal of Jewish Studies* 42 (1991): 1–14.

12. "Gods Change, Prayers Are Here to Stay," no. 2, 39.

13. On the figurative image of God, see, for example: Yehuda Liebes, "De Natura Dei: On the Development of the Jewish Myth," in his *Studies in Jewish Myth and Jewish Messianism*, trans. Batya Stein (New York: State University of New York Press, 1993), 1–64;

Yair Loberbaum, *Image of God* [in Hebrew] (Jerusalem: Schocken, 2004). On theurgical trends that depict God as a weak figure, see, for example: Moshe Idel, *Kabbalah: New Perspectives* (New Haven, CT: Yale University Press, 1988), 156–199; Charles Mopsik, *Les Grands Textes de la Cabale: Les Rites qui Font Dieu* (Paris: Verdier, 1993).

14. Rabbi Meir Ibn Gabai, Tola'ath Ya'akov (Constantinople, 1560), 4a. On this source and its meanings see, Idel, *Kabbalah: New Perspectives*, 175.

15. "Gods Change, Prayers Are Here to Stay," no. 10, 42.

16. I would like to thank Yakir Paz for this translation of the poem.

17. Babylonian Talmud (BT), *Berakhot*, [Neusner], 7a.

18. "Gods Change, Prayers Are Here to Stay," no. 3, 40.

19. *Bereshit Raba*, A1 in Jacob Neusner, *Genesis rabbah: the Judaic commentary to the book of Genesis: a new American translation* (Atlanta: Scholars Press, 1985), A:1.

20. "Gods Change, Prayers Are Here to Stay," no. 21, 46.

21. See, for example: Shifra Asulin, "The Flaw and its Correction: Impurity, the Moon and the Shekhinah—An Inquiry into *Zohar* 3:79 (Aharei Mot)" [in Hebrew], in *Kabbalah* 22 (2010): 193–252; Havivah Pedayah, "Sabbath, Sabbatai and the Diminution of the Moon—The Holy Conjunction, Sign and Image" [in Hebrew], *Eshel Beer-Sheva* 4 (1996): 150–153; Elliot R. Wolfson, "The Face of Jacob in the Moon: Mystical Transformation of an Aggadic Myth," in *The Seductiveness of Jewish Myth: Challenge or Response*, ed. S. D. Breslaur (Albany: State University of New York Press, 1997), 235–270.

22. Tzahi Weiss, "Listening to the Silent Crying of the Shekhinah: Mysticism in Modern Hebrew Literature—Between Textual Influence and Mythical Narrative" [in Hebrew], in *Literature Kabbalah and Mysticism*, ed. A. Elkayam and Sh. Mualem (Jerusalem: Magnes Press, 527–546, in press).

23. See "The Language of Love and Tea with Roasted Almonds," no. 12, 97, and "In My Life, on My Life," no. 13, in *Open Closed Open*, 114.

24. "Gods Change, Prayers Are Here to Stay," no. 19, 46.

SIXTEEN

The Politics of Negative Theology

MARTIN KAVKA

In an important article written over a quarter century ago, Kenneth Seeskin claimed that "the most obvious contribution of negative theology is the extent to which it forces us to take the limits of human reason seriously."[1] This is a deeply important intellectual claim in contemporary Jewish thought. The contribution of negative theology is obvious in part due to our own post-Holocaust context. We know all too well the destructive power of the program of "civilization" and the reasons invoked to defend it;[2] we know all too well the importance of acknowledging reason's limits. Nevertheless, it is also an important philosophical-theological claim, regardless of the historical moment at which the claimer makes it. There are good reasons why negative theology should be compelling for monotheists who place authority both in the Bible and in certain strands of Western philosophy. These reasons stem from the broad set of questions about how human language might refer to God.[3] If God is one in the sense of being radically simplex—as the post-Aristotelian tradition of divine oneness and transcendence has it—then God cannot be the subject matter of a sentence with typical "S is P" subject-predicate structure. This is because predicating something of God's nature is to introduce a relationship of otherness between God and the predicate, and thus multiplicity. Two somewhat silly examples might suffice to explain. If we were the kind of people who were in the habit of saying that "God is blue," we would be positing a relationship between God and a property in a way that no longer makes God simply one. God may be blue, but just as blue rock has other qualities besides its color, so a blue God would have other qualities. (While all things are colored, no thing is only colored; a thing also has weight, extension, texture, etc.) "Blue" would only get us part of the way to giving an account of God's essence, of what it means for God to be God. And as soon as we say that naming one of a subject's predicates gets us only *part* of the way to knowing the essence of a subject, we have introduced multiplicity into the subject, simply because we have (even if unintentionally) broken the one subject into multiple parts. Similarly, if we were the kind of people who were in the habit of saying "God is blueness," then we would be explaining God in such a way that would imply that God is not the first cause of the world (as biblical monotheists believe). After all, color appears as a result of a process of absorbing and reflecting light, a light that comes from a source other than any color. And so these kinds of definitional explanations of God implicitly contradict the account of God as a simplex creator to which biblical monotheists are committed. As a result, all sentences about God except for tautologies such as "God is God" are irresponsible. We must learn to negate all of our positive predications and explanations of God, and this is something that monotheists committed to a God who transcends the world must learn if their commitment is not to be held in bad faith.

Therefore, such an argument about the intimacy between monotheism and negative theology entails a claim about the fundamental limits of human reason, as Seeskin rightly sees. If the premise of negative theology is that no non-tautologous assertions can be made about God, then there is no dogma about God's nature or identity that one could hold with any certainty. Such an argument also entails a political claim. For if the premise of negative theology is that no non-tautologous assertions can be made about God, then there is no dogma about God's nature or identity—over and above being a simplex creator—that one could lord over one's neighbors in a polity. As Seeskin's essay in this volume states, a culture that would adhere to negative theology would take as a virtue the cultivation of "a feeling of awe and wonderment" that cannot translate into definitive knowledge about the ground of that feeling and wonderment, except that it is great enough to cause that feeling.[4] Accordingly, for Seeskin, no one's claims about God's proper name(s) can be taken as prima facie wrong (or right); no one is blameworthy (or praiseworthy) simply for holding or for refusing to hold a belief. One might restate what is so appealing to Seeskin about negative theology by pointing out that a polity whose members acknowledge the limits of human reason is a polity marked by religious pluralism. Negative theology is, on his account, a solution to the problem of how a polity might cope with reasonable disagreement about religious matters. It takes religion out of politics and gets adherents of different religious (or at least monotheistic) traditions to agree with each other that God transcends any and all humans' concepts of God.

This is an appealing account, and it is one that I largely endorse. (I remain unclear as to how negative theology might justify to the inclusion of non-monotheists, or atheists and agnostics, as equal citizens in a polity.) However, if one were to look at the primary site of negative theology in the Jewish philosophical tradition—Moses Maimonides's twelfth-century *Guide of the Perplexed*—one would find neither the separation of religion from politics, nor the recipe for inter-monotheist comity that Seeskin finds in negative theology.[5] We find a theory of rulership, and an anti-Christian polemic. The following two paragraphs expand on this claim.

The first chapters in the *Guide* that treat negative theology are criticisms of earlier figures in the Jewish philosophical canon, specifically the tenth-century philosopher Saadia Gaon and the eleventh-century philosopher Bahya ibn Paquda. Those thinkers were also worried, as was Maimonides, about introducing multiplicity into God. As a result, in his treatment of what he took to be God's three essential attributes (life, omnipotence, and omniscience), Saadia cautions his reader: "For it is not to be imagined that the Eternal, blessed and exalted be He, possesses several distinct attributes. All these attributes are rather implied in His being a Creator. It was only our need to transmit it that impelled us to formulate this concept in three expressions."[6] Similarly, Bahya wrote that any "plurality in the Creator's attributes does not, however, exist in His glorious essence but is due to the inadequacy of language on the part of the speaker."[7] However, these were insufficient cautions for Maimonides, in part because he thought that the content of belief was inextricably bound up with the language used to express belief. Language must mirror belief. This was paired with another consideration:

> If, however, you belong to those whose aspirations are directed . . . to gaining certain knowledge with regard to God's being One by virtue of a true Oneness, so that no composition whatever is to be found in Him . . . then you must know that He, may He be exalted, has in no way and in no mode any essential attribute. . . . If, however, someone believes that He is one, but possesses a certain number of essential attributes, he says in his words that He is one, but believes Him in his thought to be many. This resembles what the Christians say: namely, that He is one but also three, and that the three are one.[8]

In this passage, negative theology does *not* serve to build common cause with members of other religious traditions. It instead serves as a technique to distinguish true religion from false religion (in this case, Christianity).[9] Maimonides's problem with the looseness of expression found in Saadia and Bahya, in which essential attributes are either implicit in God's creative act(s) or a side effect of the limitations of human language, is that such imprecision blurs the difference between Jews and Christians, a difference that Maimonides was invested in maintaining. This is not necessarily simply for social or cultural reasons. The Jew who portrays God as Saadia or Bahya do introduces multiplicity into God, and thereby sounds like an idolator. Negative theology prevents one from being led so astray by one's concept of God that one becomes functionally equivalent to a polytheist, or a Christian.

Therefore, something different from Seeskin's ideal of interreligious tolerance is present in Maimonidean negative theology. Similarly, Maimonides's political application of negative theology is quite different from Seeskin's. While

Seeskin appropriates negative theology as part of a pluralist politics, Maimonidean negative theology involves learning how to rule others properly.[10] If one cannot be confident of predicating anything about God's nature, lest God no longer be thought of as truly one, then it is unjustified to claim that God has a psyche that could be variably moved in response to human action. (A psyche is a part of a being; a simplex God cannot have parts.) God is dispassionate, and this should be imitated by rulers who seek to receive an overflow from the divine (as prophets did):

> With reference to these actions He is called "jealous" and "avenging" and "keeping anger" and "wrathful," meaning that actions similar to those that proceed from us from a certain aptitude of the soul—namely jealousy, holding fast to vengeance, hatred, or anger—proceed from Him, may He be exalted, because of the deserts of those who are punished, and not because of any passion whatever, may He be exalted above every deficiency.... It behooves the governor of a city, if he is a prophet, to acquire similarity to these attributes, so that these actions may proceed from him according to a determined measure and according to the deserts of the people who are affected by them and not merely because of his following a passion.[11]

In Maimonides's negative theology, those who have political authority over others indeed will use their reason, and it seems not to be limited by negative theology; indeed, the rationally perfected ruler knows what to do in any given situation. The correct judgment of what others deserve for their actions is readily discernible. The ruler who imitates God's dispassionateness governs differently than the constant skepticism, deferral, and second-guessing that would be endemic to governance if negative theology were truly about the limits of human reason, as Seeskin has suggested it is.

My aim in introducing this essay with an account of the gaps between Maimonides's negative theology and the understanding of that negative theology on the part of one of the most influential commentators on Maimonides in the secondary Anglophone literature is not to lay claim to some correct, or even better, understanding of Maimonides. I endorse the consequences of Seeskin's negative theology. Indeed, I prefer them to the consequences of Maimonides's negative theology, and I want to bolster Seeskin's negative theology by linking it to another strand of the Jewish tradition. For negative theology in Maimonides is an odd thing. On the one hand, negative theology takes knowledge away, for God's essential attributes are unknowable. On the other hand, negative theology gives knowledge: the knowledge that Judaism is truer than Christianity, and the knowledge of how to properly rule over others. Scholarship on negative theology in

Maimonides has tried to resolve this apparent contradiction, often by focusing on his description of God as intellect.[12] Yet perhaps what is called for is not a resolution of the Maimonidean dilemma, but an argument for choosing one and only one of its horns. For the problem of thinking through negative theology is simply a narrower version of the problem of thinking through revealed religion. Revealed religion is a turn to God as the source of revelation, and thereby an authority who must be imitated: think of Leviticus 19:2 ("Be ye holy as I am holy"). Nevertheless, it also posits *humans* as the recipients of revelation, and those humans thereby also become authorities themselves: think of Deuteronomy 30:11–14 ("Surely this Torah which I enjoin upon you is not too baffling for you, nor is it beyond reach. . . . No, the thing is very close to you, in your mouth and in your heart, to observe it.")

The Maimonidean model takes the first horn of this dilemma and makes God's radical otherness from humans into an argument for the justified nature of divine commands; the Law produces a good people who live alongside each other in an orderly fashion, and it produces good persons "of noble and excellent character."[13] Because we cannot know God's essence, *imitatio dei* requires imitating God's actions. Torah teaches us how to do this and thereby to take an unknowable God as an authority figure. Yet this path of thinking turns away from the claim that Torah is already "in your mouth and in your heart" when God speaks it to the people of Israel. For those scholars who want to argue for a Jewish theology that embraces *that* claim, and grasp the other horn of the dilemma articulated earlier in this paragraph, it will not be necessary to depart from negative theology. For the theologian who values this verse from Deuteronomy—either because of a belief that it makes for a stable polity, or because of an attachment to a liberal political theory—God will remain functionally absent. God does not tell humans what they do not already know. As a result, there is nothing uniquely divine about the law, and no need to value theologians' authority in the public sphere, as they tell us what God knows and we do not. (In other words, as Miriam Galston pointed out long ago, "divine law" is not identical to "revealed law" in Maimonides's *Guide*.[14]) The site of authority is the people—the *demos*—and its acts of reason-giving and learning from its past. God is not the site of authority. Still a negative theology insofar as it acknowledges that human concepts do not mirror divine realities, such a theory opens up a space for democracy. It is this political vision that I take to be implicit in Seeskin's vision of a polity that is self-aware of the limits of its reason.

An exemplar for this kind of negative theology is the late Jacob Taubes (1923–1987), who left behind a quite idiosyncratic corpus: a wide range of essays on Jewish and Christian philosophical theology, and most notably, a series of lectures on the apostle Paul that were published in the late 1980s. Yet all of his writings are explorations of the inability of religious believers either to make confident assertions about the supernatural (which is inaccessible), or about the meaning of the historical order (which appears groundless). Contrary to what one might expect, Taubes's corpus does not constitute a manifesto for tragedy. Rather, it reflects an anthropocentric Jewish theology that politically expresses itself as democracy.[15] As such, Taubes's position is similar to the recent argument of Elliot Wolfson that, given the structural problems endemic to negative theology—apophatic utterances are still assertions, no matter how many attributes they negate—"what is necessary, although by no means easy, is the termination of all modes of representation, even the representation of the nonrepresentable."[16] When we do this, we give up talking about the *content* of our God-talk (and about how, or whether, it represents God), and turn to ourselves, our *desire* for such God-talk and its functions. Given the absence of God from history, theology is a human science; in Wolfson's poetic words, "what we think of as reality in contrast to the dream is naught but a dream of there being reality apart from the dream."[17]

Although I take Taubes as a thinker of democracy, this is not how Taubes's work is usually described in the secondary literature, which largely focuses on his lectures on Pauline political theology. In this section I will read those lectures against the grain, before turning in the next section to two of Taubes's essays from the 1950s that develop Taubes's theology of democracy further.

As someone whose academic fame has been primarily posthumous, Taubes and scholarship on Taubes depend on guardians of his memory; such guardians have shaped the reception of Taubes's work. The lectures on Pauline political theology, given in Heidelberg near the end of his life in 1987, were transcribed and edited by a group of scholars led by the Egyptologist Jan Assmann and his spouse Aleida, a scholar of English literature. Along with Wolf-Daniel Hartwich, a scholar of romanticism, they wrote an afterword to the published version of those lectures, titled *The Political Theology of Paul*. There, they summarized Taubes's thought as an endorsement of Pauline political theology and describe his stance as a "negative political theology," following up on a phrase that Taubes used in a previous lecture course on Paul given in 1986. (This course remains unpublished.) For them, a negative political theology is purely irruptive and refuses "all positive political form. This is why all oppressed peoples and groups can identify with it."[18] Thus, a negative political theology refuses legitimacy to all human political orders (including that of a church), because the only legitimate authority is a divine authority. This kind of theocentrism supports no political plan; instead, it serves to mark the impossibility of all political plans to fulfill their aims and stabilize a community's historical situation, regardless of whether such plans are promulgated in the name of God. Taubes's theology, on this account, is a kind of nihilism. The secondary literature continues to spin off this model. Most notable in this regard is Marin Terpstra and Theo de Wit's important article showing how Taubes's analysis of Walter Benjamin's "Theologico-Political Fragment" from the 1920s linked Benjamin's call for a nihilist method of "world politics" to Paul's use of the formula "as if not [ōs mē]" in 1 Corinthians 7—since time is short, those who have wives should act as if they have none, those who mourn should act as if they were not mourning, etc. And in the excellent treatment of Taubes that Joshua Robert Gold published before his untimely death, he described Taubes as endorsing a kind of apocalyptic nihilism, centered around the principle that "terrestrial power is destined for oblivion."[19]

Taubes may have very well been a nihilist. There are several passages in works that he published in his lifetime that suggest that such a nihilist or tragic reading of Taubes is indeed the *echt* Taubes. For example, in his 1957 essay on Freud, republished in *From Cult to Culture*, Taubes takes Freud's interpretation of Paul in *Moses and Monotheism* to entail the claim that progress is impossible, for Paul's gospel also contained an "implicit confession of guilt . . . the evangel was at the same time a dysangel," proclaiming the bad news of original sin.[20] Paul becomes the main figure for Taubes's argument that progress is a sham, for "history is caught in an eternal cycle of constructing and destroying. It is illusory to hope for man ever to break the cycle."[21] Similarly, Taubes's corpus contains many claims about human understandings of religion failing to represent religion adequately; the finitude of human thinking and action is part and parcel of humans' being in the world. For example, in a 1967 essay against Buber's utopianism, Taubes claims that "the call for realization and action which fill [sic] the pages of Buber's writings remains a gesture so long as it is not admitted that in the process of realization and action man's original purity of intention must be transformed and sullied by the complexity of the recalcitrant reality."[22] The wisdom received from the past can never be put into action; therefore, claims that such wisdom can be a source of power or happiness are simply false. This dynamic is actually quite similar to a Freudian one. If one's purity of intention were always compromised by the real world, the repetition of this experience would lead agents to *remember* this gap between interior motivation and the pragmatics of action when formulating social-ethical plans. Yet Buber—at least on Taubes's account—failed to do this.[23] So in this case too, Buber's creativity in hearkening back to prophetic accounts of human agency and its possibilities is *also* always a forgetting, a repression of human finitude.

If such a reading of Taubes were an accurate report of his views, one could easily find biblical antecedents for it. In an essay on monotheism and trauma, intended to show Freudian dynamics in biblical texts, Jan Assmann gave a compelling account of the simultaneity of memory and forgetting, and the instability such simultaneity produces, in the book of Deuteronomy.[24] Corresponding to the scroll found during King Josiah's reign in 622 BCE, when the Assyrian Empire had already exiled the northern kingdom of Israel and was threatening the southern kingdom of Judah, Deuteronomy sought to forestall the exile of the southern kingdom by exhorting the people of Israel to devote itself to the covenant. It did this by requiring externalized memory-symbols and rites of memorialization by which the people's collective identity is maintained: memorization of divine teaching, religious education, wearing tefillin, having mezuzot on doorjambs, depositing a written document of divine teaching in a public place, and hastening the transformation of agricultural festivals into holidays of historical memory. As Assmann pointed out, "the entire book is based on the deep fear of forgetting that will inevitably occur once the people have entered the cities they have not built, the wells they have not dug, and once they have eaten and drunk the bread and wine they have not produced" in the Promised Land. As a result, "the people are expected to master the trick of remembering privation in the midst of abundance, and to recollect their nomadic lifestyle while living a settled existence in towns or in the fields."[25] There would be no reason to legislate practices such as those delineated at Deuteronomy 6:6–9, 27:2–8, or 16, unless the author(s) of Deuteronomy either had observed the people of Israel's forgetting the covenant, or feared their doing so in the near future. Yet the process of remembering the covenant requires that the Israelite be in two time frames simultaneously: now in the time frame that is doing the remembering, as well as in the past that is being remembered. Assmann described this kind of collective memory as "counterfactual," as a way of getting at the dynamic in which revealed religion produces a feeling of simultaneous at-home-ness and not-at-home-ness in the world. Since "revealed knowledge is by definition knowledge of something outside the world," counterfactual memory is simply part and parcel of revealed religion, commanded and yet impossible.[26] Because monotheism renders human beings homeless (by calling them to the supernatural) at the same time that they are making their home in the world, "the duty to forget one's pagan faith is never quite fulfilled."[27] It is simply impossible for the believer to be both supernatural and historical, both in the past and in the present, at once. I should be *then*, but I am always *now*; I need to travel in time because God says that I must do so if I am to flourish in the here and now, but I sadly cannot travel in time. Because the duty of counterfactual memory can never be fulfilled, there is no monotheism without guilt.

However, in his discussion of Freud in *The Political Theology of Paul*, Taubes did suggest that classical Judaism also gives evidence of contesting such a tragic reading. The eternal cycle of constructing and destroying in history can be suspended, in a move that both absents God from history and speaks in the name of the God who is no longer present. Negative theology undoes itself dialectically, and it does so because negative theology remains in force, insofar as the Jewish tradition allows Jews to construct a true fiction in which they place themselves in God's stead. While God is absent and radically beyond, humans are present, relieving history of the anxiety caused by negative theology.

Taubes made this suggestion on the second day of the four days of lectures preserved in *The Political Theology of Paul*, in the course of a lengthy exegesis of B. Berakhot 32a (and its interpretation of Exodus 32) that was one part of a longer treatment of the liturgy of Yom Kippur.[28] On Yom Kippur, according to Taubes, the I is *not* powerless to relieve the guilt produced by negative theology—by a God before whom we are always in the wrong, because of the impossibility of fulfilling the demand of counterfactual memory. The believer remembers his or her sins on Yom Kippur, acknowledges them, and utters prayers of acknowledgment that have the effect of achieving forgiveness of his or her sins. Some kind of harmony is produced. And yet it should *not* have been produced, because of the qualitative difference between God and humankind. Taubes found acknowledgments in the tradition that such harmony is produced by *human* action, and not by God. One of these is the Kol Nidre prayer, which creates a legal fiction by which all the believer's oaths over the next year are deprived of any and all force, making it impossible for the believer to be judged negatively for having broken oaths that were made in undue haste.[29] This suspension of oaths, while post-Talmudic, coheres with the "point" of B. Berakhot 32a.[30] When Moses implores God in Exodus (32:11) not to turn away from the people of Israel for having built the golden calf, he is not simply beseeching God, but, as the Talmud points out, also taking upon himself the power to break God's own vow to correlate the people's sin with divine punishment. As Taubes narrated the *sugya* to his audience (the two bracketed passages of English text are Taubes's editorial comments): "*And Moses besought* [va-yeḥal] *the Lord his God* [Exodus 32:11]. Rabbi Eleazar said: This teaches that Moses stood in prayer before the Holy One, blessed be He, until he wearied Him. Raba said [and now comes the crux]: Until he remitted His vow for Him. It is written here *va-yeḥal*, and it is written there [that is, for the vow] *lo yeḥal devaro, he shall not break* [yeḥal] *his word* [Numbers 30:3]."[31] The lexical creativity of the rabbi (the third-/fourth-century CE rabbi, Rava) in whose name one finds the opinion that Taubes finds to be the point of the Talmudic passage, is quite staggering. Trying to unpack the meaning of *va-yeḥal* in Exodus 32:11 (from the root *ḥ.l.h*), where Moses "pleads" or "beseeches" God not to be angry with the people of Israel, Rava suggests that it is identical with the meaning of another word that appears in Numbers 30:3, *yaḥel* in the Masoretic text (from the root *ḥ.l.l*), meaning to break or to violate a pledge. Inserting the meaning of this second verb back into the verse from Exodus leads to understanding Moses's "Let not your anger blaze forth against Your people" not as a prayer that *asks* for a vow to be undone, but as a prayer that *performs* a cessation of God's vow to punish a sinful people according to their deserts.

Rava does not engage in this lexical creativity because he is attributing the predicate of mercy to God. Rather, he says this—on Taubes's interpretation—because the terms of the covenant have such intense psychic costs that they *must* be suspended on a regular basis in the liturgical cycle. The gap between the believer's position in the historical present and God's position in the past (or outside of the present moment) is simply unsustainable. Mercy is *required* by the trauma of revelation. On the one hand, when Rava reads Numbers 30:3 into Exodus 32:11, this reading becomes part of the content of revelation; it is simply the case that revelation asserts that humans have the power to change the terms of the covenant through their religious acts. On the other hand, it is *at the same time* a human annulment of the covenant, which depends upon the blessings-and-curses aspect of its formula for its force: if the people of Israel follow the commandments of the Torah, then they will be blessed, but if not they will be cursed. Because divine transcendence is given *to* human historicity, it undoes itself—not due to logical necessity, but out of a psychodynamic necessity. There can be no monotheism without what Taubes describes, overtly returning to Freud, as the "primal scene [*Urszene*]" of "the suspension [*Aufhebung*] of the destruction that was pledged by God."[32]

Compare this to Maimonides's account of negative theology. On the Maimonidean account, God's literal apathy with regard to humans—God's inability to respond to human actions because God cannot have a psyche that could sense such acts—means that there is no way to relieve the sense that suffering is deserved. God does not directly punish humans, leading them to suffer. Yet God has ordained permanent rules that promise blessedness or suffering in accordance with what naturally follows from various human norms and dispositions: "Actions similar to those that proceed from us from a certain aptitude of the soul—namely jealousy, holding fast to vengeance, hatred, or anger—proceed from Him, may He be exalted, because of the deserts of those who are punished."[33] Maimonides's perfectionist rationalist ethic ignores the need to moderate the stresses of that life through some kind of liturgical structure. (Note that Maimonides's law code, the *Mishneh Torah*, never makes mention of the Kol Nidre prayer.)

To be sure, Taubes did not *deny* divine transcendence. He claimed only that it needed some regular structure in which human conceptual labor did theological work, so that the ill effects of belief would be minimized. In this way, the power of God could be exercised by humans, despite the difference between humans and God. Instead of being constricted by God-made laws, humans can make laws for themselves. Only on such an account is it possible to understand Moses's plea to God, which cancels God's oath to judge the people of Israel on the basis of what they deserve.[34]

If we are to take Taubes's discussion here seriously, then the term "negative political theology" used by Hartwich and the Assmanns, as well as Terpstra and de Wit, is not an apt descriptor for Taubes's work. For them, the phrase means a refusal of all political structure. But if Moses denies God's authority to judge the people of Israel for their acts, as Rava suggests, then this is *not* a refusal of all political power. Rather, it is *only a refusal of all political power that forgets that its power is granted by those over whom it rules (and not by God)*. The ruled are simultaneously the rulers, for Moses and for Taubes. A negative political theology that blurs the distinctions between theology and anthropology, by allowing humans to take the reins of the covenant from God, grants humans the power to change norms and/or the effects of not abiding by norms (as Moses does in the passage from B. Berakhot). It is thereby democratic and populist. This political model requires the absence of God from both history and human understanding that negative theology grants.[35]

It still remains to extend this account of Taubes's negative political theology, which portrays Taubes as a radical democrat in the lectures on Paul (going against the grain of much of the secondary literature on Taubes), and to show its upshot for contemporary polities. To show that Taubes himself linked negative theology with democracy requires turning to other works of Taubes besides *The Political Theology of Paul*, and even to essays that are not collected in *From Cult to Culture*. In the following, I will focus on two of those uncollected essays, further concretizing the link between Taubes's theology and Taubes's politics.

The first of these essays is "Theology and the Philosophic Critique of Religion," which appeared in the journal *Cross Currents* in 1955.[36] The biographical sketch of Taubes at the bottom of the essay's opening page notes that "portions of this article appeared, in altered form, in the *Journal of Religion*." This is true. The opening section and most of the closing section are lifted from "On The Nature of the Theological Method," Taubes's critique of Paul Tillich's theology that had appeared early in 1954 in *Journal of Religion*, while the treatment of Karl Barth and dialectical theology that makes up the essay's middle section is borrowed from "Theodicy and Theology," which had also appeared in *Journal of Religion* later in 1954.[37] In addition, the essay's first paragraph also appeared in 1955, in the journal *Social Research*, as the first paragraph of "Theology and Political Theory."[38] This essay would appear to be nothing but a tapestry of self-plagiarism.

And yet there is a key alteration that appears in the final sentence of "Theology and the Philosophic Critique of Religion." It reads as follows: "When the first revolutionary impetus of dialectical theology came to a halt and the conservative restoration of dogmatics began [in other words, when Barth shifted from the style of his commentary on Paul's epistle to the Romans to that of the *Church Dogmatics*], the attempt to develop theology on the level of man's transtheistic consciousness had proven itself abortive."[39] The earlier version of this sentence, in "On the

Nature of the Theological Method" ends with the judgment that "the attempt to develop theology on the level of man's actual situation had proven itself abortive."[40] What does this change from "actual situation" in 1954 to "transtheistic consciousness" in 1955 signify? What is "transtheistic consciousness" anyway, or the "transtheistic stage of consciousness," a phrase that Taubes had used earlier in "Theology and the Philosophic Critique of Religion," as well near the end of "Theodicy and Theology," to describe what Barth's commentary on Romans meant to herald?[41]

What Taubes definitely did *not* mean to imply by using the language of "transtheistic" was some impersonal and über-transcendent God beyond God, as was the case with the brief appearance of this word in the opening pages of Paul Tillich's *The Courage to Be*, which had appeared in 1952.[42] Yet giving an account of what Taubes *did* mean requires a brief reconstruction of his evaluation of Barth's theology in several essays that Taubes published in the 1950s.

While Taubes was critical of the first edition of Barth's commentary on Paul's letter to the Romans for keeping too closely to the spirit of nineteenth-century liberal theology, it is not clear to me that Taubes outright favored the second edition of Barth's commentary on Romans in which "man in his totality takes on demonic features and functions only as an antithesis in the divine drama of redemption."[43] While the second edition indeed made advances, insofar as it acknowledged the relation of alterity between the divine and the human, Taubes also pointed out that describing the human-divine relationship strictly as one of negativity makes it impossible for humans to engage in responsible God-talk. The problem of Barth's dialectical theology is the same as the problem of negative theology in general. Barth affirmed revelation and claimed to know that revelation was valid. But at the same time, Barth criticized the human capacity to know God. Thus, while Barth in his commentary on Romans opened "the possibility of a religious language in an age of the eclipse of the divine,"[44] he was unable to justify his own theocentrism, in which revelation would take precedence over reason. For Taubes, the postwar era had shown the reality of evil and the absence of any reconciliation in history between the immanent and the transcendent realms. As a result, the only valid theology for Taubes would be one that was "ready to take upon itself the form of incognito," becoming an entirely ordinary kind of talk. Such a theology would be anthropocentrist, but still theology. It would not be naturalist, because it was theology. It would not be supernaturalist, because of its suspicion of human language's ability to speak of a radically transcendent God. If neither naturalism nor supernaturalism were live options for Taubes, then "transtheism" would do. The word suggests the erasure of the difference between naturalism and supernaturalism. In affirming that naturalism and supernaturalism are identical, it also affirms that theology is also anthropology, that salvation history is world history, and that anthropology is pneumatology.[45] Human "transtheistic consciousness" would this affirm that theology is *not* about a transcendent God, because theology is uttered by finite humans, in a determinate historical situation.

This, at least, is Taubes's claim about the necessity of rooting theology in humans' transtheistic consciousness. His argument, however, is not as clear from the critique of Barth in "Theology and the Philosophic Critique of Religion" as it is in the critique of Tillich in "On the Nature of Theological Method." In the latter essay, Taubes pointed out that "an ontology that stops short at describing objective structures without recourse to the subjective source of this act remains ungrounded."[46] In other words, if negative theology prohibits knowledge of the divine, then if theology is still to be possible, theism can no longer be a mode of belief in which God is only an object for humanity. If theism is to mean anything, it must be concrete. But once it is concrete it is no longer a theism that has something wholly other than humankind as its subject matter. Theism becomes a belief in which humankind and God recognize each other as each other's ground. If God is the creator of humans, it remains the case that God only has meaning due to humans' conceptualizing God. For humans to be self-conscious that their conceptualizing work is at the ground of God's (or "God's") effectiveness in a community is for humans to know that they are not alienated from the object of which they speak; God is in their mouths, and in their hearts. The human and the divine are ideally reconciled within human history only when humans are self-conscious of their own conceptual work as the origin of God. This refusal of the subject-object distinction is what makes the consciousness of humankind transtheistic.

The political upshot of Taubes's theology appeared in another essay published in 1955, "On the Symbolic Order of Modern Democracy."[47] This appeared in the journal *Confluence*, edited by Henry Kissinger while he was a graduate student at Harvard, running the Harvard International Seminar. The journal was, in effect, Kissinger's calling card. It had a very large print run and few subscribers; according to Walter Isaacson's biography of Kissinger, copies of the journal were usually gifts for those whose favor Kissinger wanted to curry.[48] "On the Symbolic Order" is mentioned briefly in one of Taubes's lectures on Paul, in the course of narrating the contours of his relationship with the Nazi jurist Carl Schmitt. Kissinger "had heard that there's someone wandering around, and no one knows who he is, why not have him come to us? And I gave a lecture about political theology, a critique of Schmitt, saying that the mystical phase, meaning the democratic phase, is passed over by Schmitt and that for him is a purely hierarchical cataract in *Political Theology*."[49] Nevertheless, on the basis of the published version of "On the

Symbolic Order," it is difficult to see the essay as a critique of Schmitt, since Schmitt appears only in two paragraphs near its end. How, then, might we reconstruct Taubes's essay as a critique of Schmitt?

Approximately at the midpoint of the essay, Taubes made some comments about the historical development of American democratic government, rooting it not in the hierarchical "federalist" model of Puritanism (as the historian Perry Miller had been arguing[50]) but in Anabaptist patterns of social organization, following the Quaker historian Rufus Jones.[51] Jones had argued that the Protestant notion of the "covenant of grace," in which believers not only receive gifts from God, but also from the Holy Spirit itself, was the antecedent of democratic forms of religious organization such as those found in the early Quakers. From Jones, Taubes inferred that democracy is essentially a mystical political movement.[52]

> Only in terms of a mystical experience does a saying like *vox populi vox Dei* make sense without falling into banality.... The democratic principle makes sense only if I assume that the general will of the people constitutes a quality that is not inherent in any single person. Such a political order [here Taubes began to quote Jones] "is at heart a mystical order. There is something more in each individual than there would be if he were operating in isolation. He becomes in a real sense *over-individual*, and transcends himself through the life of others."[53]

This claim about democracy advances the argument about transtheistic consciousness that Taubes had made the previous year in "Theology and the Philosophic Critique of Religion." Transtheistic consciousness knows that God-talk is always already human talk. Yet this is not the end of the story. Transtheistic consciousness is not a reproduction of social-Gospel–style liberal theology. In a move of negative theology, it posits a transcendent God that is other than humanity; in a move that undoes negative theology, it is self-conscious of itself as positing that God. (Similarly, in B. Berakhot 32a, Moses both prays to a transcendent God, and has power over that God by releasing God from his oath.) In such a blurring of the subject-object distinction, there is no stable epistemological point from which an individual can claim final knowledge of God.

However, this is not a recipe for religious anarchy, in which each person goes about proclaiming his or her own knowledge of God, and ridiculing everyone else's claims. This is the case because one's claims about God still need verification. They can go far, but they can only go so far as the community that endorses them; as Jones pointed out, the Society of Friends aimed at unanimity.[54] Sovereignty therefore is distributed across the community as a whole.[55] As transtheistic consciousness grounds divine authority in communal authority, so does democracy acknowledge that its president "is president only by the grace of the people, and is therefore not fit to represent the sovereignty of God in the language of faith."[56] In following Jones, Taubes offered a model of a democratic political theology that suspends authoritarian policies that either explicitly imitate or are secularized versions of theologies in which a present God manifests himself as commander. Polities that seek a form of government in which God and humanity are only opposed to each other—without the realization that meaning is accomplished through human acts of meaning-giving—will produce authoritarian policies. Taubes continued in the essay to claim that this is the lesson of Kierkegaard, of the Spanish political theorist Juan Donoso Cortés, as well as that of the anarchist Pierre-Joseph Proudhon, all of whom apply "dictatorial attributes" to God.[57]

In the closing pages of the essay, where Schmitt finally appears explicitly, Taubes attempted to use Jones's scholarship to break through the logic of the last essay of Schmitt's *Political Theology* (1922). There, Schmitt agreed with Donoso Cortés that humans have only three political options: to decide for Catholicism, to decide for atheist socialism, or worst of all, to be a member of the bourgeoisie and discuss the matter further.[58] Schmitt and Donoso Cortés agreed with the first of these options. However, in an aside, Schmitt briefly imagines a fourth, Hegelian, option, which denies "that there was at all something to be decided upon"—an option that, for Schmitt, "must have appeared to be a strange pantheistic confusion" between God and the people.[59] Although Schmitt dismissed this option as even worse than bourgeois liberalism, it was such a pantheistic confusion on which Taubes seized in the 1950s. Democracy is the secularized, or incognito, version of the theological concept of the mystical body of the religious community. Only in a democratic polity is transtheistic consciousness achieved. Schmitt had argued, thought Taubes, that in liberalism "the divine was eliminated from secular life," and therefore that "a democratic constitutional state had no legitimizing principle and was therefore doomed to end in a new Caesarism."[60] To this Taubes responded, in effect, by saying that democracy only eliminated the divine as a being who is set over and against the people. Yet if *vox populi* and *vox Dei* are identical in substance as well as in content—as the pantheistic confusion would dictate—then one can accept Schmitt's critique of bourgeois liberalism without feeling pushed into thinking that the only other option was to support dictatorship (as Schmitt and Donoso Cortés did).

The description of Taubes's negative political theology as nihilist therefore seems to me to be either unjustified, or based on an overly narrow reading of Taubes's work. Rather, Taubes's work remains a resource for resisting the authoritarian overtones that result from classical accounts of negative theology. On the Maimonidean model, knowledge of divine substance is made impossible. But a fixed order of rules remains in effect. So even if God cannot be a present authority for a people (because God cannot be brought to language), humans themselves do not become sites of authority. A prophet may become authoritative, or another kind of ruler who enforces laws that are presumed to produce welfare for the people. Hierarchy is in place; someone who is not God takes the place of the divine sovereign. It is only in a more rigorous negative theology—one that takes the role of the subject in making knowledge-claims seriously and sees that once the subjective element is taken into account, God is forced to withdraw from the world, leaving democracy in God's wake—that any and all objective claims about not only the divine substance or psyche, but divine will and a divine law, and even the right and the good, can be doubted. God at that point may still exist for a community, but God will be *theirs*.[61] Only such a negative theology can fulfill the promise that Kenneth Seeskin has articulated, and allow humans to live in the liberation and the humility that comes with the full awareness of the limitations of human reason.[62]

Notes

1. Kenneth Seeskin, "The Positive Contribution of Negative Theology," in *Jewish Philosophy in a Secular Age* (Albany: State University of New York Press, 1990), 61.

2. See Zygmunt Bauman, *Modernity and the Holocaust* (Ithaca, NY: Cornell University Press, 1989); and Max Horkheimer and Theodor W. Adorno, *Dialectic of Enlightenment: Philosophical Fragments*, trans. Edmund Jephcott (Stanford, CA: Stanford University Press, 2002).

3. For treatments of negative theology in Moses Maimonides (1135–1204) that emphasize its relationship with philosophy of language, see Ehud Benor, "Meaning and Reference in Maimonides's Negative Theology," *Harvard Theological Review* 88 (1995): 339–360, and the reply in Hilary Putnam, "On Negative Theology," *Faith and Philosophy* 14 (1997): 407–422.

4. Seeskin, chap. 2, p. 56, this volume.

5. This is the case despite Seeskin's own attempt to link his understanding of negative theology back to Maimonides. See "The Positive Contribution of Negative Theology," 35–50.

6. Saadia Gaon, *The Book of Beliefs and Opinions*, trans. Samuel Rosenblatt (New Haven, CT: Yale University Press, 1948), 102.

7. Bahya ibn Paquda, *Duties of the Heart*, trans. Moses Hyamson (New York: Feldheim, 1970), 1:103.

8. Moses Maimonides, *The Guide of the Perplexed*, trans. Shlomo Pines (Chicago: The University of Chicago Press, 1963), 111 [I:50].

9. Maimonides's views of the truth-status of Islam are complex, and so I have not tried to classify Islam along this axis. What we read in the *Guide* does not overlap with the *Epistle to Yemen* (1172); see Joel L. Kraemer, *Maimonides: The Life and World of One of Civilization's Greatest Minds* (New York: Doubleday, 2008), 237–242.

10. Compare with the accounts of pluralism at William Connolly, *Pluralism* (Durham, NC: Duke University Press, 2005), 140–145, and Michael Warner, *Publics and Counterpublics* (New York: Zone Books, 2002).

11. Maimonides, *Guide,* 126 I: 54.

12. See Diana Lobel, "'Silence Is Praise to You': Maimonides on Negative Theology, Looseness of Expression, and Religious Experience," *American Catholic Philosophical Quarterly* 76 (2002): 25–51; Martin Kavka, *Jewish Messianism and the History of Philosophy* (Cambridge: Cambridge University Press, 2004), 75–81.

13. Maimonides, *Guide,* 511 (III 27).

14. Miriam Galston, "The Purpose of the Law According to Maimonides," *Jewish Quarterly Review* 69 (1968): 27–51, esp. 32.

15. Such democratic Jewish theology need not depend on Taubes. For another route to a populist negative theology, see Seth Sanders's analysis of Deuteronomy's privileging of a scroll of divine text over a king, in *The Invention of Hebrew* (Urbana: University of Illinois Press, 2010), 152–154.

16. Elliot R. Wolfson, *A Dream Interpreted within a Dream: Oneiropoiesis and the Prism of Imagination* (New York: Zone Books, 2011), 31.

17. Ibid., 274.

18. Taubes, *Die Politische Theologie des Paulus* (Munich: Wilhelm Fink, 1993), 152; Taubes, *Political Theology of Paul,* trans. Dana Hollander (Stanford, CA: Stanford University Press, 2004), 121.

19. See Wolf-Daniel Hartwich, Jan Assmann, and Aleida Assmann, "Nachwort," in *Die Politische Theologie des Paulus,* 143–181; Hartwich, Assmann, and Assmann, afterword to *The Political Theology of Paul,* 115–142; Marin Terpstra and Theo de Wit, "'No Spiritual Investment in the World as It Is': Jacob Taubes's Negative Political Theology," in *Flight of the Gods: Philosophical Perspectives on Negative Theology,* ed. Ilse N. Bulhof and Laurens ten Kate (New York: Fordham University Press, 2000), 319–353; Joshua Robert Gold, "Jacob Taubes: 'Apocalypse from Below,'" *Telos* 134 (2006): 140–156 (quotation at 156). A more nuanced account of Taubes's relationship to nihilism can be found in Bruce Rosenstock, "*Palintropos Harmoniê*: Jacob Taubes and Carl Schmitt '*im liebenden Streit,*'" *New German Critique* 41.1 (2014): 55–92.

20. Jacob Taubes, "Religion and the Future of Psychoanalysis," in *From Cult to Culture,* ed. Charlotte Elisheva Fonrobert and Amir Engel (Stanford, CA: Stanford University Press, 2010), 338.

21. Ibid., 339.

22. Taubes, "Martin Buber and the Philosophy of History," in *From Cult to Culture,* 25.

23. I have offered a somewhat different, more chastened view of Buber, in "Verification (*Bewährung*) in Martin Buber," *Journal of Jewish Thought and Philosophy* 20 (2012): 71–98.

24. Assmann, "Monotheism, Memory, and Trauma: Reflections on Freud's Book of Moses," in *Religion and Cultural Memory: Ten Essays,* trans. Rodney Livingstone (Stanford, CA: Stanford University Press, 2006), 46–62. Some of the argument in this essay requires a knowledge of the examples given in the book's introduction (18–19).

25. Assmann, "Monotheism, Memory, and Trauma," 52–53.

26. Ibid., 54.

27. Ibid., 58.
28. Taubes, *Die politische Theologie*, 43–55; Taubes, *Political Theology*, 28–38.
29. Taubes, *Die politische Theologie*, 49; Taubes, *Political Theology*, 33.
30. Taubes used "die Pointe" (45) and the idiom "der Witz der Sache" (54) in his text; Hollander translates both of these phrases as "crux," a word whose etymology jibes somewhat uncomfortably with Taubes's text. See Taubes, *The Political Theology of Paul*, 30, 37.
31. Taubes, *Die politische Theologie*, 45; Taubes, *Political Theology*, 30.
32. Taubes, *Die politische Theologie*, 67; Taubes, *Political Theology*, 47. For Freud on the traumatic power of the primal scene, see the discussion of the Wolf Man in "From the History of an Infantile Neurosis," in Sigmund Freud, *Complete Psychological Works of Sigmund Freud*, translated from the German under the general editorship of James Strachey, in collaboration with Anna Freud, assisted by Alix Strachey and Alan Tyson (London: Hogarth, 1955), 17:7–122.

As Michael Fagenblat has suggested to me in personal correspondence (November 12, 2013), a fascinating comparison can be made between Taubes's reading of traditional texts about Yom Kippur and the deconstruction of Christianity in recent work by Jean-Luc Nancy. For Nancy, the kenotic element of the incarnation narrative of the Gospels, in which "renunciation becomes the proper act of God . . . undoes theism, that is to say, the presence of the power that assembles the world and assures this sense." A similar comparison might also be made to the work of Gianni Vattimo, for whom "secularization is precisely a positive effect of Jesus's teaching, and not a way of moving away from it." Insofar as humans release God from his vows in the Talmudic *sugya*, the sense of the world is immanent to it and not transcendent to it in a way that is similar to the kenotic (post)theology of Nancy and Vattimo. Nevertheless, Nancy's and Vattimo's work—explicitly (as in Nancy) or only implicitly (as in Vattimo) similar to Marcel Gauchet's history of Western secularization in terms of the development of a "religion for departing from religion"—slightly differs from Taubes's argument. The distinction is one between assenting to the truth of the matter and shaping the truth of the matter. In Nancy, Vattimo, and Gauchet, theological development is taken as the development of better reports on objective theological matters. In the Talmudic *sugya*, the subjective element of theological development is clearly at the surface of the text, as Rava uses the biblical text to *force* theology to become anthropology. In Christian and post-Christian accounts of kenosis, God becomes man and withdraws of God's own accord; kenosis is thus the core of a theism that undoes itself, yet this self-undoing is the very essence of theism. In B. Berakhot 32a, man makes God withdraw; the undoing of theism is both explicitly human work *and* part of divine teaching (as Oral Torah).

See Jean-Luc Nancy, *Dis-Enclosure: The Deconstruction of Christianity*, trans. Bettina Bergo, Gabriel Malenfant, and Michael B. Smith (New York: Fordham University Press, 2008), 36; Gianni Vattimo, *Belief*, trans. Luca D'Isanto (Stanford, CA: Stanford University Press, 1999), 41 (and 47); Marcel Gauchet, *The Disenchantment of the World*, trans. Oscar Burge (Princeton, NJ: Princeton University Press, 1997), 33–34 and 101–161. For Nancy on Gauchet, see *Dis-Enclosure*, 142. For a helpful introduction to Nancy's writings on Christianity, see Alena Alexandrova, Ignaas Devisch, Laurens ten Kate, and Aukje van Rooden, "Reopening the Question of Religion: Dis-enclosure of Religion and Modernity in the Philosophy of Jean-Luc Nancy," in *Re-treating Religion: Deconstructing Christianity with Jean-Luc Nancy*, ed. Alena Alexandrova, Ignaas Devisch, Laurens ten Kate, and Aukje van Rooden (New York: Fordham University Press, 2012), 22–40.

33. Maimonides, *Guide*, 126 [I 54].

34. However, we could also read the Maimonidean model somewhat differently. For if God does not directly punish the people of Israel, then is this not already a suspension of heteronomous law, and of the blessings-and-curses aspect of the covenant formula? As Maimonides suggests in his discussion of the law, what makes norms worth endorsing is not their having been promulgated by God, but their production of social welfare, their productions of effects that can be acknowledged by mere observation. See Maimonides, *Guide*, 381 (II 29). See also Galston, "Purpose of the Law According to Maimonides," 32: "it is not precluded that a *nomos* [a humanly created "secular" law] may be divine." Menachem Lorberbaum argued against Galston in *Politics and the Limits of Law: Secularizing the Political in Medieval Jewish Thought* (Stanford, CA: Stanford University Press, 2001), 169n34; I tried to resolve the differences between them in "What Is Immanent in Judaism?: Transcending *A Secular Age*," *Journal of Religious Ethics* 40 (2012): 130.

35. Compare with Jean-Luc Nancy, *The Truth of Democracy*, trans. Pascale-Anne Brault and Michael Naas (New York: Fordham University Press, 2010), 33: " 'Democracy' is thus first of all the name of a regime of sense whose truth cannot be subsumed under any ordering agency whether religious, political, scientific, or aesthetic; it is, rather, that which wholly engages 'man' as the risk and chance of 'himself.' " Again, I thank Michael Fagenblat for suggesting this fruitful link.

36. Taubes, "Theology and the Philosophic Critique of Religion," *Cross Currents* 5 (1955): 323–330. The bibliography of Taubes's writings given in *Abendländliche Eschatologie: Ad Jacob Taubes*, ed. Richard Faber, Eveline Goodman-Thau, and Thomas Macho (Würzburg: Königshausen and Neumann, 2001), 561–570, mistakenly gives the essay a 1954 publication year.

37. Taubes, "On the Nature of the Theological Method: Some Reflections on the Methodological Principles of Tillich's Theology," now reprinted in *From Cult to Culture*, 195–213. For evidence of this essay's influence on American death-of-God theology in the 1960s, see its earlier reprinting in *Toward a New Christianity: Readings in the Death-of-God Theology*, ed. Thomas J. J. Altizer (New York: Harcourt, Brace, and World, 1967). Taubes, "Theodicy and Theology: A Philosophical Analysis of Karl Barth's Dialectical Theology," in *From Cult to Culture*, 177–194.

38. Taubes, "Theology and Political Theory," in *From Cult to Culture*, 222–232.

39. Taubes, "Theology and the Philosophic Critique of Religion," 330.

40. Taubes, "On the Nature of the Theological Method," 199.

41. For "transtheistic state of consciousness," see Taubes, "Theology and the Philosophic Critique of Religion," 329; Taubes, "Theodicy and Theology," 194.

42. Paul Tillich, *The Courage to Be* (New Haven, CT: Yale University Press, 1952), 9.

43. Taubes, "Theology and the Philosophic Critique of Religion," 226; Taubes, "Theodicy and Theology," 185.

44. Taubes, "Theology and the Philosophic Critique of Religion," 229; "Theodicy and Theology," 193. See also "On the Nature of the Theological Method," 213.

45. Taubes would affirm the identity of salvation history and world history in 1963 in "Nachman Krochmal and Modern Historicism," in *From Cult to Culture*, 28–44. He would affirm the identity of anthropology and pneumatology in 1971, in "The Dogmatic Myth of Gnosticism," in *From Cult to Culture*, 61–75, esp. 74: "I have attempted to present the thesis that late ancient Gnosticism signifies a crisis in the monotheistic religion of revelation itself: in this crisis, the doctrine of the transworldly creator-God becomes questionable."

46. Taubes, "On the Nature of Theological Method," 206.

47. Taubes, "On the Symbolic Order of Modern Democracy," *Confluence, An International Forum* 4 (1955): 57–71.

48. Walter Isaacson, *Kissinger: A Biography* (New York: Simon and Schuster, 1992), 72–74.

49. Taubes, *Die politische Theologie des Paulus*, 135–136; Taubes, *Political Theology of Paul*, 100.

50. Perry Miller, "The Marrow of Puritan Divinity," in *Errand into the Wilderness* (Cambridge, MA: Belknap/Harvard University Press, 1956), 48–98; Miller, *The New England Mind: The Seventeenth Century* (Cambridge, MA: Harvard University Press, 1939), 365–462.

51. Rufus Jones, *Mysticism and Democracy in the English Commonwealth* (Cambridge, MA: Harvard University Press, 1932). For his account of Puritanism, implicitly critiquing Perry Miller's work, see p. 49. For more on Jones, see Matthew S. Hedstrom, "Rufus Jones and Mysticism for the Masses," *Cross Currents* 54 (2004): 31–44.

52. For Jones on covenant theology, see Jones, *Mysticism and Democracy*, 130–133. For Jones on the Society of Friends as a form of "religious democracy," see ibid., 56.

53. Taubes, "Symbolic Order of Modern Democracy," 63. The quotation is from Jones, *Mysticism and Democracy*, 25. These sentences are also quoted in the work of the late Unitarian theologian James Luther Adams, *An Examined Faith: Social Context and Religious Commitment* (Boston: Beacon Press, 1991), 310.

54. Jones, *Mysticism and Democracy*, 56.

55. See also Bonnie Honig's remarks on a non-Schmittian understanding of miracle in *Emergency Politics: Paradox, Law Democracy* (Princeton, NJ: Princeton University Press, 2009), 108. My thanks to Joshua Lupo for suggesting this parallel.

56. Ibid., 64.

57. Ibid., 67.

58. Carl Schmitt, *Politische Theologie: Vier Kapitel zur Lehre von der Souveränität* (Berlin: Duncker and Humblot, 1979), 62–64; Schmitt, *Political Theology: Four Chapters on the Concept of Sovereignty* (Cambridge, MA: MIT Press, 1985), 58–60.

59. Schmitt, *Politische Theologie*, 65–66; Schmitt, *Political Theology*, 61–62.

60. Taubes, "Symbolic Order of Modern Democracy," 70.

61. In personal correspondence (July 17, 2015), my student Joshua Lupo asks me if I am being willfully blind to the possibility that I am endorsing a realized eschatology, or in other words to the possibility that the vox populi can be just as authoritarian a force as the Maimonidean God against which I am counterposing Taubes's negative theology. While I remain open to this problem, I do think that those who would want to follow Taubes by taking the vox in, say, ethnocratic ways are missing the implication of Jones's claim, endorsed by Taubes, that the democrat who is an over-individual *continues to engage in self-*

overcoming, and does not limit the "others" through whom she transcends herself. Indeed, in order to transcend herself, the democrat must always live with others who test and contest the pretense of the vox populi to be equivalent to the general will.

62. My thanks to Ken Seeskin for his expert stewardship of the community of those who inquire into the meanings and powers of Jewish philosophy; to Seeskin, Lenn Goodman, David Novak, and Michael Fagenblat, before whom a very preliminary version of this chapter served as a response at the 2011 annual meeting of the Association for Jewish Studies; to Michael Fagenblat for asking me to expand upon my remarks on that occasion; and to Joshua Lupo for an extensive conversation about this essay for which I am exceedingly grateful. The responsibility for all remaining faults and weaknesses of this essay remains mine and mine alone.

CONTRIBUTORS

AGATA BIELIK-ROBSON is Professor of Jewish Studies at the University of Nottingham and Professor of Post-Secular Studies at the Polish Academy of Sciences in Warsaw. She is the author of *The Saving Lie: Harold Bloom and Deconstruction* and *Jewish Cryptotheologies of Late Modernity: Philosophical Marranos*.

IDIT DOBBS-WEINSTEIN is Associate Professor of Philosophy, Jewish Studies, and Graduate Department of Religion. Her most recent book is *Spinoza's Critique of Religion and Its Heirs: Marx. Benjamin, Adorno* (2015).

MICHAEL FAGENBLAT is Senior Lecturer at the Open University of Israel. He is the author of *A Covenant of Creatures: Levinas's Philosophy of Judaism* and numerous articles in modern Jewish philosophy and European phenomenology.

LENN E. GOODMAN is Professor of Philosophy and Andrew W. Mellon Professor in the Humanities at Vanderbilt University. His books include *God of Abraham, On Justice,* and *In Defense of Truth.*

JAMES JACOBSON-MAISELS teaches at Haifa University and the Pardes Institute of Jewish Studies. He received his PhD from the University of Chicago in 2015. His most recent publication is "Embodied Epistemology: Knowing through the Body in Late Hasidism," forthcoming in the *Journal of Religion.*

MARTIN KAVKA is Professor in the Department of Religion at Florida State University. He is the author of *Jewish Messianism and the History of Philosophy* (Cambridge University Press), which was awarded the Jordan Schnitzer Award in Philosophy and Jewish Thought by the Association for Jewish Studies in 2008. He is the coeditor of four books, including *Judaism, Liberalism, and Political Theology* (2014, with Randi Rashkover), and with his colleague Aline Kalbian, coedits the *Journal of Religious Ethics.*

SAM LEBENS is Research Fellow at the Rutgers Center for Philosophy of Religion. He has had articles published in a number of philosophical journals, including: *Philosophical Studies*, *Religious Studies*, and the *International Journal for Philosophy of Religion*.

ADAM LIPSZYC is a Professor in the Institute of Philosophy and Sociology of Polish Academy of Science. He is the author of *Justice on the Tip of the Tongue: Reading Walter Benjamin* (in Polish).

DAVID NOVAK is J. Richard and Dorothy Shiff Chair of Jewish Studies as Professor of Religion and Philosophy in the University of Toronto. He is the author of seventeen books, most recently, *Natural Law: A Jewish, Christian, and Islamic Trialogue* and *Zionism and Judaism: A New Theory*, and is a member of the Editorial Board of *First Things*. In 2017, he is to deliver the Gifford Lectures at the University of Aberdeen, Scotland.

SARAH PESSIN is Professor of Philosophy and Judaic Studies at the University of Denver. She is the author of *Ibn Gabirol's Theology of Desire: Matter and Method in Jewish Medieval Neoplatonism* and numerous articles on Jewish and Islamic medieval philosophy and Greek, Jewish, Islamic, and Christian Neoplatonisms.

KENNETH SEESKIN is Philip M. and Ethel Klutznick Professor of Jewish Civilization at Northwestern University. He has written several books in the field of Jewish philosophy including *Searching for a Distant God*, *Maimonides on the Origin of the World*, and *Jewish Messianic Thoughts in an Age of Despair*. His most recent book is titled *Thinking about the Torah: A Philosopher Reads the Bible*.

DAVID SHATZ is the Ronald P. Stanton University Professor of Philosophy, Ethics, and Religious Thought at Yeshiva University. He is the author of *Jewish Thought in Dialogue* and editor of *Philosophy and Faith: A Philosophy of Religion Reader* and will be featured in a volume of the series *Library of Contemporary Jewish Philosophers*, published by Brill.

SANDRA VALABREGUE is a painter and an independent scholar of Medieval Jewish thought. She is the author of *Concealed and Revealed: "Eyn Sof" (Infinity) in Theosophic Kabbalah* (in Hebrew).

TZAHI WEISS is an Associate Professor of Jewish Mysticism and Modern Hebrew Literature at the Open University of Israel. His most recent book is *Cutting the Shoots: The Worship of the Shekhinah in the World of Early Kabbalistic Literature* (in Hebrew).

ELLIOT R. WOLFSON is the Marsha and Jay Glazer Chair Endowed Chair in Jewish Studies at the University of California, Santa Barbara. He is the author of many essays and books including, most recently, *A Dream Interpreted within a Dream: Oneiropoiesis and the Prism of Imagination* (2011), which won the American Academy of Religion's Award for Excellence in the Study of Religion in the Category of Constructive and Reflective Studies, 2012, and *Giving Beyond the Gift: Apophasis and Overcoming Theomania* (2014). He is presently working on a book titled *Heidegger and the Kabbalah: Hidden Gnosis and the Path of Poiesis*.

SHIRA WOLOSKY is Professor of English Literature at the Hebrew University. She has written books and articles on literary theory, poetics, and religion, including Language Mysticism, and is currently working on a book on Jewish Thought and Postmodern Theory. Her awards include a Guggenheim, American Council of Learned Societies, Fellowships at the Institute of Advanced Studies in Princeton and Israel, and Drue Heinz professor at Oxford

INDEX

Abraham (biblical figure), 110–11
absence of God, 20, 116, 129n27, 239–40, 250–53, 256n60, 263
absolute music, 208, 211n34
Abulafia, Abraham, 263
Adam (biblical figure), 79, 137, 141, 153n
Adams, James Luther, 354n53
Adonai, 263, 327
Adorno, Theodor: after Auschwitz, 200, 202; on antisemitism, 208–9; Walter Benjamin and, 202, 204, 205, 206; critics on, 199–200, 210n6, 210n14; on delusion, 205–6; disassociation between consciousness and thing/material object, 201; exegesis presented by, 206, 211n27; Jewish affiliation of, 199, 200, 210n6; on Judaism, 10, 27n35; on Kabbalah, 210n7; negative dialectics, 202–6; on opposition to Mahler's and Schoenberg's music, 208; on prohibition against graven images, 201, 202, 204, 205, 209; rhetoric, hostility to, 207
afissat hamahsava (annihilation of thought), 40
Agamben, Giorgio, 236n64, 267, 270, 273
ahdout shavah (equal unity), 38–39
Alcibiades (Socrates), 68
al-falā sifa. *See* Neoplatonism
Al-Farabi, 32, 34, 65, 83, 195n18
Al Kindi, 32, 43n6
almond motif: in Celan's poetry, 316, 317–18, 319, 320–21
al-Mukammas, David ibn Merwan, 32
Alter, Robert, 279n20
Altmann, Alexander, 69
Amichai, Yehuda: on the images of God, 21, 325–28; influences on poetry of, 21; ironic rhetoric in poetry of, 323, 327; knowledge of Jewish sources, 324, 326; on limits of belief, 327–28; Maimonideanism contested by, 21; on prayer, 329–30; rebellion against patriarchal Judaism, 331–32
Amida prayer, 65
animal, cruelty to, 292, 301nn33, 34, 302n42
annihilation: and reaching the state of '*ayin*, 116, 118–21, 129n45
anniyya (Thatness of God), 229–31, 252
Anscombe, Elizabeth, 98
anthropology, 345, 346–47, 352n32, 354n45
anthropomorphism, 4, 25n19, 59, 66, 71, 224, 226
antinomianism, 19–21, 158n84, 262, 264, 267–68, 269–70
antisemitism, 208, 213–14
Apollonius, 69
apophasis. *See* negative theology
Aqiba, Rabbi, 51, 227
Aquinas, 6, 172, 201
Aristotle, 67; on foundations of philosophy, 85; God of, 244–45; on the Intellect, 195n18; law of non-contradiction, 91; perfection of divine activity, 64; on prayer, 2; union of matter and form, 78
Armstrong, A. H., 166, 177n41
Arugat ha-Bosem (ibn Ezra), 33
Aschenglorie (Celan), 315
Assembly of Israel *(kenesset yisrael)*, 133, 135–37, 153n25, 154n37, 155n39
Assmann, Aleida, 340, 341–42, 344–45
Assmann, Jan, 340, 342, 344–45

atheism: God's existence, 3, 23n7, 88–89, 149, 158n91, 240; Levinas on, 165; of Maimonides, 72; nonconceptual atheism, 3, 23n9; the pious atheist, 265, 278n15; Rav Kook on, 17, 148–50, 158n91; skepticism, 3, 6, 35, 38, 226–28, 227, 235n54, 236n56; transatheism, 348–49
Atlan, Henri, 131
attributes of action, 242–44
Augustine, 79–80, 164, 182, 196n33, 275
Austin, John L., 230
authority: people (*demos*) as site of, 339
autobiography, 218, 220
Avicenna, 32, 63, 64, 150, 195n18, 229
'*ayin* (nothing): attainment of, 117–23, 124, 129n45; corporeality, 66–67, 122–23, 126; creation/creativity, 111–13, 115–16; Ecclesiastes 3:19, 13, 38; engagement with material world, 119–20, 122–26, 130n59; and existential unity, 116; as fear and awe, 111, 116–17, 126, 129n29; Grounding Element, 186; humility, 12, 15, 55–56, 59, 102, 116–20, 126, 145; in Ibn Gabirol's poetry, 186; metaphysical transformation, 113, 128n16; Rav Kook on, 290; and the spiritual process, 113–14; transcendence of, 125; *tsimtsum* (contraction), 13, 25n21, 28n45, 142, 173, 261–62, 264, 278n16; unifying role of, 112–14, 117–20, 121–22, 126, 128n16; wisdom as, 125. See also *yesh*
'*ayn sof* (the Infinite), 25n21, 36, 122; apophatic v. anthropomorphic notions of, 37, 87; God as, 39, 173, 255n21; historical background of, 46n49; as indifferent oneness (*aḥdout ha-shaveh*), 145; Levinas on, 172, 173–74; Rav Kook on, 145, 147, 150; *sefirot*, 39–46n49, 115, 125, 145, 159n101, 252, 327; *shi'ashu'a* and the stirrings within, 280n34
Azriel of Gerona, 41, 116, 129n27, 147

Bachofen, Johann Jakob, 266, 267–68, 272–73
Bacon, Francis, 205
Badiou, Alain, 72
Band, Arnold, 324
ban on graven images, 201, 204, 205, 209
baqashah, 245
Barth, Karl, 26n26, 259–61, 277n7, 345–46
being: "beyond Being," 161, 162, 163–64, 165, 223; constitution-as-interruption, 185; doing compared with, 240; *ehyeh asher ehyeh*, 77, 230, 251, 262, 328; God as, 6, 64–66, 191, 230, 244–45, 251–52; *hester panim*, 240, 262; *khōra*, 181–85, 188–92, 195n18; *tsimtsum* (contraction), 13, 25n21, 28n45, 142, 173, 261–62, 264, 278n16. See also '*ayin* (nothing); transcendence; *yesh*
Benjamin, Walter: Adorno, Theodor, 202, 204, 205; on the antinomian trace, 270; autonomy of the subject, 206; dialectics of nothingness, 265–68, 273, 278n18, 307; on the Exodus from Egypt, 269–70, 279n27; form of immersion in the details of tradition, 206; Haggadah, 269, 275, 279n26, 281n37; on Halakhah/Torah Law, 269–70; hiddenness associated with Christianity, 262; the hunchback motif, 269, 280n29; influence of Bachofen on, 266, 267–68, 272–73; integration of disciplines in works of, 304–5; on the Kafkan universe, 264–65; language of (*reine Sprache*), 138–39; on Law-the Torah, 268–69; on the messianic, 278n18; on revelation, 20; Schmitt's analyses of politics, 305; on scripture in Kafka's works, 308; separation of law from life, 264–65; on storytelling, 269–72, 279n26; Taubes' analysis of "Theologico-Political Fragment," 341; *theologischer Schachzug*, 278n16; theology deployed by, 305; on tradition, 206. See also Scholem, Gershom
ben Sheshet, Jacob, 38

ben Uzziel, Jonathan, 66
"beyond Being," 161, 162, 163–64, 165, 223
Bialik, Hayyim Nahman, 279n26, 281n37
biblical anthropomorphism, 5, 66–67, 70, 72
biblical hermeneutics, 206, 211n27
binah, 40
Blanchot, Maurice, 11
Blau, Yitzhak, 293, 294, 295, 302n46
Bleich, J. David, 301n34
Bloch, Ernst, 17, 259, 261, 281n37
Bloom, Harold, 11–12, 259, 276n4, 280n31
Book of Beliefs and Doctrines (Saadya Gaon), 89
Book of Causes, 32
breaking of the vessels *(shevirat hakeilim),* 118–19
Brentano, Franz, 201
"Brisker school," 295
brit (covenant), 246–47, 249–50, 255n39, 255n41, 344
Brod, Max, 265, 266
brokenness *(shevirah),* 118–19
Buber, Martin, 247–48, 251, 341
Buddhism, 139, 156n
Burke, Edmund, 9

Caesarism, 349
Camp, Elizabeth, 101
Cappadocian Fathers, 87
Caputo, John, 26n25, 182
Carabine, Deidre, 4
Carlson, Thomas A., 24n10
catastrophe, theory of, 55
Catholicism, 7, 349
cave, parable of, 167
Celan, Paul: Christian theology, 311, 315, 318, 319, 320; dualism in poetry of, 12–13; formal regression in poetry of, 316, 317; German-Jewish negative theology of, 10; influences on, 309, 310; Jewish motifs in poetry of, 275–76, 316, 317; on Kafka's definition of writing, 308; *the Meridian* (Celan), 275–76, 308, 309–10, 320; negative theology in works of, 309–10; *Die Niemandsrose* (Celan), 311–12; nothingness of on, 315; pun on

niemand in poetry of, 312–13; on revelation, 312; theologico-literary negativity of, 304
cherubim (monsters), 48
Christianity: almond imagery in, 318; analytic philosophy, 85–86; apophasis, 193n1; apophatic theology in, 87; bearing God's name in vain, 202; biblical hermeneutics, 206; Derrida on, 190–91, 193n3, 214, 216; *deus absconditus in,* 260; Good beyond being, 223; on graven images, 202; on *hamartia,* 275; incarnation narrative of the Gospels, 352n32; Jewish God in, 324; kenosis, 191–92, 352n32; messianic reversal, 260, 261, 263; negative theology in, 203–4; presence of God, 18; on the presence of God, 18; transcendence of Christian mysticism, 203–4; *via negativa,* 18, 274
Christological imagery: in Celan's poetry, 311, 315, 318, 319, 320
Chrysostom, John, 87
Citron, Gabriel, 87–89, 106n15
clinamen, 11, 14, 162, 259, 260, 271, 273, 277n5
Cohen, Hermann, 1, 12, 220–21, 312
commandments, 9–10, 12, 246, 255n39, 276n4
concealed *(ne'elam),* 14, 37, 38, 138
Confessions (Augustine), 164
Conic Sections (Apollonius), 69
contraction *(tsimtsum),* 13, 25n21, 28n45, 142, 173, 261–62, 264, 278n16
corporeality, 66–67, 122–23, 126
counter-person, 170
the covenant *(ha-brit),* 246–47, 249–50, 255n39, 255n41, 344
creation: *'ayin* (nothing), 111–12; destruction, 48; dissolution as path to, 112–13; emanation, 168, 169; God created by human prayer, 330, 331; positivity of, 173; *tsimtsum* (contraction), 13, 25n21, 28n45, 142, 173, 261–62, 264, 278n16
creationism, 169

creator, God as, 12, 71–76, 83n59, 84n73, 87–89, 172, 330
Crescas, Hasdai, 36

Davidson, Herbert, 72, 83n54
de Leon, Moses, 13, 21, 38, 42
Deleuze, Gilles, 194n16
delusion, 205–6
democracy, 339, 340, 345, 348–49, 351n15, 354n35
Denys, 180, 181, 183, 191, 193n1. *See also* Pseudo-Dionysius
Derrida, Jacques: *adieu*, 191–92; Augustine, 182; on being Jewish, 213–14, 216; on Christianity, 190–91, 193n3, 214, 216; *égarés*, 213, 214, 226, 228–29; emancipation of Jewishness from Judaism, 219, 222, 233n22; *époché* of theology, 227; explicit predication rejected by, 224; on God, 193n1, 217–19, 280n36; on Haggadah, 279n25; intuitionless mysticism, 226, 236n56; Jewish identity of, 218–19; *khōra*, 182–84; language of, 230–31; Maimonides in works of, 220–21; Marranoism, 215–16, 217; messianicity of, 197n38; on prayer, 224, 227, 234n40, 236n59; on representation, 8, 27n27; on Saint Augustine, 213–14, 217; on the self, 188, 218; on silence, 225, 235n48; speaking/speaking of the unspeakable/not speaking, 218–19
Descartes, René, 8, 52–55, 85, 164
desire, 117, 122–23, 184–85, 189, 190
determinate negation, 208, 212n35
deus absconditus, 36, 258–59, 276n3; God in Celan's poetry, 309–10; hiddenness as, 262, 276n3; in Protestantism, 19–20, 258–59, 260–61; Scholem on, 36, 260; *tsimtsum* (contraction) compared with, 261–62
devastation: catastrophe, theory of, 55
de Vries, Hent, 191, 193n4
de Wit, Theo, 341, 344–45
dialectical theology, 65, 345–46
dialogue between God and his people Israel, 247

difference: double relationality of, 172–73
dissent *(kefirah)*, 146, 148
distortion *(Entstellung)*, 271
Dobbs-Weinstein, Idit, 10, 78–79
Donoso Cortés, Juan, 249
Dostoyevsky, Fyodor, 306
double-person theory of the soul, 170
double relationality, 172–73
Dov Baer, Maggid of Mezherich, 13–14, 17, 110; on *'ayin*, 112–13, 116–19, 123–26, 125, 128n16; on the creation of humanity, 124; on the mystical union between God and man, 121–22; on world engagement, 117, 129n37
dualism, 12–13, 167, 168, 170–71, 177n41, 261
Duties of the Heart (ibn Paquda), 33

Eckhart, Meister, 6, 199, 200, 220, 222, 309, 310
ecstatic religion, 134, 171, 178n62, 263
efes (nothingness), 113, 122, 126
Ehud (biblical figure), 231–32
ehyeh asher ehyeh, 77, 230, 251, 262, 328
ein sof. See *'ayn sof* (the Infinite)
Eleazar, Rabbi, 343
emanation, 164, 168, 169, 183–84, 194nn13, 16
Die Engführung (Celan), 276, 281n39
entity (term), 99
époché, 227, 228
equal unity (*ahdout shavah*), 38–39
equanimity, conception of, 38
equanimity of values *(hishtawwut shel arakhim)*, 143
Eriguena, Johannes Scotus, 44n16
Eros, birth of, 185–96
es gibt, 181, 190
esotericism, 132–34, 133–35, 141, 144, 150n
ethical value, hierarchy of, 166–67, 168–69, 177n30
Eve (biblical figure), 79
evil, 85–86, 145–46
existence (use of term), 150, 159n100
Exodus from Egypt, 269–70, 275–76, 279n27
external v. internal divine relationality, 251
extremism, 55

Fagenblat, Michael, 158n91, 170, 179n73, 352n32
faith *(emunah)*, 143, 147, 157n62
Feinstein, Moshe, 297
feminine divinity, 331–32
Feuerbach, Ludwig, 261
Fine, Kit, 94
finitude, 170
Finlayson, Gordon, 199, 200, 209n4
Fons Vitae (Ibn Gabirol), 33
four rabbis entered the garden *(pardes)*, 51, 227
Frank, Jacob, 17
Franke, William, 28n38
Frege, Gottlob, 97, 99
Freud, Sigmund, 219, 271, 272, 276n4, 280n31, 341, 342, 344; on the traumatic power of the primal scene, 344, 352n32

Galston, Miriam, 339, 353n34
Garden of Eden, banishment from, 48
Gauchet, Marcel, 352n32
Geach, Peter, 98
Gersonides, 101, 288
Ghazālī, 32, 64, 65, 72, 75, 76, 80n4
Gibbs, Robert, 192n1, 197n38
Gikatilla, Joseph, 4, 38
Gilson, Etienne, 161
Glory, 231–32, 240
glory *(kavod)*, 48
Gnosticism, 176n30, 354n45
God: absence of, 20, 239–40, 250–53, 256n60, 263; in Amichai's poetry, 21, 325–28; *anniyya* (Thatness of God), 229–31, 252; of Aristotle, 244–45; authority of, 305, 338–39, 348–49; as being, 6, 64–66, 191, 244–45, 251–52; in Celan's poetry, 309–10, 312–13; covenant with, 246–47, 249–50, 255n39, 255n41, 344; as creator, 12, 71–76, 83n59, 84n73, 87–89, 172, 330; Descartes on the existence of, 52, 53; descent into the world, 122–23; describing, 48–51, 56–58, 103, 106nn15, 16, 148, 202, 241–44, 288–90, 335–36; disappearance of, 264–65; divine punishment, 343, 344, 353n34;

ehyeh asher ehyeh, 77, 230, 251, 262, 328; evil, 85–86; face of, 14–15, 240, 262; free relationality of *(da-sein)*, 251–52; as a *Gegenprinzip*, 262; in Haggadah, 269, 275, 279n26, 281n37; in history, 248–49, 256n51, 325–26; human language on, 56–58, 66, 250, 335–36; *imitatio dei*, 28n44, 56, 57–58, 202, 242–44, 339; *kavod* (glory) of, 231–32, 240; knowledge of, 31–32, 40–41, 43n6, 51–57, 70, 102, 144, 221, 226, 290; as mirror of the self, 69, 82n35; Moses and, 56–57; names of, 35, 101, 148, 157n78, 201–2, 227, 263, 327; perfection of, 64, 71–76, 77, 83n59, 290; rational conjunction *(ha-devequt ha-sikhlit)* contrasted with, 157n78; relations with humans, 48, 58, 72–74, 83n59, 135–37, 172, 344; revelation of, 185, 187, 193n1, 253n2, 290; Sabbath, 274–75; secret of *(sod ha-shem)*, 141; Shekhinah, 120, 122–25, 123, 124–25, 132–33, 310–11, 331; Tetragrammaton (YHWH), 35–36, 51, 77, 229–30, 255n31, 263, 269–70, 327; thirteen attributes of, 285, 299n11; *tsimtsum* (contraction), 13, 25n21, 28n45, 142, 173, 261–62, 264, 278n16; unity of, 32–33, 64, 78, 231–32; voice of/recognition of, 217–19; withdrawal of, 306–7. *See also* atheism; *deus absconditus*; hiddenness; idolatry; the One
Gold, Joshua Robert, 341
Goodman, Micah, 34
goodness, 65, 164, 166, 184, 185–96, 193n1, 195n18, 223, 241–42
graven images, ban on, 201–4, 202, 204, 205, 209
Grice, Paul, 224
der Griffel, 314
Grounding Element, 183–84, 186, 195n18
Guide of the Perplexed (Maimonides), 80n2; on biblical anthropomorphism, 5, 66–67, 70, 72; Derrida on, 213–16, 223, 226, 235n48; on Glory, 231; God as creator, 83n59, 84n73, 245; on God's attributes, 33, 56–58, 70,

Guide of the Perplexed (Maimonides) *(cont.)* 150, 242–44, 245; on idolatry, 202; on introduction of multiplicity into God, 337; on language mirroring belief, 337; on *mitzvot*, 290, 299n11; on oneness of God, 229–31, 252; pantheism, 237n72; on prayer, 23n5, 57, 224, 227–28

Habermas, Jürgen, 199, 200, 209n4, 210n6
Hadot, Pierre, 261, 262
Haggadah, 206, 268–70, 275–76, 279n25, 281n37
Halakhah: adjudication of, 293–94; analysis of, 293–95, 302n46; authority of, 20; commitment to, 288–89; divine providence in, 297; Haggadah, 206, 268–70, 279n25, 281n37; immunity to the antinomian negativity of revelation, 21; negative theology and commitment to, 283; observance of, 282, 283–84; primacy of practice in observance of, 282; status of women in, 302n38; theological basis of, 296–98. See also *mitzvot*
Haninah, Rabbi, 228
Hannah (biblical figure), 227, 329
happiness, 145, 157n78, 227
Hartwich, Wolf-Daniel, 340, 344–45
Hasidism. See Dov Baer, Maggid of Mezherich
Hegel, Georg Wilhelm Friedrich, 9–10, 11, 26n26, 202, 260
Heidegger, Martin, 11, 217, 220, 231, 282, 289, 291
heresy *(harisah)*, 146, 147, 148
hester panim (concealment of God's presence), 240, 262
Hick, John, 289
hiddenness: distortion *(Entstellung)* as protection, 271–72; forgetting, 272; *ne'elam,* (conceal), 14, 37, 38, 138; revelation, 36, 185, 258–63, 276n3; of Torah, 266–67
hineni (I am), 240, 254n6
hishtawwut shel arakhim (equanimity of values), 143

history, philosophy of, 202
hohmah, 40
Holocaust, 21, 200, 310, 325
Horkheimer, Max, 27n35, 199, 201n6
hotza'at shem ra', 224
hukkim, 292
human body, sanctity of, 79–80
humans/human nature: discovery of God, 68–70; God's relations with, 48, 58, 72–74, 83n59, 135–37, 172, 344; humility, 12, 15, 55–56, 59, 102, 116–20, 126, 145; *imitatio dei,* 28n44, 56, 57–58, 202, 242–44, 339; inadequacy of human language, 57, 66, 230, 250, 335–36; incomprehensibility of God, 52–54; influence of Torah on, 135–37, 154nn29, 31; practitioner as infinite, 122; pursuit of perfection, 71, 82n; reaching the state of *'ayin* (nothing), 116, 118–23; response to divine absence, 240, 250–51, 256n60; transcendence, 239–40; transmission of mystical knowledge to, 135. See also prayer
Hume, David, 75, 246
humility, 12, 15, 55–56, 59, 102, 116–20, 126, 145
hymnic theology (Pseudo-Dionysius), 180

Ibn al-'Arabi, 34–35
ibn Bajja, 26n23
Ibn Ezra, Moshe, 33
Ibn Gabirol, Solomon, 18; *'ayin* in works of, 186; on creation, 186; on the creation of being, 188; criticism of, 191; on God, 183–84, 186–87; Grounding Element, 190; his system of emanating matters, 183–84, 194n13; influence on Kabbalah, 33; matter-apophasis, 185; as medieval Jewish Neoplatonist, 5, 33; origin of being, 183; on Plotinus, 183–85, 187, 190; Theology of Desire, 185; unitive-intuitive type, 6
Ibn Paquda, Bahya, 5, 6, 33, 337
Ibn Sina, 86

ibn Tamim, Dunash, 33
Ibn Tibbon, Shmuel, 35, 83n60
Ibn Zaddik, Joseph, 32
iḍāfa, 83n59
Idel, Moshe, 19–20, 37, 179n74, 258–59, 260
idolatry: ban on graven images, 8, 201, 202, 204, 205, 209; Maimonides on, 202; of ontotheology, 191–92; Rav Kook on, 148–49, 154n33; Second Commandment, 9–10, 12, 276n4
imitatio dei, 28n44, 56, 57–58, 202, 242–44, 339
immanence, 12, 173, 239, 315
the infinite. See *'ayn sof* (the Infinite)
insomnia, 189, 190, 196n32
integration of disciplines, 304–5
Intellect, 15, 44n19, 70, 77–80, 137, 164, 175n8, 183, 185, 195n19
intelligibility, privation of, 164, 176n11
intuitionless silence, 226
inwardness, belief in, 213–14
Isaac the blind, 47n58
Ishmael, Rabbi, 329–30
Ish-Shalom, Benjamin, 132, 133, 152n8, 152n10, 153n16, 156n54
Islamo-Judeo-Greek tradition of *khōra*-of-*khōra*, 182–84
Israel, land of, 17, 136, 141, 153n21, 153n25, 249–50, 297
Israel, nation of, 135–37, 136–37, 153n21, 153n25
Israel, people of: collective identity of, 342–43; election of, 246–47, 255n39, 255n41, 344; God's relation with, 326, 341–42; *kenesset yisrael* (Assembly of Israel), 133, 135–37, 153n25, 154n37, 155n39; rites of memorialization, 342
Israeli, Isaac, 6
Izzi, John, 175n8

Jabes, Edmund, 1
Jacob (biblical figure), 117, 218
Jacobs, Jonathan, 85, 93, 94–95, 107n29
Jacobs, Louis, 296–97, 303n56
Jacob's dream, 71
Jesus Christ, 62, 260, 261, 263, 315, 318, 352n32

Jewishness, 219, 222, 233n22
Jewish people: Assembly of Israel *(kenesset yisrael)*, 133, 135–37, 153n25, 154n37, 155n39; chosenness of, 136–37; chosenness of/uniqueness of, 136–37, 154n37, 155n39; compared with other nations, 136–37; covenant with God, 246–47, 249–50, 255n39, 255n41, 344; land of Israel, 17, 136, 141, 153n21, 153n25, 249–50, 297; and the propagation of mystical knowledge, 135–36, 153n16; in relation to other nations, 135–37, 153n21, 153n25
John of Damascus, 87
Jonas, Hans, 276n3
Jones, Rufus, 348, 349
Judeité, 214–15, 219

Kabbalah: in Celan's works, 309, 310; conceptions of God in, 37; creation in, 173; distortion *(Entstellung)*, 271; divine-human relationship in, 246, 255n39; on divine relations, 256n68; divine unification, 38; esotercism, 133–34, 150n; God's essence in, 37–38; knowing God, 290; secret *(sod)* in, 20–21, 139–40; *sefirot*, 39–40, 46n49, 115, 125, 145, 159n101, 252, 327. See also *'ayn sof* (the Infinite)
kaddish, 218, 219, 250–51
Kafka, Franz, 1, 13, 204; Aggadic elements in, 308; Benjamin on, 268–69; on the distortion of existence, 271; on the Exodus from Egypt, 269–70, 279n27; German-Jewish negative theology of, 10; Haggadic parables of, 269, 279n26; on Halakhah/Torah Law, 269–70; Jewish exegetical tradition, 206, 268; on Jewish tradition, 310; on the Law (Torah), 269–70, 279n27; negativity of, 19–20, 310; *der Nichts der Offenbarung*, 264, 265; as pious atheist, 278n15; theology in works of, 306–8; on writing as prayer, 308
Kalām, 32, 64, 65

Kant, Immanuel, 77, 201; Adorno on, 202; *Ding an sich,* 242; epistemology of, 288n11; on the existence of God, 9–11, 23n7, 248; *Grenzbegriff,* 252; on Judaism, 9–10; on reason, 24n24, 253n2

Karaitism, 259–60

Kasher, Hannah, 67–68, 80

kataphatic philosopy, 24n11, 139, 143–44, 148, 187, 258–59

Kaufman, Gordon, 86, 87

kavannah, 226–27

kavod (glory), 231–32, 240

kavvanah, 244

Kearny, Richard, 181–82

Kedushat Levi , 106n15

kefirah (heresy), 146, 148

kenesset yisrael (Assembly of Israel), 133, 135–37, 153n25, 154n37, 155n39

kenosis, 191, 192, 221, 352n32

keter (first *sefirah*), 39–40, 159n101

khōra, 181–85, 188–92, 195n18

khōra -of- *khōra*: apophasis of the trace in, 188–89; on being, 190; goodness, 184–85, 190; Grounding Element as, 186; intelligible matter, 195n18; Islamo-Judeo-Greek tradition of, 182–84, 188–89, 191; nothing-space of, 184; "not-yet" emphasized in, 192; Same by Other, 190; the unattainable sought by, 189

Kierkegaard, Søren, 26n26, 55, 259, 260–61, 349

Kol Nidre prayer, 343, 344

Kook, Abraham Isaac: absolute reality, 140–41, 156n; on atheism, 148–50, 158n91; on the *'ayn sof,* 290; esotericism of, 132, 133–34, 150n; on evil, 145; existence as signifier for God, 150, 159n100; faith described by, 143, 157n; on the faith of Israel, 147–48; on the intellect, 79, 137; on Israel's distinctiveness, 135–38, 153nn21, 25, 154n31, 155n39; on language, 138–40; on Maimonides, 150, 152n11, 158n91, 159n100; messianism, 146–47; on the mysteries of Torah (*sitrei torah*), 133; philosophy (*filosofyah*) v. esotericism (*soddiyut*), 141; *razei torah* (mysteries of Torah), 132; rhetoric of secrecy in teachings of, 131; on the ṣaddiq, 146–47; sufferings of the righteous, 146, 157n; on the teaching of Torah, 135–37, 154nn29, 31, 268; theistic depictions of God, 148, 158n91; on transmission of knowledge, 134–36, 153n16; on the *via contemplativa,* 139–40; on world religions, 136–37, 154n29, 154n37, 155n40; Zionism of, 141

Kook, Zvi Yehuda, 17

language: approaches to reading, 97–98; as compositional, 98–99; of esoteric wisdom, 138–39; fundamentals of reality and its relationship to, 97; limitations of, 57, 66, 140, 230, 250, 335–36; on the limitations of, 139–40; Maimonides on, 3, 34, 230, 337; in negative theology, 34; of prayer, 57–58, 228; puns in poetry of Celan, 312–13; *of razim* (mysteries), 137–38; *safah berurah* (pure language), 138–39; of secrecy, 137–38

lashon ha'rah (gossip, wrongful speech), 224

Law (Torah): *imitatio dei,* 339; Sinaitic revelation, 269–70, 279n27

Leibniz, Gottfried W. L., 201

Leibowitz, Yeshayahu (Isaiah): on God's existence, 68, 299n9; on Halakhah, 228, 282, 283–84, 302n38; on Maimonidean negative theology, 158n91, 228; on performance of *mitzvot,* 291; on predications of prayer, 2–3; on the status of women in Halakhah, 302n38

Levinas, Emmanuel: *adieu,* 191–92; on atheism, 158n91; on being, 163–64, 167; creationism, 169, 170; on Descartes, 52–53; on emanation, 164; on the *En Sof,* 172; on the infinite, 52; on insomnia, 189, 190, 196n32; on Judaism, 10; *khōra* -of- *khōra,* 188–89; logic of messianicity, 190; on love, 179n86; negative theology as ethical, 18, 162; on Nietzsche, 18; parable of

Index   369

the Cave, 167; on philosophy, 161–62, 164, 167, 168–70; the trace, 188–89; on transcendence, 171–72, 254n7; on *tsimtsum,* 262
light of the mysteries of God *(razei el),* 140
likutey Moharan (Nachman of Bretslav), 29n47
Linzer, Dov, 292
liturgy: God-human dialogue in, 245–48, 255n35; God's beneficence celebrated through, 248–50, 256n48; human responses to God's silence, 250–51, 256n60; of Yom Kippur, 343, 352n32
Loberbaum, Menachem, 353n34
Loewe, Judah (Maharal of Prague), 153n16, 296
logic: species-neutrality of, 85, 105n1
Lorberbaum, Menachem, 34
love, 175, 179n86
Lurianic Kabbalah: breaking of the vessels *(shevirah),* 118–19; *tsimtsum* (contraction), 13, 25n21, 28n45, 142, 173, 261–62, 264, 273–74, 278n16
Luther, Martin, 9, 261
Lutheranism, 260–61
Lyotard, Jean-François, 11

the Maggid. *See* Dov Baer, Maggid of Mezherich
Maggid Devar la-Yaacov (Maggid of Mezherich), 17, 110–11
mah (something), 120
Mahler, Gustav, 208, 211n34, 212n38
mahshavah tehorah (pure thoughts), 40
mahshavah (thoughts), 244
Maimonides, Abraham, 295–96
Maimonides, Moses: argumentative structures in works of, 104; on biblical anthropomorphism, 5, 66–67, 70, 72; on challenges of describing God, 50–51; on closeness to God, 58–59; denial of divine attributes, 62, 63; Derrida on, 213–16, 223, 226, 235n48; *ehyeh asher ehyeh* , 77, 230, 251; on Exodus 33, 49; on figurative interpretation, 233n22; on gender roles, 78–79; Gersonides on, 101; God as creator, 83n59, 84n73, 245; on God's apathy towards humans, 344; on God's attributes, 33, 56–58, 70, 150, 242–44, 245–46, 256n68; on God's existence, 89–90, 95, 150, 159n100; on God's unity, 63, 64; on goodness, 241–42; his theory of knowledge, 34–35, 56–57; on human behavior, 56, 59, 68, 79; *iḍḍāfa,* 57–58, 242–44; influence on Kabbalists, 133, 152n11; on the inwardness of faith, 226; on Jacob's dream, 71; on Jewishness, 233n22; *kavannah,* 226; on language, 3, 34, 230, 337; law of noncontradiction, 93; Marranoism of, 215–16; on *mitzvot,* 290, 299n11; and the monotheism of Judaism, 158n91; Nachmanides compared with, 41; natural theology of, 75, 240; on negation, 50–51, 199, 222–23, 226, 236n56; negative theology of, 33–34, 172, 221, 222–23, 226, 287–88, 289; on oneness of God, 229–31, 252; pantheism, 237n72; *Perek Helek* (Maimonides), 82n49; on the Perfection of God, 71–76; political application of negative theology, 337–38; on prayer, 23n5, 57, 224, 227, 228; on reflexivity of conceptual thought in man and God, 69; on relations between God and humans, 58, 67, 72–76, 83n59, 344; "relation" used by, 75; replacement of physical destruction, 51; on Revelation, 76; on silence, 225–26, 227, 235n46; skepticism of, 6, 23n5, 226, 236n56; on systematic theology, 102; on the Tetragrammaton, 35, 36, 230; theistic depictions of God, 148, 158n91; theory of attribution, 241; *Tractatus Logico-Philosophicus* (Wittgenstein), 100, 101; on transcendence, 66, 68; on what is God, 241–42
Mandelshtam, Osip, 314, 317–18

Mandorla (Celan), 316–21
Marconite Gnostic dualism, 261
Marion, Jean-Luc, 11, 26n25, 180, 193n1, 197n38, 234n40
Marranoism, 215–16, 217
materiality, 115, 119–20, 122–26, 130n59, 168, 201, 204
mathematics, 53
Matt, Daniel, 38
McGinn, Benjamin, 220
medical ethics, 297
Meir Ibn Gabai, 328
Mendelssohn, Moses, 9, 10
mercy: and the trauma of revelation, 343–44
the Meridian (Celan), 275–76, 308, 309–10, 320
Merleau-Ponty, Maurice, 253n3
Mersenne, Marin, 53
Mesland, Denis, 53
messianicity, 184, 185, 186–87, 191, 192n1
messianic negative theology (Cohen), 12
messianism, 20, 55, 140, 146–47; ascendancy of atheism, 148–49; defined, 192n1; election of Israel, 249; hiddenness, 271–72; messianic reversal, 263, 265, 268, 276, 281n39; *Mutterrecht* compared with, 272–73; narratives of, 271; preparation for the messianic age, 202; Sabbatianism, 147; Zionism, 297
milekhet mahshavet (thoughtful work), 244
Mirsky, Yehuda, 132, 155n40
Mishneh Torah (Maimonides), 56
mitzvot, 282, 290–96, 299n11, 302n44
modesty, 232
monotheism, 149, 150, 158n91, 327; fanaticism, 55; of Kalām, 32, 64, 65; negative theology, 335–36; polytheism compared with, 49; and the suspension of the desctruction that was pledged by God, 343–44; uniqueness of God, 49
monsters *(cherubim)*, 48
Moore, G. E., 19
Mortley, Raoul, 25n19, 27n28
Moses: encounters with God, 56, 59, 251, 343; God's authority challenged by, 343, 345; God's *kavod*, 48; hidden in the cleft of a rock, 56; humility of, 56, 59; knowledge of God, 56–57; practice of *'ayin*, 126; prayers to, 343, 348; theophany of, 56, 59, 64
Mosès, Stephane, 278n18, 279n26
Munk, Solomon, 83n59, 194n16
music: alienation by, 209, 212n38; ban on images, 208, 209, 211n34; determinate negation, 208, 212n35
Muʿtazilites, 32, 62, 65, 259
mysteries *(razim)*, 132–33, 137–38, 139, 141
mysticism, 100, 121–22, 169, 172, 179n74, 221–22, 329–30

Nachmanides, 14, 37–38, 41, 42, 248–49, 301n33
Nachman of Bratslav, 29n47
naïve set theory, 91, 92
names of God, 35, 101, 148, 157n78, 201–2, 227, 263, 327
Nancy, Jean-Luc, 352n32
Naor, Bezalel, 159nn100, 101
Narbonne, J.-M., 166, 167–68, 178n62
Nathan ben Saʾadyah Harar, 263
natural beneficence, 249–50
natural history, 248–49
natural theology, 239
navel motif, 308, 309, 321n7
neant *('ayin)*, 37, 38, 40
Necessary Existence, 231
ne'elam (concealed), 14, 37, 38, 138
negative dialectics, 202–3, 207, 209
Negative Dialectics (Adorno), 202–6
negative political theology, 340–41, 345
negative theology: absence of God, 240, 250–53, 256n60, 263; analytic defense of, 93–98; and commitment to Halakhah, 283; in Continental philosophy, 286–87; epistemological formulations of, 3–4, 285–86, 288; graven images, ban on, 201, 204; kataphatic philosophy, 24n11, 139, 143–44, 148, 187, 258–59; limits of, 310; monotheism, 335–36; neant *('ayn)*, 37, 38, 40; *ne'elam* (conceal), 14, 37, 38, 138; negative dialectics, 203; nihilism, 162, 174,

265, 278n15, 340, 349–50, 351n19; ontological formulations of, 2, 286; origins of, 2, 286–87; political application of, 337–38; prohibition on representation in, 8, 201, 202, 204, 205, 208, 209, 211n34; rational theology, 5; skepticism, 3, 6, 34–35, 38, 226–28, 235n54, 236n56; *via negativa*, 1, 2, 131, 144, 219, 274; in Western tradition, 170. *See also* Adorno, Theodor; atheism; *'ayn sof* (the Infinite); Celan, Paul; Derrida, Jacques; *khōra* headings; Kook, Abraham Isaac; language; Maimonides, Moses; nothingness; the One

Neoplatonism, 18, 63; "beyond Being," 161, 162; body in, 168; on divine unity, 5, 32–33, 63–64, 164; Maimonides, Moses on, 78; on negation, 236n56; schema of return and union, 175n8

neshamah (soul), 132

Newman, Barnett, 1, 22n1

Nichtes Gottes (nothingness of God), 260, 265

Nichts der Offenbarung, 265

Niederschrift, 272

Die Niemandsrose (Celan), 311–15, 317

Nietzsche, Friedrich, 18, 161, 162, 174, 240, 266

nihilism, 162, 174, 265, 278n15, 340, 341, 349–50, 351n19

nisba (relation), 15, 72–74, 73, 83n, 83nn59, 60

nissim mefursamim (public supernatural divine mainfestations), 248–49

ha-nistar (hidden), 37, 38

noēsis noēseōs noēsis (thought-thinking-itself), 244–45

nolens volens, 261

nominalism, 207

non-being, 165, 166, 176n26

nonconceptual atheism, 3, 23n9

nonsemes (Badiou), 72

nothingness: attainment of, 109, 113, 117–23, 129n29; in Celan's poetry, 312–13, 315, 316, 319–21; dialectics of, 266, 278n18; *khōra*, 181–85, 188–92, 195n18; revelation, 265, 266–67, 273, 307, 315. *See also 'ayin* (nothing)

Ockham's razor, 241

the One, 37, 63–64; as beyond being, 164, 166; historicization of the spirit of, 221; Levinas on the return to, 171; multiplicity, 164, 166, 168, 174, 176n30; and non-beings, 166, 176n26; otherness, 169; in Platonist tradition, 164; priority of, 166, 177n31; singularity of God, 252; status of the world of multiplicity, 165; transcendence of, 165, 172; as unity, 164; world, separation of, 167

Onkelos, 66

"On the Symbolic Order of Modern Democracy" (Taubes), 347–48

Otto, Rudolf, 68

paganism: motif of hiding nature, 261

pantheism, 237n72

paradox of the preface (Priest), 92

paramārtha-satya, 139, 155n47

Pauline political theology, 340–41

Perek Helek (Maimonides), 82n49

perfection, 64, 71–76, 77, 83n59, 172, 290

"perhaps" (Derrida), 230–31

Philo of Alexandria, 4, 24n15, 31–32, 62

philosophy, rhetorical element of, 207

Pines, Shlomo, 6, 15, 34, 67, 68, 72

pious atheist, 265, 278n15

Plantinga, Alvin, 15–16, 86, 87, 105

Plato, 4, 71; on being, 164, 166, 223; Eleatic notion of being in philosophy of, 164; on ethics, 85; on the good, 164, 166, 223, 241–42; *khōra* of, 183–84; monotheism, 18; ontological tradition of negative theology, 162; on unity, 166

Plotinus: on "beyond Being," 164, 165–66; Christian theologians on, 193n3; criticism of, 193n3; dualism of, 168, 170, 177n41; hierarchies in writings of, 168; Ibn Gabirol on, 183–85, 187, 190; on Intellect, 80, 185; on intelligible matter, 164, 171, 183, 185, 190, 195n18; mystical union

Index

Plotinus: on "beyond Being," (cont.)
  as *ecstasis*, 169; *to noein*, 185; on the return to the One, 164, 165–66, 168–69; on silence, 51; on unity, 165–66
The Political Theology of Paul, 21–22, 340, 342–43, 345
prayer: achievement of *ayin*, 125; as address, 2, 223–24; *Amida* prayer, 65; Aristotle on, 2; kaddish, 218, 219, 250–51; *kavannah*, 226–27; Kol Nidre, 343, 344; language of, 57–58, 187, 228; silence, 139, 226, 227, 236n59, 329; thirteen attributes of God, 285, 299n11; women's prayers, 227, 329, 331–32; writing as, 308
Priest, Graham, 16, 91, 92, 93
Principle of Sufficient Reason, 64, 65
pronoia (divine caring), 77
Protestantism, 220–21; biblical hermeneutics, 206; *deus absconditus* in, 19–20, 258, 260–61; Jewish God in, 260–61; Marconite Gnostic dualism, 261
Proudhon, Pierre-Joseph, 349
Proust, Marcel, 306
Psalm (Celan), 317, 318, 319, 320
Pseudo-Dionysius, 86, 100, 193n1, 225, 228, 236n64
psychoanalysis, 205, 211n23
public supernatural divine mainfestations *(nissim mefursamim)*, 248–49
puns: in Celan's poetry, 312–13, 315, 316, 317
Purcell, Michael, 179n74
pure gift in theology, 191–92
pure language *(safah berurah)*, 138–39
pure messianism: defined, 192n1
pure prayer, 224, 226
Pyrrhonian skepticism, 227, 235n54

Quakers, 348
quietism, 114, 123, 145

Rackman, Emanuel, 293
radical negativity, 227–28
Rambam. *See* Maimonides
Ramsey, Frank P., 97–98
Rava, 343, 345, 352n32

Rāzī, 82n49
razim (mysteries), 132–33, 137–38, 141, 142
rebelliousness *(meridah)*, 146
redemption, 245–46, 255n35, 305, 315
Reformation, 220–21
repentance *(teshuvah)*, 146, 247
resurrection, 140, 193n3
Rettung, 13
returning (term), 164
revealed religion, 338–39
revelation: antinomianism, 19–20, 270; believers on, 290; divine hiddenness, 36–38, 258–63, 276n3; of God, 36, 37–38, 56, 258–63, 276n3; hiding, 271–73; mercy and the trauma of, 343–44; *der Nichts der Offenbarung* (Kafka), 264; Nothingness, 265, 266–67, 270, 273, 307, 315; self-revelation of God, 290; of Torah, 266–67; *tsimtsum* (contraction), 13, 25n21, 28n45, 142, 173, 261–62, 264, 273–74, 278n16; withdrawal as, 264–65, 307
Revelation, 76
rose imagery: in Celan's poetry, 311–14
Rosenzweig, Franz, 1, 10–12, 251, 305–6, 307, 312
Rothko, Mark, 1, 22n1
Russell, Bertrand, 85, 91, 97, 99, 253n2
Rynhold, Daniel, 282, 291, 299n9

Saadya Gaon: apophatic theology of, 32–33, 87–89; argumentative structures in works of, 104; cataphatic-claims of, 102; on God's attributes, 32–33, 74, 95, 337; law of noncontradiction, 93; Maimonides on, 77; on rational knowledge and prophecy, 32; on systematic theology, 102; *Tractatus Logico-Philosophicus* (Wittgenstein), 101
Sabbath, 263, 274–75
Sabbatianism, 147
ṣaddiq, 119, 120, 121, 124, 130n59, 146–47
safah berurah (pure language), 138–39
Sagi, Avi, 282
Saint Augustine, 213–14, 217
Saint Thomas, 223

saṃvṛti-satya, 139, 155n47
Saruk, Israel, 280n34
Schatz-Uffenheimer, Rivka, 109, 114, 127
Schelling, Friedrich Wilhelm Joseph, 261, 262
Schmitt, Carl, 304, 305, 308, 347–48, 349
Schocken, Salman, 278n15
Schoenberg, Arnold, 208, 209, 211n34
Schoeps, Hans-Joachim, 259
Scholem, Gershom: on the antinomian lesson of the Jewish Law, 266–67; on the antinomian trace, 270; on concept of modern authenticity, 259–60; correspondence with Schoeps, 259–60; *deus absconditus* v. *deus revelatus*, 36; dialectics of nothingness, 266, 278n18; on divine contracting, 12; on divine meaninglessness, 274; on early Hasidism, 126; eulogy for Rosenzweig, 305–6, 307; on extreme behaviour in monotheism, 55; German-Jewish negative theology of, 10; on Kabbalah, 12, 273–74, 280n34; on Kafka's works, 265–66, 278n18; on the messianic, 20, 278n18; on *Nichtes Gottes* (nothingness of God), 260; *Nichts der Offenbarung*, 264, 265, 275; nihilism of, 278n18; on nothingness, 265–66; nothingness of revelation, 19–20, 273, 307; relations of theology and literature, 308; separation of law from life, 264–65; on the shadow of the Law, 266, 267; on "that which thought cannot attain," 40; theological issues in literature, 306–7; unitive mysticism, 179n74; Walter Benjamin's correspondence, 19, 20
Schroeder, Brian, 169
Schwartz, Yosef, 220
Schweid, Eliezer, 67–68, 132
science, 76–77
Scruton, Roger, 72
Searl, John, 230
Second Commandment, 9–10, 12, 276n4
secrecy, 131, 132, 137–38, 140–41

secularism, 203–4, 278n18, 305
ṣedeq (justice), 137
Seeskin, Kenneth, 6, 16, 235n46, 335–36, 338
sefirot, 39–40, 46n49, 115, 125, 145, 159n101, 252, 327
Segal, Aaron, 287
the self: erasure, and reaching the state of 'ayin, 113, 116, 117–23, 129n45; human contact, 118–19; as mirror of God, 69, 82n35; the mystical union between God and man, 121–22; peace, 118; self-abnegation, 118–19; wholeness, 118
self-annihilation: and reaching the state of 'ayin, 116, 118–21, 129n45
"separated being no longer participating" (Levinas), 167
set (term), 91
sexuality, 79–80
Shaddai, 157n78
shalom, 51, 227
Shekhinah, 120, 122–25, 132–33, 310–11, 331
Shem Tov ibn Shem Tov, 41
Shneur Zalman of Liadi, 154n33
Shoah, 21, 200, 310, 325
showing, apophaticism of, 100–101, 104
Sider, Ted, 94
silence: absence of God, 250–53, 256n60; duplicity of, 224–25; in prayer, 51, 139, 226, 236n59; Scholem on, 281n38
Silesius, Angelus, 309, 310
skepticism, 3, 6, 34–35, 38, 226–28, 235n54, 236n56
Smith, David, 85
Society of Friends, 348
Socrates, 68, 69, 85, 163–64
sod: as *peshat*, 21
Soloveitchik, Hayyim (1853–1918), 295
Soloveitchik, Joseph, 282, 293, 296
soul *(neshamah)*, 82n49, 132, 140–41, 146, 170
Spinoza, Baruch, 9, 17, 77, 78, 80
Star of David theology, 306, 307
Star of Redemption (Rosenzweig), 306, 307
Statman, Daniel, 283, 290
Steinsaltz, Adin, 153n16

Stern, Josef, 6, 26n19, 225, 226, 227, 236n56
storytelling, 269–72, 275–76, 279n26, 280n28
Strauss, Leo, 67
subject, autonomy of, 206
Sufism, 34–35
swerve, 11, 14, 162, 259, 260, 271, 273, 277n5
Swinburne, Richard, 86
Symposium (Plato), 71, 185–86

ta'amei ha-mitzvot (reasons for the commandments), 293, 294, 296
Taubes, Jacob: anthropocentrist theology, 346–47; on Buber's utopianism, 341; democratic political theology, 348–49; on dialectical theology, 345; on divine transcendence, 259, 339–40, 344, 351n15; on Karl Barth, 345–46; nihilism of, 340, 341, 349–50, 351n19; on Paul Tillich's theology, 345, 346; *The Political Theology of Paul*, 21–22, 340–43; on progress, 341; on transatheistic consciousness, 348–49; on Yom Kippur liturgy, 343, 352n32
tefillin, 19, 342
Terpstra, Marin, 341, 344–45
Tetragrammaton (YHWH), 35–36, 51, 77, 229–30, 255n31, 263, 269–70, 327
the Infinite. See *'ain sof* (the Infinite)
theism, 193n4, 352n32
theodicy, 145–46, 325
theology: anthropology, 345; defined, 238–39, 254n1; political notions as secularized categories of, 305; pure gift in, 191–92; in works of literature, 305
"Theology and the Philosophic Critique of Religion" (Taubes), 345, 348
Theology of Aristotle, 195n18
Theology of Desire (Ibn Gabirol), 185
theosophy, 134
therapeutic falsehood, 96–97, 104–5
Thomas Aquinas, 251
thoughtful work (*milekhet mahshavet*), 244
thought-thinking-itself (*noēsis noēseōs*), 244–45

Tillich, Paul, 193n3, 345, 346
Timaean *khōra*. See *khōra*
tiqqun olam (rectification of the world), 137
Torah: adjectives describing God in, 288; anthropomorphisms in, 71; Benjamin, Walter on, 268–69; creation of the world, 330–31; fading of, in Scholem-Benjamin correspondence, 266–67; human language of, 206; interpretation of, 141, 266; mysteries of *(hashra'at razei torah)*, 140–41; and the propagation of mystical knowledge, 135; revelation of, 135, 266–67, 269–70, 279n27; soul of *(nishmata de-orayyta)*, 141; teaching of, 135–37, 154nn29, 31, 268
totality, 175n8
Totality and Infinity (Levinas), 162
"touching and not touching": tensions between *yesh* and *'ayin*, 124–25
"Toward Understanding Schoenberg" (Adorno), 209
the trace, 188–89
Tractatus Logico-Philosophicus (Wittgenstein), 96–101
transatheism, 348–49
transcendence: Adorno on, 203–4; in Celan's poetry, 315; in ethical negative theology, 170; God's presence, 239–40; immanence, 12, 173, 239, 278n18, 315; Levinas on, 171, 176n17, 177n38, 188–89; Maimonides on, 66–67; Taubes on divine transcendence, 344, 346; unity, 32–33, 114, 117–20, 126, 143, 145, 162–68
transtheism, 22, 345–47, 346
transtheistic consciousness, 345, 346
the Trinity, 18, 260
truth, 93–96, 155n47, 206–7, 289
tsimtsum (contraction), 13, 25n21, 28n45, 142, 173, 261–62, 264, 278n16

unitive mysticism, 172, 179n74
unity, 32–33, 114, 116, 117–20, 121–22, 126, 143, 145, 162–68

utopianism, 137, 154n, 155n, 207–8, 211n34, 341

van Inwagen, Peter, 85, 86, 89
Vattimo, Gianni, 352n32
va-yeḥal, 343
via contemplativa, 139–40
via negativa, 1, 2, 7, 25n19, 131, 144, 219, 226, 274
von Harnack, Adolf, 261, 277n7
von Rosenroth, Christian Herr, 26n
vox populi, 22, 348, 349, 354n61

Warranted Christian Belief (Plantinga), 86
Weigel, Sigrid, 271, 272
Wellhausen, Julius, 9
Westphal, Merold, 289
White, Roger, 98, 100
Wittgenstein, Ludwig, 16, 96–100, 242, 252
Wohlfarth, Irving, 278n16, 280n28
Wolfson, Elliot, 7, 31, 37, 179n74, 188, 193n4, 235n48, 340
Wolterstorff, Nicholas, 24n11
women, 78–79, 227, 302n38, 329, 331–32
word play: in Celan's poetry, 312–13, 314, 315, 317
Wyschogrod, Edith, 171, 175, 197n38
Wyschogrod, Michael, 10

Xenophanes, 80

yeḥidah (unique), 132–33, 152n7
Yerushalmi, Yosef Hayim, 219, 280n28
yesh: characteristics of, 122, 125, 126, 129n27; and insubstantiality, 145; keter, associations with, 159n101; materiality, 119–20, 122–26, 130n59, 168, 201, 204; relations with ayin, 110, 112–17, 122, 124–25, 127n3
YHWH (Tetragrammaton), 35–36, 51, 77, 229–30, 255n31, 263, 269–70, 327
Yom Kippur, 343, 352n32

ẓaddik, 119, 120, 121, 124, 130n59, 146–47
Zähle die Mandel (Celan), 317
zakhor (remember), 247–48
Zionism, 17, 141, 297
Zohar: on Abraham's sacrifice, 112; apophaticism of, 87; on the 'ayn sof, 87, 124–25; on the Divine Sovereignty, 274; on the human soul, 13; in Rav Kook's writings, 145, 146; on the soul, 232
Zohar, Noam, 297

CITATION GUIDE

Pentateuch

Genesis
    1:32, 56
    2:4, 256n68
    3:24, 48
    9:9, 254n6
    14:22, 255n29
    17:4, 254n6
    21:33, 255n29
    22:1, 254n6
    22:11, 254n6
    22:13, 110–111
    24:2, 79
    33, 58

Exodus
    2:23, 255n35
    3:4, 254n6
    3:6, 56
    3:14, 148, 251, 255n30
    4:21, 126
    14:10, 255n35
    19, 48
    19:17, 279n27
    20:8, 255n42
    24:11, 56
    25:31–35, 317
    31:2, 255n27
    32, 343
    32:11, 343
    32:13, 255n41, 256n43
    33, 49, 50, 52, 56, 59, 299n11
    33:20, 48
    33:21, 254n6
    34:6, 255n30, 255n31
    34:6–7, 285, 299n11
    35:33, 244

Leviticus
    19:2, 339

Numbers
    6:26, 253n5
    10:2, 121
    12:3, 56
    30:3, 343
    33:53, 256n58

Deuteronomy
    5:23, 251
    6:4, 256n67
    6:5, 71
    6:6–9, 342
    8:10, 249, 253n5, 256n57
    22:6, 301n33
    25:17, 255n42
    25:19, 255n42
    27:2–8, 342
    27:16, 342
    29:13, 255n41
    30:11–14, 339
    31:17, 253n5
    34:6, 275

Prophets

Joshua
    7:11, 255n41

Judges
    3, 231

1 Samuel
    1, 227
    3:16, 254n6

Isaiah
  2:1–4, 256n56
  6:8, 254n6
  40:17, 51–52
  43:10, 255n39
  44:6, 255n39
  45:21, 252
  46:5, 50
  52:6, 254n6
  55:8, 244
  64:3, 252

Jeremiah
  1:5, 217
  1:11–12, 317
  2:21, 136
  9:23, 243
  12:16, 81n6
  14:8–9, 250
  44:26, 254n6

Ezekiel
  1:26, 121
  34:10, 254n6
  34:31, 137

Hosea
  4:15, 81n6
  14:10, 147

Amos
  8:14, 64

Habakkuk
  2:20, 250

Zephaniah
  3:9, 256n56

Zechariah
  14:9, 256n56

Writings

Psalms
  4:5, 225, 256n60
  18:46, 6n
  22:2, 250
  27:131–34, 253
  42:3, 146
  56, 56
  65, 51, 56
  65:2, 224–25, 256n60
  95, 256n51
  104:24, 112
  111:10, 111, 125
  116:6, 303n57
  142:3, 255n33
  143:8, 223
  145:9, 243
  147:8, 123

Proverbs
  3:19, 111
  7, 78
  22:17, 223
  27:19, 120
  31, 78

Job, 56
  19:25, 247
  28:12, 111
  34:29, 253n5

Lamentations
  2:9, 118

Ecclesiastes
  3:9, 13
  3:19, 13, 38

Esther
  3:15, 226

Mishnah

Avot
  2:21, 82n49
  2.21, 82n

Berakhot
  9.3, 255n33

Kelim
  26.8, 255n27

Citation Guide

Makhshirin
    6.1, 255n27

Nedarim
    10a, 241

Babylonian Talmud

Berakhot
    4a, 256n72
    4b, 255n34
    7a, 256n68
    20b, 253n5
    21a, 256n57
    28b, 255n32
    32a, 255n41, 343–44, 348, 352n32

Shabbat
    88a, 279n27
    88b, 279n27
    128b, 302n41
    129b, 303n57

Pesahim
    64b, 303n58
    106a, 255n42

Betsah
    13b, 255n27

Rosh Hashanah
    17b, 255n31

Taanit
    31a, 122

Hagigah
    5a–b, 253n5

Megillah
    18a, 255n42

Kiddushin
    39b, 256n44

Bava Metzia
    32a–33a, 302n41

Bava Qama
    38a, 154n31

Sanhedrin
    10 (Heleq), 256n67
    44a, 255n41

Shevuot
    39a, 255n41

Avodah Zarah
    7b, 255n33

Menahot
    43b, 255n42

Jerusalem Talmud

Berakhot
    7.1, 256n57
    11a, 256n57

Orla
    1c, 123

Shekalim
    6:3, 303n58

Yoma
    1:4, 303n58

Hagiga
    77:a–b, 124

Yevamot
    12b, 303n57

Tosefta

Tosefta Hagiga
    20:6, 124

Midrash

Beresheet Rabbah
    12.15, 256n68
    36, 253n5

Shemot Rabbah
    21.5, 255n35
    44.7, 256n43

Zohar

Zohar
    I:16b, 125
    I:120b, 110, 111
    I:135a, 255n38
    I:264b–265a, 237n71
    II:114b, 47n56
    3:79, 334n21
    59, 275

New Testament

1 Corinthians
    7, 341

Guide of the Perplexed (Maimonides)

Introduction, 66, 70, 81n14, 82n45, 82n46
1:26, 288, 300n21
1:46, 288, 300n21
1:54, 298, 303n65
1.1, 68, 82n28
1.5, 35, 61n25
1.11, 73, 83n58
1.15, 71, 82n48
1.21, 70, 82n44
1.23–24, 71, 82n50
1.26, 242, 250, 254n15, 256n59
1.27, 66, 81n15, 81n16
1.28, 66n17, 81n17
1.32, 32, 60n10, 227, 236n58
1.33–36, 67, 81n24
1.35, 32, 36, 60n5, 61n27
1.36, 67, 81n18
1.38, 70, 82n44
1.39, 243–244, 254n25
1.46, 76, 84n74
1.47, 71, 82n47
1.50, 72, 83n56, 226
1.51, 62, 80n3, 89
1.52, 31, 60n1, 65, 72, 81n11, 83n57, 89, 172, 244, 254n26

1.54, 31, 36, 60n2, 61n26, 64, 70, 81n9, 82n44, 172, 178n71, 243, 254n21, 344, 353n33
1.56, 32, 60n6, 223, 338, 351n11
1.57, 222, 226, 231, 234n31
1.58, 32, 60n7, 70, 82n44, 222, 225, 226, 234n31, 235n48, 235n52, 242, 254n15
1.59, 2, 5, 23n5, 24n12, 33, 34, 37, 44n19, 60n11, 61n22, 61n29, 69, 75, 82n39, 84n68, 224, 228, 236n62, 250, 256n60
1.61, 32, 60n8, 230
1.64, 76, 84n72, 231, 232, 237n72
1.65, 62, 80n2
1.68, 63–64, 68, 69, 70, 81n6, 82n29, 82n31, 82n32, 82n33, 82n34, 82n43
1.70, 227, 236n58
1.73, 69, 82n38
1.111, 226
1.124, 243, 254n21
1.130, 223
1.132, 222, 234n31
1.133, 226, 231
1.134, 222, 234n31
1.135, 226, 231, 235n52
1.137, 225, 235n48
1.139, 228, 236n62
1.140, 228, 236n62
1.141, 224
1.148, 230
1.156, 231
2.1, 89
2:25, 285, 300n12
2:48, 298, 303n65
2.6, 72, 83n55
2.13, 245, 255n29
2.25, 219, 233n22
2.29, 344, 353n34
3:13, 285, 300n12
3:25–28, 285, 299n11
3.9, 31, 60n3
3.15, 34, 61n18
3.16–17, 69, 82n41
3.17–18, 71, 82n50
3.19, 73, 83n59
3.21, 73, 83n59
3.27, 339, 351n13
3.51, 223, 225, 234n36
3.54, 36, 61n28, 202, 243, 254n221
3.618, 223, 234n36

www.ingramcontent.com/pod-product-compliance
Lightning Source LLC
Chambersburg PA
CBHW021336300426
44114CB00012B/976